American Museum Sourcebooks in Anthropology, under the general editorship of Paul Bohannan, are published for The American Museum of Natural History by the Natural History Press. Directed by a joint editorial board made up of Dr. Bohannan and members of the staff of the Museum and the Natural History Press, this series is an extension of the Museum's scientific and educational activities, making available to the student and reader inexpensive, up-to-date, and authoritative books in the field of anthropology. The Natural History Press is a division of Doubleday & Company, Inc., and has its editorial offices at Doubleday & Company, Inc., 277 Park Avenue, New York, New York, 10017, and its business offices at 501 Franklin Avenue, Garden City, New York 11530.

PREHISTORIC AGRICULTURE

EDITED BY STUART STRUEVER

AMERICAN MUSEUM SOURCEBOOKS IN ANTHROPOLOGY

PUBLISHED FOR

THE AMERICAN MUSEUM OF NATURAL HISTORY

THE NATURAL HISTORY PRESS

1971 · GARDEN CITY, NEW YORK

The illustrations for this book
were prepared by the Graphic Arts Division of
The American Museum of Natural History.

CONTENTS

Part I | INTRODUCTION

1 THE DOMESTICATOR
OF PLANTS AND ANIMALS

Richard A. Watson and Patty Jo Watson

ADVANCED HUNTERS and gatherers are nomadic to the extent required by the animals they hunt and the plants they collect, but they are semi-sedentary according to the seasonal life cycles of these animals and plants. And, in those times when men are living on stored food, they may have regularly recurring blocks of leisure time for craft specialization, art, and speculation. Semi-sedentary conditions are essential also to the development of the invention that has had the most revolutionary impact on man's way of life: domestication of plants and animals. Elemental men are simply important animals in the ecological community; advanced hunters and gatherers have an important effect on the ecological community, but do not control it; domesticators of plants and animals, however, exert a great deal of influence on the physical environment and often actually control its ecological balance. Domestication has revolutionary importance because it results in a kind of food specialization that makes possible a vast increase in the quantity and degree of stabilization of the food supply. This potentially great increase in food supplies, if realized, allows for a resultant, correlative increase in population, and since large populations are necessary for the development of the civilized way of life, domestication is at the foundation of civilization.

Let us begin with the essential territorial requirements for the domesticators' way of life. The physical environment must contain plants and animals amenable to domestication. Among animals, those that live in herds are most easily domesticated. Herd behavior is such that most animals follow the lead of some dominant member or all members stay close together and move together. If a man can gain control of the movements of a few members of a herd, the other members will be likely to follow. Among plants, those like the grasses, which tend to grow densely and widely at the expense of other species, and tropical plants, which are easily transplanted, are most amenable to control by man, although it is highly unlikely that these plants, or any others, would be domesticated at any great distance from places where they grow naturally.

Domesticators must also have a semi-sedentary way of life. People who are continually on the move do not have time to experiment with domestication, but people who have at least seasonal home bases will probably observe two things that suggest the possibility of domestication. Around the areas where wild grain and seeds are stored or eaten or where garbage is thrown, plants grow from lost seeds. Men are certain to take advantage of these accidentally sown plants, harvesting them even though they were not intentionally planted. Young animals that have been captured alive by hunters will probably be brought to the home base. Such animals are dependent on the people who tether or cage them, and often become quite tame. They are obviously a potential food source, even though they were not consciously captured for this purpose.

A semi-sedentary life in a physical environment with appropriately domesticable species is a necessary but not sufficient condition for the invention of domestication. Man must also be, and is, intelligent enough to understand the possibilities and to act on them. What a semi-sedentary way of life provides, with regularly recurring intervals of leisure, is the time and place for experimentation. We still cannot say that in such conditions domestication is necessarily invented; however, these are the conditions under which it could and most likely would be invented by man.

Men who live a way of life in which they are primarily dependent on domesticated plants and animals for food are more bound to limited areas than are elemental men or advanced hunters and gatherers. The latter feel a sense of ownership of the wild plants and animals on their territory, but their degree of control over these plants and animals is small. Domesticators, who have direct control over domesticated plants and animals, have an explicit notion of property; they can manipulate and dispose of property as they will. And since it is necessary for the growth of their domesticates that sufficient land be available, the notion of territory that belongs to the group is refined: land becomes property that is more consciously and explicitly owned, either privately or communally, than is the territory of elemental men or of advanced hunters and gatherers. To the extent that the entire group still depends on the joint produce of its members, property will be communal. However, work and distribution along kinship lines—which is most likely—tends to divide communal property into family holdings. The very great productivity of farming and herding is what permits this separation. Each family can, through its own labor, produce enough food for its own needs. In the simplest situation, work can be organized and supervised along kinship lines, with each family maintaining its own flocks and fields. Each family would ordinarily be self-sufficient, but in times of need could share the produce of other families in the group.

Farmers who concentrate mostly on the growing of plants have territories—or land holdings—which are extremely small compared to those of hunters and gatherers. An extended family of a dozen members may farm no more than a few acres. A dozen such families grouped together in a village community may hold no more than a few square miles of land, the bulk of which would be grazing land for the herds or flocks. Herdsmen, who concentrate mostly on the nurture of their animals, usually have much larger territorial claims than farmers. Larger herds and flocks will require more grazing land and not uncommonly will force the herdsmen to migrate seasonally for hundreds of miles with their animals to find adequate supplies of grass. Even such nomads, however, may own fields in which they sow grain at one season, returning to reap their crop at a later season. Agriculture and animal husbandry are usually combined to some degree, although absolute specialization in one or the other is a possible self-sufficient way of life.

Small village communities offer many advantages to predominantly agricultural people. Several families can group their houses, storage bins, and stables together in order to provide protection for themselves, their stored foods, and their animals. A substantial body of people is also available in case of need to defend growing crops or flocks in the field. No special group organization beyond that of the advanced hunters and gatherers is necessary for a small village community. However, the amount of property owned by individuals and families gives rise to problems of ownership. Most basic are those concerning ownership of house and field plots. Property lines are established through mutual agreement and by occupation of worked plots of land, with disputes mediated by the more experienced and respected members of the village community. These community leaders are also most likely to take charge of communal distribution of food supplies in case of group shortages due to crop failure, raiding, or other reasons.

A crisis might arise in a village community from population increase as a result of substantial food production. If an extended family grows too large to be supported on its land holdings, then new holdings will have to be found. If open land is not available within a reasonable distance from the village, men may set out to establish villages of their own on new territory. Such expansion will first occur throughout areas where agriculture is supported by natural precipitation. However, if fields are irrigated, crops can be grown in drier climates than would support the plants normally. Once agriculture is established in temperate lands, the need for the proper amount of rain to fall on the crops at the proper time is established as one of man's enduring topics of conversation. The relationship between growing plants and water is easily enough understood, and where rainfall is insufficient most men are probably intelligent enough to see the possibility of carrying water from rivers or springs to the fields or of digging artificial channels to divert water from these sources to the fields. We cannot say what it takes to motivate men to actualize such possibilities, but need in time of drought would surely be enough in some cases. When village farms do move out of the areas in which their crops will ordinarily grow under natural rainfall to areas so dry that irrigation is necessary, then they begin to exert even greater control over the environment than before and thus become dependent on an artificial environment they create. Agriculture might also begin in marginal areas where rivers provide naturally irrigated flood plains.

The development of agriculture and animal husbandry in itself suggests a climate of thought in which men are receptive to innovation; that is, the domestication of plants and animals requires some experimentation. Men must choose and try various species; they must think of possibilities, plan in order to actualize these possibilities, and then evaluate the results. Even if domestication arose out of accidental garbage-plot gardens and keeping pets, once it suggested a way of life, men would experiment with different species and ways of growing them, sometimes through the force of circumstances but also out of curiosity. Besides direct concerns with animals and plants, efforts would be expended on the invention and elaboration of tools to care for them. Although all individuals of a given age and sex would be engaged in more or less the same kinds of work for subsistence, they would naturally tend to specialize in different crafts. A partial division of labor could thus develop. There would also be individual specialization in the conduct of ritualistic celebrations and in the production of art forms. Craft, ritual, and art skills might be perfected further in games and contests of some utilitarian value.

The domesticator's way of life is adaptable to many different environments. Just as the overall pattern of the way of life of hunters and gatherers might be followed in various plant and animal environments, so might the techniques of domestication, agriculture, and animal husbandry. In many cases, it is the pattern alone that is transferred from one environment and one group of people to another, rather than the content. However, many domesticated plants and animals are also quite adaptable to new environments, and so are transferred along with the way of life. Domesticators improve their crops and animals by breeding selectively for large, healthy, and manageable producers. It is both the wide applicability of the pattern and the malleability of the domesticates that permit the wide distribution of this way of life.

To be potential domesticates, plants and animals must occur in sufficient numbers and be hardy enough to survive the changes man imposes on them by confining them to ways that suit his own purposes. They must be able not only to survive but to respond to his efforts to train them to new ways. Most important, they must continue to reproduce as domesticates. These conditions being fulfilled, men might simply keep control of the movements of their herds and continue to sow a part of the seeds from the crops they harvest. However, the crucial feature of domestication is man's control over the breeding of his domesticates. He improves his crops by sowing only selected seeds and his animals by allowing only those with desirable features to breed. This requires the knowledge that characteristics of plants and animals are passed on to successive generations; few domesticators have failed to understand and take advantage of this fact. It has led to the development of wooly sheep and heavy-headed grains. In fact, many varieties of animals and plants of the same species are adapted to such different environments that extreme varieties of a single species often cannot survive in the same environment.

Man's control of the breeding of his domesticates sometimes becomes so complete that some of them could not survive without his aid. This is especially true of animals that have been bred to be docile and stupid and then cannot protect themselves from wild predators, and of varieties of grain that have been developed with tough stems to retain seeds, which then resist natural sowing by wind and weather. Domesticates depend for life on man, but man himself depends on them. Thus in securing his food supply through agriculture and animal husbandry, man becomes very dependent on his own creations.

Domesticators must care for and, in a broad sense, cultivate the earth itself. Land must be prepared for sowing by hoeing or raking and some attention must be given to the eradication of competing wild plants. Animals must be herded as much as possible so that they do not overgraze an area, killing plants that otherwise would recover and grow to provide new grazing. In dry regions, canals must be dug and natural water courses altered for irrigation. Small barrage dams may be built to store water from occasional rains, and springs may be dug out and improved. From this man gains a notion of the malleability and manipulability not only of the raw materials from which he makes his tools and the plants and animals he domesticates, but also of the earth—the land itself. Man learns that much of the physical environment is amenable to his control and that success in its control means a rich food supply and a correspondingly secure life. He can mold to his desires wood and stone, plants and animals, and overcome to some extent even the imperatives of climate and weather by altering land surfaces and water courses. An expression of major environmental control is the invention of the well. Villages can be established outside the range where natural rainfall is sufficient for agriculture if a water supply is available for irrigation. But even in areas of sufficient rainfall, villages must be located close enough to rivers or springs so that men and animals have water to drink. Once the principles and techniques of well digging are developed, more land is opened to village farming, and more freedom is possible in choosing village sites.

Each group of domesticators, whether it concentrates primarily on village farming or on nomadic pastoralism, is a self-sufficient unit. All the subsistence needs of the group are provided for from their crops and animals and from the immediate environment. Techniques such as skin curing, weaving, and sewing, which occur among advanced hunters and gatherers, are elaborated. Among man's ways of life we have described so far, this is the first that is so successful that it can provide enough food to allow a large increase in population. Although it involves specialized dependence on only a few species of plants and animals, as does the life of hunters and gatherers, the new way is not simply a method for procuring food—hunting and gathering what nature offers—but a method for *producing* food. Agriculture and animal husbandry have been mechanized in modern times, but the basic principles remain the same. Farmers and herdsmen are almost the sole producers of food for human beings today. Modern food supplies are supplemented only to a small degree by products of hunting and gathering—primarily sea animals and wild plants.

The increase in population made possible by more food is paralleled by an increase in density of population made possible by the new techniques of food production that require relatively small plots of land. Such increases in turn make possible more interaction among people—interaction of both a friendly and an antagonistic nature. Friendly interchanges within and among villages can include some trading in both essential and nonessential goods. Trade could develop naturally among newly sedentary peoples who may have roamed over several ecological zones and been exposed to a wide variety of resources before they settled as villagers with limited territory. No man survives through his skill in any particular craft, be it making hoe handles or music, but he can certainly add to the amenities of his life by trading the products of his special abilities. Some obvious antagonistic encounters would be individual theft, group raiding, and warfare among villages. But again, neither the craftsmen nor the warriors would be full-time specialists in these activities. Certain men may have better memories and imaginations for tradition and ritual, and other men may be more adept at measuring, calculating, and recording; but every man must work in the same way as farmers or herdsmen to survive. There is no full-time specialization in non-food-producing work.

Although individuals are not identified by separate craft specializations, since they are all primarily engaged in the same kind of work, there are still various classifications based on age and property holdings. Labor is divided between the sexes, and within each sex there is also division based on age. Young boys often work with their mothers and sisters, learning their jobs. As they grow older, they help their fathers, and then at maturity work as do the other men. But, since some men and some families will inevitably work harder and more shrewdly than others, they will accumulate and maintain larger holdings of land. Such property will pass down hereditary lines in the families and can be enlarged or decreased through marriage. Class distinctions may develop between large and small property holders, but these distinctions will have little impact on the basic social structure of the villages, since the imperatives of hand labor will not allow greatly diverse property holdings. Leadership, however, will probably more often fall to larger property holders in recognition of the fact that those who control a large property must be intelligent and hardworking.

The control the domesticator of plants and animals exerts over the physical environment is control of the basic source of food energy. Plants capture the radiant energy of the sun and reorganize and store it in the production of seeds and vegetable matter. Animals can utilize the stored energy of plants by eating them and their seeds. By domesticating plants, man gains control over the primary food source for animals. By domesticating animals, he gains control over living organisms that eat plants and greatly concentrate the energy they derive in the form of animal protein. Thus man taps the primary source of food energy by controlling plants, and he assures himself high protein food by controlling animals. In the most general sense, domestication allows man to gain indirect control over some of the sun's radiant energy. Through this control he increases his food supply, with the result that he can live longer and reproduce in greater numbers; both of these facts promote further alterations of the physical environment by man.

The invention of domestication permits a way of life which is extremely successful in solving the problem of food procurement for man. Equally important, it promotes the notion in man that he can modify the physical environment at will to serve his own purposes more fully. A culminating expression of the malleability of the earth is the invention of pottery. Clay can be molded into many forms, and many villagers use it to make unfired bricks for buildings and walls. Long before the invention of pottery, men become familiar with the plastic qualities of clay and with the fact that the application of heat or fire can lead to changes in materials. Particularly in cooking, many chemical and physical changes take place which are of great utility to man. Elemental men use fire to form and harden the wooden points of spears and to cook food. The villagers learn that molded clay can be hardened in fire so that vessels can be made that are impervious to insects, small rodents, and water. The control of such an important process of transforming the raw materials of the earth is of parallel importance to the control of plants and animals. The principles of kiln firing are basic to the techniques of metallurgy, which we will discuss in the next chapter, and the alterations of raw materials controlled in these processes spur men to the experimentation that results in modern chemistry and that ultimately gives man much greater control over the physical environment. For all the control the simplest forms of farming and animal husbandry allow—and they are sufficient for changing the face of the earth and altering the worldwide ecological balance—the actual amount of energy controlled by man with these techniques is very small, since all the work he accomplishes is the result of hand labor.

Part II | HYPOTHESES TO EXPLAIN THE INITIAL SHIFT TO AGRICULTURE

2 THE NEOLITHIC REVOLUTION

(EXCERPT)

V. Gordon Childe

THE PERIOD when the food-producing economy became established was one of climatic crises adversely affecting precisely that zone of arid sub-tropical countries where the earliest farmers appear, and where the wild ancestors of cultivated cereals and domestic animals actually lived. The melting of the European ice sheets and the contraction of the high pressures or anticyclones over them involved a northward shift in the normal path of the rain-bearing depressions from the Atlantic. The showers that had watered North Africa and Arabia were deflected over Europe. Desiccation set in. Of course the process was not sudden or catastrophic. At first and for long, the sole harbinger would be the greater severity and longer duration of periodical droughts. But quite a small reduction in the rainfall would work a devastating change in countries that were always relatively dry. It would mean the difference between continuous grasslands and sandy deserts interrupted by occasional oases.

A number of animals that could live comfortably with a twelve-inch annual rainfall would become a surplus population if the precipitation diminished by a couple of inches for two or three years on end. To get food and water, the grasseaters would have to congregate round a diminishing number of springs and streams—in oases. There they would be more exposed than ever to the attacks of beasts of prey—lions, leopards, and wolves—that would also gravitate to the oases for water. And they would be brought up against man too; for the same causes would force even hunters to frequent the springs and valleys. The huntsman and his prey thus find themselves united in an effort to circumvent the dreadful power of

Extracted from "The Neolithic Revolution," in *Man Makes Himself*, 1951, pp. 67–72. Reprinted by permission of the publisher, C. A. Watts & Co. Ltd., London.

drought. But if the hunter is also a cultivator, he will have something
to offer the famished beasts: the stubble of his freshly reaped fields
will afford the best grazing in the oasis. Once the grains are
garnered, the cultivator can tolerate half-starved mouflons or wild
oxen trespassing upon his garden plots. Such will be too weak to run
away, too thin to be worth killing for food. Instead, man can study
their habits, drive off the lions and wolves that would prey upon
them, and perhaps even offer them some surplus grain from his
stores. The beasts, for their part, will grow tame and accustomed
to man's proximity.

Hunters today, and doubtless in prehistoric times, have been
accustomed to make pets of young wild animals for ritual ends
or just for fun. Man has allowed the dog to frequent his camp
in return for the offal of his prey and refuse from his feasts. Under
the conditions of incipient desiccation the cultivator has the chance
of attaching to his ménage not only isolated young beasts, but the
remnants of complete flocks or herds, comprising animals of both
sexes and all ages. If he just realizes the advantage of having a
group of such half-tamed beasts hanging round the fringes of his
settlement as a reserve of game easily caught, he will be on the
way to domestication.

Next he must exercise restraint and discrimination in using this
reserve of meat. He must refrain from frightening the beasts un-
necessarily or killing the youngest and tamest. Once he begins to
kill only the shyest and least amenable bulls or rams, he will have
started selective breeding, eliminating untractable brutes, and consequently favoring the more docile. But he must also use his new
opportunities of studying the life of the beasts at close range. He
will thus learn about the processes of reproduction, the animals'
needs of food and water. He must act upon his knowledge. Instead
of merely driving the herd away when the time comes round for
sowing his plots again, he must follow the beasts, guide them to
suitable pastures and water, and continue to ward off predatory
carnivora. It can thus be imagined how with lapse of time a flock
or a herd should have been bred that was not only tame, but
actually dependent upon man.

That result could happen only provided the peculiar climatic
conditions continued long enough, and suitable animals were haunt-
ing human settlements. No doubt experiments were tried with various species; herds of antelopes and gazelles were kept by the

Egyptians about 3000 B.C. These and other unknown experiments were fruitless. Luckily, cattle, sheep, goats, and pigs were included in the wild fauna of the desiccated regions in Asia. These did become firmly attached to man and ready to follow him.

At first the tame or domesticated beast would presumably be regarded only as a potential source of meat, an easily accessible sort of game. Other uses would be discovered later. It might be noticed that crops flourished best on plots that had been grazed over. Ultimately the value of dung as a fertilizer would be realized. The process of milking can only have been discovered when men had had ample opportunity of studying at close quarters the suckling of calves and lambs and kids. But once the trick was grasped, milk would become a second staple. It could be obtained without killing the beast, without touching your capital. Selection would again be applied. The best milkers would be spared, and their young reared in preference to other calves, lambs, or kids. Still later the hair of sheep or goats would win appreciation. It could be treated by processes, perhaps originally applied to plant fibers, and woven into cloth or else beaten into felt. Wool is entirely the artificial product of selective breeding. On wild sheep it is merely a down between the hairs. It was still unknown to the Egyptians even after 3000 B.C. But in Mesopotamia sheep were being bred for their wool before that date. The harnessing of animals to bear burdens or draw plows and vehicles is a late adaptation, and will be considered among the steps leading up to the second revolution in human economy.

The minimal characteristics of simple cultivation have already been considered. But these must now be pictured as combined with stock-breeding if we are to understand the basic economy revealed in neolithic settlements in North Africa, Hither Asia, and Europe. If the number of animals kept remains quite small, the account already given will hold good: the animals will be put to graze on the stubble after the harvest and at other seasons on natural pastures round the settlement. Beyond telling off a few youths to look after the herd, the communal economy can be left as already described. But as soon as the flocks exceed a low limit, special provision may have to be made for them. Trees and scrub may be burned off to make room for grass. In a river valley it may be thought worth-while to clear or irrigate special meadows to serve as pasture for cattle. Crops may be deliberately grown, harvested, and conserved to serve exclusively as fodder. Or the animals may be driven far afield to find pastures in the dry season. In Mediterranean lands, Persia, and Asia Minor there is good summer grazing on the hills which in winter are snow-clad. And so sheep and cattle are driven up to hill pastures in the spring. And now a regular company of the village's inhabitants must accompany the herds to ward off wild beasts, to milk the cows and ewes. The herders must generally take with them supplies of grain and other equipment. In some cases the fraction of the community that migrate with their gear to the summer pastures is quite small. But in hot and dry countries, like Persia, parts of the Eastern Sudan, and in the northwestern Himalayas, the bulk of the community abandons its village in the stifling valley and accompanies the herds to the cooler hills. Only a few stay behind to look after the fields and dwellings.

From this it is no far cry to a purely pastoral economy in which cultivation plays a negligible role. Pure pastoral nomadism is familiar, and is illustrated by several peoples in the Old World; the Bedouin of Arabia and Mongolian tribes of Central Asia are the best-known examples. How old such a mode of life may be is uncertain. Pastoralists are not likely to leave many vestiges by which the archaeologist could recognize their presence. They tend to use vessels of leather and basketry instead of pots, to live in tents instead of in excavated shelters or huts supported by stout timber posts or walls of stone or brick. Leather vessels and baskets have as a rule no chance of surviving; tents need not even leave deep post holes to mark where they once stood. (Though wood decays, modern archaeology can recognize the hole made by a post five thousand years ago.)

The failure to recognize prehistoric settlement sites or groups of relics belonging to pure pastoralists is not in itself any proof that such did not exist. To that extent the postulate of the "historical school," that pure pastoralism and pure hoe-culture were originally practiced independently by separate peoples and that mixed farming resulted from their subsequent fusion, is irrefutable. Yet Forde has recently emphasized the instability of pure pastoralism. Many typical pastoral tribes today, like the patriarchs in Genesis, actually cultivate grain, though in an incidental and rather casual manner. If they grow no grain themselves, pastoral nomads are almost always economically dependent upon settled peasant villages. The cultivators may be tributaries or serfs to the pastoralists, but they are essential to their subsistence.

Whatever its origin, stock-breeding gave man control over his own food supply in the same way as cultivation did. In mixed farming it becomes an equal partner in the food-producing economy. But just as the term "cultivation" covers many distinct modes of gaining a livelihood, so the single phrase "mixed farming" marks an equal disparity and diversity. The several different modes of cultivation may be combined in varying degrees with distinct attitudes to the livestock. The diversity of the permutations and combinations has just been suggested. The multiplicity of concrete applications of the food-producing economy must never be forgotten.

It must be remembered, too, that food-production does not at once supersede food-gathering. If today hunting is only a ritual sport and game is a luxury for the rich, fishing is still a great industry, contributing directly to everybody's diet. At first hunting, fowling, fishing, the collection of fruits, snails, and grubs continued to be essential activities in the food-quest of any food-producing group. Grain and milk began as mere supplements to a diet of game, fish, berries, nuts, and ants' eggs. Probably at first cultivation was an incidental activity of the women while their lords were engaged in the really serious business of the chase. Only slowly did it win the status of an independent and ultimately predominant industry. When the archaeological record first reveals neolithic communities in Egypt and Iran, survivals from the food-gathering régime clearly stand on an equal footing with grain-growing and stock-breeding. Only subsequently does their economic importance decline. After the second revolution, hunting and fowling have become, as with us, ritual sports, or else, like fishing, specialized industries practiced by groups within the community or by independent societies, economically dependent upon an agricultural civilization.

Two other aspects of the simple food-producing economy deserve attention. In the first place, food-production, even in its simplest form, provides an opportunity and a motive for the accumulation of a surplus. A crop must not be consumed as soon as it is reaped. The grains must be conserved and eked out so as to last till the next harvest, for a whole year. And a proportion of every crop must be set aside for seed. The conservation is easy. But it means on the one hand forethought and thrift, on the other receptacles for storage.

These are quite as essential as, and may actually be more elaborate than, dwellings. In the neolithic villages of the Fayum, perhaps the oldest of their kind, excavated silos, lined with straw basketry or matting, are the most substantial constructions that have survived.

Again, livestock that has been laboriously carried over the dry season must not be indiscriminately slaughtered and devoured. The young cows and ewes at least must be spared and reared to provide milk and to augment the herd or flock. Once these ideas have been driven home, the production and accumulation of a surplus are much easier for food-producers than for food gatherers. The yield of crops and of herds soon outstrips the immediate needs of the community. The storage of grain, the conservation of live meat "on the hoof" is much simpler, especially in a warm climate, than the preservation of stocks of slaughtered game. The surplus thus gathered will help to tide the community over bad seasons; it will form a reserve against droughts and crop failures. It will serve to support a growing population. Ultimately it may constitute a basis for rudimentary trade, and so pave the way to a second revolution.

Secondly, the economy is entirely self-sufficing. The simple food-producing community is not dependent for any necessity of life on imports obtained by barter or exchange from another group. It produces and collects all the food it needs. It relies on raw materials available in its immediate vicinity for the simple equipment it demands. Its constituent members or households manufacture the requisite implements, utensils, and weapons.

This economic self-sufficiency does not necessarily spell isolation. The variations in the simple food-producing economy already indicated, the simultaneous pursuit of several methods of obtaining nourishment by different groups, are liable to bring the several communities concerned into mutual contact. Driving their flocks to summer pastures, the herdsmen from one village are likely to meet their counterparts from another. On hunting expeditions across the desert, huntsmen from one oasis may cross parties from another. In such ways the isolation of each community is liable to be broken down. Far from being a scattering of discrete units, the neolithic world should be viewed as a continuous chain of communities. Each would be linked to its neighbors on either side by recurrent, if infrequent and irregular, contacts.

The simple food-producing economy just described is an abstraction. Our picture is based on a selection of supposedly distinctive traits from materials afforded by ethnographers' observations on modern "savages" and inferences from particular archaeological sites. The precise stage of economic development here adumbrated may never have been fully realized in precisely this concrete form. Archaeology alone could justify the presentation of a "neolithic" economy as a universal historical stage in the progress towards modern civilization. But all archaeology can do at present is to isolate temporary phases in what was really a continuous process. We have tacitly assumed that similar phases were realized nearly simultaneously in several areas. But in prehistoric times such simultaneity cannot be proved, even in the cases of regions so close together as Tasa in Middle Egypt, the Fayum, and the Delta. Strict parallelism in time between Egypt and, say, North Syria would be hard to establish. To claim it as between Egypt and North Europe would be almost certainly false; our best examples of a simple food-producing economy in Britain or Belgium are to be dated in terms of solar years perhaps thirty centuries later than their counterparts in Egypt. And we have deliberately cited contemporary savage groups as illustrating the same economic stage.

3 POST-PLEISTOCENE ADAPTATIONS

Lewis R. Binford

THIS PAPER will examine some of the major assumptions underlying the current systematics of the archeological remains of the
post-Pleistocene period. The paper falls into three parts: (1) a
brief survey of the history of research on the immediately post-
Pleistocene period, with particular attention to the conditions affecting research orientation and, consequently, systematics; (2) an assessment of the utility of current concepts, schemes, and arguments
which are advanced to explain cultural events of the post-Pleistocene
period; and (3) the outlining of a different approach for understanding the nature and extent of cultural changes occurring during
the period.

The archeological remains of the immediately post-Pleistocene
period are generally termed Mesolithic. They are characterized over
wide areas by the appearance of small, highly specialized flint implements; these occur frequently on later sites in the coastal and
riverine regions in the context of the systematic exploitation of
aquatic resources.

Until 1892, there was widespread agreement among European
scholars that there was a break, or "hiatus," in the archeological
record between the Paleolithic and Neolithic epochs (Brown 1893;
G. deMortillet 1885:479–84; Breuil 1946:25).

> It has generally been assumed that a break occurred between the
> periods during which this country, and in fact the continent of
> Europe, was inhabited by Palaeolithic Man and his Neolithic suc-
> cessors, and that the race or races of Palaeolithic folk who hunted the
> elephant, rhinoceros, cave bear, hippopotamus, reindeer, *ursus*, bison,
> etc., were completely seperated as by a chasm from the agricultural
> people, the herdsmen with their oxen and sheep, and the tillers of the

Reprinted from Sally R. Binford and Lewis R. Binford, editors, *New Perspectives in Archeology* (Chicago: Aldine Publishing Company, 1968); copyright © 1968 by Sally R. Binford and Lewis R. Binford.

soil of the so-called Neolithic epoch, implying that man in Britain had changed suddenly from the low savage hunter to a half-civilized farmer and drover.

A. C. Carlyle who conducted archeological investigations in the Vindhya Hills of Central India between 1868 and 1888 was the first to use the term "mezolithic." Carlyle was also one of the early questioners of the validity of the hiatus between the Paleolithic and Neolithic. Carlyle's excavations yielded typical crescents, trapezoids, and other geometric microliths; it was asserted that these implements were found both with late Paleolithic tools and pottery. This led him to propose that there was no hiatus in India and that the microliths constituted an intermediate industry to which he applied the term "mezolithic." These materials were exhibited in England in 1888 at the Royal Albert Hall.

Carlyle's findings served to stimulate John Allen Brown (1889) who published an article summarizing Carlyle's work. In this article, Brown asked if there had been similar microlithic forms found in the British Isles, pointing out that they were already reported from Tunis, Egypt, Italy, Palestine, France, Portugal, and the Crimea. Brown's main concern was with documenting the widespread occurrences of microliths, and he offered no chronological interpretation. Wilson (1894) reported that in 1892, the U. S. National Museum acquired much of Carlyle's material, and he proposed the acceptance of the Mesolithic as a transitional period between the Paleolithic and Neolithic.

The following year Brown (1893) published an extensive paper in which he discussed the problem of the hiatus. He went on to argue in favor of an unbroken continuity between the Paleolithic and Neolithic, setting forth four stages: Eolithic, Paleolithic, Mesolithic, and Neolithic. He based this four-fold division on the transformational sequence of axes, from the crude forms of the "Drift" to the well-made polished types of the Neolithic. He documented finds of "intermediate" forms and used a scale of crude-to-fine as evidence for historical continuity, citing Pitt-Rivers' (1906:20–44) argument that such a transformational sequence indicated historical continuity. Occupation of the same caves by Paleolithic and Neolithic populations is cited as further support for the claim of continuity.

The following year, Boyd Dawkins (1894:243) challenged Brown's views:

I shall first of all address myself to the point as to continuity in this country. Is there any evidence that the Palaeolithic shaded off into the Neolithic age in this country without any such break as I have mentioned above? Next, I shall examine the facts bearing on the point outside of the British Isles, premising that the evolution of the Neolithic from the Palaeolithic stage of culture in some part of the world may be accepted as a high probability, although we may be unable to fix with precision the land where this transition took place.

Dawkins (1894:274) went on to question the validity of the reasoning behind the claims for continuity and concluded: "The exploration of caverns has not, I submit, yet resulted in establishing a 'continuity' but simply a sequence."

The English literature of the early 1890's is full of arguments on these issues, and similar questions were also occupying continental scholars. The formal changes in the archeological record were the subject of controversy, both with regard to the meaning of the observed changes and the reality of a hiatus. Lartet and G. de-Mortillet claimed as early as 1872 that the apparent break in the archeological record was in reality simply a gap in knowledge and did not represent a period during which Europe was not occupied (Piette 1895b:235–36). Cartailhac, on the other hand, stated that the hiatus consituted a major break in the occupancy of the continent. In 1875 the Congress of Prehistory held a meeting at Nantes, and an argument was presented which attempted to disprove Cartailhac's position by pointing to formal similarities between the flints from Solutré and those of the Neolithic period (Piette 1895b: 238).

Shortly after this, artifacts were found which were dated to the period between the remains of the Magdalenian, or "reindeer," period and that of the Lake Dwellers, the Robenhausian. In 1879 Vielle discovered microliths at Fère-en-Tardenois (1890:961). Almost ten years later Piette made his discoveries at Mas d'Azil where microliths were found in association with modern fauna. The deposits in question overlay the Magdalenian and lacked the features then considered diagnostic of the Neolithic (Piette 1895a). These finds were followed by surveys of locations with microliths (A. de-Mortillet 1896), and there was a proliferation of names for these industries which were said to fill the hiatus (see Coutil 1912). New excavations were also carried out (deLoe 1908; Herve 1899).

In the years following World War I, there was a marked increase of interest in the post-Pleistocene period, and a number of regional syntheses were made (Kozlowski 1926; Clark 1932; 1936; Childe 1931; 1937). Further, there was an extension of European terms to non-European materials which were considered intermediate between the Paleolithic and Neolithic (Garrod 1932; Garrod, Bate 1937). Some general works also appeared in which data from various regions were summarized and compared (Obermaier 1924a; Osborn 1919; deMorgan 1924; MacCurdy 1924; Menghin 1929). Specific syntheses of the Mesolithic period proper have appeared (Burkitt 1925; Gimbutas 1956; 1963). In these various summary and interpretive writings, there are several distinct lines of reasoning, leading to a diversity of opinion as to the historical significance of the archeological record.

One line of argument sought to demonstrate that the Mesolithic represented a way of life, and a subsistence base, intermediate in a developmental sequence between the reindeer hunters of the terminal Pleistocene and the food-producing villagers of the Neolithic. For example, Piette claimed that there was evidence for the domestication of the horse by the Solutreans, reindeer by the Magdalenians, and cattle by the occupants of Mas d'Azil who also, according to Piette, domesticated plants (Piette 1895b). Less extravagant claims have recently been made for the transitional nature of the Baltic materials (Troels-Smith 1953) and those from Central Europe (Pittioni 1962b). Few workers, however, have seriously considered the European Mesolithic as a stage transitional to the later food-producing societies.

Other workers were more concerned with the problem of the continuity (or lack of it) between the human groups responsible for the Paleolithic and Mesolithic. Osborn (1919:457) saw in each change in form of archeological assemblages evidence for the invasion of new "races." Others argued that the presence or absence of discrete traits was diagnostic of population stability or change. For example, Grahame Clark (1932:2) and Menghin (1929) based their claims for historical continuity between the Paleolithic and Mesolithic on the continued use of core tools. Obermaier (1924a:324), on the other hand, viewed the shift to the exploitation of aquatic resources in Ertebølle and the Auterian as justifying the postulation of movement of new people into Western Europe. DeMorgan (1924:74) saw the adoption of microliths and the loss of graphic arts as "revolutionary" and as proof of a major break in historical continuity. Childe (1925:2), Clark (1932:1), Gimbu-

tas (1956) and Braidwood (1967) are in general agreement that
the Mesolithic of Europe is a continuation of the Paleolithic way
of life and that the observed archeological changes can be related
directly to the major climatic changes of the post-Pleistocene
period. These authors do differ, however, on the degree to which
changes in the form of archeological assemblages can be explained
by reference to new populations or to "influences" from other cultures.

We have attempted to show in this brief historical survey that
Mesolithic research has been characterized by a series of changing
questions and that the answers to any one question have tended to
generate new questions. The initial problem was to determine
whether or not Europe was occupied between the end of the
Paleolithic and the beginning of the Neolithic. The affirmative answer to this problem led to the question of historical continuity. Consideration of this problem necessitated consideration of the criteria
for evaluation of formal archeological variations in terms of their
meaning for population change or lack of change. There was considerable diversity of opinion on this question.

Although problems of interpretive theory and method were never
solved (S. R. Binford 1968; Sackett 1968), they began to occupy
scholars less and less as more detailed knowledge of the archeological record accumulated. Local sequences were worked out, and
a more limited geographical perspective led to greater conservatism
in interpretive viewpoints. Most recent workers have used a dif-
fusionist model for interpreting geographic variations in archeological data, with the postulation of actual movement of peoples
playing a minor role (see, for example, Waterbolk 1962). The
problem of historical continuity *vs.* population movement has not
been so much solved as circumvented; this circumvention has involved two means: first, application of one's own criteria to an extremely detailed sequence in a very limited area making it almost
impossible for other workers to judge interpretations offered; and
second, stressing certain widespread "traits" in macroregional syntheses, traits which are usually so generalized that one might question
their relevance to the measurement of detailed changes in culture
history.

The work of the past 100 years has resulted in the accumulation
of sufficient data to justify some generalizations made by workers in
the field of European Mesolithic studies. Some of the generalizations
made in distinguishing the Paleolithic from the Mesolithic are:

1. *There was a major shift in the centers of population growth in Western Europe.* "During the Upper Magdalenian, the density of population was relatively high in France, as evidenced by the great number of sites occupied for the first time, and by the richness of the sites. . . . The end of the glacial times was fatal to this striking human expansion. The disappearance of the cold fauna and the replacement of the steppe, rich in game, by forests was followed by the demographic recession and breakup of the Upper Paleolithic cultures resulting in the traditions which are grouped together under the general name of Mesolithic" (deSonneville-Bordes 1960; 1963a:354; 1963b; Sackett 1968).

2. *There was a major change in the form of stone tools.* "Small, geometric flints became very common, and the bow and arrow became widespread during the immediately post-Pleistocene period. The changes have occasionally been taken as defining features of the Mesolithic" (Childe 1956:96; Gabel 1958a:658).

3. *There is greater geographic variety in cultural remains suggesting more specific responses to local environmental conditions.* See deMorgan (1924:74); Garrod, Bate (1937:121); Braidwood, Willey (1962b:333); Schwabedissen (1962:260); Pittioni (1962b:218); deSonneville-Bordes (1960:497–500; 1963) for specific statements of this generalization.

4. *There was a marked increase in the exploitation of aquatic resources and wild fowl.* This statement scarcely requires documentation since it is practically a definiens of the Mesolithic (cf. Gabel 1958a:661).

5. *There was a "trend" toward small game hunting.* Braidwood (1962:332) notes that this phenomenon has traditionally been explained as a response to the extinction of large mammals at the close of the Pleistocene. He points out, however, that this trend occurs before the end of the Pleistocene and characterizes Africa and India as well as Europe (see also Gimbutas 1956:14).

6. *The Mesolithic represents cultural degeneration when compared with the Upper Paleolithic.* This is generally cited in the context of discussions of the Western European materials and the loss of graphic arts (see Osborn 1919:456; deMorgan 1924:73; Clark 1932:1; Sollas 1924:595; deSonneville-Bordes 1960:498). Reference is also made to the less prestigeful activity of fishing and shellfish collecting, as opposed to reindeer hunting (Osborn 1919:457).

These generalizations which summarize archeological observations have been conceived by most European scholars in the following manner (see Clark 1962:100):

1. There are major changes in cultural remains which serve to differentiate the cultural systems of the terminal Pleistocene from those of the immediately post-Pleistocene period.

2. This immediately post-Pleistocene period is further characterized by major changes in pollen profiles, fossil beach lines, and the geomorphology of major drainage systems.

3. The demonstrable correlation between the dramatic cultural and environmental changes at this time is evidence for the systematic articulation of cultural and environmental systems.

Therefore:

a) Archeological differences observed between the terminal Paleolithic and the Mesolithic can be explained by reference to environmental changes.

b) Differences not explained by reference to environmental changes are the result of new social contacts; such social contacts were a result of movement of populations in response to local climatic deterioration (for example, the "desiccation" of North Africa cited by Clark 1936:xiv).

This argument is a relatively straightforward mechanistic approach and is completely compatible with a materialistic, systemic approach to the understanding of cultural change. The extent to which this approach might be questioned and the particulars of its application tested depends upon the degree to which: (1) equally radical changes in culture can be demonstrated in the absence of analogous environmental changes, and/or (2) major environmental changes can be demonstrated to vary independently of analogous changes in cultural systems.

Such test situations can be found either at a contemporary time period outside the area directly affected by the retreat of glacial ice or in the same regions under similar environmental conditions at a different time period. Researchers concerned with the initial appearance of food-production, as well as those workers operating in a variety of non-Western European regions, are the ones to whom we now turn for an evaluation of the explanatory approach commonly used on Western European materials.

The shift from food-procurement to food-production has been examined by many scholars; Childe (1925) termed this change the Neolithic Revolution. In *The Dawn of European Civilization* Childe suggested that the investigation of the origins of the Neolithic and its spread into Europe would be a major step in the understanding of the post-Mesolithic history of Western Europe. In his *New Light on the Most Ancient East* Childe (1952) offered a model to explain the beginnings of the Neolithic Revolution. Until this point, several other workers had considered the problems of understanding the conditions surrounding the origins of agriculture, and some offered idealistic progressions of conditions under which man would have gained sufficient knowledge of plant and animal biology to permit cultivation (Darwin 1875:326–27; Roth 1887). Others offered mechanistic generalizations about the conditions under which man would have been most likely to have implemented his knowledge (Tylor 1881:214; deCandolle 1959). Childe's (1951b:23–25) consideration of the problem was the most influential, since he presented a series of propositions specific enough to be tested through the collection of paleoenvironmental and paleoanthropological data:

> Food production—the deliberate cultivation of food plants, especially cereals, and the taming, breeding and selection of animals . . . was an economic revolution . . . the greatest in human history after the mastery of fire. . . . The conditions of incipient desiccation . . . would provide the stimulus towards the adoption of a food-producing economy. Enforced concentration by the banks of streams and shrinking springs would entail an intensive search for means of nourishment. Animals and men would be herded together in oases that were becoming increasingly isolated by desert tracts. Such enforced juxtaposition might promote that sort of symbiosis between man and beast implied by the word domestication.

If it was Childe who first provided a set of testable propositions as to the conditions under which food-production was achieved, it was Braidwood who actively sought the field data to test Childe's propositions. For a short history of the Iraqi-Jarmo project, the reader is referred to Braidwood and Howe (1960:1–8); we shall simply summarize the findings of Braidwood and his co-workers with specific reference to the validity of the oasis theory and to the materialistic approach to the understanding of culture change. In discussing the oasis theory Braidwood (1951a:85) states:

> So far this theory is pretty much all guess-work, and there are certainly some questions it leaves unanswered. I will tell you quite frankly that there are times when I feel it is plain balderdash.

Braidwood (1951a:86) also questioned the relevance of the postu-
ated environmental changes to the origins of food-production:

> There had also been three earlier periods of great glaciers, and long
> periods of warm weather in between. . . . Thus the forced neighbor-
> liness of men, plants and animals in river valleys and oases must also
> have happened earlier. Why didn't domestication happen earlier too,
> then?

Braidwood has made the above point on numerous occasions, but
it is in more recent publications (Braidwood, Willey 1962b:342)
that the comment is less directly aimed at the oasis theory and
more toward questioning the role of environmental change in bringing about food-production.

Braidwood's work in the "hilly flanks" zone of the Fertile Crescent
was carried out over a number of years and involved the collaboration of a number of scientists from the fields of zoology, paleontology,
geology, palynology, paleobotany, etc. Their investigations had been
directed toward the identification of the physical effects of domestication on plants and animals and the documentation of the environmental events of the period between 10,000 B.C. and the appearance of "settled village life." The climatological-environmental
results have allowed Braidwood (1952b:11) to generalize:

> It seems most unlikely that there was any really significant difference
> between then and now in the general land forms and rainfall patterns.
> In southwestern Asia . . . our colleagues in the natural sciences see no
> evidence for radical change in climate or fauna between the levels
> of the Zarzian and those of the Jarmo or Hassunah phases (Braid-
> wood, Howe 1960:181).

Discussing specifically the relationship between environmental
change and the beginnings of food-production, Braidwood and Howe
(1960:142) state:

> We do not believe that the answers will lie within the realm of en-
> vironmental determinism and in any direct or strict sense . . . we and
> our natural-science colleagues reviewed the evidence for possible
> pertinent fluctuations of climate and of plant and animal distribu-
> tions . . . and convinced ourselves that there is no such evidence
> available . . . no evidence exists for such changes in the natural en-
> vironment . . . as might be of sufficient impact to have predetermined
> the shift to food production.

Thus Braidwood argues that: (1) environmental conditions analogous to those at the close of the Pleistocene had occurred previously
without having brought about food-production, and (2) there is no

evidence to support major climatic changes in the Near East of sufficient magnitude to have "predetermined the shift to food production." These observations are not only directed against the oasis theory but also against the argument that food-production constituted an alternative adaptation to changed environmental conditions at the close of the Pleistocene. Braidwood also argues against the causative role of environmental change in his consideration of the applicability of the term Mesolithic to non-European areas (Braidwood, Willey 1962b:332). Garrod (1932) called the Natufian of Israel a Mesolithic industry, and the appropriateness of this terminology has been questioned by Braidwood and Willey (1962b: 332):

> . . . the usual conception of the Mesolithic is as a cultural readaptation to post-Pleistocene environments but the conception has become an awkward one, on a world wide scale, since as we have just seen, there is evidence that the same trends toward readaptation and intensification of collecting activities had begun to manifest themselves in certain areas before the conventional date for the end of the Pleistocene. One of us is of the opinion that there was no Mesolithic sensu stricto, in southwestern Asia, at least.

There is also increasing evidence that there were cultural changes parallel to those occurring in Western Europe in regions where there were no correlated major climatic changes (see, for example, Perrot 1962:147, 151–53).

Braidwood presents a strong case that there was major cultural change in areas where environmental change was minor or absent, as well is in areas such as Western Europe where environmental change was marked. This, together with the fact that earlier interglacial warm periods were not accompanied by drastic cultural changes of analogous form, is sufficient to invalidate the argument that the magnitude of environmental and cultural change can be expected to vary directly in a simple stimulus-response pattern. These data also raise questions about the positive correlations claimed for the form of environmental and cultural changes.

Braidwood, however, is not completely consistent in his application of these findings. He argues *against* the causative role of environmental change in the Near East, yet *for* such an explanation for the cultural changes observed in Western Europe (Braidwood, Willey 1962b:341). We do not propose here that there is no relationship between environmental and cultural change in Western Europe but rather argue against the direct and simple causative role of environmental change in view of Braidwood's own findings. What we must seek is a set of explanatory variables which will be valid on a world-wide scale at the terminal- and post-Pleistocene periods. If Braidwood rejects environmental change as the principal explanation in the Near East, what does he propose instead? After apologizing for Childe's "materialistic philosophy of history" (Braidwood, Howe 1960:7), Braidwood (1960a:134) offers his "nuclear zone" theory:

> In my opinion there is no need to complicate the story with extraneous "causes." The food producing revolution seems to have occurred as the culmination of the ever increasing cultural differentiation and specialization of human communities. Around 8,000 B.C. the inhabitants of the hills around the fertile crescent had come to know their habitat so well that they were beginning to domesticate the plants and animals they had been collecting and hunting. . . . From these "nuclear" zones cultural diffusion spread the new way of life to the rest of the world.

A nuclear zone is defined as follows:

> A region with a natural environment which included a variety of wild plants and animals, both possible and ready for domestication . . . (Braidwood 1963:106).

In his statements Braidwood proposes that cultivation is the expected, natural outcome of a long, directional evolutionary trend, limited only by the presence in the environment of domesticable plants and animals. This is clearly an orthogenetic argument (see Simpson, 1949:130–59 for a critical discussion of orthogenesis). The vital element responsible for the directional series of events appears to be inherent in human nature; it is expressed by Braidwood (1963:106) in such phrases as "increased experimentation" and "increased receptiveness" (1963:97–98, 137–38). These behavioral traits made it possible for man to "settle into" his environment (Braidwood, Reed 1957:20), and they serve as the basis for Braidwood's taxonomy of subsistence-settlement types (1960b: 143–51) in which three long-run trends can be seen: (1) increased localization of activity within the territory of a group, (2) more specific exploitation of the habitat, and (3) increased group size. (For a playful treatment of Braidwood's frame of reference see Binford and Binford 1966b.) It is when we have these trends, based on inherent human nature, operating in the context of a "nuclear zone" that things begin to happen:

> Now my hunch goes that when this experimentation and settling down took place within a potential nuclear area . . . where a whole constellation of plants and animals possible of domestication were available . . . the change was easily made . . . (Braidwood 1963: 110).

The explanation for absence of food-production during earlier interglacial periods is that: "culture was not ready to achieve it" (Braidwood, Willey 1962b:342).

It is argued here that vitalism, whether expressed in terms of inherent forces orienting the direction of organic evolution or in its more anthropocentric form of emergent human properties which direct cultural evolution, is unacceptable as an explanation. Trends which are observed in cultural evolution require explanation; they are certainly not explained by postulating emergent human traits which are said to account for the trends.

In summary, post-Pleistocene research began with the question of whether or not Western Europe was populated between the close of the Pleistocene and the first appearance of the later Neolithic settlements. When this question was answered affirmatively, emphasis shifted to the question of continuity—were the "intermediate" populations indigenous or were they intruders? In seeking to solve this problem scholars were involved in the methodological question of what archeological data could be cited as proof or disproof of continuity. As local sequences became better documented, this question was dropped, and there was an increasing tendency to view variability as a direct response to local environments which had radically changed with the retreat of the ice. This stimulus-response reasoning was generalized not only for the European foraging adaptation but was also used to explain the origins of food-production (the propinquity or oasis theory). Field investigation in the relevant parts of the Near East showed that dramatic environmental change did not characterize the crucial periods of time. The oasis theory has fallen into disfavor, and Braidwood's nuclear zone theory has tended to replace it. We have sought to demonstrate in our analysis that this theory is based on a kind of vitalism and a postulation of causal factors which are incapable of being tested. We also propose that current explanations for the form and distribution of post-Pleistocene cultures in Europe are implicitly, and often explicitly, based on simple and direct environmental determinism which the data from non-European parts of the world tend to refute. What follows is an examination of post-Pleistocene data within a different theoretical framework and the formulation of explanatory hypotheses which, it is hoped, are both more generally applicable and also testable.

If our aim is the explanation of cultural differences and similarities in different places and at different times, we must first isolate the phenomena we designate "cultural." Culture is all those means whose forms are not under direct genetic control (that is, extra-somatic [White 1959:8]) which serve to adjust individuals and groups within their ecological communities. If we seek understanding of the origins of agriculture or of "the spread of the village-farming community," we must analyze these cultural means as adaptive adjustments in the variety of ecosystems within which human groups were participants.

Adaptation is always a local problem, and selective pressures favoring new cultural forms result from non-equilibrium conditions in the local ecosystem. Our task, then, becomes the isolation of the variables initiating directional change in the internal structuring of ecological systems. Of particular importance is understanding the conditions which favor the rearrangement of energy-matter components and their linked dependencies in a manner which alters the effective environment of the unit under study.

The term "effective environment" (Allee *et al.* 1949:1) designates those parts of the total environment which are in regular or cyclical articulation with the unit under study. Changes in the effective environment will produce changes not only in the boundaries of the ecological community but also in the internal organization of the community. Both of these changes in turn set up conditions favoring adaptive adjustments among the components of the community. In dealing with sociocultural systems and in trying to understand the conditions under which such systems undergo adaptive change, we are necessarily concerned with the effective environment of a given system.

> Cultural systems relate man to habitat, and an equilibrium can be established in this relationship as in others. When an equilibrium has been established culturally between man and habitat, it may be continued indefinitely until it is upset by the intrusion of a new factor (White 1959:284).

If we hope to understand culture change in general, and the changes of the post-Pleistocene period in particular, we must seek the conditions which have brought new factors into play in the effective environments of the cultural systems at the close of the Pleistocene.

Before undertaking our analysis, one further distinction needs to be made—the distinction between functional and structural differences in ecological niches. *Functional differences* are those which result from differences in the form of the elements of a system and which do not necessarily imply differences in the kind of articulation which exists between a cultural system and the ecological community of which it is a part. *Structural differences* refer to communities made up of non-analogous components which are integrated in different ways. In citing functional variability between niches, we are referring to differences in the form of the gross environment in which ecological communities occur; in such cases there would be no necessary structural differences in the organization of the ecological communities of the system, but only in the form of their environments. A case in point might be two cultural systems, both of which are solely dependent upon terrestrial resources within their home ranges and neither of which possesses the technological means for food storage or circulation beyond the locus of procurement. If one such system were located in a tropical rain forest and the other in a temperate deciduous forest, we would observe numerous formal differences between the cultural elements in the two systems, yet both can be said to occupy similar ecological niches within their habitats. Despite obvious differences in raw materials, the form of implements, differences in phasing of activities, and even in social organization, all such differences are explicable directly by reference to differences in gross environment. Therefore, we would term these differences functional, not structural.

Structural differences in ecological niches, on the other hand, refer to differences in the modes of integration between cultural and other components within ecological communities. Such differences imply a different set of relationships between the cultural unit and the variables in the gross environment with which the cultural unit is articulated. Cultural systems which occupy different ecological niches would therefore have different effective environments. An example of two cultural systems in the same gross environment but occupying different ecological niches would be the commonly occurring case where horticulturalists and hunters and gatherers live side by side. Each cultural group is in articulation with quite different elements of the gross environment and is integrated with the environment differently. Such cultural systems would be subject to qualitatively different types of selective pressure.

We would argue that understanding the selective pressures favoring the adoption of adaptive means as radical and as new as animal husbandry and cultivation in the post-Pleistocene requires the application of the ecological principles outlined above. A first step would be to determine whether food-production constitutes a functional variant of analogous ecological niches in different environments, or whether it is a structurally new adaptive means in an ecological niche not previously occupied by cultural systems.

Braidwood's nuclear zone theory is an argument for the former interpretation; the differences between the post-Pleistocene cultures in the hilly flanks and elsewhere are explicable by reference to formally unique elements in the plant and animal populations of the piedmont regions of the Near East. Childe's position is a statement of the latter interpretation, and he cites changes in the physical environment as the cause for bringing about new structural relationships between plants, animals, and men. Our argument also favors the second interpretation but with demographic, rather than gross environmental, variables responsible for the generation of pressures favoring new ecological niches.

> At certain times and places in the course of culture history, the threat of a diminished food supply, coming from an increase of population through immigration, or from a decline in local flora due to climatic or physiographic change, was met by various measures of cultural control over plant life, which collectively, we call agriculture (White 1959:285).

White's citation of population increase through immigration as a relevant variable in explaining the appearance of agriculture is a radical departure from traditional interpretations.

In the traditional approach, changes and variation in the available food supply have been cited as the major factors which regulate population equilibrium systems (Childe 1958:98; Dumond 1965: 310).

> Man must eat to live at all; food is perhaps the one absolute and overriding need for man. In early and primitive societies the quest for food was and is the most absorbing preoccupation for all members of the group. The enlargement of the food-supply was therefore presumably the indispensable condition for human progress (Childe 1944:12).

The community of food-gatherers had been restricted in size by the food supplies available (Childe 1951b:61).

Similar statements have been made by Braidwood (1963:121–22), among others.

The inference about population dynamics to be made from these statements is that populations will grow until the food requirements of the group begin to exceed the standing crop in the local habitat. No population could ever achieve a stable adaptation, since its members would always be under strong selective pressure to develop new means of getting food. This assumption of the available food supply as the critical variable in population dynamics has prevented consideration of population variables themselves as possible sources of disequilibrium.

Recent studies in demography have argued strongly against the direct control of population density by the availability of food.

> We have the strongest reasons for concluding . . . that population density must at all costs be prevented from rising to the level where food shortage begins to take a toll of the numbers—an effect that could not be felt until long after the optimum density had been exceeded. It would be bound to result in chronic over-exploitation and a spiral of diminishing returns (Wynne-Edwards 1962:11).

> Long term population equilibrium . . . implies some kind of restraint. . . . "Food supply" offers a quick answer, but not, I think, the correct one. At any rate, a forest is full of game for an expert mouse-hunter, and a Paleolithic man who stuck to business should have found enough food on two square kilometers instead of 20 or 200. Social forces were probably more powerful than mere starvation in causing men to huddle in small bands (Deevey 1960:6).

Most demographers agree that functional relationships between the normal birth rate and other requirements (for example, the mobility of the female) favor the *cultural* regulations of fertility through such practices as infanticide, abortion, lactation taboos, etc. These practices have the effect of homeostatically keeping population size below the point at which diminishing returns from the local habitat would come into play. (See Carr-Saunders 1922; Wynne-Edwards 1962; 1964; Birdsell 1958; 1968; Deevey 1960; Hainline 1965; Dumond 1965; Halbwachs 1960).

The arguments of demographers are supported by a number of recent ethnographic studies which document the abundance of food available to even marginal hunters. Some cases of importance are J. D. Clark (1951) on the Barotse, Lee (1965) on the !Kung

Bushmen, Woodburn (n.d.) on the Hadza, and Huntingford (1955) on the Dorobo. Similar conditions of relative abundance have been reported for Australia. For example, life on the Daly River in the Northern Territory led McCarthy (1957:90) to generalize: "for the uncontaminated bush native the food problem hardly exists." Ease in food procurement is also reported for Arnhemland (McCarthy 1957:90; McCarthy, McArthur 1960:145–93). Quimby has described the truly impressive quantities of food obtained in the course of a single year by a Chippewa family in the Lower Peninsula of Michigan in 1763 (Quimby 1962:217–39). In a quantitative study of food intake by the Onge hunters of Little Andaman, Bose (1964:306) states: "The region surrounding Toke-buea can supply more food than the requirement of the local people."

These data suggest that while hunting-gathering populations may vary in density between different habitats in direct proportion to the relative size of the standing food crop, nevertheless within any given habitat the population is homeostatically regulated *below* the level of depletion of the local food supply.

There are two corollaries of the assumption that population size is regulated almost exclusively by food supply which we also need to examine. The first corollary is: *Man would be continually seeking means for increasing his food supply.* In other words, there would be ubiquitous and constant selective pressure favoring the development of technological innovations, such as agriculture, which serve to make larger amounts of food available to a group. There is a large body of ethnographic data which suggests that this is not the case.

Carneiro (1957) in his study of the Kuikuru, who are horticulturalists, demonstrated that these people were capable of producing several times the amount of food they did. A small increment in the amount of time devoted to planting and harvesting would have brought about substantial increases in the available food, yet the Kuikuru chose not to do this. Enough food was produced to meet local demands, and it was at that point that production stopped. Equilibrium had been reached, and neither population nor production increased.

In writing about the Southeastern United States, Caldwell concerned himself with the question of why no effective early prehistoric agriculture was developed in the region. He concluded:

We have suggested that so many natural foods were available that to place any reliance on cultivation . . . might have seemed risky or irrelevant. The hunting-gathering pattern was developed to a peak of efficiency and jelled, so to speak, in the very heart of eastern cultures (1958:72).

If we recognize that an equilibrium system can be established so that populations are homeostatically regulated below the carrying capacity of the local food supply, it follows that there is no necessary adaptive pressure continually favoring means of increasing the food supply. The question to be asked then is not why agricultural and food-storage techniques were not developed everywhere, but why they were developed at all. Under what set of conditions does increasing the supply of available food have adaptive advantage?

The second corollary to be examined concerns leisure time: *It is only when man is freed from preoccupation with the food quest that he has time to elaborate culture.* A fairly representative statement of this corollary has been made by Childe (1951b:61) and is cited above. Also, Braidwood and Braidwood (1950:189) write:

Proper village life now came into being, and with it a completely new kind of technology. This latter depends on the fact that time now became available for pursuits other than that of simply collecting food.

Braidwood reiterates the same argument in more detail in another place (1963:121–22). The view of the hunter constantly involved in scrounging a bare subsistence and existing on the brink of starvation has recently received some rather pointed comments by Sahlins (1968):

Almost totally committed to the argument that life was hard in the Paleolithic, our text books compete to convey a sense of impending doom, leaving the student to wonder not only how hunters managed to make a living but whether, after all, this is living. The spectre of starvation stalks the stalker in these pages. His technical incompetence is said to enjoin continuous work just to survive, leaving him without respite from the food quest and without the "leisure time to build culture."

There is abundant data which suggests not only that hunter-gatherers have adequate supplies of food but also that they enjoy quantities of leisure time, much more in fact than do modern industrial or farm workers, or even professors of archeology. Lee (1965), Bose (1954), McCarthy and McArthur (1960), and

Woodburn (n.d.) have shown that hunters on a simple level of technology spend a very small percentage of their time obtaining food. On these grounds we can reasonably question the proposition that cultural elaboration is caused by leisure time which is available for the first time to agriculturalists.

In rejecting the assumption that hunter-gatherer populations are primarily regulated by the available supply of food, we put the problem of the development of new types of subsistence in a different light. As long as one could assume that man was continually trying to increase his food supply, understanding the "origins of agriculture" simply involved pinpointing those geographic areas where the potential resources were and postulating that man would inevitably take advantage of them. With the recognition that equilibrium systems regulate population density below the carrying capacity of an environment, we are forced to look for those conditions which might bring about disequilibrium and bring about selective advantage for increased productivity. According to the arguments developed here, there could be only two such sets of conditions:

1. A change in the physical environment of a population which brings about a reduction in the biotic mass of the region would decrease the amounts of available food. The previous balance between population and standing crop is upset, and more efficient extractive means would be favored. This is essentially the basis for Childe's propinquity theory.

2. Change in the demographic structure of a region which brings about the impingement of one group on the territory of another would also upset an established equilibrium system, and might serve to increase the population density of a region beyond the carrying capacity of the natural environment. Under these conditions manipulation of the natural environment in order to increase its productivity would be highly advantageous.

The remainder of this paper is devoted to the exploration of this second set of conditions. The first step of our analysis is to build models of different types of population systems under different conditions. One such type of system is termed a *closed population system* (Hyrenius 1959:476) in which a steady state is maintained by internal mechanisms limiting numbers of offspring at the generational replacement level. Techniques such as abortion, contraception, abstinence, and infanticide serve to lower the birth rate and increase the mortality rate so that a given population would be homeostatically regulated at a given size or density.

The second type of system, the *open population system,* is one in which size and/or density is maintained by either the budding off of new groups or by the emigration of individuals. This would be an *open system of the donor type.* If the size or density of the system is altered through the introduction of immigrants from other population groups, we have an *open system of the recipient type.*

Given these two types of population systems—closed and open, the latter including two sub-types, recipient and donor—we can begin to analyze differences in the ways in which the two system types can be articulated in a given region.

CLOSED SYSTEMS

We can identify the population of a region as a whole as a closed system, yet find that within the region there would be some variability in optimum group size as a response to geographical differences in the regional distribution of resources. Further, each local group within the region may operate periodically as an open system, since we would expect some variability in the degree to which local groups have achieved equilibrium. There would therefore be some redistribution of population between groups which would promote a more uniform and steady density equilibrium system over the region as a whole.

We would expect selection favoring cultural means of regulating population to occur in situations where the density equilibrium system for the region as a whole was in fact a closed system, and where there were significant imbalances in the losses and recruits for the local subsegments of the regional population. There would be differential selective advantage for cultural regulation of population growth between two closed population systems in different environmental settings if there were discrepancies between the actual birth and death rates on the one hand and the optimal rates for maintaining population size on the other.

OPEN SYSTEMS, DONOR TYPE

We would expect to find this type of population system in areas which are not filled to the point at which density dependent factors are brought into play. The peopling of a new land mass, such as the New World or Australia, would be an example of such a situation in which there would be positive advantage for this type of system.

The rate of expansion of open donor systems into uninhabited territory has been discussed in the literature, and models for this type of expansion have been built (Bartholomew, Birdsell, 1953; Birdsell, 1957; 1958; 1968; Yengoyan, 1960). Birdsell (1957:54) has made two observations which are particularly relevant here. First, the budding off of new groups occurs *before* optimum local population size has been reached.

This observation demonstrates the role of emigration in bringing about and maintaining equilibrium and also shows that the unit on which selection for emigration operates is a subunit of the local population, since conditions favoring segmentation appear before the regional population is under pressure from density dependent factors.

Second, the adaptation of any given sociocultural system will determine in part the locus of selection within the social system and the particular selective advantages for different fertility rates. Birdsell (1968) writes:

> In a population stabilized at the carrying capacity of its given environment, some limitation on procreative activities naturally filter down to the level of the biological family. These may be examined most profitably in terms of the requirements which affect the spacing of the natal survivors. Generalized hunters with their requirements of high mobility present the most exacting model. Australian data indicate that the inability of a mother to carry more than one child at a time together with her female baggage impose the first insurmountable barrier to a large number of children. Strongly reinforced by an equally limiting incapacity to nurse more than one child simultaneously imposes a minimum of a three-year spacing upon children designed for survival. Since human female reproductive physiology does not reliably prevent conception while still nursing, children are frequently conceived and born which cannot be reared. The result is systematic infanticide.

We have seen that two frequent means of maintaining homeostasis are emigration and cultural regulation of births and deaths. The relative importance to any group of one of these means *vs.* the other will be conditioned by such factors as mobility requirements of the group. Another conditioning factor would be the type of articulation between segments of the population which can directly affect the ease with which budding-off can occur. A third factor would be the degree to which the region as a whole is occupied which would affect the expectations of success in the establishment of daughter communities.

OPEN SYSTEMS, RECIPIENT TYPE

This type of system could occur under only two sets of conditions; the first would be where there is the expansion of a donor system into an uninhabited region. The frontier of the region would contain a number of population units which could, for a short time, serve as recipient systems. Their change from recipient to donor systems would depend upon the extent to which optimal densities were achieved locally and the frontier continued to advance.

The second set of conditions promoting systems of the recipient type is more relevant to the consideration of early agricultural developments. This is the situation in which two or more different kinds of sociocultural systems occupy adjacent environmental zones. If the adaptation of one sociocultural unit is translatable into the adjacent environmental zone, it may expand into that zone at the expense of resident systems. Cases of this type have been cited by Kaplan (1960) as examples of the Law of Cultural Dominance, and a specific instance referred to by Sahlins (1961) are the Tiv and the Nuer. We would expect expansion of the dominant system until the zone to which the system was adapted was occupied; at this juncture there would be selection for increased efficiency of production and/or for increased regulation of the birth rate.

A different kind of situation would obtain in the case of sociocultural systems occupying adjacent zones if the adaptation of the more rapidly growing group is not translatable into the adjacent zone. Population growth within the area occupied by the parent group might well be so great that daughter communities would frequently be forced to reside in an environment which is incompatible with their particular cultural adaptation. There could be a number of effects under these circumstances.

From the standpoint of the populations already in the recipient zone, the intrusion of immigrant groups would disturb the existing density equilibrium system and might raise the population density to the level at which we would expect diminishing food resources. This situation would serve to increase markedly for the recipient groups the pressures favoring means for increasing productivity.

The intrusive group, on the other hand, would be forced to make adaptive adjustments to their new environment (for an example of this situation see L. R. Binford 1968b). There would be strong selective pressures favoring the development of more efficient subsistence techniques by both groups.

It should be pointed out, however, that such advantage does not insure that these developments will inevitably occur. In many cases these problems are met by changes which might be called regressive in that the changes in adaptation which occur may be in the direction of less complex cultural forms. Examples of this sort of change can be seen among the hunter-gatherers of the non-riverine tropical forest zones in South America. Steward and Faron (1959: 378) write of the Siriono and Guayaki:

> These Indians retreated . . . to inaccessible regions where they largely abandoned horticulture to rely on a predominantly hunting and gathering subsistence. Other enclaves of nomads isolated in the tropical forests and interfluvial regions may also have experienced similar deculturation.

Lathrap (1968) has offered the possibility that perhaps all of the less sedentary South American groups are "the degraded descendants of peoples who at one time maintained an advanced form of Tropical Forest Culture."

While in these examples the adaptations along population frontiers were in the direction of less complexity, it is in the context of such situations of stress in environments with plant and animal forms amenable to manipulation that we would expect to find conditions favoring the development of plant and animal domestication. Such situations would be characterized by disequilibrium between population and resources which, in turn, would offer selective advantage to increases in the efficacy of subsistence technology. Rather than seeking the locus for the origins of agriculture in the heart of a "natural habitat zone," we would argue that we must look to those places where a population frontier or adaptive tension zone intersects a "natural habitat zone." This means that archeological investigations might well concentrate on those areas within the natural habitat zone where there is an archeologically demonstrated major shift in population density. The presence of such a shift might well indicate a population frontier where rapid evolutionary changes were taking place.

Another archeological clue to be exploited is the degree to which settlements are characterized by sedentism. The frontier zones would be expected between regions which differed widely in the degree of sedentism practiced by resident groups. In those areas with highly sedentary population, problems of transport of young and belongings would be reduced. Reduced mobility of social units in general and in the daily routines of females in particular would in turn reduce the selective advantages accruing to cultural means of controlling population growth. Therefore, under conditions of increased sedentism we would expect population growth. A consequence of such growth would be the increased relative importance of emigration as a mechanism for maintaining the local group within optimal size and density limits.

Therefore where there is a marked contrast in degree of sedentism between two sociocultural units within a relatively restricted geographical region, there would be a tension zone where emigrant colonies from the more sedentary group would periodically disrupt the density equilibrium balances of the less sedentary group. Under these conditions there would be strong selective pressure favoring the development of more effective means of food production for both groups within this zone of tension. There would also be increasing pressures against immigration, given the failure to develop more effective extractive technologies.

It is proposed here that it was in the selective context outlined above that initial practices of cultivation occurred. Such selective situations would have been the consequence of the increased dependence on aquatic resources during the terminal and immediately post-Pleistocene period. Not all portions of rivers and shorelines favor the harvesting of fish, molluscs, and migratory fowl; it is with the systematic dependence on just these resources that we find archeological remains indicating a higher degree of sedentism in both the Archaic of the New World and the terminal Paleolithic and Mesolithic of the Old World. This hypothesis is lent strong support by the fact that it is also in the terminal Paleolithic-Mesolithic and Archaic that we find, associated with increased sedentism, evidence for marked population growth and for the development of food-storage techniques, the latter being functionally linked to the highly seasonal nature of migratory fowl and anadromous fish exploited as food crops (for an example of the importance of anadromous fish see L. R. Binford 1964).

Since the systematic exploitation of these food sources (and of markedly seasonally available terrestrial forms as well—for example, reindeer) characterized adaptations of this time range in a wide variety of environments, we would expect that tension zones, with their concomitant selective pressures favoring increased subsistence efficiency, would be widely distributed also. This expectation is in accord with the empirical generalizations that: (1) There were a number of independent loci of the development of cultivation techniques—the Near East, Asia, and the New World—and all the developments of these techniques occur within the time range in question; and (2) These loci were distributed across widely different environmental types—root crops in the tropics and cereals in semiaridlands, for example.

The widespread nature of conditions favoring increased subsistence efficiency also accounts for the rapid transmission and integration of contributing innovations from one cultural system to another. Many authors have cited the rapid "diffusion" of cultural elements as characterizing the immediately post-Pleistocene period.

Finally, in the traditional view the "Neolithic Revolution" is characterized by the appearance of a number of traits which are thought to be linked to the shift to food production. The manufacture of ceramics and textiles, relatively permanent houses, and craft specialization are only a few of those frequently cited (cf. Braidwood 1963:122–23). These traits constitute part of the definition of the "village farming way of life," and the assumption is that they originated in the "nuclear area" from which they spread as a complex, the spread being achieved by diffusion, stimulus diffusion, and/or migration. As more data have been accumulated, it becomes increasingly clear that these traits are not mutually dependent; indeed, it seems to be quite clear that ceramics, for example, were first used in the Old World in coastal Japan (Griffin 1961:92), with a cluster of radiocarbon dates averaging *ca.* 7000 B.C. This is about the same time that effective grain agriculture was initially practiced in the Near East (Mellaart 1961b; 1963; Hole 1966; Young, Smith 1966), and the occupations in question have yielded no ceramics. Given our model, such traits insofar as they are functionally linked to sedentism and/or food-production would be expected to appear in a variety of regions as the result of numerous independent but parallel inventions.

Further utility for the model presented here can be shown by the degree to which it provides explanatory answers for a series of questions posed by Braidwood and Willey (1962b:342)—questions which cannot be satisfactorily answered within the traditional framework.

Why did incipient food production not come earlier? Our only answer at the moment is that culture was not yet ready to achieve it.

We believe that a more complete answer is possible. The shift to the exploitation of highly seasonal resources such as anadromous fish and migratory fowl did not occur until the close of the Pleistocene. This shift, probably linked to worldwide changes in sea level, with attendant increase in sedentism, established for the first time conditions leading to marked heterogeneity in rates of population growth and structure of the ecological niche of immediately adjacent sociocultural systems. This new set of conditions brought about, in turn, conditions favoring improved subsistence technology. It was not that culture was unready, but rather that the selective conditions favoring such changes had not previously existed.

What were the . . . cultural conditions favoring incipient cultivation or domestication? Certainly there is nothing in the archeological record to indicate that those few instances of cultural build-up and elaboration, as manifested by the varying art styles of the upper paleolithic from western Europe into Siberia . . . provided a favorable ground for incipient food production. On the contrary, those instances of incipient cultivation or domestication of greatest potential are found in contexts of a much less spectacular character (Braidwood, Willey 1962b:343; see also Willey 1966:141–42).

According to our model, we would *expect* to find the selective situation favoring "incipient cultivation" in "contexts of a much less spectacular character"—in those tension zones where less sedentary populations are being moved in on by daughter groups from more sedentary populations. These are the areas where the development of greater productive means is most advantageous.

The perplexing question of what kinds of natural environmental settings were most propitious for the early development of incipient food production is by no means solved. Nevertheless, the data on hand suggest that generally semi-arid regions . . . with adequate but not overabundant collectible food resources were the hearths of the most important beginnings of cultivation and domestication (Braidwood, Willey 1962b:342).

If we look at the semi-arid areas where the crops referred to (wheat and barley in the Old World; maize in the New World) were developed, it turns out that they are adjacent to areas which already supported settled (that is, sedentary) villages whose populations depended in large part upon aquatic resources. The Natufian of the Near East (Kenyon 1959b; Perrot 1960; 1962) and the coastal settlements of Mexico and Peru (Willey 1966:144; see also Flannery and Coe 1968) are cases in point.

The explanation of the distribution noted above of the hearths of domestication of most economically significant crops within semi-arid regions lies in the nature of the seeds produced by the plants in such regions. Seeds of xerophytic plants normally have low moisture requirements and can therefore remain viable without being subject to rots which attack many other kinds of seeds. Their economic value also lies in the fact that semi-arid regions are areas with low diversity indices (Odum 1954:281), which means that there will typically be many individuals of a given species within a very limited space.

We would like to note in passing that the post hoc evaluation of some "beginnings of cultivation" as "most important" (because of the ultimate economic significance of the crops produced) and the limitation of question-asking to these instances has served to prevent the recognition of the general conditions under which cultivation may have been initiated.

> *How* did the new elements spread into Europe; how shall we conceptualize the nature of the cultural mechanisms of "diffusion" and the spread of new "influences" through a vast area of already functioning cultural and environmental adaptations? (Braidwood, Willey 1962b:347).

While wheat and barley might have constituted "new influences" in Europe, it has been suggested above that cultivation arose as a response to similar pressures many times and in many places. Given the existence of the selective situation favoring food-production and the response to this adaptive situation occurring in a number of places, including Europe, the adoption of easily storable high-yield crops such as wheat and barley becomes readily understandable. However, it is important not to confound the adoption of specific crops with the "spread of the village-farming way of life."

If the model presented here has value above and beyond that of a logical exercise, it must be tested by the formulation of hypotheses and the collection of data. While the outlining of a program of research is beyond the scope of and irrelevant to the aims of this paper, a few predictions follow which, if borne out by field research, would empirically validate some of our assertions.

1. Evidence for the initial domestication of plants and animals in the Near East will come from areas adjacent to those occupied by relatively sedentary forager-fishers. One such area is that adjacent to the Natufian settlements in the Jordan Valley. These settlements have yielded evidence of heavy dependence upon fish and migratory fowl (Perrot 1960:20) and the architecture suggests a sedentary way of life. The areas just beyond these villages would have received "excess" population and would therefore have been areas of disequilibrium in which adaptive change would have been favored. Intermontane valleys and foothills which supported migratory hunters far removed from the kind of villages described above will not yield information on the earliest transition to dependence on food-production, regardless of the density of wild ancestors of domesticates.

2. Evidence for independent experimentation leading to the development of agriculture as well as animal domestication will be found in European Russia and south-central Europe. We would expect the relevant areas to be adjacent to those where there was effective exploitation of anadromous fish and migratory fowl. Such areas appear to be the rivers flowing into the Black Sea (Clark 1948b:50).

3. As further research is carried out in Europe, Asia, and the New World, there will be evidence for numerous independent innovations paralleling forms appearing in other areas. Post-Pleistocene adaptations are viewed as the result of the operation of local selective pressures, and the development of food production is one instance of such adaptations. Parallel innovations can be expected where structurally similar ecological niches were occupied, regardless of differences in the general form of the environment.

In conclusion, it is hoped that the theoretical perspective offered here will serve to generate a new series of questions, the answers to which may increase our understanding of the major cultural changes which occurred at the close of the Pleistocene.

4 ORIGINS AND ECOLOGICAL EFFECTS OF EARLY DOMESTICATION IN IRAN AND THE NEAR EAST

Kent V. Flannery

INTRODUCTION

LATE IN the Pliocene there began a series of movements of the earth's crust, which caused the central plateau of Iran to be drawn closer to the stable massif of Arabia. The land between, caught in the grip of these two far-heavier formations, was compressed and folded into a series of parallel mountain ridges or anticlines. Gradually the centre of this compressed zone collapsed and subsided, so that the parallel ridges, trending from north-west to south-east, appear to rise out of it like the successive tiers of a grandstand, eventually reaching the Arabian and Iranian plateaus to either side. The sunkland in between, still settling and filling with the erosion products of the mountains, became the rolling and irregular plain known as Mesopotamia; the parallel ridges to the east of it are the Zagros Mountains (Lees, Falcon 1952:24–39).

The result was an area in which altitudinal differences produce a great number of contrasting environments in a relatively limited geographic area—a mosaic of valleys at different elevations, with different rainfall, temperature, and vegetational patterns. Like some of the other areas where early civilizations arose—Mesoamerica and the Central Andes, for example—the Near East is a region of "vertical economy", where exchanges of products between altitude zones are made feasible and desirable by the close juxtaposition of four main environmental types: high plateau (*c.* 5000 ft.), intermontane valleys (1500–4000 ft.), piedmont-steppe (600–1000 ft.),

Reprinted from Peter J. Ucko and G. W. Dimbleby, editors, *The Domestication and Exploitation of Plants and Animals* (Chicago: Aldine Publishing Company, 1969); copyright © "Research Seminar in Archaeology and Related Subjects, 1969."

and alluvial desert (100–500 ft.). A similar pattern arose in the Levant, where the same late Pliocene tectonic movements produced the great Jordan Rift Valley, flanked by the wooded Lebanon-Judean mountains and the arid Syrian Plateau. It was in this kind of setting that the first steps toward plant and animal domestication were made.

Stages in Near Eastern prehistory

In a recent article, Frank Hole and I have divided the prehistory of Western Iran into three main adaptive eras (Hole, Flannery 1967). The first was a period of semi-nomadic hunting and gathering, which lasted until roughly 10,000–8000 B.C. The second era we have called the period of early dry-farming and Caprine domestication, and it seems to have involved predominantly emmer wheat (*Triticum dicoccum*), two-row hulled barley (*Hordeum distichum*), goats (*Capra hircus*), and sheep (*Ovis aries*). This period lasted until about 5500 B.C., and its hallmarks are already familiar to members of this symposium: permanent villages, early hornless sheep, goats with medially-flattened and/or helically-twisted horn cores, and cereal grain samples which show a mixture of wild (tough-glumed, brittle rachis) and domestic (brittle-glumed, tough-rachis) characteristics. The third adaptive era was one which involved the previously-mentioned cultivars plus bread wheat (*Triticum aestivum*); six-row barley which might be either hulled or naked (*Hordeum vulgare*); lentils; grass peas; linseed; domestic cattle (*Bos taurus*); pigs (*Sus scrofa*); and domestic dogs (*Canis familiaris*), and featured irrigation in those zones where its use was feasible without elaborate technology. This era culminated, in the lowlands at least, in the rise of walled towns, about 3000 B.C. (Adams 1962).

There is no reason to believe that the entire Near East went through these eras synchronously; in addition, evidence suggests that each of the cultivars may have appeared earlier in some areas than in others. Nevertheless, with these caveats in mind, I find this framework useful enough so that I will follow it in this paper, and apologize in advance for viewing the rest of South-western Asia through Iranian eyes. The stages are, it should be emphasized, ones of farming adaptation: they imply nothing about level of social and political development. They allow, in other words, for the simultaneous existence of tiny four-acre villages in Kurdistan and immense, 32-acre sites like Çatal Hüyük in Anatolia.

The basic argument of the paper is as follows. An important change in subsistence pattern, midway through the Upper Palaeolithic in the Near East, set the stage for domestication of plants. This shift, which represented a trend toward "broad spectrum" wild resource utilization, continued long after cultivation had begun. In this sense, our Western view of early cultivation as a drastic change or "improvement" in man's diet is erroneous, as is the frequently-cited notion that early agriculture gave man a "more stable" food supply. Given the erratic nature of rainfall in Southwest Asia, the era of early dry-farming was still one of unpredictable surpluses and lean years, with considerable reliance on local wild products. I suggest that early caprine domestication, apart from its food aspects, represented a way of "banking" these unpredictable surpluses in live storage, analogous to the use of pigs by Melanesian peoples (Lees 1967) or the exchange of imperishable, exotic raw materials which characterized early village farmers in Mesoamerica (Flannery 1968a). Early irrigation modified this pattern, and also aggravated environmental destruction to the point where the return to a wild resource economy would have been nearly impossible. It also set the stage for both dramatic population increases in the lowlands and "ranked" or stratified societies in which a hereditary elite controlled the small percentage of the landscape on which the bulk of the food was produced. A bit of indulgence on the reader's part will be required by the fact that in a paper of this length only the meagrest documentation can be offered for these points of view.

Prime movers and subsistence change

A basic problem in human ecology is why cultures change their modes of subsistence at all. This paper, while not relying on the facile explanation of prehistoric environmental change, is hardly destined to settle that problem. The fact is, however, that for much of South-west Asia we have no evidence to suggest that late Pleistocene or post-Pleistocene environmental changes forced any of the significant subsistence shifts seen in the archaeological record. I will therefore use, as one possible mechanism, a model of population pressure and disequilibrium relative to environmental carrying capacity, drawn from recent enthnographic data on hunting and gathering groups.

A growing body of data supports the conclusion, stated with increasing frequency in recent years, that starvation is not the principal factor regulating mammal populations (Wynne-Edwards 1962). Instead, evidence suggests that other mechanisms, including their own social behaviour, homeostatically maintain mammal populations at a level *below* the point at which they would begin to deplete their own food supply. The recent conference on "Man the Hunter", held at Chicago in 1966, made it clear that this is probably also true of human populations on the hunting-gathering level (Birdsell 1966). In addition, a number of current ethnographic studies indicate that, far from being on a starvation level, hunting-gathering groups may get all the calories they need without even working very hard (McCarthy 1957; Bose 1964; Lee 1965). Even the Bushmen of the relatively desolate Kalahari region, when subjected to an input-output analysis (Lee 1969), appeared to get 2100 calories a day with less than three days' worth of foraging per week. Presumably, hunter-gatherers in lusher environments in prehistoric times did even better. This is not to say that palaeolithic populations were not limited by their food supply; obviously, they were. But *in addition*, they engaged in behaviour patterns designed to maintain their density below the starvation level.

What, then, would persuade a hunter-gatherer to modify his subsistence pattern significantly—for example, to adopt agriculture? In the course of this paper I would like to apply the equilibrium model recently proposed by Binford (1968a) as a means of explaining post-Pleistocene changes in the archaeological record. This model will be used to offer tentative explanations for subsistence changes which took place in the Near East at the three critical points mentioned in the start of this paper: the Upper Palaeolithic, the beginning of domestication, and the beginnings of irrigation.

Binford, drawing on both Birdsell and Wynne-Edwards, postulates that prehistoric hunting populations, once reasonably well-adapted to a particular environment, tended to remain stable at a density below the point of resource exhaustion. He argues that their adaptation would change only in the face of some disturbance of the equilibrium between population and environment. Two kinds of disturbances might take place: either (1) a change in the physical environment which would bring about a reduction in the density of chosen plant and animal foods, or (2) a change in demography which would raise local human populations too close to the carrying capacity of the immediate area. The first kind of disturbance might be reflected in the palynological record; the second might be reflected in a shift in site density and settlement pattern in the archaeological record. Disturbances of both kinds occurred in the prehistoric Near East, but it is perhaps the second kind which is most useful theoretically, because it does not rely on the *deus ex machina* of climatic change, an event which does not seem to have taken place with sufficient frequency to explain all (or even most) prehistoric cultural changes (Binford 1968a).

Binford points out that, even in the hunting-gathering era, certain areas supported higher populations than others because of their high level of edible resources. Butzer (1964) makes the same point, singling out the "grassy, tropical deciduous woodlands and savannas; the mid-latitude grasslands; (and) the lower latitude Pleistocene tundras" as having the optimal carrying capacity for hunting-gathering populations. In the case of the Near East, for example, it would appear that the mixed oak woodland of the Levant Coast supported higher upper palaeolithic populations than some of the treeless inland steppe areas, at least where survey has been comparably extensive. One sees, therefore, a mosaic of "optimal" habitats, with a somewhat higher carrying capacity and population density, separated by "less favourable" habitats with a somewhat lower carrying capacity and population density. Binford argues that one source of stimulus for culture change is the cyclical demographic pressure exerted on these marginal habitats by their optimal neighbours. It is the optimal habitats which are regional growth centres; it is in them that populations rise, followed by buddings-off and emigrations of daughter groups before the carrying capacity has been strained (Birdsell 1957). They are the "donor systems"; the marginal habitats are the "recipient systems". And it is in the marginal habitats that the density equilibrium would most likely be periodically disturbed by immigrations of daughter groups, raising populations too near the limited carrying capacity. Thus Binford argues that pressures for the exploitation of new food sources would be felt most strongly *around the margins* of population growth centres, not in the centres themselves.

The first change I would like to deal with took place in the upper palaeolithic period, before 20,000 B.C., and amounted to a considerable broadening of the subsistence base to include progressively greater amounts of fish, crabs, water turtles, molluscs, land snails, partridges, migratory water fowl (and possibly wild cereal grains in some areas?).

The Upper Palaeolithic of the Near East has a number of chronological phases and regional variants, from the "Antelian" and "Kebaran" of the Mediterranean Coast (Howell 1959) to the "Baradostian" and "Zarzian" of the Zagros Mountains (Solecki 1964a). Its environmental context in the coastal Levant may have been an open Mediterranean woodland not unlike today's (Rossignol 1962; 1963), while the Zagros Mountains seem at that time to have been treeless *Artemisia* steppe (Van Zeist, Wright 1963; Van Zeist 1967). In both areas, hunting of hoofed mammals accounted for 90% of the archaeological animal bones, and when weights of meat represented are calculated, it appears that ungulates contributed 99% (Flannery 1965). In the Zagros, archaeological settlement patterns suggest that the basic residential unit was a "base camp" composed of several families, which shifted seasonally; from this base, hunting parties made periodic forays to "transitory stations", vantage points from which they stalked and eventually killed game, which was then cut up into portable sections at temporary "butchering stations" (Hole, Flannery 1967). There are indications that a similar pattern may have characterized the Levant. On the basis of multivariant factor analysis of flint tools, Binford and Binford (1966a) have described the various living floors of Rockshelter I at Yabrud as brief "work camps" made at varying distances from a base camp, sometimes for hunting, sometimes for processing plant material. Near the Wadi Antelias, where Ksar Akil was presumably the "base camp", Ewing (1949) describes "hunting sites on the surface higher up in the mountains", some of which may be analogous to the transitory stations or butchering stations of the southern Zagros.

Midway through the "Antelian" or "Baradostian" phases, one can see the aforementioned trend toward increasing use of small game, fish, turtles, seasonal water fowl, partridges, and invertebrates—the latter including terrestrial and marine snails, freshwater mussels, and river crabs. It would be oversimplified to view this as a "shift from large to small game", for even at late palaeolithic sites, ungulates contributed 90% of the meat supply. The trend is rather from exploiting a more "narrow spectrum" of environmental resources to a more "broad spectrum" of edible wild products. This "broad spectrum" collecting pattern characterized all subsequent cultures up to about 6000 B.C., and I would argue that it is only in such a context that the first domestication could take place. It is a pattern in which everything from land snails (*Helix* sp.) to very small crabs (*Potamon* sp.), and perhaps even cereal grasses, was viewed as potential food. It was also accompanied by a number of "pre-adaptations" for early cultivation.

One of these was the development of ground stone technology. At sites like Ksar Akil in Lebanon (Ewing 1951) and Yafteh Cave in Iran (Hole, Flannery 1967), small coarse grinding stones occasionally appear; abraders are increasingly common in later Zarzian sites in the Zagros, where they come to include grooved rubbing stones (Hole, Flannery 1967; Garrod 1930). Evidence suggests that these implements were at first used mainly (but not necessarily solely) for milling ochre. However, the ground stone technology was there, and when man eventually turned to the cereal grasses, he had only to adapt and expand a pre-existing technology in order to deal with grain processing.

Still another "pre-adaptation" for what was to follow can be detected in the later stages of the Palaeolithic in the Near East: the development of storage facilities, which are not at all well-represented in earlier phases. In the Zarzian level at Shanidar Cave, for example, "several pits . . . which may have been storage pits" are reported by Solecki (1964a; 1964b). These features increase with time; many sites of the period 9000–7000 B.C. are reported to have subterranean pits, e.g. Zawi Chemi Shanidar (Solecki 1964a; 1964b), Karim Shahir (Braidwood, Howe 1960), and Mureybat (van Loon 1966). Some were plastered, evidently for storage, e.g. at Aïn Mallaha (Perrot 1966), while others may have been used for roasting grain over heated pebbles, e.g. at Mureybat (Braidwood, Howe 1960). In any event, these subterranean pits seem to be a feature of the broad-spectrum collecting era, and would presumably have been more effective for storing or processing invertebrate or vegetal foods (snails, acorns, pistachios, etc.) than for any activity connected with ungulate hunting.

It seems unlikely that the shift to a broad spectrum pattern was a direct result of environmental change. It is true that the earlier Pleistocene "big game" of the Near East—elephant, rhinoceros, hippopotamus, and so on—had vanished, but as pointed out by Howell (1959), these species disappeared midway in the Mousterian period, that is, many thousands of years before we can see any substantial increase in the use of fish, invertebrates, and (possibly) vegetal foods. Moreover, use of these latter foods is more striking in some areas than others. For example, in the Levant area none of the Mount Carmel caves shows much in the way of invertebrate foods (Garrod, Bate 1937), while "thousands" of *Helix* snails are reported from Ksar Akil in the Wadi Antelias. In the Zagros, certain caves like Palegawra have more abundant remains of snails, mussels, and crabs than do those in other areas (Ewing 1949), (Reed, Braidwood 1960); we recovered virtually no land snails from our Khorramabad Valley caves (Hole, Flannery 1967).

Regional variations like those mentioned above suggest that Binford's model of disturbed density equilibrium may not be far wrong: pressure for the use of invertebrates, fish, water fowl, and previously-ignored plant resources would have been felt most strongly in the more marginal areas which would have received overflow from the expanding populations of the prime hunting zones, raising their densities to the limit of the land's carrying capacity. At this point they would tend to turn, I suggest, not to small *mammals*—which do not appear to be a very secure resource anywhere in the Near East—but to those smaller resources which are readily and predictably available in some quantity at certain seasons of the year. These are water fowl, fish, mussels, snails, and plants. Many of these resources are storable, and though small, are not to be scoffed at. Land snails, for example, although less rich in protein than ungulate meat, are actually much richer in calcium (Platt 1962), especially in limestone mountain regions, since they use lime to synthesize their protective mucous (Hesse *et al.* 1951). Mussels supply vitamin A and acorns and pistachios are very high calorie foods, much more so than wild game (Platt 1962). Present data tentatively suggest that the "broad spectrum revolution" was real, that it was nutritionally sound, and that it originally constituted a move which counteracted disequilibria in population in the less favourable hunting areas of the Near East. Once established, however, it spread to and was eventually taken up even by the favourable areas. And one other aspect of it might be noted: the invertebrate (and vegetal?) foods involved are ones which could easily have been collected by women and children, while the men continued ungulate hunting. The broad spectrum collecting pattern may therefore have contributed to the development of division of labour in the late Pleistocene and early post-Pleistocene era.

EARLY DRY FARMING

The environmental context of early domestication

The "broad spectrum" revolution set the cultural stage for domestication, and with the close of the Pleistocene the oak woodland belt expanded over the upland Near East, even into areas of the Zagros which had formerly been treeless steppe (Van Zeist, Wright 1963). This "optimum" wild resource zone, which includes the densest stands of edible nuts, fruits, and wild cereal grasses had apparently been present in the Levant throughout the last glaciation (Rossignol 1962; 1963), but was now available over a much wider area.

A number of environmental characteristics of this zone today (which presumably have characterized it since the Pleistocene drew to a close) should be mentioned here, for they are variables which affected man's use of the region and set the environmental stage for domestication. Low average precipitation inhibits dense forest growth, but cool, moist air from the Mediterranean in winter results in enough rain (or snow) to guarantee some spring growth of edible grasses and legumes. Hot, dry air circulating out of Eurasia in the summer (plus even hotter local winds off Arabia) produces a prolonged rainless period which inhibits the growth of perennials; most of the vegetation thus consists of annuals which have a peak growing season in March or April, after which they must be harvested in a three-week period. This set the seasonal collecting pattern. Further, like most arid or semi-arid regions, the zone has a low vegetation diversity index (Odum, Odum 1959), which means that certain species (like wild cereal grasses) may form nearly pure stands. This is true of the fauna as well; while the number of mammalian species is low (relative to wetter areas), many of these are species which tend to form herds, e.g. sheep, goat, gazelle, and onager. Harlan and Zohary (1966) have discussed the implications of the nearly-pure cereal stands, and Reed (1959; 1960) has considered the pre-adaptive role of "herd behaviour" in the ungulates which were first domesticated.

The origins of cultivation

The beginning of cultivation is a second shift which may have taken place in the less favourable valleys and wadis around the periphery of the zone of maximum carrying capacity.

For many years it was assumed, quite logically, that domestication must have begun in the zone where the wild ancestors of the domesticates are most at home. Then, in an eye-opening paper, Harlan and Zohary (1966) revealed that "over many thousands of hectares" within this zone "it would be possible to harvest wild wheat today from natural stands almost as dense as a cultivated wheat field". Harlan (1967) then proceeded to do just that: armed with a flint-bladed sickle, he harvested enough wild wheat in an hour to produce one kilo of clean grain—and the wild grain, after chemical analysis, proved to be almost twice as rich in protein as domestic wheat. Harlan and Zohary (1966) therefore closed with a warning: "Domestication may not have taken place where the wild cereals were most abundant. Why should anyone cultivate a cereal where natural stands are as dense as a cultivated field? . . . farming itself may have originated in areas adjacent to, rather than in, the regions of greatest abundance of wild cereals."

Harlan's wild wheat harvest also suggested that a family of experienced plant-collectors, working over the three-week period when wild wheat comes ripe, "without even working very hard, could gather more grain than the family could possibly consume in a year" (Harlan 1967). Such a harvest would almost necessitate some degree of sedentism—after all, where could they go with an estimated metric ton of clean wheat?

This was, of course, what archaeologist Jean Perrot (1966) had been saying for years about the Natufian culture in Palestine—that they had been semi-sedentary, based on intensive wild cereal collection. A further suggestion of this nature has since come from Tell Mureybat, a site on the terrace of the Euphrates River in inland Syria, dating to *c.* 8000 B.C. Preliminary analyses of carbonized barley and einkorn wheat from pre-pottery levels at the site—which have clay-walled houses, grinding stones, and roasting pits presumably used to render the cereal glumes brittle for threshing—suggest that the grain may be all wild (Van Loon 1966). Such data indicate that sedentary life based on wild cereal collecting and hunting may be possible, and that consequently pressures for domestication may not be as strong in the heart of the wild cereal habitat as elsewhere.

This impression is reinforced by the fact that some of our most ancient samples of morphologically domesticated grain (e.g. emmer wheat) come from "marginal" habitats well outside the present wild range of that plant; for example, in the Wadi Araba region (Kirkbride 1966) and the Khuzistan steppe (Helbaek 1969), in areas where dense stands could only be produced by deliberate cultivation. It is possible, therefore, that cultivation began as an attempt to produce artificially, around the *margins* of the "optimum" zone, stands of cereals as dense as those in the *heart* of the "optimum" zone. Binford had already suggested that this might have taken place in response to population pressure exerted on the marginal habitats by expansion of sedentary food-collectors from the heart of the wild cereal zone. It appears that efforts at early cultivation were probably soon reinforced by favourable mutations in the cereals themselves, such as toughening of the rachis, polyploidy, and loss of tough glumes.

The spread of the early dry-farming complex across the Near East is striking; where surveys are adequate, it appears that very few environmental zones were without farming communities at this time, although population densities were higher in some areas than others. In the Zagros Mountains, densities of sites are highest in intermontane plains with a high sub-surface water table and frequent marshy areas (Hole, Flannery 1967), suggesting that a critical resource sought by early farmers were lands of high water-retention, where soil moisture helped the planted cereals to survive annual fluctuations in rainfall. At Ali Kosh on the lowland steppe of Southwest Iran, early farmers planted their cereals so near swamp margins that seeds of club-rush (*Scirpus*) were mixed in with the carbonized grain samples (Helbaek 1969). This is analogous to the practices of early farmers in parts of arid highland Mesoamerica, who also utilized permanently-humid bottomlands and high-water table zones (Flannery *et al.* 1967). Such types of farming may also have facilitated the spread of agriculture out of the Near East and into Europe, which took place sometime during this time period.

More complicated techniques accompanied the extension of early dry-farming to its limits in very marginal habitats to the north-east (e.g. the Turkoman steppe), and the south-west (e.g. the Wadi Araba region). At Beidha, in the south Jordan desert, it is possible that farming sites were located in such a way as to take advantage of rainfall run-off concentrated by steep nearby cliffs (Kirkbride 1966). On the Turkoman steppe, early cultivators used small "oasis" situations where streams from the Kopet Dagh formed humid deltas along the base of the mountain range (Masson 1965). In all such cases, where rainfall agriculture must have been pushed to its absolute limit, barley seems to have been the main crop (Helbaek 1966a; 1966b; Masson 1965), otherwise, wheat was preferred.

A detailed look at the early dry-farming diet

In archaeology, one concrete example is often worth more than a whole chapter of generalization. At this point, I would therefore like to present in some detail our dietary data from the site of Ali Kosh, a small early dry-farming village on the Khuzistan steppe of south-western Iran (Hole, Flannery 1967). Excavations at Ali Kosh produced *c.* 45,000 carbonized seeds, which on analysis by Helbaek (n.d.) could be grouped into 40-odd species of plants; it also produced more than 10,000 identifiable bones from approximately 35 species of animals. I have listed only the most common categories in Table 1. In addition, I have estimated the pounds of

TABLE 1 Most common foods recovered in debris at Ali Kosh, an early village in the plain of Deh Luran, south-western Iran (see Helbaek 1969; Hole, Flannery 1967).

TEPE ALI KOSH (7500–5600 B.C.)

(a) Emmer wheat	Caper
(a) Two-row barley, hulled	Pistachio
(a) (Rare traces of other cultivars)	Gazelle
	Onager
(a) Goats	Pig
(a) Sheep	Aurochs
Small wild legumes (*Astragalus, Trigonella, Medicago*)	Fox (and other small mammals)
	Miscellaneous birds
Wild two-row barley	Ducks and geese
Goat-face grass (*Aegilops*)	
Ryegrass (*Lolium*)	Water turtles
Wild oat grass (*Avena*)	
Canary grass (*Phalaris*)	Fish (carp, catfish)
Vetchling (*Lathyrus*)	
Shauk (*Prosopis*)	Freshwater mussels

(*a*) Domesticated items.

usable meat represented by minimum individuals of each type of animal, using the system proposed by White (1953) and adult weights taken from Walker (1964) and my own field notes (Table 2). A further chart (Table 3) gives average representative nutritional values for some of the important plant and animal foods at the site, taken from Platt (Platt 1962),[1] plus some estimates of the amount of each food source needed to make a kilogram.

Three periods of the early dry-farming era were represented at the site of Ali Kosh. These have been called the Bus Mordeh (7500–6750 B.C.), Ali Kosh (6750–6000 B.C.), and Mohammad Jaffar (6000–5600 B.C.) phases (Hole, Flannery 1967). Counts of the animal bones and carbonized seeds by species will be given in the final reports on the site (Helbaek 1969; Hole *et al.* 1969). I can present here only an abbreviated summary of the results.

The subsistence pattern in the earliest, or Bus Mordeh phase, had five main aspects: (1) the cultivation of cereals, whose grains amounted to only about 3% of the carbonized seeds, but because of their greater size constituted perhaps a third of the total weight of plant food; (2) collecting of small wild legume seeds of clover-alfalfa type, which constituted about 94% of the carbonized seeds, but amounted probably to no more than a third of the total weight of plant food; (3) collecting of the seeds of wild grasses, constituting only about 1% of the carbonized seeds and about 15% of the weight of plant food; (4) herding of domestic goats and sheep, whose bones constituted about 67% of the faunal material, but which contributed only about a third of the total weight of meat represented (see Table 2); (5) hunting of wild ungulates, which accounted for only 25% of the animal bones, but contributed more than 60% of the total weight of meat.

The remainder of the food supply was made up by elements such as nut meats, fruits, small mammals, fish, water fowl, and mussels, which although nutritionally important constituted a small percentage of the total weight of meat and plant food. Unfortunately, in the absence of coprolites, we have no way of calculating what percentage of the diet was made up by plant foods and what percentage was meat. It appears, however, that the Bus Mordeh

---

[1] Obvious difficulties were encountered in finding values for some of the wild foods at Ali Kosh. For gazelle meat, I have used the values for lean goat meat; for onager, those for lean beef. Small legume values are those given for fenugreek (*Trigonella* sp.), etc.

villagers ate a good deal more meat than the average modern Iranian peasant; Watson (1966) reports that animal bones are "rather rare" on village dump heaps today.

Nowadays, as May (1961) points out, "most Iranian meals are of the one-pot type", with many ingredients thrown in, such as grain, lentils, meat, onions, etc. This may also have been true prehistorically—at least during the later part of the dry-farming era, when cooking pots are known. The early cereals (emmer wheat and two-row hulled barley) are largely unsuitable for breadmaking, and their grains seem to have been pounded up and eaten right along with fragments of the woody spikelet base (Helbaek 1969). A lack of scorched or carbonized bone suggests that most meat was cooked after it had been cut off the carcass, or else boiled; there is little evidence to indicate direct roasting of the meat while still on the bone. Thus, it is possible that a typical meal of the early dry-farming era consisted of a gruel of cereal grains, spikelet bases, wild legumes, and chunks of ungulate meat cooked up together.

During the three periods represented at Ali Kosh, the only significant change in meat resources seems to have been an increase of sheep relative to goats; hunting was just as important when the site was abandoned as when it was founded. On the other hand, the changes in plant species percentages through time are more striking. They reflect (1) increases in cultivated cereal grains, (2) decreases in the use of local wild legumes, (3) increases in crop weeds, and (4) increases in plants typical of fallowed agricultural land (see below). In Tables 2 and 3 I have added comparative data from a nearby site, Tepe Sabz, which was occupied during the later era of simple irrigation farming (5500–3700 B.C.).

In terms of total food supply, hunting and wild plant collecting were not "supplements" to the Bus Mordeh diet; they were major subsistence strategies. Most of the total weight of meat and plant foods of this period came from wild resources. These resources had been available throughout the preceding upper palaeolithic period, and some of them (e.g. aurochs meat, pistachios, small wild legumes) are intrinsically richer in calories, protein (or both) than most of the domestic foods eaten in the Bus Mordeh phase. In this sense, there is no reason to believe that the early "food-producers" were significantly better nourished than their "food-collecting" ancestors. Nor was their subsistence base necessarily

TABLE 2 Estimated kilograms of usable meat represented in middens at Ali Kosh and Tepe Sabz, in the plain of Deh Luran, Iran. Broken down by category of animal, and cultural phase (except in the case of Tepe Sabz) (For method of calculation, see White 1953).

| | | | TEPE ALI KOSH | |
| | | | Bus Mordeh Phase | |
Animal	Estimated adult weight (kg.)	Kg. of usable meat	Minimum no. of individuals	Kg. of usable meat
Sheep Goat	50	25	(49)	1225
Gazelle	50	25	(16)	400
Onager	350	175	(3)	525
Aurochs	800	400	(3)	1200
Domestic cattle	500	250	—	—
Pig	100	70	(2)	140
Wolf (?)	26	13	—	—
Red fox	9	4.5	(2)	9
Hyaena	40	20	—	—
Wild cat	1	0.5	—	—
Marten	1	0.5	—	—
Weasel	0.2	0.1	—	—
Hedgehog	0.8	0.4	—	—
Duck-size birds	1.5	1	—	—
Goose-size birds	2	1.4	(2)	2.8
Partridge-size birds	0.2	0.14	(1)	0.14
Hawk-size birds	1	0.7	—	—
Turtle	0.5	0.25	(8)	2
Fish	0.5	0.25	(29)	7.25
Crab	0.01	0.005	—	—
Mussel	0.01	0.005	(123)	0.62

more "reliable"; attempts at dry-farming in the Deh Luran plain today meet with failure two or three years out of every five (Hole, Flannery 1967).

The one real advantage of cereal cultivation is that it increases carrying capacity of the land in terms of kilograms per hectare. Dry farming of wheat in northern Khuzistan, for example, yields an average of 410 kilos per hectare (Adams 1962). This is equal to the weight of usable meat from sixteen sheep, or the weight of more than 400 million small legume seeds. There is probably no other food in the Bus Mordeh phase debris which will produce as many kilos from so small an area as the cereals. Cultivation thus

TEPE ALI KOSH

	Ali Kosh Phase		Moh. Jaffar Phase		TEPE SABZ (all phases)
Minimum no. of individuals	Kg. of usable meat	Minimum no. of individuals	Kg. of usable meat	Minimum no. of individuals	Kg. of usable meat
(102)	2550	(40)	1009	(44)	1100
(59)	1475	(18)	450	(18)	450
(12)	2100	(4)	700	(8)	1400
(6)	2400	(2)	800	—	—
—	—	—	—	(9)	2250
(3)	210	(3)	210	(5)	350
(2)	26	(2)	26	—	—
(3)	13.5	(7)	31.5	(6)	27
—	—	(1)	20	—	—
(2)	1	(2)	1	(1)	0.5
—	—	—	—	(1)	0.5
—	—	(1)	0.1	—	—
(2)	0.8	(1)	0.4	(1)	0.4
—	—	(2)	2	—	—
(2)	2.8	(1)	1.4	(1)	1.4
(6)	0.84	(7)	0.98	(6)	0.84
—	—	—	—	(2)	1.4
(4)	1	(4)	1	(4)	1
(47)	12.25	(44)	11	(4)	1
(3)	0.015	(3)	0.015	—	—
(166)	0.83	(111)	0.56	(8)	0.04

represented a decision to replace the native, high-protein wild legume ground cover with a lower-protein grass which would grow more densely and probably was less work to harvest, in spite of the risk of crop failure.

Nutritional aspects of early dry-farming in Iran

Still another fact which emerges from an examination of Tables 1–3 is that the early farmers of south-western Iran were still in the "broad spectrum" era: they made a living by *diversifying* their subsistence strategies, rather than concentrating on one food source. In fact, the synergistic effect of their various food combinations—

TABLE 3   Estimated values of some of the foods commonly eaten at Ali Kosh and Tepe Sabz, in the plain of Deh Luran, Iran.[a]

ESTIMATED VALUE PER KILOGRAM OF EDIBLE PORTION

Food	Calories	Protein (gm.)	Fat (gm.)	Carbohydrate (gm.)
Wheat	3440	115	20	700
Barley	3390	120	20	680
Lentils	3390	240	10	590
Lathyrus	2930	250	10	460
Small wild legumes	3350	290	52	500
Miscellaneous wild grasses	3880	120	75	680
Pistachio	6260	200	540	150
Almond	6570	200	590	120
Goat	1450	160	90	—
Sheep	1490	170	90	—
Gazelle	1450	160	90	—
Onager	2020	190	140	—
Aurochs	2020	190	140	—
Domestic cattle	2020	190	140	—
Pig	3710	140	350	—
Ducks/Geese	1390	190	70	—
Turtle	790	160	10	20
Fish	950	180	25	—
Mussels	700	100	20	30

(a) Based on tables given by Platt, B. S. (1962).

ungulate meat, grasses, legumes, nut meats, mussels and so on—probably resulted in better nutrition than would specialization on a narrower range of products.

Highest on the list of calorie-producing foods used at Ali Kosh and Tepe Sabz were the almonds and pistachios, followed by cereal grasses and wild legumes. The wild legumes, judging by analyses of *Trigonella* (Platt 1962), seem to have been higher in protein than most other food sources. Most calories probably came from these plant foods, since none of the meat sources (with the possible exception of pig) has a very high caloric value.

Minerals like calcium came from a variety of foods: mussels, water turtles, fresh water crabs, almonds, and pistachios. The

ESTIMATED VALUE PER KILOGRAM OF EDIBLE PORTION

Calcium (mg.)	Iron (mg.)	Vitamin A (IU)	Vitamin C (mg.)	Approximate amount needed for 1 kilo
300	35	—	—	±33,000 grains
350	40	—	—	±45,000 grains
700	70	1000	—	±25,000 lentils
1100	56	700	—	Tens of thousands
1800	220	—	—	>1,000,000 seeds
600	50	—	—	>30,000 grains
1400	140	1000	—	±2750 nuts
1500	35	—	—	±1000 nuts
110	25	—	—	1/25 of one animal
110	25	—	—	1/25 of one animal
110	25	—	—	1/25 of one animal
100	30	—	—	1/175 of one animal
100	30	—	—	1/400 of one animal
100	30	—	—	1/250 of one animal
100	20	—	—	1/70 of one animal
150	15	—	—	1 bird (or less)
1000	10	—	—	4 turtles
500	10	—	—	4 fish
1500	100	200	—	200 mussels

mussels, pistachios, and various of the wild legumes are also good vitamin A sources. (It is interesting to note, however, that all these calcium-vitamin A sources probably became insignificant once the milking of domestic animals was established—an event for which we still have no archaeological evidence.)

None of the foods listed in Table 3 is a decent vitamin C source; the fruit of the wild caper (*capparis*) probably filled this role. Other sources existed in the environment, and probably were used, although it cannot be proved archaeologically. These include fresh ungulate liver, the fruit of the jujube tree (*Zizyphus*), and the growing shoots of *Medicago* and other wild legumes (Platt 1962). In short, combinations of the twenty or so major foods used by the early dry farmers probably left them far better nourished than today's Iranian villager (May 1961).[2]

Cropping, herding, and erratic rainfall in the dry-farming era

One aspect of dry-farming in Western Iran—or elsewhere in the Near East, for that matter—is that its outcome is unpredictable. Our figure of 410 kilos per hectare for northern Khuzistan is an average; in a good year the yield might be 1000 kilos, in a bad year almost nothing.

We have already mentioned the hazards of dry-farming in the Deh Luran plain. Watson (1966) gives roughly similar figures for Iranian Kurdistan, where annual rainfall is higher (but still erratic). There a farmer may plant 300 kilos of wheat, and if the rain comes on time and in sufficient amounts, he might even get a ten-fold yield (3000 kilos). On the other hand, Watson's informants lost their entire wheat crop in 1958, 1959, and 1960 because of insects. What early farmers needed, therefore, was a way of levelling out the years of unpredictable bumper crops.

Primitive peoples, in the prehistoric record and in the ethnographic present, seem to use three main methods for dealing with unpredictable surpluses. They can store them; they can convert them into craft items of imperishable, exotic raw materials, which can be used as media of exchange during lean years (Harding 1967; Flannery 1967); or they can convert them into live storage, i.e. domestic animals, which can be used either directly (as food) or

---

[2] The synergistic value of food combinations was brought home to me in 1963 while I worked closely in the field with my friend and colleague, Frank Hole, excavating the Palaeolithic caves of Iran's Khorramabad Valley. As we sat in our camp in the evening—partaking of barley in its most appealing form—we used to share a large paper sack of Kurdistan pistachios (*pistacia atlantica*). Wild products being what they are, the 1963 pistachio crop was riddled with small live caterpillars which had bored into the nuts and lay waiting for the unwary eater. I examined each pistachio carefully as I opened it, and as a consequence had to discard about half; but I noticed that Hole was able to eat 100% of the ones he selected, and I commented on his luck. To which he replied: "I'm just not looking." I later learned that a kilo of dried caterpillars may contain 3720 calories, 550 grams of protein, 2700 milligrams of calcium, and a generous supply of thiamine, riboflavin, and iron (see Platt 1962). In fact, the protein content is double that of the pistachios themselves, and a combination of the two foods probably has a synergistic effect exceeding the value of the nuts alone. Hole's wise decision to diversify his subsistence base brought him out of the field season a good thirty pounds heavier than me.

for inter-group exchanges which set up reciprocal obligations and maximize sharing during lean years (Lees 1967). These second two alternatives amount to a kind of "banking" of surpluses. (Lees 1967).

While early farmers in Mesoamerica relied fairly heavily on exchanges of exotic raw materials, the early Near Eastern farmers seem to have used mainly storage and domestic animals. Sheep and goats, for example, may be purchased with agricultural surpluses in good years, then exchanged for grain in lean years. They may be allowed to graze on growing cereal grain fields in good years (Adams 1965), and at some time periods were fed stored or surplus barley (Adams 1962). Archaeological and ethnographic evidence suggest that plant cultivation and animal herding, far from being two separate subsistence activities, are interrelated in ways which help "bank" surpluses and even out the erratic fluctuations of the Near Eastern environment.

Effects of early cultivation on the wild plant cover

One effect of cultivation was an extensive alteration of the native plant cover of areas like the south-west Iranian steppe, which may actually have prevented a return to previous food-gathering patterns.

We have mentioned already the heavy dependence of Bus Mordeh phase farmers on local wild plants between 7500 and 6750 B.C. Nine-tenths of the seeds identified by Helbaek from these levels were from small annual legumes and wild grasses native to northern Khuzistan. Most abundant were the clover-like legumes *Medicago* (wild alfalfa), *Astragalus* (spiny milk vetch), and *Trigonella* (a small plant of the pea family, related to fenugreek); but they also collected oat grass (*Avena*), Bermuda grass (*Cynodon*) and Canary grass (*Phalaris*). However, these wild plants have the same general growing season as wheat and barley, which the Bus Mordeh people cultivated, and they also compete for the same alluvial soil with low salinity which the cereals require. As cultivation of wheat and barley increased, therefore, these wild legumes and grasses assumed the status of weeds, and were removed to make way for cultivated grains.

Their place did not remain unfilled for long, however—what happened was that new crop weeds from the mountains were introduced, probably in imperfectly cleaned batches of grain brought down to the steppe. These included various strains of *Aegilops* (goat-face grass), *Lolium* (ryegrass), and other grasses. Once established, the newcomers proved stubborn; Adams (1965) reports that today ryegrass is one of the major crop weeds requiring eradication in the Mesopotamian lowlands.

One of the native plants which did not compete with the cereal crops was *Prosopis,* a woody perennial legume with an edible pod, related to the mesquite plant of the American West. Adams points out that *Prosopis* matures in a different season of the year from the cereals, and its deep root system survives even after ploughing. This woody wild legume may therefore even *increase* along with cultivation and fallow land, and Helbaek has in fact detected an increase in *Prosopis* seeds through time through three periods at Ali Kosh. Evidently the early cultivators responded in a reasonable way: as *Prosopis* increased, they ate more of it.

Fallowing practices also modified the landscape in other ways. Today in Khuzistan, three-fourths of all arable land is fallow during any given year. Helbaek's study of carbonized seeds from the Mohammad Jaffar Phase at Ali Kosh indicate that by *c.* 6000 B.C. such fallowing systems were already taking their toll of the previously dominant grasses and legumes, which were increasingly being replaced by pasture plants like mallow (*Malva*), plantain (*Plantago*), fumitory (*Fumaria*) and bedstraw (*Galium*).

The tiny annual legumes retreated to the margins of the cultivated land and the talus slope of the mountains. Their role as a major human food was played out by 6000 B.C. But they were not forgotten or ignored; they became food for sheep and goats. Today, from Iran west across the Near East, and even as far as the Tuareg Country of North Africa (Nicolaisen 1963), *Astragalus* and *Trigonella* have become two of the most common plants collected as fodder for domestic caprines. Man continues to derive energy from them, but through an animal converter.

EARLY IRRIGATION FARMING

Origins of irrigation

Irrigation may be yet a third example of an innovation which took place in a less-favourable habitat adjacent to an area of population growth. Our earliest evidence for this new technology comes not from the well-watered uplands of Kurdistan and Luristan, where early dry-farming was so successful, but from the lowland steppe of Khuzistan, a treeless plain receiving only 300 mm. of annual rainfall.

There is some reason to believe that the Khuzistan steppe was, indeed, receiving overflow populations from the mountain woodland. One line of evidence is the aforementioned field weeds in early levels at Ali Kosh—including *Aegilops* and *Lolium,* which are more at home in the mountains than on the steppe. The implication is that the whole complex, both cereals and field weeds, came into the steppe from the uplands. Another line of evidence is the strong resemblance of steppe artifact assemblages to those in the mountains (Hole *et al.* 1969).

Although survey has been far from exhaustive, what we know of the Zagros region at that time does suggest that population densities were higher in the large intermontane valleys than on the steppe. (Hole, Flannery 1967). Under conditions of rainfall agriculture, the carrying capacity of the steppe is limited, soil salinity is an ever-present danger, and considerable fallowing is required. Parts of the steppe, however, had great potential for irrigation: areas like the upper Khuzistan plains, where "increased surface gradients and widespread underlying gravel deposits provide sufficient natural drainage . . . to minimize the problems of salinization and waterlogging that usually attend irrigation agriculture" (Adams 1962). Once irrigation appeared, the steppe greatly increased its carrying capacity and became, in fact, the dominant growth centre of the Zagros region between 5500 and 4000 B.C. Yet, interestingly enough, this new mode of production did not spread rapidly out of South-west Asia as earlier systems of dry-farming had: it seems to have been a peculiarly Near Eastern development.

Early irrigation on the lowland steppe was accompanied by a shift in settlement pattern (Hole *et al.* in press). Instead of locating sites near the margins of swampy areas, where the high water table could be used to ameliorate fluctuations in rainfall, some villages now occurred in linear arrangements along fossil stream courses from which water could be drawn by small, shallow canals. Table 4 lists the major plant and animal food sources from Tepe Sabz, an early irrigation site in south-western Iran.

Archaeological evidence for early irrigation comes from a variety of approaches. It was Adams (1962) who first pointed out that there were alignments of later prehistoric sites in Khuzistan (5500–3500 B.C.) which seemed to follow such water courses south into

TABLE 4 Common foods recovered from Tepe Sabz,
in the plain of Deh Luran, south-west Iran (Helbaek 1969).

TEPE SABZ (5500–3700 B.C.)

(a) Emmer wheat	Shauk (*Prosopis*)
(a) Two-row barley, hulled	Caper
(a) Bread wheat	Pistachio
(a) Einkorn wheat	Almond
(a) Six-row barley, hulled	
(a) Six-row barley, naked	
(a) Linseed	Gazelle
(a) Lentils	Onager
(a) Grass peas	Pig
(a) Goats	Fox (and other small mammals)
(a) Sheep	Miscellaneous birds
(a) Cattle	
Goat-face grass (*Aegilops*)	Water turtles
Ryegrass (*Lolium*)	
Vetchling (*Lathyrus*)	Fish

(*a*) Domesticated items.

the zone where rainfall alone is inadequate for cultivation. Implications of the settlement pattern were that irrigation, consisting of the simple breaching of the natural levees of small streams flowing at the surface of the plain, enabled prehistoric farmers to partially counteract the erratic and frequently inadequate rainfall of the steppe. A similar survey by Wright (1967), recently undertaken in the vicinity of Ur, shows that Ubaid baked-clay sickles and sickle fragments found on the land surface tend to be restricted to a band five kilometres wide to either side of fossil stream channels, giving us an estimate of the area watered by the small canals serving the fields.

Ecological effects of irrigation

Irrigation in Khuzistan, according to Adams (1962) tends to increase crop yields from 410 kilos per hectare to 615 kilos per hectare. In addition, the actual physical size of the crop plants themselves seems to have been increased. For example, Helbaek's studies suggest that seeds of flax or linseed (*Linum bienne*) grown by rainfall alone have a maximum length range between 3.29–4.03 mm., while irrigated flax has a maximum length range of 4.39–6.20

mm. Flax seeds of this large size do not appear in the Deh Luran deposits until 5500–5000 B.C., after which they are present in large numbers (Helbaek 1960a; 1960b; 1969). However, as many authors have already pointed out, irrigation if unaccompanied by proper drainage may bring salt to the surface through capillary action in areas which were not previously saline. Agriculture then necessitates a strategy in which the advantages of irrigation water are weighed against soil salinity. One strategy employed in the lowlands of Iran and Mesopotamia was to concentrate on barley, which has a shorter growing season and higher salt tolerance than wheat. It is no accident that barley and sheep (see below), with their relatively greater ability to withstand the rigours of the hot, dry, saline lowland steppe and alluvium, were among the most important food resources of Elamite civilization (Adams 1962; Hole, Flannery 1967).

One by-product of irrigation was that the canal became a new semihumid niche on which specialized plants could be grown, apart from those which the water was originally intended to irrigate. It is known, for example, that onions and date palms were grown on canal banks in early historic times in Mesopotamia. (Adams 1960). Unfortunately, the canal vegetation is also served as a haven for crop pests such as the bandicoot-rat (*Nesokia indica*) which otherwise would have been less abundant in the region.

Sleep versus Stipa: *a by-product of the origins of wool*

An interesting chain of events followed the domestication of *Ovis orientalis,* an animal which still roams the foothills and intermontane plains of the Zagros and Taurus ranges in herds of up to fifteen individuals. These sheep have a coat which is reddish-buff above, white below, and is little different from that of a deer or gazelle. The coat is composed of hair from two kinds of follicles: "primaries", which produce the visible coat, and "secondaries", which produce the hidden, woolly underfur (Ryder 1958).

In the wild, these sheep use a number of wild grasses as forage. One of the best of these is a plant known as *Stipa,* or "feathergrass", which grows over much of the area from the Khuzistan and Assyrian steppes to the high mountains of the Iran-Iraq border. Many species of *Stipa* are classed by Pabot (1960) and others as among the better forage species in terms of nutrition. *Stipa* has a rather interesting seed implantation mechanism: the seed has a sharp callus, which easily penetrates the soil, and a number of short stiff hairs which oppose its withdrawal. The bent and twisted awn of the seed, which is hygroscopic, serves as a driving organ, twisting and untwisting with changes in humidity. Thus, over a period of alternating wet and dry days, the feathergrass seed literally "screws itself into the ground".

Now, to set the stage, let us domesticate *Ovis orientalis* in the Zagros area sometime between 9000 and 8000 B.C. It appears (at the present state of our knowledge) that the first genetic change following domestication was the loss of horns in some sheep, probably females. One hornless sheep specimen is known from the Bus Mordeh phase in the Deh Luran plain of Iran, dating to about 7500 B.C. (Hole, Flannery 1967), and others are known from early villages near Kermanshah, Iran, and in Anatolia (personal communications from S. Bökönyi and D. Perkins, Jr.). A later change, and one still not radiocarbon dated,[3] was the appearance of wool in domestic sheep, which we know took place prior to 3000 B.C. (Hilzheimer 1941). Ryder (1958) has shown that this was brought about when the "secondary" follicles increased in number and changed their spacing, causing the "underfur" to become the principal component of the sheep's coat.

It has long been known that sheep survive high temperatures and desertic conditions better than most other domestic animals. Recent studies by Schmidt-Nielsen (1964) and his associates suggest that this is due to a number of factors: a "panting" mechanism which "permits an efficient ventilation of the upper respiratory tract, where most of the evaporation takes place" (Schmidt-Nielsen 1964) and also—believe it or not—their wool. Thermometers were used to measure the internal, skin-surface, and outer-wool temperatures of sheep exposed to extreme conditions of heat and sun. It was observed that while the wool temperature reached 87° C, skin temperature remained at 42° C; in other words, "4 cm. of wool sustained a gradient of 45° C between tip and skin" (Schmidt-Nielsen 1964). It appears that while wool acts not only as a reflection to divert light and heat rays, but also as a layer of insulation which allows air circulation to cool the skin without exposing it to the sun. There may thus be some adaptive advantage

---

[3] Textiles from Çatal Hüyük, once thought to be perhaps the earliest wool known, have been examined now by Ryder (1965), and it appears that they are mostly flax fibre.

for woolliness in domestic sheep maintained in captivity in hot climates, especially if they are deprived of a chance to spend the mid-day hours in the shade of a thicket, as they do in the wild. (Obviously, however, the *extreme* degree of woolliness in modern breeds is an artificial condition maintained by man, since feral sheep rapidly lose it.)

One of the side-effects of this process becomes apparent when woolly sheep are allowed to graze in meadows of *Stipa:* the feather-grass seed catches in the wool and often, through the same process of wetting and drying with which it plants itself, may burrow right into the animal's skin, causing considerable discomfort and even infection (Reeder 1967). In some parts of Iran today, for example, shepherds even avoid taking their flocks into areas dominated by this plant (Pabot 1960), which must have been one of the most useful foods of the hairy wild sheep. Such little ecological chains of events give us some idea of how complex the whole process of domestication must have been.

Effects of changing land-use on sociopolitical structure

An interesting relationship appears when one plots the increasing population of prehistoric Iran against today's figures for different kinds of land use, as I have done in Figure 1. It would appear that while early dry-farming and irrigation were pushing population densities up at a rapid rate, the relative amount of land which could be considered "prime", or "highly productive" was decreasing with equal rapidity. Let me explain.

Hole and I (Hole, Flannery 1967) have already presented estimates of population densities for parts of south-western Iran during the prehistoric era. These estimates are based on numbers of sites recovered by our surveys and those of Adams (1962), using figures of approximately 100 persons per 1-hectare village site, and so on; it is presumed that whatever inaccuracies are present apply equally to all periods, so the general shape of the population growth curve should be reasonably reliable. Briefly, our estimates go from 0–1 persons per square kilometre in the late Palaeolithic, to 1–2 persons per square kilometre under conditions of early dry-farming, and up to 6 or more persons per square kilometre after irrigation appears in the archaeological record. In other words, population increased at least sixty-fold in the space of about six thousand years.

Now consider the figures given by May (1961), which are based on the 1956 Iranian census, plus studies by FAO-WHO and the

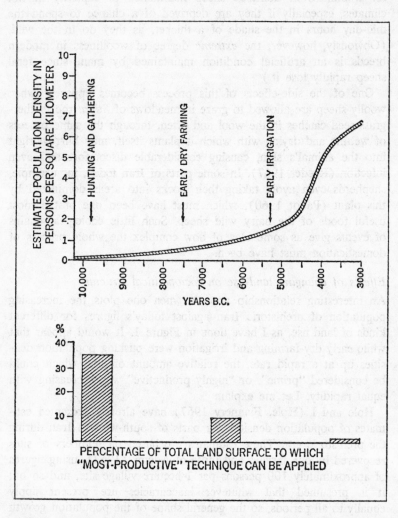

TABLE 5 Inverse ratio between population growth and percentage of total land surface to which "most productive" technique (hunting and gathering, dry farming, early irrigation) could be applied at various stages of Iranian prehistory.

U. S. Foreign Agricultural Service. First of all, these studies indicate that a very large part of Iran—about 65%—is taken up by nearly uninhabitable deserts and lands of extremely marginal productivity. These may have been used by late Palaeolithic man, but surely it would have been the other 35% which provided him with the best hunting-gathering opportunities; included in the latter would be the intermontane plains of the limestone mountain area and the great winter grasslands of northern Khuzistan. These zones had the wild game, as well as the edible fruits, grasses, and legumes which supplied its sustenance and presumably also man's.

Begin dry-farming, however, and the picture changes; for only 10% of Iran's land surface is considered "arable" (May 1961; Cressey 1960). This means that although population increased by twenty times, most of its food was now produced on one-tenth of the land surface. And with the start of irrigation the ratio changed drastically again; today, only 10% of the arable land in Iran, or 1% of the total land surface, is irrigated (and that includes large areas irrigated today by underground chain wells or *qanats,* for which we have no evidence in prehistory; the area over which stream or canal irrigation can be practised is even smaller). Add to this the fact that in any one year three out of every four hectares of arable land are fallow, and it appears that a very small area feeds many millions of people. In fact, the irrigated 1% of the country produces 30% of the yearly crop (May 1961).

Such an inverse ratio between population and "most productive" land characterized other areas where early civilizations arose— Mesoamerica, for example. As Palerm and Wolf (1957) have suggested, early agriculture in Mexico and Guatemala probably depended on rainfall alone; but as time went by, increasingly more productive techniques arose, such as flood-water farming, canal irrigation, dams, and *chinampas* or "floating gardens". As these techniques appeared they were "applicable to an ever-decreasing number of areas" (Palerm, Wolf 1957). The area over which the most productive techniques could be applied was miniscule relative to Mesoamerica as a whole—yet such areas fed millions of Indians.

Perhaps the most important consequence of the inverse ratio is that it set the stage for social stratification. As May (1961) has pointed out, one of the salient characteristics of Near Eastern agriculture is what he politely calls "inequitable systems of land ownership and tenure". It is not just that 100% of the food is produced on 10% of the land; it is the fact that in some cases 1% of the population owns the 1% of the land which produces 30% of the food. This kind of differential access to strategic resources, including the means of production, is at the heart of "ranked" or "stratified" society. It is not a result of agricultural success, or "surplus", but a product of the widening gap between the size of the population and the size of the critical land surface on which it was most dependent. It is probably no accident that highly stratified societies followed this adaptive era in the alluvial lowlands of the Near East.

CONCLUSIONS

Like many semi-arid mountain regions, the Near East is a mosaic of woodland or parkland areas, relatively rich in wild products, surrounded by steppes or grasslands which are less rich in wild products. The changes leading to intensive food production are here viewed as a series of responses to disturbances of density equilibrium in human populations around the margins of the favoured areas, caused by the fact that those areas were the zones of population growth and emigration. Obviously, a definition of "favourable" depends on the technological level at the time: i.e., hunting, wild plant collecting, early dry-farming, or early irrigation.

Recent ethnographic studies do not indicate that hunters and gatherers are "starving", or that starvation is the major factor limiting their populations. Nor does the archaeological record in the Near East suggest that the average Neolithic farmer was any better nourished than the average Palaeolithic hunter. Moreover, over much of the Near East, farming does not necessarily constitute a "more stable" subsistence base or a "more reliable" food supply. The real consequence of domestication was to (1) change the means of production in society, (2) make possible divisions of labour not usually characteristic of hunter-gathers, and (3) lay the foundations for social stratification by continually reducing the zone of "optimum" productivity while allowing the population to expand at a geometric rate. It also (4) increased man's potential for environmental destruction, so that eventually it would have been impossible for him to return to his former means of subsistence, had he wanted to.

In this respect, early Near Eastern agriculture represents yet another example of the "second cybernetics" (Maruyama 1963; Flannery 1968b). Starting with a relatively stable configuration of plant and animal species at 10,000 B.C., early cultivation took two genera of cereal grasses and two genera of small ungulates out of their habitat and artificially increased their numbers while they underwent a series of genetic changes, many of which were favourable from man's standpoint. These favourable changes made feasible a still greater investment of human labour in the cereals and caprines, and a greater artificial expansion of their range at the expanse of other species. At this point, the ecosystem was no longer cybernating, or "stable"; all former rules which had kept species in check were off. What had been a minor deviation from equilibrium at 8000 B.C. had been amplified into a major subsystem at 5000 B.C., by which time irrigation had been employed to produce single-species stands of cereals, where none had even existed in the wild. When equilibrium was momentarily reached again, perhaps around the time of the Sumerian state, a great many species —like the aurochs, the onager, and the red deer—had been driven completely on to marginal land. Today they are locally or universally extinct in the Near East. The new niches opened up by agriculture and irrigation were not for them, but for the crop pests and weeds which accompanied the cereals into foreign habitats and became, in some cases, part of the dominant biota. So great was the change in the Near East that today we see its original configuration only in the pollen record and the Palaeolithic bone debris.

5 ARCHEOLOGICAL SYSTEMS THEORY AND EARLY MESOAMERICA

Kent V. Flannery

INTRODUCTION

A s work on the early periods of Mesoamerican prehistory progresses, and we learn more about the food-collectors and early food-producers of that region, our mental image of these ancient peoples has been greatly modified. We no longer think of the preceramic plant-collectors as a ragged and scruffy band of nomads; instead, they appear as a practiced and ingenious team of lay botanists who know how to wring the most out of a superficially bleak environment. Nor do we still picture the Formative peoples as a happy group of little brown farmers dancing around their cornfields and thatched huts; we see them, rather, as a very complex series of competitive ethnic groups with internal social ranking and great preoccupation with status, iconography, water control, and the accumulation of luxury goods. Hopefully, as careful studies bring these people into sharper focus, they will begin to make more sense in terms of comparable Indian groups surviving in the ethnographic present.

Among other things, the new data from Mesoamerica strain some of the theoretical models we used in the past to view culture and culture change. One of these was the model of a culture adapted to a particular environmental zone: "oak woodland," "mesquite-grassland," "semitropical thorn scrub," "tropical forest," and so on. New data suggest, first, that primitive peoples rarely adapt to whole "environmental zones" (Coe, Flannery 1964:650). Next, as argued in this article, it appears that sometimes a group's basic

Reprinted by permission of the Anthropological Society of Washington, from *Anthropological Archeology in the Americas* (Betty J. Meggers, ed.), 1968, pp. 67–87, and by permission of the author.

"adaptation" may not even be to the "micro-environments" within a zone, but rather to a small series of plant and animal genera whose ranges cross-cut several environments.

Another model badly strained by our new data is that of culture change during the transition from food-collecting to sedentary agriculture. Past workers often attributed this to the "discovery" that planted seeds would sprout (MacNeish 1964a:533), or to the results of a long series of "experiments" with plant cultivation. Neither of these explanations is wholly satisfying. We know of no human group on earth so primitive that they are ignorant of the connection between plants and the seeds from which they grow, and this is particularly true of groups dependent (as were the highland Mesoamerican food-collectors) on intensive utilization of seasonal plant resources. Furthermore, I find it hard to believe that "experiments with cultivation" were carried on only with those plants that eventually became cultivars, since during the food-collecting era those plants do not even seem to have been the principal foods used. In fact, they seem to have been less important than many wild plants which never became domesticated. Obviously, something besides "discoveries" and "experiments" is involved.

I believe that this period of transition from food-collecting to sedentary agriculture, which began by 5000 B.C. and ended prior to 1500 B.C., can best be characterized as one of gradual change in a series of procurement systems, regulated by two mechanisms called seasonality and scheduling. I would argue that none of the changes took place during this period arose *de novo,* but were the result of expansion or contraction of previously-existing systems. I would argue further that the use of an ecosystem model enables us to see aspects of this prehistoric culture change which are not superficially apparent.

In the course of this paper I will attempt to apply, on a prehistoric time level, the kind of ecosystem analysis advocated most recently by Vayda (1964) and Rappaport (1967), with modifications imposed by the nature of the archeological data. Man and the Southern Highlands of Mexico will be viewed as a single complex system, composed of many sub-systems which mutually influenced each other over a period of over seven millennia, between 8000 B.C. and 2000 B.C. This systems approach will include the use of both the "first" and "second" cybernetics (Maruyama 1963) as a model for explaining pre-historic culture change.

The first cybernetics involves the study of regulatory mechanisms and "negative feedback" processes which promote equilibrium, and counteract deviation from stable situations over long periods of time. The second cybernetics is the study of "positive feedback" processes which amplify deviations, causing systems to expand and eventually reach stability at higher levels. Because I am as distressed as anyone by the esoteric terminology of systems theory, I have tried to substitute basic English synonyms wherever possible.

PROCUREMENT SYSTEMS
IN THE PRECERAMIC (HUNTING AND GATHERING) ERA

Let us begin by considering the subsistence pattern of the food-collectors and "incipient cultivators" who occupied the Southern Highland of Mexico between 8000 and 2000 B.C.

The sources of our data are plant and animal remains preserved in dry caves in the Valley of Oaxaca (Flannery, Kirkby, Kirkby, Williams, 1967) and the Valley of Tehuacán (MacNeish 1961, 1962, 1964a). Relevant sites are Guilá Naquitz Cave, Cueva Blanca, and the Martínez Rock Shelter (near Mitla, in the Valley of Oaxaca), and MacNeish's now-famous Coxcatlán, Purrón, Abejas, El Riego, and San Marcos Caves, whose food remains have been partially reported (Callen 1965; Smith 1965a). Tens of thousands of plants and animal bones were recovered from these caves, which vary between 900 and 1900 meters in elevation and occur in environments as diverse as cool-temperate oak woodland, cactus desert, and semi-tropical thorn forest. Because most of the material has not been published in detail as yet, my conclusions must be considered tentative.

Preliminary studies of the food debris from these caves indicate that certain plant and animal genera were always more important than others, regardless of local environment. These plants and animals were the focal points of a series of procurement systems, each of which may be considered one component of the total ecosystem of the food collecting era. They were heavily utilized—"exploited" is the term usually employed—but such utilization was not a one-way system. Man was not simply extracting energy from his environment, but participating in it; and his use of each genus was part of a system which allowed the latter to survive, even flourish, in spite of heavy utilization. Many of these patterns have survived to the present day, among Indian groups like the Paiute and Shoshone (Steward 1955: Chapter 6) or the Tarahumara of northern Mexico (Pennington 1963), thus allowing us to postulate some of the mechanisms built into the system, which allowed the wild genera to survive.

Each procurement system required a technology involving both implements (projectiles, fiber shredders, collecting tongs, etc.) and facilities (baskets, net carrying bags, storage pits, roasting pits, etc.). In many cases, these implements and facilities were so similar to those used in the ethnographic present by Utoaztecan speakers of western North America that relatively little difficulty is encountered in reconstructing the outlines of the ancient procurement system.

1. Plants

Literally hundreds of plant species were used by the food-collectors of the Southern Mexican Highlands. There were annual grasses like wild maize (*Zea*) and fox-tail (*Setaria*), fruits like the avocado (*Persea*) and black zapote (*Diospyros*), wild onions (*Allium*), acorns and pinyon nuts, several varieties of pigweed (*Amaranthus*), and many other plants, varying considerably from region to region because of rainfall and altitude differences (Callen 1965; Smith, 1965b, and personal communication). However, three categories of plants seem to have been especially important wherever we have data, regardless of altitude. They are:

(1) The maguey (*Agave* spp.), a member of the Amaryllis family, which is available year-round; (2) a series of succulent cacti, including organ cactus (*Lemaireocereus* spp.) and prickly pear (*Opuntia* spp.), whose fruits are seasonal, but whose young leaves are available year-round; and (3) a number of related genera of tree legumes, known locally as mesquites (*Prosopis* spp.) and guajes (*Lucaena, Mimosa,* and *Acacia*), which bear edible pods in the rainy season only.

System 1: Maguey Procurement. Maguey, the "century plant", is most famous today as the genus from which pulque is fermented and tequila and mezcal are distilled. In prehistoric times, when distillation was unknown, the maguey appears to have been used more as a source of food. Perhaps no single plant element is more common in the dry caves of southern Mexico than the masticated cud or "quid" of maguey (Smith 1965a:77). It is not always realized, however, that these quids presuppose a kind of technological breakthrough: at some point, far back in preceramic times, the Indians learned how to make the maguey edible.

The maguey, a tough and phylogenetically primitive monocotyledon which thrives on marginal land even on the slopes of high, cold, arid valleys, is unbearably bitter when raw. It cannot be eaten until it has been roasted between 24 and 72 hours, depending on the youth and tenderness of the plant involved.

The method of maguey roasting described by Pennington (1963: 129–130) is not unlike that of the present-day Zapotec of the Valley of Oaxaca. A circular pit, 3 to 4 feet in diameter and of equal depth, is lined with stones and fueled with some slow-burning wood, like oak. When the stones are red-hot, the pit is lined with maguey leaves which have been trimmed off the "heart" of the plant. The maguey hearts are placed in the pit, covered with grass and maguey leaves and finally a layer of earth, which seals the roasting pit and holds in the heat. After one to five days, depending on the age and quantity of maguey, the baking is terminated and the hearts are edible: all, that is, except the indigestible fiber, which is expectorated in the form of a "quid" after the nourishment is gone. Evidence of the roasting process can be detected in maguey fragments surviving in desiccated human feces from Coxcatlán Cave (Callen 1965:342).

The Zapotecs of the Valley of Oaxaca, like most Indians of Southern Mexico, recognize that the best time to cut and roast the maguey is after it has sent up its inflorescence, or *quiote*. The plant begins to die after this event, which occurs sometime around the sixth or eighth year of growth, and a natural fermentation takes place in the moribund plant which softens it and increases its sugar content. The sending up of this inflorescence is a slow process, which can culminate at any time of the year. The large numbers of *quiote* fragments in our Oaxaca cave sites indicate that the Indians of the preceramic food-collecting era already knew that this was the best point in the plant's life cycle for roasting.

The discovery that maguey (if properly processed) can be rendered edible was of major importance, for in some regions there is little else available in the way of plant food during the heart of the dry season. And the discovery that maguey was best for roasting *after* sending up its inflorescence and starting its natural fermentation meant that the plants harvested were mostly those that were dying already, and had long since sent out their pollen. Thus the

maguey continued to thrive on the hillsides of the southern highlands in spite of the substantial harvests of the preceramic food-collectors: all they did was to weed out the dying plants.

System 2: Cactus Fruit Procurement. Organ cacti of at least
four species were eaten at Tehuacán and Oaxaca, and their fruits—
which appear late in the dry season—are still very common in
Mexican markets. Most are sold under the generic terms *pitahaya*
and *tuna,* but the best known "tuna" is really the fruit of the prickly
pear (*Opuntia* spp.), the ubiquitous cactus of Mexican plains and
rocky slopes. Most cactus fruit appears some time toward the end
of the dry season, depending on altitude, but the tender young
leaves may be peeled and cooked during any season of the year.

The collecting of cactus fruit had to take place before the summer
rains turned the fruit to mush, and had to be carried on in competition with fruit bats, birds, and small rodents, who also find the fruit
appetizing. The fruits are spiny, and some of the Tehuacán caves
contained wooden sticks which may have been "tongs" for use in
picking them off the stem (MacNeish, personal communication).
The spines can be singed off and the fruits transported by net
bag or basket, but they cannot be stored for long. By sun-drying,
the fruit can be saved for several weeks (Pennington 1963:117–
118), but eventually it begins to rot. It is worth noting, however,
that harvest of most of these wild fruits must be done quickly and
intensively because of competition from wild animals, rather than
spoilage.

The harvesting and eating of cactus fruits, no matter how intensive it may be, does not appear to diminish the available stands
of cactus nor reduce subsequent generations of tuna and pitahaya—
for the seeds from which the plant is propagated almost inevitably
survive the human digestive tract and escape in the feces, to sprout
that very year. It is even possible that such harvests are beneficial
for the prickly pear and columnar cacti, in affording them maximum
seed dispersal. This is only one example of the self-perpetuating
nature of some of the procurement systems operating in preceramic
Mexico.

System 3: Tree Legume Procurement. Mesquite is a woody
legume which prefers the deep alluvial soil of valley floors and river
flood plains in the highlands. During the June to August rainy
season it bears hundreds of pods which, while still green and tender,

can be chewed, or boiled into a kind of syrup (called "miel" in the Oaxaca and Tehuacán Valleys).

Such use of mesquite extended from at least the Southern Mexican Highlands (where we found it in caves near Mitla) north to the Great American Southwest, where it was evident at Gypsum Cave and related sites (Harrington 1933). *Guajes,* whose edible pods mature in roughly the same season, characterize hill slopes and canyons, and were abundant in both the Mitla and Tehuacán caves (C. Earle Smith, personal communication).

The amount of food available when mesquite and guajes are at the peak of their pod-bearing season is truly impressive. Botanist James Schoenwetter, standing outside one of our Mitla caves in 1966 during the optimum mesquite-guaje season, personally communicated to us his suspicion that a family of four Indians could have collected a week's supply of legume pods there "practically without moving their feet."

The pod-bearing pattern of mesquite and guaje demands a seasonal, localized, and fairly intensive period of collecting. The pods can be hand-picked, and probably were transported in the many types of baskets and net carrying bags recovered in the Oaxaca and Tehuacán caves (MacNeish 1964a:533; Flannery, unpublished data). Both pods and seeds can be dried and stored for long periods, but they must be picked at the appropriate time or they will be eaten by animals, like deer, rabbit, and ring-tailed cat.

II. Mammals

Mammals were an important year-round resource in ancient Mesoamerica, where winters are so mild that many animals never hibernate, as they do at more northern latitudes. Deer, peccary, rabbits, raccoons, opossums, skunks, ground squirrels, and large pocket gophers were common in the prehistoric refuse (Flannery 1967). However, wherever we have adequate samples of archeological animal bones from the Southern Highlands of Mexico, it appears that the following generalization is valid: white-tailed deer and cottontail rabbits were far and away the most important game mammals in all periods, and most hunting technology in the preceramic (and Formative) eras was designed to recover these two genera. Our discussion of wild animal exploitation will therefore center on these animals.

System 4: White-Tailed Deer Procurement. The white-tailed deer, a major food resource in ancient times, continues to be Mesoamerica's most important single game species. Part of its success is due to the wide range of plant foods it finds acceptable, and its persistence even in the immediate vicinity of human settlement and under extreme hunting pressure. White-tailed deer occur in every habitat in Mesoamerica, but their highest populations are in the pine-oak woodlands of the Sierra Madre. The tropical rain forests, such as those of the lowland Maya area, are the least suitable habitats for this deer. Within Mesoamerica proper, highest prehistoric populations would have been in areas like the mountain woodlands of the Valley of Mexico, Puebla, Toluca, Oaxaca, and Guerrero.

These deer have relatively small home ranges, and although they often spend part of the daylight hours hiding in thickets, they can be hunted in the morning and evening when they come out to forage. Deer have known trails along which they travel within their home ranges, and where ambush hunters can wait for them. In other words, they are susceptible to daylight hunts, on foot, by men armed with nothing more sophisticated than an atlatl or even a fire-hardened spear, such as used by the Chiapanecs of the Grijalva Depression (Lowe 1959a:7). On top of this, they can stand an annual harvest of 30 to 40 per cent of the deer population without diminishing in numbers (Leopold 1959:513). Archeological data (Flannery 1967) suggest that the hunters of Tehuacán and Oaxaca Valleys did not practice any kind of conservation, but killed males, females, fawns and even pregnant does (as indicated by skeletal remains of late-term foetuses). This does not seem to have depleted local deer populations in any way. In fact, by thinning the herds during times of optimum plant resource availability, it may even have prevented the starvation of deer during the heart of the dry season.

System 5: Cottontail Procurement. I have already discussed the ecology of Mexican cottontails in a previous paper (Flannery 1966) and will only recapitulate briefly here: cottontails are available year-round (though most abundant in the rainy season) and can best be taken by means of traps or snares. Throwing sticks are also effective, and the Indians of northern Mexico use a figure-four rock trap or "deadfall" (Pennington 1963:90 and Plate XII). In the Tehuacán caves there were fragments of whittled sticks and fiber loops or slip knots which may be trap fragments (MacNeish 1964a:533 and

personal communication); similar fragments showed up in one of our
Oaxaca caves in 1966. The best feature of cottontail trapping is that
the only investment of labor is in the manufacture and setting of the
trap; it works for you while you go about other tasks. And cottontails
are such prolific breeders that no amount of trapping is likely to wipe
them out.

REGULATORY MECHANISMS

The ecosystem in which the hunters and collectors of ancient Mexico
participated included many regulatory mechanisms, which kept the
system successful, yet counteracted deviation from the established
pattern. I will discuss only two of these—"seasonality" and "scheduling." "Seasonality" was imposed on man by the nature of the wild
resources themselves; "scheduling" was a cultural activity which resolved conflict between procurement systems.

I. Seasonality

The most important divisions of the Mesoamerican year are a winter
season (October to May), which is dry, and a summer season (June
to September), when most of the annual rain falls. Many edible
plants and animals of the area are available only during one season,
or part of a season. For example, in the semiarid highlands of
Mexico some plants like the *pochote* or kapok tree (*Ceiba
parvifolia*), as well as many species of columnar cacti, bear fruit in
the late winter just before the rains begin, so that their seeds will
sprout that same year. Other trees, like the oak (*Quercus* spp.) and
the *chupandilla* (*Cyrtocarpa* sp.) bear fruit after the summer season,
so their seeds will lie dormant through the winter and sprout during
the following year. These differences, which are of adaptive value
to the plant (allowing each species to flower and seed itself during
the time of year when it is most advantageous), somewhat predetermined the collecting schedule of the pre-agricultural bands in
Mesoamerica: often these Indians had to be able to predict to
within a week or two when the maturation of the plant would take
place, and then they would have to harvest furiously before the
plants were eaten by birds, rodents, or other small mammals.

MacNeish (1964a;1964b) has shown some of the ways in which
human groups reacted to seasonality. During the rainy season, in
areas where many wild plant resources were available, they often

came together in large groups which MacNeish calls "macrobands," probably consisting of a series of related families (cf. Steward 1955:Chapter 6). During the heart of the dry season, when few edible plants are available, the group fragmented into "microbands," which may have been individual family units. These small units scattered out widely over the landscape, utilizing resources too meager to support a macroband.

The seasonally-restricted nature of resources made it impossible for groups to remain large all year, and effectively counteracted any trends toward population increase which might have been fostered by the intensive harvests of the rainy-season macrobands. Thus populations never grew to the point where they could effectively overreach their wild food resources. MacNeish (1964a:Fig. 4) postulates that as late as 3000 B.C. the population of the Tehuacán Valley was no higher than 120–240 persons, in an area of 1400 square miles.

II. Scheduling

So many possibilities for exploitive activity were open to these ancient Mesoamericans that it would have been impossible to engage in all of them, even seasonally. It happens that there are times of the year when a number of resources are available simultaneously, producing a situation in which there is some conflict for the time and labor of the group. Division of labor along the lines of sex, with men hunting and women collecting, is one common solution to these conflicts, but not all conflicts are so easily resolved.

The solution for more complex situations may be called "scheduling," and it involves a decision as to the relative merits of two or more courses of action. Such "scheduling decisions" are made constantly by all human groups on all levels of complexity, often without any awareness that a decision is being made.

It is not necessarily true that the lower the level of social complexity, the fewer the conflict decisions, for hunting and gathering groups of arid America had many scheduling problems to resolve. Food gathering bands of the Great Basin, for example, often depended on "scouting reports" from relatives who had passed through certain areas several weeks in advance. If they noticed an unusually high concentration of antelope or rabbit in a particular valley, or if they saw that a particular stand of wild fruit would come ripe within the next two weeks, they would advise other scattered bands of foragers about this resource (Steward 1955:105–106). Often, while they descended on the area to harvest that particular species, new reports would come in from other areas concerning still another resource. This was not the kind of "hit and miss" pattern of exploitation one might think, for the Great Basin Indians had a rough idea that acorns and pinyon nuts would be available in the autumn, wild legumes and grasses in the rainy season, and so on. The outlines of a schedule, albeit with conflicts, were present; the "scouting reports" helped resolve conflicts and gave precision to the dates of each kind of resource exploitation, depending on individual variations in growing season from year to year.

These individual variations, which are a common feature of arid environments, combined with the scheduling pattern to make it unlikely that specialization in any one resource would develop. This prevented over-utilization of key plants or animals, and maintained a more even balance between varied resources. Because scheduling is an opportunistic mechanism, it promoted survival in spite of annual variation, but at the same time it supported the *status quo:* unspecialized utilization of a whole range of plants and animals whose availability is erratic over the long run. In this sense, scheduling acted to counteract deviations which might have resulted in either (1) starvation, or (2) a more effective adaptation.

EVIDENCE FOR SCHEDULING IN THE FOOD-COLLECTING
AND "INCIPIENT CULTIVATION" ERAS (8000–2000 B.C.)

Thanks to the plants and animal bones preserved in the dry caves of Oaxaca and Tehuacán, we can often tell which season a given occupation floor was laid down in. Because of the work of botanists like Earle Smith, Lawrence Kaplan, and James Schoenwetter, we know the season during which each plant is available, and hence when its harvest must have taken place. Even the use of animal resources can often be dated seasonally; for example, in the Tehuacán Valley, we studied the seasonality of deer hunting by the condition of the antlers, which indicates the time of year when the animal was killed.

Assuming that each occupation floor in a given cave represents the debris of a single encampment, usually dating to a single season (an assumption that seems to be borne out by the quantity and nature of the refuse), the combinations of plant and animal remains observed in a given level tell us something about prehistoric scheduling decisions. Analyses of our Oaxaca caves and MacNeish's Tehuacán Caves, by roughly the same group of specialists (MacNeish 1962, 1964a; Flannery 1967, suggest the following tentative generalizations:

(1) *Dry season camps* (October–March), depending on their elevation above sea level, may have great caches of fall and winter plants—for example, acorns in the Mitla area, or Ceiba pods in the Coxcatlán area—but in general they lack the variety seen in rainy season levels. And perhaps most significantly, they have a high percentage of those plants which, although not particularly tasty, are available year-round: maguey, prickly pear leaf, *Ceiba* root, and so on. These are the so-called "starvation" plants, which can be eaten in the heart of the dry season when little else is available. These same levels also tend to have high percentages of deer bone. Some, in fact, have little refuse beyond maguey quids and white-tailed deer.

(2) *Rainy season camps* (May–September), as might be expected, show great quantities of the plants available at that time of the year: mesquite, guajes, amaranth, wild avocado, zapotes, and so on. They also tend to be rich in small fauna like cottontail, opossum, skunk, raccoon, gopher, and black iguana. Although deer are often present in these camps, they frequently represent only a small percentage of the minimum individual animals in the debris. Nor are the "starvation" plants particularly plentiful in these rainy-season levels.

(3) What these generalizations suggest, for the most part, is that scheduling gave preference to the seasonality of the *plant* species collected; and when conflict situations arose, it was the *animal* exploitation that was curtailed. I would reconstruct the pattern as follows:

A. In the late dry season and early rainy season, there is a period of peak abundance of wild plant foods. These localized resources were intensively harvested, and eaten or cached as they came to maturity; this appears to have been a "macroband" activity. Because "all hands" participated in these harvests, little deer hunting was done; instead the Indians set traps in the vicinity of the plant-collecting camp, an activity which does not conflict with intensive plant harvests the way deer-hunting would.
B. In the late fall and winter, most plants have ceased to bear fruit, but deer hunting is at its best. Since this is the mating season, male

deer (who normally forage by themselves) fall in with the does and fawns, making the average herd larger; and since this is also the season when the deciduous vegetation of the highlands sheds its leaves, the deer can be more easily followed by hunters. As the dry season wears on, however, the deer grow warier and range farther and farther back into the mountains. This is the leanest time of the year in terms of plant resources, and it was evidently in this season that man turned most heavily to plants available year round, like the root of the Ceiba (which can be baked like sweet manioc) or the heart of the maguey plant (which can be roasted). These appear to have been "microband" activities.

C. By chewing roots and maguey hearts, the preceramic forager managed to last until the late spring growing season, at which point he could wallow in cactus fruit again. Essentially, his "schedule" was keyed to the seasonal availability of certain wild plants, which climaxed at those times of the year which were best suited for small-game-trapping. He scheduled his most intensive deer hunting for the seasons when big plant harvests were not a conflicting factor.

D. Climatic fluctuations, delays in the rainy season, or periodic increases in the deer herds at given localities probably kept the picture more complex than we have painted it, but this cannot be detected in the archeological record. The constant evolution of new bags, nets, baskets, projectile points, scrapers, carrying loops, and other artifacts from the caves of the Southern Highlands suggests slow but continual innovation. To what extent these innovations increased the productivity of the system is not clear.

Because the major adaptation was to a series of wild genera which crosscut several environmental boundaries, the geographic extent of the ecosystem described above was very great. This adaptation is clearly reflected in the technological sphere. Implements and facilities of striking similarity can be found in regions which differ significantly in altitude and rainfall, so long as the five basic categories of plants and animals are present. This can be illustrated by an examination of the Coxcatlán Phase (5000–3000 B.C.) as it is represented at Coxcatlán Cave, Puebla (Mac-Neish 1962) and at Cueva Blanca, Oaxaca (Flannery, Kirkby, Kirkby, Williams, 1967).

Coxcatlán Cave, type site for the phase, occurs at 975 meters in an arid tropical forest characterizes by dense stands of columnar cacti; kapok trees (*Ceiba parvifolia*); chupandilla (*Cyrtocarpa* sp.); cozahuico (*Sideroxylon* sp.); and abundant Leguminosae, Burseraceae, and Anacardiaceae (Smith 1965b:Fig. 31). Cueva Blanca occurs at 1900 meters in a temperate woodland zone with scattered oaks; *Dodonaea;* ocotillo (*Fouquieria*); wild zapote (*Diospyros*);

and other trees which (judging by archeological remains) may originally have included hackberry (*Celtis*) and pinyon pine.

In spite of environmental differences, implements at the two sites are nearly identical; even the seasonal deer hunting pattern and the size of the encamped group are the same. In the past, such identity would have inspired the traditional explanation: "a similar adaptation to a similar arid environment." But as seen above, the two environments are not that similar. The important point is that the basic adaptation was not to a zone or even a biotope within a zone, but to five critical categories—white-tail deer, cottontail, maguey, tree legumes, prickly pear, and organ cactus. These genera range through many zones, as did the Indians who hunted them, ate them, propagated their seeds, and weeded out their dying members. This is not to say that biotopes were unimportant; they played a role, but they were also crosscut by a very important system.

Seasonality and scheduling, as examined here, were part of a "deviation-counteracting" feedback system. They prevented intensification of any one procurement system to the point where the wild genus was threatened; at the same time, they maintained a sufficiently high level of procurement efficiency so there was little pressure for change. Under the ecosystem operating in the Southern Mexican Highlands during the later part of the food-collecting era, there was little likelihood that man would exhaust his own food resources or that his population would grow beyond what the wild vegetation and fauna would support. Maintaining such near-equilibrium conditions is the purpose of deviation-counteracting processes.

POSITIVE FEEDBACK AND CULTURE CHANGE

Under conditions of fully-achieved and permanently-maintained equilibrium, prehistoric cultures might never have changed. That they did change was due at least in part to the existence of positive feedback or "deviation-amplifying" processes. These Maruyama (1963:164) describes as "all processes of mutual causal relationships that amplify an insignificant or accidental initial kick, build up deviation and diverge from the initial condition."

Such "insignificant or accidental initial kicks" were a series of genetic changes which took place in one or two species of Mesoamerican plants which were of use to man. The exploitation of these plants had been a relatively minor procurement system compared with that of maguey, cactus fruits, deer, or tree legumes, but positive feedback following these initial genetic changes caused one minor system to grow all out of proportion to the others, and eventually to change the whole ecosystem of the Southern Mexican Highlands. Let us now examine that system.

System 6: Wild Grass Procurement. One common activity of the food-collecting era in the Southern Highlands was the harvesting of annual grasses. Perhaps the most useful in pre-agricultural times was fox-tail grass (*Setaria*) (Callen 1965:343), followed by minor grasses like wild maize (*Zea mays*), which may have been adapted to moist barrancas within the arid highland zone (Smith 1965a:95).

We know very little about the nature of the early "experiments" with plant cultivation, but they probably began simply as an effort to increase the area over which useful plants would grow. For example, Smith (1965a:77–78) has suggested that the preceramic food-collectors may have attempted to increase the density of prickly pear and organ cactus stands by planting cuttings of these plants. For the most part, judging by the archeological record, these efforts led to little increase in food supply and no change in emphasis on one genus or another, until—sometime between 5000 and 2000 B.C. —a series of genetic changes took place in a few key genera. It was these genetic changes, acting as a "kick," which allowed a deviation-amplifying system to begin.

As implied by Maruyama, many of these initial deviations may have been accidental and relatively minor. For example, beans (1) became more permeable in water, making it easier to render them edible; and (2) developed limp pods which do not shatter when ripe, thus enabling the Indians to harvest them more successfully (Kaplan 1965). Equally helpful were the changes in maize, whose genetic plasticity has fascinated botanists for years. While *Setaria* and the other grasses remained unchanged, maize underwent a series of alterations which made it increasingly more profitable to harvest (and plant over wider areas) than any other plant. Its cob increased in size; and, carried around the highlands by Indians intent on increasing its range, it met and crossed with its nearest relative, *Zea tripsacum,* to produce a hybrid named *teocentli.* From here on its back-crosses and subsequent evolution, loss of glumes, increase in cob number and kernel row number, have been well documented by Mangelsdorf, MacNeish, Galinat (1964).

Another important process, though somewhat less publicized, was the interaction between corn and beans recently emphasized by Kaplan (1965). Maize alone, although a reasonably good starch source, does not in itself constitute a major protein because it lacks an important amino acid—lysine—which must therefore be made up from another source. Beans happen to be rich in lysine. Thus the mere combining of maize and beans in the diet of the southern highlands, apart from any favorable genetic changes in either plant, was a significant nutritional breakthrough.

Starting with what may have been (initially) accidental deviations in the system, a positive feedback network was established which eventually made maize cultivation the most profitable single subsistence activity in Mesoamerica. The more widespread maize cultivation, the more opportunities for favorable crosses and back-crosses; the more favorable genetic changes, the greater the yield; the greater the yield, the higher the population, and hence the more intensive cultivation. There can be little doubt that pressures for more intensive cultivation were instrumental in perfecting early water-control systems, like well-irrigation and canal-irrigation (Neely 1967; Flannery, Kirkby, Kirkby, Williams 1967). This positive feedback system, therefore, was still increasing at the time of the Spanish Conquest.

What this meant initially was that System 6, Wild Grass Procurement, grew steadily at the expense of, and in competition with, all other procurement systems in the arid highlands. Moreover, the system increased in complexity by necessitating a *planting* period (in the spring) as well as the usual *harvesting* season (early fall). It therefore competed with both the spring-ripening wild plants (prickly pear, organ cactus) and the fall-ripening crops (acorns, fruits, some guajes). It competed with rainy-season hunting of deer and peccary. And it was a nicely self-perpetuating system, for the evolution of cultivated maize indicates that no matter how much the Indians harvested, they saved the best seed for next year's planting; and they saved it under storage conditions which furthered the survival of every seed. Moreover, they greatly increased the area in which maize would grow by removing competing plants.

As mentioned earlier, (1) procurement of "starvation" plants like *Ceiba* and maguey seems to have been undertaken by small, scattered "microbands," while (2) harvests of seasonally-limited plants, abundant only for a short time—like cactus fruits, mesquite and guajes, and so on—seem to have been undertaken by large "macrobands," formed by the coalescence of several related micro-bands. Because of this functional association between band size and resource, human demography was changed by the positive feedback of early maize-bean cultivation: an amplification of the rainy-season planting and harvesting also meant an amplification of the time of macroband coalescence. MacNeish (1964b:425) anticipated this when he asked:

> "Is it not possible as the number of new agricultural plants increased that the length of time that the microbands stayed in a single planting area also increased? In time could not perhaps one or more microbands have been able to stay at such a spot the year around? Then with further agricultural production is it not possible that the total macroband became sedentary? Such would, of course, be a village."

Actually, it may not be strictly accurate to say that sedentary village life was "allowed" or "made possible" by agricultural production; in fact, increased permanence of the macroband may have been *required* by the amplified planting and harvesting pattern.

"RE-SCHEDULING" IN THE EARLY AND MIDDLE FORMATIVE PERIODS (1500–200 B.C.)

An aspect of early village agriculture in Mexico not usually dealt with in the literature is the extent to which increased concentration on maize production made it necessary to "re-schedule" other procurement systems. It is not possible in a paper of this length to discuss all the subtleties of Formative agricultural systems. The basic distinction I would like to make is this: given the technology of the Early Formative as we understand it at present, there were regions where maize could be grown only during the rainy season, and regions where maize could be grown year-round. All differences in scheduling to be considered in this paper ultimately rest on this dichotomy.

Regions where we postulate that agriculture was practiced only during the rainy season include areas with an extremely arid climate like the Tehuacán Valley, or higher valleys where frosts occur in October and continue until April, as is the case in the Valley of Mexico (Sanders 1965:23). Regions where we postulate that agriculture was practiced year-round include very humid areas in the frost-free coastal lowlands (such as the southern Gulf Coast or the Pacific coasts of Chiapas and Guatemala), and areas in the frost-free parts of the interior where one of two techniques was possible: (1) intensive cropping of permanently humid river bottomlands, such as in the Central Depression of Chiapas (Sanders 1961:2) or (2) very primitive water control techniques like "pot-irrigation," such as in the western Valley of Oaxaca (Flannery, Kirkby, Kirkby, Williams, 1967).

What did this mean, region by region, in terms of "scheduling"? It meant that, in regions of year-round agriculture, certain seasonal activities were curtailed or even abandoned, and emphasis was placed on those year-round resources that did not conflict with farming schedules. In regions where farming was conducted only in the rainy season, the dry season was left open for intensive seasonal collecting activities. Even exploitation of permanent wild resources might be deferred to that time of year. Let me give a few examples:

The Re-Scheduling of Deer Hunting. Deer hunting in the Formative differed greatly from region to region, depending on whether agriculture could be practiced year-round, or only seasonally. In the Valleys of Mexico and Tehuacán, remains of white-tailed deer are abundant in Formative sites (Vaillant 1930a; 1935a; Flannery 1967), but wherever we have accurate counts on these fragments it is clear that by far the most intensive deer hunting was done in the late fall and winter. Projectile points and obsidian scrapers of many types are plentiful in these sites (MacNeish 1962; Vaillant 1930a, 1935a). On the Guatemalan coast, at Pánuco, or in the western Valley of Oaxaca, deer remains are absent or rare, and projectile points nonexistent (Coe, Flannery 1967; MacNeish 1954). It has occasionally been suggested that the lowland areas had such intensive agriculture that hunting was "unnecessary," whereas the highland areas needed deer "as a supplement to their diet." I do not believe this is the case; it is more likely a matter of scheduling. It so happens that the best season for deer hunting in the oak woodlands of highland Mesoamerica is late fall, after the maize crop has been harvested and the frosts are beginning. This made intensive fall and winter deer hunts a logical activity. By contrast, lowland peoples concentrated on those wild resources that were available year-round in the vicinity of the village. Exploitation of these resources could be scheduled so as not to siphon off manpower from agricultural activities. On the Guatemalan Coast, for example, the very rich perennial fish resources of the lagoon and estuary system were relied upon. Some villages, located near mangrove forests, collected land crabs; others, located at some distance from the mangroves, ignored them (Coe 1961; Coe, Flannery 1967). None of these resources conflicted with the farming pattern.

Similar "re-scheduling" of wild plant collecting took place in the highlands. The plants that dwindled in importance were the ones that ripened during the seasons when corn would have to be planted or harvested. Plants like maguey, whose exploitation could be deferred until the winter, were still exploited intensively, and in fact eventually came to be cultivated widely in areas where a winter maize crop is impossible. In the arid Mitla region of the Valley of Oaxaca today, maguey is as important a crop as maize, and some years it is the only crop that does not fail (personal communication, Aubrey W. Williams, Jr.).

System 7: Procurement of Wild Water Fowl. Until now, we have not mentioned Mesoamerica's great water fowl resources, since we still have no good archeological evidence from the food-collecting and "incipient cultivation" periods in any of the lake and marsh areas where those fowl congregate. But beginning with the Formative period, we do have data on wild fowl exploitation from the lakes of highland Mexico and the swamps and lagoons of the coast.

Water fowl in Mesoamerica are as restricted in availability as the seasonal plant resources mentioned above. Only four species breed in Mexico. All the others (perhaps some two dozen species or more of ducks and geese) spend the summer in the prairie marshes of western Canada, principally in Alberta, Saskatchewan and Manitoba. Before the formation of winter ice in November, these ducks and geese head south down a series of four well defined routes, of which only two will be considered here: the Pacific and Central Flyways. Ducks coming down the Central Flyway, terminating at the lakes of the Central Mexican Plateau (Texcoco, Patzcuaro, Cuitzeo, Chapala), include the pintail (*Anas acuta*), the shoveler (*Spatula clypeata*), and the green-winged teal (*Anas carolinensis*). The coot (*Fulica americana*) is resident year-around in Lake Texcoco, but constitutes only three per cent of the water fowl. Ducks coming down the Pacific Flyway reach the extensive lagoon-estuary system of the Chiapas and Guatemala coasts. Among the most numerous ducks taking this route are the pintail (*Anas acuta*), blue-winged teal (*Anas cyanoptera*), and baldpate (*Mareca americana*). There are also a few resident species like the black-bellied tree duck (*Dendrocygna autumnalis*), but they constitute less than one percent of the waterfowl. In other words, between 97 and 99 percent of the duck population of Mesoamerica is available only between November and March; by March or April most of these species are either back in Canada or on their way. This necessitated an intense seasonal exploitation pattern similar to that required by perishable seasonal fruits.

It is difficult to compare the relative abundance of waterfowl on the Pacific coast lagoons with Lake Texcoco, because the lake system of the Valley of Mexico was drained by the Spanish, and is now a pale shadow of what it was in the Formative. In 1952, an estimated 33,540 migratory ducks spent the winter in Lake Texcoco (Leopold 1959:Table 4), while the totals for the Chiapas Coast during the same period were over 300,000; some 27,000 of these were in the area between Pijijiapan and the Guatemalan Coast alone, a stretch of only 100 miles of coastline.

The Early Formative villagers responded quite differently to these populations of winter waterfowl. Every Formative site report from the Lake Texcoco area stresses the abundance of duck bones in the refuse. Vaillant 1930a:38) claimed that the animal bones from Zacatenco indicated "considerable consumption of the flesh of birds and deer," and his illustrations of bone tools suggest that bones of waterfowl were well represented. Worked bird bone also appears at El Arbolillo (Vaillant 1935a:246–7). Piña Chán (1958:17) likewise lists "bones of deer and aquatic birds" from Tlatilco. At Ticomán, bird bones were also common, and the larger ones apparently were ducks (Vaillant 1931). Recently, I have had a chance to examine faunal remains from Tolstoy's new excavations at El Arbolillo, Tlatilco, and Tlapacoya, as well as the Late Formative site of Temesco near Lake Texcoco (Dixon 1966), and ducks of the genera *Anas* and *Spatula* are abundant, confirming Vaillant's impressions.

On the Guatemalan Pacific Coast, as suggested by Coe and Flannery (1967) the extensive duck populations were virtually ignored. Although rich in fish and mollusks, the Formative middens have yielded not a single bone of the ducks that flew over our heads as we traveled upriver to the site each day. Since other birds, like the brown pelican, were sometimes killed and eaten, we assume that ducks must occasionally have been consumed. But the paucity of their remains is in striking contrast to the Lake Texcoco sites.

I suggest that in areas where agriculture was practiced year-round, heavy exploitation of winter duck resources would have conflicted with farming, and hence was not practiced. In areas like the Valley of Mexico, where winter frosts prevent agriculture, ducks arrive during the very time of the year when farming activity was at its lowest ebb, and hence they could be heavily exploited. This may be one further example of the kind of "scheduling" that characterized the Formative.

CONCLUSIONS

The use of a cybernetics model to explain prehistoric cultural change, while terminologically cumbersome, has certain advantages. For one thing, it does not attribute cultural evolution to "discoveries," "inventions," "experiments," or "genius," but instead enables us to treat prehistoric cultures as systems. It stimulates inquiry into the mechanisms that counteract change or amplify it, which ultimately tells us something about the nature of adaptation. Most importantly, it allows us to view change not as something arising *de novo,* but in terms of quite minor deviations in one small part of a previously existing system, which, once set in motion, can expand greatly because of positive feedback.

The implications of this approach for the prehistorian are clear: it is vain to hope for the discovery of the first domestic corn cob, the first pottery vessel, the first hieroglyphic, or the first site where some other major breakthrough occurred. Such deviations from the pre-existing pattern almost certainly took place in such a minor and accidental way that their traces are not recoverable. More worthwhile would be an investigation of the mutual causal processes that amplify these tiny deviations into major changes in prehistoric culture.

6 THE ORIGINS OF AGRICULTURE: AN EVALUATION OF THREE HYPOTHESES

J. Thomas Meyers

I. INTRODUCTION

THIS PAPER will summarize several hypotheses which discuss the development of agriculture, and evaluate these hypotheses using archeological data from Mesoamerica.

The hypotheses considered were developed by Robert Braidwood, Lewis Binford, and Kent Flannery.

The data used to evaluate them were that of the Tehuacán Archaeological-Botanical Project. The Tehuacán Valley in southern Mexico represents one of the few world areas from which an archeological sequence spanning preagricultural and agricultural adaptations has been recovered. This Tehuacán sequence suggests that the Valley was an early center of Mesoamerican plant domestication. Though much of the Tehuacán project's data has not yet been reported, enough has that an evaluation of Tehuacán prehistory is possible (cf. Byers 1967a; 1967b).

The plan of this paper will be to summarize the three hypotheses and briefly outline the prehistory of the Tehuacán Valley. The hypotheses will then be discussed on the basis of the Tehuacán sequence.

II. THE THREE HYPOTHESES

Braidwood's hypothesis for the development of agriculture is explicitly directed at Near Eastern prehistory. However, it may be equally relevant to the prehistory of Mesoamerica.

Braidwood (1960; 1967) claims that causes for the development of agriculture were entirely cultural.

He first rejects V. Gordon Childe's (1952:15–26) argument

Unpublished article reprinted by permission of the author.

that there was extreme climatic change in the Near East at the end of the Pleistocene. Thus he discards the theory suggested by Childe that such climatic change forced the invention of Near Eastern agriculture (Braidwood 1960:134). That is, although Braidwood (1967:91) allows that post-Pleistocene climatic shifts did occur in the Near East, he argues that they were too minor to have significantly altered man's environment.

Braidwood argues further that climatic changes similar to those which did occur at the close of the Pleistocene had occurred during previous Pleistocene interglacial periods without bringing about agriculture.

Therefore, according to Braidwood, there was nothing in the nature of the environment at the end of the Pleistocene which predetermined a shift in human adaptation from hunting-and-gathering to agriculture.

Braidwood (1960:134) states:

> The food-producing revolution seems to have occurred as the culmination of the ever increasing cultural differentiation and specialization of human communities. Around 8000 B.C. the inhabitants of the hills around the fertile crescent had come to know their habitat so well that they were beginning to domesticate the plants and animals they had been collecting and hunting.

The hills near the fertile crescent constituted one of several "nuclear zones," where there were natural varieties of plants and animals which had the potentiality for domestication (Braidwood 1967:94). The process involved in the invention of agriculture was one of "settling-in," by which the ancient Near Easterners came to understand and then to manipulate the plants and animals around them. Agriculture had not been achieved before the end of the Pleistocene simply because culture had not been ready to achieve it (Braidwood 1967:91).

From the nuclear zones where it began, domestication diffused to other parts of the world, together with an entire complex of traits characterizing the "village farming" way of life. These traits included sedentism, ceramic manufacture, simple architecture, etc.

Thus, to Braidwood the development of an agricultural way of life was the natural result of the cultural evolution of any group which lived *in* a suitable environment and which lived *by* hunting-and-gathering. The causative force behind the development of agriculture was inherent "human nature." Once agriculture had been developed, it spread throughout the world as part of a complex called "village farming."

I will critically evaluate the Braidwood hypothesis in section IV of this paper.

Binford (1968) rejects the Braidwood theory. He claims first that it cannot be archeologically tested, and further that existing evidence demonstrates that *testable* factors more concrete than "human nature" caused the development of food production.

On the basis of ethnographic data, Binford (1968:327–28) argues that in regions where *environment* and *demography* have remained constant (as Braidwood argues they did in the terminal-Pleistocene Near East), population and food-procurement have tended to reach equilibria. Under such stable conditions, Binford maintains, cultural groups live at food-consumption levels far below the maximum food-production potentials of their environments. Contrary to Braidwood's contention, such groups need not constantly seek new food supplies.

Binford (1968:328) goes on to state that only two testable factors *could* explain the post-Pleistocene development of sedentary agriculture:

1. A change in the physical environment of a population which brings about a reduction in the biotic mass of the region would decrease the amounts of available food. The previous balance between population and standing crop is upset, and more efficient extractive means would be favored. . . .

2. Change in the demographic structure of a region which brings about the impingement of one group on the territory of another would also upset an established equilibrium system, and might serve to increase the population density of a region beyond the carrying capacity of the natural environment. Under these conditions manipulation of the natural environment in order to increase its productivity would be highly advantageous.

Of these two types of changes, Binford argues that post-Pleistocene climatic changes were too minor to have directly caused the invention of agriculture. He therefore maintains that demographic factors were crucial to the development of food production (1968:328).

Such demographic factors could be of two types: *internal demographic stress,* resulting from population growth within a region; or *external stress,* as a result of emigration from a region where population was increasing into an area where the population level was otherwise stable.

Binford claims that external demographic stress actually favored the development of agriculture. He argues (1968:332) that agriculture could have been invented at locations where zones of external demographic stress intersected "natural habitat zones," or regions with low rainfall and populations of potentially domesticable xerophytic plants. Binford states that after the close of the Pleistocene, demographic stress zones intersected natural habitat zones within at least four major world areas (the Near East, Asia, Mesoamerica, and South America). Each of these areas was near a seacoastal plain. These coastal plains, Binford notes, were geologically new features, for there *had been* significant terminal Pleistocene climatic change at the world's seacoasts, in the form of a general rise in sea levels. This resulted in the formation of extremely productive littoral and estuarine ecozones, and favored the development of sedentary (but non-agricultural) "fisher-forager" adaptations. Some of these newly sedentary marine-oriented culture groups lived at localities directly adjacent to inland regions populated by much less sedentary hunting-and-gathering cultures. Binford argues that the populations of the marine-cultures tended to continually increase, and that this tendency led to emigration from the coasts to the inland regions.

> ... Where there is a marked contrast in degree of sedentism between two sociocultural units within a relatively restricted geographical region, there would be a tension zone where emigrant colonies from the more sedentary group would periodically disrupt the density equilibrium balances of the less sedentary group. Under these conditions there would be strong selective pressure favoring the development of more effective means of food production for both groups within this zone of tension (Binford 1968:332).

In sum, Binford's hypothesis states that after the close of the Pleistocene there was a flow of population from parts of the world's seacoasts to less populated inland areas, as a result of environmental changes at the coasts. The resultant demographic stress made the development of agriculture adaptively advantageous for both the old and new inhabitants of those inland areas with the proper environments.

I will also critically discuss Binford's hypothesis in section IV of the paper.

Flannery (1964:38; 1966:801), like Braidwood and Binford,

rejects the proposition that post-Pleistocene climatic changes brought about the development of agriculture. And he rejects Braidwood's "settling-in" familiarization as an explanation for the beginnings of plant domestication. Flannery (1968:68) states:

> We know of no human group on earth so primitive that they are ignorant of the connection between plants and the seeds from which they grow, and this is particularly true of groups dependent (as were the highland Mesoamerican food-collectors) on intensive utilization of seasonal plant resources.

Instead, Flannery (1968:68; Coe, Flannery 1964:651) has proposed that the shift from nomadic hunting-and-gathering to sedentary agriculture was a gradual one. It involved a reduction in the number and spatial concentration of resources that cultural groups were collecting by a series of resource procurement systems.

These resource procurement systems operated in two distinct ways. One type was regulated by negative feedback processes which promoted equilibrium and counteracted deviation from the systems. The other was regulated by positive feedback, which amplified changes in the systems, causing them to expand until they reached equilibria at higher levels of integration (Flannery 1968).

Flannery argues that negative feedback operated within five major resource procurement systems in Mesoamerica: *maguey, cactus fruit, tree legume, white-tailed deer,* and *cottontail rabbit* procurement. These five systems, which characteristically crosscut a variety of microenvironmental zones, supplied the great bulk of food resources utilized by early hunters-and-gatherers in highland Mesoamerica. Flannery (1968:76) maintains that the difficulty of altering either the systems themselves or the relationships between them prevented the systems' users from starving, but also kept them from developing more effective subsistence techniques.

Mechanisms regulating the five "deviation-counteracting" systems were *seasonality* (i.e., certain resources were available to man only at certain times of the year) and *scheduling* (i.e., certain resources were preferred by man over other, simultaneously available ones). Preagricultural adaptations in Mesoamerica were characterized by procurement of resources which were available seasonally and collected according to schedules not conflicting with one another.

The deviation-counteracting procurement systems operated essentially as follows: Overdepletion by man of a given resource one year would require him to depend on other resources during the same season of the next year. However, a balanced use of all five major resources would allow him to continue the same procurement pattern year after year. Where such a balanced use occurred, there would be a continuous exploitation of a limited range of resources. But overexploitation of any given resource would cause only a shifting of procurement patterns within the limited range. Thus, variations in seasonal availability and the necessity for scheduling would act to prevent specialization on any one of the five resource types. A long-term *status quo* of broad-spectrum resource utilization would result.

Such a *status quo* of resource exploitation could exist indefinitely only if each procurement system tended to be either adversely affected or unaffected by human utilization. If there were resource procurement systems which tended to increase in productiveness when exploited, they would tend to become more important at the expense of systems which failed to increase. That is, systems whose productiveness increased would respond to exploitation and manipulation in a pattern of *positive feedback,* rather than the negative feedback pattern characterizing deviation-counteracting systems.

Such a positive feedback mechanism, Flannery suggests (1968: 79–81), affected *wild grass* procurement in Mesoamerica. The considerable genetic plasticity shown by grasses of the genus *Zea* allowed them to respond to exploitation by a series of genetic changes. This supplied an "initial kick" for a positive feedback loop, making it possible for man to develop a geometrically progressing dependence on grasses once he had begun to utilize them. It gradually led to the expansion of the wild grass procurement system at the expense of the seasonal procurement schedules of other ("negative feedback") resources.

The process involved in this feedback loop might have been one in which there was transplantation of minor amounts of maize to new environments and crosses between this grass and its near relatives. This would have increased maize's productiveness, and favored a further increase in man's use and manipulation of maize, which in turn would have led to still greater increases in its productivity. Flannery argues that such a positive feedback process allowed maize and several other plant species, originally only minor resources in Mesoamerica, to gradually become the major food resources there.

At the same time that use of maize would have been increasing, the use of certain *wild resources* (i.e., those which would have been collected during the seasons when maize must be tended) would have been decreasing. On the other hand, seasonality and scheduling would have allowed the continued collection of wild resources whose procurement did not interfere with that of maize, and, in fact, may even have increased the *seasonal* productivity of those resources which formerly had been collected year-round (e.g., deer).

III. THE TEHUACÁN VALLEY

A brief discussion of the prehistory of the Tehuacán Valley may allow me to more thoroughly discuss the three hypotheses.

The Tehuacán Valley, located in southern Puebla and northern Oaxaca, Mexico, is 110 kilometers long and 30 kilometers wide. The elevation of the Valley's floor ranges from 1200 to 1600 meters above sea level, and the Valley's walls rise an average of 1500 meters above its floor. Local rainfall is only 300 to 500 millimeters per year, and the mean annual temperature ranges from 19° to 24° C. The Valley is frost free. The flora and fauna resulting from these conditions are drought resistant and diverse, but have little tolerance for cold (MacNeish 1964:531; Flannery 1964:21).

The Tehuacán Valley can be divided into four major micro-environments and four specialized sub-niches (Coe, Flannery 1964; Flannery 1964:24–37). These are:

Zone 1: *The Alluvial Valley Floor and West Travertine Slopes.* Before the natural flora was destroyed by agriculture, this area was mesquite grassland, with a small population of tree legumes. In it were deer, rabbits, and other small mammals.

A specialized niche in Zone 1 includes several *Wet Arroyos,* each of which supported lush vegetation and a large animal population before intensive agriculture was introduced.

Another specialized niche on the Valley Floor is a barren *Salt Plain* which supports little life.

Zone 2: *The Limestone-Travertine Slopes and West Valley Edge.* This is a piedmont zone, and is largely barren, with little soil or vegetation and a very low animal population. However, there are two rich sub-niches in Zone 2.

One of these specialized niches includes the *Wet Secondary Valleys,* which are cut off from the rest of the Valley's alluvium by a barren travertine flat. In the Wet Secondary Valleys are found mesquite, grasses, and other non-xerophytic plants. Rabbits and other small mammals are common here. This sub-niche would have been an ideal location for the growth of wild maize.

Another sub-niche within this Valley zone includes the area of the *El Riego Mineral Springs,* where barren rock surrounds a spring-fed oasis of vegetation. Rabbits, deer, and small mammals are abundant in this niche.

Zone 3: *The Coxcatlán Alluvial Thorn Forest.* With respect to the rest of the Tehuacán Valley, this is a very moist zone. It offered prehistoric men more hunting and collecting resources than any other Tehuacán microenvironment. Present in the Thorn Forest were tree legumes, wild fruit trees, seed-bearing plants, edible cacti, many deer and rabbits, and abundant small game.

Zone 4: *The Narrow Canyons and Dissected Alluvial Slopes of the Southeast Valley Edge.* This is an area similar to the Coxcatlán Thorn Forest, but less humid. It offers correspondingly more limited food resources.

Within this physical and biological setting, human culture has existed for over 9000 years.

The Tehuacán Archaeological-Botanical Project, an interdisciplinary research program, was organized by Richard S. MacNeish to document the origins and domestication of maize. Members of the project have extensively surveyed and excavated Tehuacán Valley archeological sites. On the basis of these investigations, MacNeish (1967a:19) has divided the prehistory of Tehuacán into nine phases:

Ajuereado	"Paleo-Indian", ? – 7000 B.C.
El Riego	Early Archaic, 7000 – 5200 B.C.
Coxcatlán	Middle Archaic, 5200 – 3400 B.C.
Abejas	Late Archaic, 3400 – 2400 B.C.
Purron	Earliest (?) Formative, 2400 – 1500 B.C.
Ajalpan	Early Formative, 1500 – 900 B.C.
Santa Maria	Middle-Late Formative, 900 – 200 B.C.
Palo Blanco	Classic, 200 B.C. – A.D. 700
Venta Salada	Post-Classic, A.D. 700 – 1500

In evaluating hypotheses for the origins of agriculture, I will discuss only the phases between Ajuereado and Ajalpan. The Ajuereado Phase apparently preceded agriculture, while agriculture had become firmly established in the Tehuacán Valley by the Ajalpan Phase (MacNeish 1967b, Table 38).

Data used in my discussion of Tehuacán Valley prehistory were taken from the following sources (unless otherwise noted in the text): a) *settlement patterns, artifact assemblages, diet:* MacNeish 1964, 1967b, 1967c; MacNeish, Nelkin-Turner, Johnson 1967a, 1967b; and Callen 1967. b) *faunal remains:* Flannery 1967. c) *plant remains:* Cutler, Whitaker 1967; Kaplan 1967; and Sauer 1969. d) *skeletal remains:* Anderson 1967. e) *miscellaneous:* MacNeish 1964; 1967b.

The Ajuereado Phase

During this phase, the Tehuacán fauna shifted from its Pleistocene configuration to an essentially modern one. The shift, however, was minor, and left few cultural traces (Flannery 1966:801).

Ten "occupations" datable to the Ajuereado Phase were examined by the Tehuacán Project.

Tools found include chipped flint knives, projectile points, end-scrapers, side-scrapers, choppers, and prismatic blades. No ground stone tools have been found. This assemblage is, according to Mac-Neish, a typical Paleo-Indian one, and was apparently used in the killing and collecting of wild animals and plants. MacNeish considers few of the Ajuereado artifacts to have been food-*processing* tools. Rather, they were used in the actual collection of plants and hunting of animals.

Faunal remains include antelope and jack rabbit from early Ajuereado occupations, and deer and cottontail from the late Ajuereado. Few plant remains have been recovered, but wear patterns on recovered human teeth indicate a plant diet consisting of gritty, unprocessed foods. MacNeish believes that the diet of the Tehuacán occupants during the Ajuereado may have been about 50 percent wild plants and 50 percent wild animals. He has found no evidence for either plant or animal domestication.

The Tehuacán population at this time may have been made up of small, wandering microbands, which migrated from microenvironment to microenvironment three or four times per year. Population for the entire Valley may have been only twenty-five to fifty people.

The El Riego Phase

The climate, flora, and fauna of Tehuacán had become essentially modern by the start of the El Riego, and remained so throughout all later phases.

The Tehuacán project recovered thirty-seven occupations associated with the El Riego Phase. From the increase in number of sites, and an increase in their sizes, MacNeish infers a population increase for the Valley.

Artifacts recovered include a few projectile points and animal processing tools of chipped flint. However, most chipped-stone tools found were choppers and scrapers, probably used to shred and pulp plants. During this phase the Tehuacán inhabitants developed the technique of using well-prepared cores in the production of flakes and blades. They also began to use ground-stone mortars and pestles for processing plants.

The wet-season diet of the Tehuacán peoples during the El Riego consisted of deer, peccary, small game, and some fish; *Setaria* (foxtail), wild maize, pochote root, *Cucurbita mixta* (squash), *Amaranthus* (pigweed), chili peppers, and avocados. Of the plants utilized, chilis, avocados, and pigweed *may* have been in the earliest stages of domestication.

The dry-season diet included large proportions of deer and of maguey and other xerophytic plants.

Fifty percent of the El Riego diet may have come from wild animals, 45 percent from wild plants, and only 5 percent from domestic plants during the El Riego Phase. The heavy tooth wear of skeletons from the El Riego may indicate a gritty diet. The high incidence of healed bone fractures in these same skeletons reflects the rugged life these people must have lived.

Along with a population increase, there occurred in the El Riego a shift in the subsistence-settlement pattern from continually wandering *microbands* to alternating microbands and *macrobands*. Wet-season macroband camps were located in the Coxcatlán Thorn Forest, on the Valley Floor alluvium, and in the Wet Barrancas, where grasses, fruits, and seeds were plentiful. Dry-season microbands exploited a wider range of niches, in search of deer and dry-season cactus and maguey.

The Coxcatlán Phase

Only fourteen occupations dating from the Coxcatlán Phase have been found in Tehuacán.

Coxcatlán Phase tool assemblages were very similar to those of the El Riego, although projectile points were much smaller (possibly because of the adoption of atlatls in place of hand-thrown spears). There were new styles of scrapers and choppers, and true manos and metates appeared. Crude stone bowls were manufactured for the first time during the Coxcatlán.

Early in the wet season, macrobands may have aggregated on the Valley Floor and in the Wet Barrancas to collect small game, pochote root, seeds, and fruits, and to plant their crops. The domesticated plants, including avocados, chilis, *Cucurbita mixta* and *C. moschata, Lagenaria* (bottle gourd), *Amaranthus,* maize, *Setaria,* and the Valley's earliest *Phaseolus* (beans), were harvested by the macrobands late in the wet season.

Dry-season resources included maguey, pochote root, sapotes, chilis, and cucurbits, plus deer, rabbit, peccary, and small game. Microbands collected dry-season foods from a wide area within the Valley.

Continued heavy tooth wear indicates a continuation of the gritty, fibrous diet of previous phases.

The Coxcatlán Phase saw a major re-emphasis in food procurement. Dependence on deer and other wild game decreased greatly, while dependence on plant resources increased. Wild plants contributed an estimated 52 percent of the Coxcatlán diet, cultivated plants 14 percent, and animals only 34 percent.

Though fewer occupations were found from the Coxcatlán Phase than from the El Riego, Coxcatlán sites were larger. MacNeish believes this reflects the aggregation of groups into plant-procuring macrobands for much longer periods during the year.

The Abejas Phase

Twenty-three occupations have been recovered which date from the Abejas Phase.

Artifacts from the Abejas remained very similar to those of earlier phases, although there were modifications. Stone bowls were improved, as were manos and metates; obsidian, not naturally available from local sources, was introduced for the manufacture of blades.

There was, according to MacNeish, a major shift in settlement patterns during the Abejas. Macrobands began to settle on river terraces, rather than in the Thorn Forest and Wet Barrancas. On the terraces, they collected wild plants and animals and grew all of their previous domesticates. In addition, they used for the first time domesticated dog (which was eaten), cavalia beans, and pre-

Chapalote and pre-Nal-Tel maize, some of which showed Teosinte introgression. Wild animals collected on or near the river terraces were cottontail, skunk, turtle, and fish.

During the dry season, microbands separated from the macro-band camps and hunted in the Coxcatlán Thorn Forest, where they took deer and peccary and collected maguey.

According to MacNeish, wild plants contributed an estimated 49 per cent of the Tehuacán diet during this phase. Domestic plants added 21 percent, and wild meat contributed 30 percent. The proportion of the diet contributed by domesticated dog was negligible.

The Purron Phase

This is the least documented phase of Tehuacán Valley prehistory. Except for the appearance of a crude, locally developed pottery, the Purron would be considered merely a continuation of the preceding Abejas.

Only two Purron occupations are known.

Tools include manos, metates, scrapers, and fine obsidian blades.

The crude, crumbly pots are of the same shapes and sizes as the stone bowls of preceding phases, and in MacNeish's opinion are a local invention.

There is no data from this phase on plant and animal dietary components, hunting patterns, or settlement patterns. However, two new domesticates can be distinguished: early tripsacoid maize and *Cucurbita pepo.*

The Ajalpan Phase

Eighteen occupations have been discovered from the Ajalpan phase. By the end of this period, full-time agriculture had become the way of life in the Tehuacán Valley.

The most characteristic artifacts for this phase are good-quality unpainted and monochrome pots. Seed jars are the most common artifact type, and ceramic figurines are common. Non-ceramic artifacts include small projectile points, manos, metates, and fine blades.

Diet during the Ajalpan was based primarily on agricultural products. Hybrid maize, *Cucurbita mixta, C. moschata,* and *C. pepo,* gourds, amaranths, beans, chilis, avocados, sapotes, and cotton were grown. Non-cultivated items in the diet included maguey, wild fruits, deer, peccary, rabbits, and other small game.

Domesticated plants had increased enormously in importance by the Ajalpan Phase, when they comprised 55 percent of the Tehuacán diet. Wild plants contributed 18 percent, and meat 27 percent.

The Valley settlement pattern may have been one of permanently occupied villages concentrated on river terraces. Single-village populations have been estimated at between 100 and 300 people. From the villages, task-specific groups were sent out seasonally to collect wild resources. Structures in the villages were of wattle-and-daub.

Summary

A set of continuing trends of change may be seen operating throughout the Archaic and Early Formative of the Tehuacán Valley.

Chipped-stone artifacts tend to become smaller and better made as one progresses through the Tehuacán culture sequence. There is a gradual shift from large plant- and meat-collecting artifacts to tools suitable for processing plants and small game. Ground-stone artifacts, used exclusively in the processing of plants, tend to increase in importance through time, reflecting the increased importance of plant resources.

The first Tehuacán ceramics virtually duplicate previously developed ground-stone bowls in form, and apparently also duplicate them as simple plant-processing artifacts. Proliferation of styles and types indicates that later ceramics were used more extensively, in the processing, storage, and consumption of plant resources (especially seeds).

Changes in diet through the Tehuacán sequence show several trends. First, there is a gradual, but definite, shift from dependence on meat in the El Riego to dependence on plants in all later phases.

The meat-collecting patterns show a development away from *hunted* large game (i.e., deer) to more easily *trapped* small game (e.g., rabbits).

Plant procurement evolves from dependence on collected wild resources to intensive use of cultivated plants.

Reflected in the Tehuacán skeletal remains is a gradual trend from a very rugged way of life with an associated coarse, gritty diet (evidenced by the high incidence both of healed bone fractures and of severely worn teeth) to a much less rugged way of life with a lower rate of bone fracture and much less tooth wear.

There seems to be a shift from a wide ranging, seasonally

wandering settlement pattern practiced by small groups to a sedentary pattern, in which subsistence is based on the practice of agriculture by large groups. Reflecting this change in subsistence-settlement pattern are the simultaneous developments of wattle-and-daub building construction and of ceramic manufacture. Both of these techniques are practical only for sedentary cultural groups.

The possible significance of these evolutionary trends is discussed in the following sections of this paper.

IV. EVALUATION OF THE HYPOTHESES

The Braidwood Hypothesis: The first prerequisite of the Braidwood hypothesis is that the environmental changes of previous Pleistocene interglacials had not led to the invention of agriculture, and thus the latest interglacial could not be expected *per se* to produce it. This cannot be tested in the New World, since no cultural groups are known to have existed in the New World during the previous interglacials.

Braidwood's second prerequisite, that there was very little post-Pleistocene climatic change in the areas where earliest agriculture appeared, is met in Mesoamerica. For the Tehuacán Valley alone, MacNeish (1967a:19), Flannery (1964:30), and C. Earle Smith (1967:222) independently argue that in fact there was little significant post-Pleistocene climatic change.

Though Braidwood's prerequisite is met, it is difficult to accept his explanation that it was simply inherent for man to domesticate useful plants and animals as soon as he had become sufficiently familiar with them. Most importantly, this explanation is untestable archeologically, since inherent "human nature" leaves no physical remains. The Braidwood hypothesis must therefore be accepted or rejected solely on the basis of logical reasoning, not archeological evidence.

Accepting Flannery's (1968:68) statement that no *advanced* hunting-and-gathering group was unaware of the means of propagation of seed plants, Braidwood's "hypothesis" becomes of more basic use, as an axiom. "Braidwood's axiom for the development of agriculture" might be stated:

> Plants and animals could have been domesticated as soon as their potential domesticators were familiar enough with them to be able to manipulate them.

Braidwood's axiom is logically necessary as a precondition in explaining the origins of both plant and animal domestication, for men could not have cultivated plants or bred animals without having a considerable familiarity with their reproductive capacities. However, as Braidwood himself has pointed out (1967:88), this axiom is not a complete explanation. If one accepts the Braidwood axiom, he must still demonstrate the "how and why" of the development of agriculture: the specific *mechanisms* by which domestication could have taken place, and the *selective pressures* which would have made agriculture more adaptive than hunting-and-gathering.

The Binford Hypothesis: In my opinion, Binford's "demographic stress" hypothesis offers an explanation for selective pressures which could have made agriculture advantageous over hunting-and-gathering. I do not wholly agree with his choice of the selective pressures involved.

In testing the Binford hypothesis, one would look for an inland region whose environment remained stable through late Pleistocene and into post-Pleistocene times. In this model, the inland region would have low rainfall and a diverse plant community, including plants with sturdy, drought-resistant seeds. The preagricultural inhabitants of the inland region are seen as originally existing by hunting-and-gathering. The inland region must be near a coastal region where the end-Pleistocene occupants' response to sea-level changes was development of sedentary or semi-sedentary fishing-foraging adaptations. Finally, groups from the expanding seacoast populations would radiate into the inland region for a period of at least several generations, after which agriculture would appear in its earliest stages within the inland region.

The Tehuacán Valley, and highland Mesoamerica in general, offers a variety of these features. Specifically, Tehuacán is a dry region with a diverse flora, in which post-Pleistocene men originally were hunters-and-gatherers. However, there are no Mesoamerican indications of sedentary, littoral post-Pleistocene cultural groups (Flannery, personal communication).

Further, because of the extreme adjustments in subsistence practices that would be required, it seems logically unlikely that even if there were high post-Pleistocene populations at the Gulf coast, population surpluses from coastal fishing cultures located in such an area of high rainfall would emigrate to a semi-arid highland valley such as Tehuacán. However, until this possibility has been examined more thoroughly, Mesoamerican data can be used neither to demonstrate nor to reject this aspect of Binford's hypothesis. It will also be necessary to investigate parallel situations in Mesoamerica, Peru, and the Near East before this segment of the Binford hypothesis can be thoroughly tested.

As an alternative to Binford's suggestion, I propose that in Mesoamerica, the demographic stress necessary to induce the development of agriculture resulted from population expansion *within* self-contained regions like the Tehuacán Valley. Binford (1968:326) states that human populations tend to increase unless regulated by artificial population control or by emigration. However, many of the ethnographic instances of artificial population control he cites are from present-day *marginal* world areas where neither emigration nor development of advanced subsistence techniques is possible (e.g., inland Australia or the Arctic).

In marginal and non-marginal areas where emigration has been possible, it has tended to take place (cf. Binford 1968:329–30). But in regions which were *not* marginal for human life and where emigration was *not* practical, I argue that population would have tended to increase until *internal* demographic stress resulted.

Prehistoric Tehuacán may have been such an area. I suggest that during the hunting-and-gathering stages of Mesoamerican prehistory, there would have been few or no localities near Tehuacán which offered sufficient resources to support man that were not already populated by human groups with population densities and cultural complexities equal to those of the Tehuacán Valley. If the Tehuacán population was in fact increasing, such a demographic situation would have effectively prevented emigration of excess population from the Valley.

Assuming that there was more than one cultural group in Tehuacán, population increase would have placed demographic stress on the competing groups within the Valley (or alternatively between groups in the Valley and their nearest neighbors). Agriculture would then have become a life mode adaptively advantageous over hunting-and-gathering (cf. Sanders, Price 1968:109).

An interesting question raised by the Binford hypothesis is why the sedentary fishing adaptations would have developed in the first place. Binford (1968:334) states:

The shift [at the seacoasts] to the exploitation of highly seasonal resources such as anadromous fish and migratory fowl did not occur until the close of the Pleistocene. This shift, probably linked to worldwide changes in sea level, with attendant increase in sedentism, established for the first time conditions leading to marked heterogeneity in rates of population growth and structure of the ecological niche of immediately adjacent sociocultural systems. This new set of conditions brought about, in turn, conditions favoring improved subsistence technology. It was not that culture was unready, but rather that the selective conditions favoring such changes had not previously existed.

It must be asked why sea-level fluctuations of previous Pleistocene interglacial periods, which were similar to the fluctuations of the terminal- and post-Pleistocene seas, did not induce culture change like that postulated for the end of the Pleistocene (i.e., sedentary fishing cultures). Binford offers no explicit reason for this.

It is, of course, obvious why earlier Pleistocene sea-level shifts induced no sedentary adaptations in *Mesoamerica*—as pointed out above, there were simply no people there.

Nonetheless, by modification, we now have "Braidwood's axiom for the development of agriculture" and the "Binford hypothesis for selective pressures favoring agriculture." We still need a hypothesis to explain the *mechanisms* of the development of agriculture. Flannery's hypothesis (1968) meets that need.

The Flannery Hypothesis: In testing Flannery's "feedback" model, one would have to seek a geographic region where culture had gradually evolved from hunting-and-gathering to full-time agriculture, with various related changes in settlement patterns, social structure, etc. In the region, sets of complementarily seasoned and scheduled resource procurement systems must have been operative. One set of systems must have been of a type that promoted a *status quo* by inherently counteracting deviations in the systems themselves. There must also have been types of resource procurement systems with the potential to respond to human manipulation by positive feedback, as a result of which changes in the systems favorable to culture would have been amplified.

Again, as with Binford's model, the essential factors for demonstrating Flannery's model were present in the prehistoric Tehuacán Valley. But I feel that Flannery's hypothesis, like Binford's, can be expanded upon.

One problem is that Flannery offers little discussion of the initial experiments with maize and other resources. He suggests that many plants may have been transplanted from localities where they were native, and that some of them responded to this by a series of genetic changes. These genetic changes supplied the initial kick for an episode of positive feedback, at the end of which maize was in the early stages of its domestication. It is here asked why and when this initial manipulation may have taken place, and how long it may have taken for various types of plants to respond to it. Assuming that men have not *always* manipulated plants, what factors influenced them to begin? When in prehistory did these factors appear?

It is doubtful that there is sufficient archeological data presently available to allow an explanation of the initial manipulation of maize, or of any other plant or animal. To develop such an explanation, it will be necessary to recover detailed information on the physical and social environments of early hunters-and-gatherers, as well as on their cultures and subsistence practices.

Another problem is that once his feedback episode has begun, Flannery provides no reason why it should continue. There must be an adaptive advantage to the entire cultural system if sub-system deviation is to be amplified. That is, procurement-sub-system change must benefit the larger cultural system, or it will simply be counter-acted by negative feedback as the larger system attempts to stabilize itself. Only if the larger system is faced with some pressure which predisposes it to change (e.g., excess population) will it accept continued sub-system change. Thus, we must understand not only the mechanisms of sub-system change (i.e., positive feedback), but we must also understand why that change would be adaptive to the entire system.

I have already argued, however, that Flannery's model is complemented by Binford's hypothesis of demographic stress. Binford outlines the adaptive advantage which agriculture would have over hunting-and-gathering. Thus, once men had begun plant manipulation, the mechanism of positive feedback would have been able to amplify manipulation of certain of the plants indefinitely, if there were some cultural advantage in their manipulation.

At this point, I hope to have demonstrated that Braidwood's axiom and Binford's and Flannery's hypotheses are not contradictory explanations of the entire process of domestication. Instead, they may be viewed as complementary parts of a larger, more inclusive hypothesis of the origins and development of agriculture.

In the concluding section of this paper, I will attempt to synthesize this inclusive hypothesis.

V. A COMBINED HYPOTHESIS

At the base of the combined hypothesis for the origins of agriculture lies Braidwood's axiom:

> Plants and animals could have been domesticated as soon as their potential domesticators were familiar enough with them to be able to manipulate them.

Since there is little evidence for extreme climatic change in those world areas where agriculture seems to have originated, post-Pleistocene climatic change is not seen as a factor in bringing about the development of food production. It is still possible, on the basis of Binford's argument, that by forcing population movement into the areas where agriculture arose, post-Pleistocene climatic change was an ultimate cause of demographic stresses which made agriculture adaptively advantageous.

However, I contend that it is equally possible that identical demographic effects could have been created by population growth *within* those areas that were the natural habitats of the important potential domesticants. Such population growth may simply have resulted from normal rates of human reproduction in non-marginal, but isolated, habitats.

Appropriate demographic stress is only one of three major factors required for a shift from hunting-and-gathering to food-production. The other two are: a proper environment, and a proper level and type of exploitative technology.

As stated, the proper demographic stress could result from population growth within each of several human groups occuping parts of the same geographic area and competing for many of the same resources. In an environment such as the Tehuacán Valley, which is non-marginal in productive potential and which may have been closed to emigration, the population would tend to increase while lacking an external outlet for its surpluses (Sanders and Price 1968: 109).

Secondly, the proper environment would be one with diverse micro-environments. These microenvironments would offer a wide variety of plant and animal resources to be utilized, and a wide variety of ecological niches into which local and exotic plants could be transplanted in the course of human manipulation. This environment would also be dry, since the potential cultigens would need tough, easily stored seeds. In addition, the food resources exploited by man in this environment would fall into two categories: 1) plants and animals which would respond to human manipulation by negative feedback, that is, by lack of response; these would provide stable resources on which hunters-and-gatherers could depend while they were initially manipulating a wider variety of resources; Flannery's (1968) "deviation-counteracting" procurement systems could be examples; and, 2) plants with the potential to respond to exploitation and (unconscious or conscious) manipulation by positive feedback; *Phaseolus* spp. and certain wild grasses in Flannery's "deviation-amplifying" procurement systems would be ideal examples.

Finally, the level of exploitative technology prerequisite to the development of agriculture would be one by which virtually any edible plant or animal resource *could* be exploited in some systematic manner. Intimately associated with such a technological level are the related factors of semi-sedentism and seasonal scheduling of resource procurement. All of these cultural factors are necessary for the development of agriculture.

If one finds that all of these cultural, environmental, and demographic elements existed prehistorically at any given location, I maintain that the potential existed there for a gradual, indigenous shift from semi-sedentary hunting-and-gathering to sedentary food-production. It may be premature to claim that these elements are sufficient to explain the origins of agriculture, but it is clear that all are necessary.

The Tehuacán Valley, between 8000 and 3000 B.C., is a case in point. There has been no major climatic change in Tehuacán for at least the last 9000 years. The Valley may have been isolated from areas of similar environment during much of its early prehistory. Tehuacán is a semi-arid region where seed plants are drought-resistant and have tough seeds. It has a diversity both of micro-environments and of plant and animal resources.

The prehistoric peoples of the Tehuacán Valley had five dependable "deviation-counteracting" resource procurement systems. These resources were available in most Tehuacán microenvironments.

The early residents of Tehuacán also utilized wild maize, which would have responded to manipulation in a pattern of positive feedback, and thus would have offered one potentially domesticable resource. It is especially noteworthy that wild maize was probably isolated in one small sub-niche of the Valley—the Wet Secondary Valleys. Its transplantation to other niches might have both required and accelerated genetic changes.

Also, the prehistoric inhabitants of Tehuacán existed at an advanced level of hunting-and-gathering immediately before they evolved into an agricultural people. Associated with this life mode were semi-sedentism and the seasonal scheduling of food-procurement activies.

The major factor of the combined hypothesis for the development of agriculture that is not demonstrably present in the prehistoric Tehuacán Valley is demographic stress—either local or external. Unfortunately, the site-size and -density data collected by the Tehuacán Project have not yet been adequately published.

When it has, this hypothesis can be thoroughly evaluated for the Tehuacán Valley.

However, to completely evaluate the combined hypothesis for the origins and development of agriculture, and to determine whether in fact such a general hypothesis is defensible, relevant data from other world areas where domestication is documented must be collected and evaluated.

7 THE ORIGIN OF PLANT CULTIVATION IN THE CENTRAL MISSISSIPPI VALLEY: A HYPOTHESIS

Melvin L. Fowler

INTRODUCTION

IN THIS PAPER I revive a hypothesis presented by earlier investigators. Gilmore in 1931 identified plant materials from dry caves in the Ozarks and attributed to a cultural unit designated as the Ozark bluff dwellers. He found seeds of giant ragweed (*Ambrosia trifida L.*), pigweed (*Amaranthus* sp.), lamb's-quarters (*Chenopodium* sp.), sunflower (*Helianthus annuus L.*), marsh elder or half-breed weed (*Iva xanthifolia (Fresen.), Nutt.*), as well as maize, beans, and squash. Because of the size and color of these seeds, he felt that they represented domesticates. Later, Jones (1936:149 ff) analyzed materials from the Newt Kash Hollow Cave in Kentucky and found most of the same plants represented as well as canary grass (*Phalaris caroliniana*). On the basis of this work, Jones, following Gilmore, proposed the hypothesis of a separate center of plant domestication in the central Mississippi Valley in which pigweed, lamb's-quarters, and sunflowers played an important part before the introduction of the typical tropical agricultural complex of maize, beans, and squash.[1]

Jones (1936) felt this was indicated by the fact that these plants were all prairie plants not normally found in the area today and

---

Unpublished paper, presented at the 1957 meeting of the American Anthropological Society, reprinted by permission of the author.

[1] Quimby (1946) has summarized the interpretations of Jones and Gilmore and correctly points out that there is no definite stratigraphic evidence of the earlier presence of the plants mentioned than of maize. He cautions that we should not accept as established that there was an Eastern Agricultural Complex before the presence of maize. Quimby also points out that the lighter color of the seeds might be due to selective gathering instead of cultivation.

that in Mammoth Cave evidence of domesticated sunflower was found in a complex lacking maize (Nelson 1917). On the basis of climatological evidence then available he was "tempted to place the site in the pre-prairie transition about 2,000 years ago . . ." (Jones 1936). Since Jones's interpretation radiocarbon dates have been determined that bear upon the age of this material. The date determined for the plant remains from the Newt Kash Hollow Cave is about 670 B.C. However, the accumulating archaeological and botanical data have caused me to revive the theory as one worthy of investigation (Crane 1956:665). The most recent dates for the Altithermal, when prairie conditions reached their peak in the eastern United States, are around 2000 B.C. or slightly later (see the radiocarbon date M-291 in Crane 1956:668; Heusser 1955).[2]

My purpose for entering into this disucssion once again is based on accumulation of new data and concepts since the time of Jones's and Gilmore's works as follows: (1) New concepts in botany bearing on the origins of plant cultivations and (2) broader understandings of the nature of the Archaic Stage have been represented.

I will discuss these two factors, propose the hypothesis growing out of them, discuss the type of evidence that is available to substantiate the hypothesis, and finally suggest avenues of investigation by which the hypothesis may be tested.

I. THE DUMP HEAP THEORY OF AGRICULTURE ORIGINS

Anderson (1952:Chapter 9) has presented a theory called the Dump Heap Theory of Agriculture. The substance of this is as follows: The wild relatives of domesticates are open habitat plants which naturally grow in river valleys, burned over regions, and other areas of disturbed soil. Such open habitats are also areas in which plant hybrids have a chance to establish themselves, whereas in closed or balanced plant habitats the hybrids lose out (Anderson 1956).

The second phase of Anderson's discussion is that a dump heap is an ideal open habitat. Kitchen middens built up of refuse from successive occupations are examples par excellence of disturbed soil where the types of plants under consideration can gain a foothold.

---

[2] The archaeological material from Newt Kash Cave is generally thought of as being Adena.

It is under these conditions that man could have begun his cultivation of plants as a source of food. Carl Sauer (1950) points out that these plants (e.g., amaranths) are nitrogen feeders and a dump heap is an ideal nitrogen source.

In a sense Anderson is proposing that a somewhat sedentary existence is almost a prerequisite for agricultural beginnings. Willey and Phillips (1955) have pointed this out in their synthesis of New World prehistory.

II. THE ARCHAIC STAGE

Throughout the eastern woodlands various archaeological assemblages have been found lacking pottery or any concrete evidence of agriculture. These complexes were given the name Archaic. In recent years the concept of the Archaic has expanded and it is now considered as a cultural stage of hunting and gathering peoples. The configuration of cultural characteristics that differentiate it from preceding and following stages has not been completely agreed upon and ranges from stone technology (see Willey, Phillips 1955:471) to a concept of semi-nomadic peoples utilizing a large number of plant resources for food and establishing themselves effectively in somewhat limited areas (see Caldwell 1957; Fowler, 1959a). Caldwell had proposed that the Archaic Stage was a time in the eastern United States in which peoples were learning to utilize the environment to its utmost and in which was being established a way of life based upon complete utilization of plant and animal resources of the forest. He terms this the establishment of primary forest efficiency. "This trend was progressive in the sense of being an increasingly successful adjustment to the eastern forest environment. It . . . culminated in Late Archaic times, at the beginning of the second millennium B.C. . . . As a result people in the areas of more abundant food resources achieved a degree of residential stability" (Caldwell 1957:6, 122).

In eastern Kentucky, Tennessee, and Alabama is abundant evidence of the stability Caldwell mentions. These sites, dating between 2000 and 3000 B.C., are large middens built up from accumulated refuse, largely shellfish remains, of successive occupations. The size and extent of the sites indicate a stable occupation and a large number of people dwelling in one place. Some idea of the number of people living on these shell middens can be gained from the over 200 burials at the Indian Knoll Site in Kentucky (Webb 1946).

There are undoubtedly semi-sedentary Archaic Stage sites in other areas of the eastern United States based upon food resources such as acorns and other nuts. A site of this nature is the Ferry Site in Hardin County, Illinois (Fowler 1957a). This site covers several areas, and a major category of artifacts found are nutting and milling stones probably used for processing plant foods such as acorns. Another Late Archaic site in which milling stones made up a significant part of the assemblage was the Read Shell Midden in Kentucky. Commenting on this, Webb and Haag (1947) pointed out that the use of plant foods must have played an important part in the economy of these peoples. An earlier site of Archaic Stage in which milling stones were again a part of the assemblage is the Faulkner Site in Massac County, Illinois (MacNeish 1947).

At Graham Cave in Missouri milling stones were an important part of the assemblage in level 6 (Logan 1952). This level has been radiocarbon dated at around 7300 B.C. (Crane 1956:666). At the Modoc Rock Shelter milling stones have been found as a part of the Archaic assemblage in the levels dating 5–6000 B.C. (Fowler 1959a).

Two things are of significance in this discussion of the Archaic Stage: (1) that the peoples of the Archaic Stage were strongly oriented toward the utilization of plant foods, and (2) that the culmination of the Archaic Stage is represented by semi-sedentary peoples extensively utilizing the food resources in a given area.

III. THE HYPOTHESIS

The hypothesis based upon the foregoing discussion is at this point fairly obvious. It can be stated as follows. (1) Most plants domesticated by man were open habitat plants, (2) in the culmination of the Archaic Stage many sites are middens of semi-sedentary peoples, (3) peoples of the Archaic Stage were strongly oriented toward the use of plant foods, (4) there are indications of plants local to the area and other than maize having been cultivated, therefore (5) plant cultivation in the eastern United States probably had its beginnings in the Archaic Stage.

IV. DATA IN SUPPORT OF THE HYPOTHESIS

In discussing the remains from the Newt Kash Hollow Cave, Jones (1936:150 ff) points out the rather extensive use of grasses as food. These include apparently domesticated varieties (*Phalaris caroliniana* and *Iva* sp.) and possibly such wild varieties as wild rye (*Elymus arkansanus*). The use of these grasses indicates to me the domestication of *local* plants. These plants do not have the continent-wide distribution that the amaranths have. Carl Sauer (1950:495) points out a similar local cultivation of grasses in Chile in aboriginal times.

Further evidence along this line concerns the origin of domesticated sunflowers. Nelson (1917) found fragments of domesticated sunflower seeds in the vestibule of Mammoth Cave in association with an apparently Archaic assemblage. Heiser (1949, 1951) points out that domesticated varieties of sunflower (*Helianthus annuus*) are native to the Midwest and that all domesticated varieties must have originally come from that region (see also Anderson 1956: 768–769).

The evidence regarding the amaranths is less conclusive; whereas they have a world-wide distribution as a cultivated plant in aboriginal times Jonathan Sauer (1950b) feels they had their origin as a domesticate in the New World.

Data on faunal materials from the Shell Mounds in the Pickwick Basin of Alabama are pertinent to this hypothesis. Morrison (1942) identified various species of land snails and found that they were forms natural to flood plain or river bottom forests. "A marked change in the abundance of both species and specimens of land snails at a level 3 feet below the surface indicates a partial clearing of the surrounding forest—such a partial forest removal means that at this level in the mound accumulation (history) there was either the beginning or marked increase in the amount of agriculture carried on by these people or that at this period the habitation of the sites changed to become more continuous as contrasted with the previous more intermittent occupations." There is evidence indicating that the level Morrison (1942) suggests as the beginning of extensive clearing of the forest is correlated with the early pottery horizons.

Further evidence bearing upon this hypothesis comes from other areas of the Western Hemisphere. In South America agriculture was practiced before the introduction of maize. Evidence has been found in Peru of sedentary fisher folk who raised cotton, gourds, peppers, and beans before 2000 B.C. (Bird 1948; Collier 1955; Willey 1955). Maize was apparently introduced in Peru around 700 B.C.

In Tamaulipas in northeastern Mexico, MacNeish has found evidence of cultures utilizing cucurbits long before the use of maize (Whitaker, Cutler, MacNeish 1957). The peoples who inhabited the area at that time were seed collectors, and plant foods made up a considerable portion of their diet (MacNeish 1955:111). Around 2500 B.C. maize became a part of the diet of these peoples. The maize was relatively primitive and was used much like other plant foods available (Mangelsdorf, MacNeish, Galinat 1956:145).

In the southwestern United States the early prefarming cultures were similar to the Archaic of the eastern woodlands. Plant utilization there apparently dates back to at least 7000 B.C. (see Jennings 1953; Jennings *et al.* 1956). The earliest cultivated plant as yet known from the Southwest is apparently maize in the form of pod corn. This is present by 2000 B.C. or slightly earlier (Dick 1954:141 ff). Cucurbits are also early in the Southwest, and perhaps in the Southeast as well. They may have functioned as supplementary foods. However, it was not until the hybridizing of maize with its near relatives that agriculture became an important food source (see Mangelsdorf, Reeves 1939; Mangelsdorf, Smith 1949; Dick 1954:143).

V. METHODS OF INVESTMENT

It is probable that very few preserved seed fragments will be found in archaeological sites in the eastern woodlands due to the moist climate. Search for dry caves in the area should be continued. Quimby (1946) has pointed out that even if cultivated plants were used by Archaic peoples the remains might not be found due to conditions of leaching in the soil.

Lacking actual seed remains other avenues of investigation must be taken. One of these avenues is in the analysis of tool assemblages to see if seed grinding tools are of importance. A method of analysis might be that suggested by Baerreis (1951) where relative predominance of different tool types is calculated. Data are accumulating that indicate the presence of several areal traditions within the Archaic Stage of the eastern woodlands (for example, Fowler 1957b). It may be possible to analyze sites within these areas to determine whether seasonal camps could be recognized. Understanding of the utilization of plant foods might be gained in this way.

More concrete methods of analysis lie in the understanding of the floral and faunal data available from prehistoric sites. The work of Morrison (1942) has already been cited. Further detailed work of this kind can yield important clues on the ecology of an area around a site. The possibilities of pollen analysis for this problem loom large. Recently techniques have been developed for extracting pollen from almost any deposit (Kurtz, Turner 1957). The presence of pollen of *Amaranthus,* or *Chenopodium,* for example, in a given level might not be indicative of plant cultivation, but a sudden influx or increase of this pollen might be. This would be especially meaningful if correlated with archaeological, zoological, and other data indicating plant utilization. It is in this method that we have our greatest hope, and no site should be excavated without a careful collection of soil samples to be used for pollen analysis.

MESOAMERICA

8 MICROENVIRONMENTS AND MESOAMERICAN PREHISTORY

Michael D. Coe, Kent V. Flannery

A CRUCIAL PERIOD in the story of the pre-Columbian cultures of the New World is the transition from a hunting-and-collecting way of life to effective village farming. We are now fairly certain that Mesoamerica[1] is the area in which this took place, and that the time span involved is from approximately 6500 to 1000 B.C., a period during which a kind of "incipient cultivation" based on a few domesticated plants, mainly maize, gradually supplemented and eventually replaced wild foods (MacNeish 1964a). Beginning probably about 1500 B.C., and definitely by 1000 B.C., villages with all of the signs of the settled arts, such as pottery and loom-weaving, appear throughout Mesoamerica, and the foundations of pre-Columbian civilization may be said to have been established.

Much has been written about food-producing "revolutions" in both hemispheres. There is now good evidence both in the Near East and in Mesoamerica that food production was part of a relatively slow *evolution,* but there still remain several problems related to the process of settling down. For the New World, there are three questions which we would like to answer.

1) What factors favored the early development of food production in Mesoamerica as compared with other regions of this hemisphere?

2) What was the mode of life of the earlier hunting-and-collecting peoples in Mesoamerica, and in exactly what ways was it changed by the addition of cultivated plants?

Reprinted from *Science,* February 14, 1964, Vol. 143, No. 3607, pp. 650–54, and by permission of the authors. Copyright 1964 by the American Association for the Advancement of Science.

[1] Mesoamerica is the name given to that part of Mexico and Central America which was civilized in pre-Columbian times. For an excellent summary of its prehistory, see G. R. Willey (1960a).

3) When, where, and how did food production make it possible for the first truly sedentary villages to be established in Mesoamerica?

The first of these questions cannot be answered until botanists determine the habits and preferred habitats of the wild ancestors of maize, beans, and the various cucurbits which were domesticated. To answer the other questions, we must reconstruct the human-ecological situations which prevailed.

Some remarkably sophisticated, multidisciplinary projects have been and still are being carried out elsewhere in the world, aimed at reconstructing prehistoric human ecology. However, for the most part they have been concerned with the adaptations of past human communities to large-scale changes in the environment over very long periods—that is, to alterations in the *macroenvironment,* generally caused by climatic fluctuations. Such alterations include the shift from tundra to boreal conditions in northern Europe. Nevertheless, there has been a growing suspicion among prehistorians that macroenvironmental changes are insufficient as an explanation of the possible causes of food production and its effects (Reed, Braidwood 1960:163),[2] regardless of what has been written to the contrary.

ETHNOGRAPHY AND MICROENVIRONMENTS

We have been impressed, in reading anthropologists' accounts of simple societies, with the fact that human communities, while in some senses limited by the macroenvironment—for instance, by deserts or by tropical forests[3]—usually exploit several or even a whole series of well-defined *microenvironments* in their quest for food.[4] These microenvironments might be defined as smaller subdivisions of large ecological zones; examples are the immediate surroundings of the ancient archeological site itself, the bank of a nearby stream, or a distant patch of forest.

---

[2] Reed and Braidwood also convincingly reject the technological-deterministic approach of V. G. Childe and his followers.

[3] See Meggers (1954) for an environmental-deterministic view of the constraining effects of tropical forest on human cultures.

[4] See Barth (1956), for a microenvironmental approach by an ethnologist to the exceedingly complex interrelationships between sedentary agriculturists, agriculturists practicing transhumant herding, and nomadic herders in the state of Swat, Pakistan.

An interesting case is provided by the Shoshonean bands which, until the mid-19th century, occupied territories within the Great Basin of the American West (Steward 1938). These extremely primitive peoples had a mode of life quite similar to that of the peoples of Mesoamerica of the 5th millennium B.C., who were the first to domesticate maize. The broadly limiting effects of the Great Basin (which, generally speaking, is a desert) and the lack of knowledge of irrigation precluded any effective form of agriculture, even though some bands actually sowed wild grasses and one group tried an ineffective watering of wild crops. Consequently, the Great Basin aborigines remained on a hunting and plant-collecting level, with extremely low population densities and a very simple social organization. However, Steward's (1938) study shows that each band was not inhabiting a mere desert but moved on a strictly followed seasonal round among a vertically and horizontally differentiated set of microenvironments, from the lowest salt flats up to piñon forest, which were "niches" in a human-ecological sense.

The Great Basin environment supplied the potential for cultural development or lack of it, but the men who lived there selected this or that microenvironment. Steward clearly shows that *how* and *to what* they adapted influenced many other aspects of their culture, from their technology to their settlement pattern, which was necessarily one of restricted wandering from one seasonally occupied camp to another.

Seasonal wandering would appear to be about the only possible response of a people without animal or plant husbandry to the problem of getting enough food throughout the year. Even the relatively rich salmon-fishing cultures of the Northwest Coast (British Columbia and southern Alaska) were without permanently occupied villages. Contrariwise, it has seemed to us that only a drastic reduction of the number of niches to be exploited, and a concentration of these in space, would have permitted the establishment of full-time village life. The ethnographic data suggest that an analysis of microenvironments or niches would throw much light on the processes by which the Mesoamerican peoples settled down.

METHODOLOGY

If the environment in which an ancient people lived was radically
different from any known today, and especially if it included
animal and plant species which are now extinct and whose behavior is consequently unknown, then any reconstruction of the
subsistence activities of the people is going to be difficult. All one
could hope for would be a more-or-less sound reconstruction of
general ecological conditions, while a breakdown of the environment
into smaller ecological niches would be impossible. However, much
if not most archeological research concerns periods so recent in
comparison with the million or so years of human prehistory that
in most instances local conditions have not changed greatly in the
interval between the periods investigated and the present.

If we assume that there is a continuity between the ancient
and the modern macroenvironment in the area of interest, there are
three steps which we must take in tracing the role of microenvironments.

1) Analysis of the present-day microecology (from the human
point of view) of the archeological zone. Archeological research
is often carried out in remote and little known parts of the earth,
which have not been studied from the point of view of natural
history. Hence, the active participation of botanists, zoologists, and
other natural scientists is highly recommended.

The modern ethnology of the region should never be neglected,
for all kinds of highly relevant data on the use of surrounding
niches by local people often lie immediately at hand. We have
found in Mesoamerica that the workmen on the "dig" are a mine
of such information. There may be little need to thumb through
weighty reports on the Australian aborigines or South African Bushmen when the analogous custom can be found right under one's
nose.[5] The end result of the analysis should be a map of the
microenvironments defined (here aerial photographs are of great
use), with detailed data on the seasonal possibilities each offers
human communities on certain technological levels of development.

---

[5] The pitfalls of searching for ethnological data relevant to archeological
problems among cultures far-flung in time and space are stressed by J. G. D.
Clark (1952:3).

2) Quantitative analysis of food remains in the archeological sites, and of the technical equipment (arrow or spear points, grinding stones for seeds, baskets and other containers, and so on) related to food-getting. It is a rare site report that treats of bones and plant remains in any but the most perfunctory way. It might seem a simple thing to ship animal bones from a site to a specialist for identification, but most archeologists know that many zoologists consider identification of recent faunal remains a waste of time (Taylor 1957).[6] Because of this, and because many museum collections do not include postcranial skeletons that could be used for identification, the archeologist must arrange to secure his own comparative collection. If this collection is assembled by a zoologist on the project, a by-product of the investigation would be a faunal study of microenvironments. Similarly, identification of floral and other specimens from the site would lead to other specialized studies.

3) Correlation of the archeological with the microenvironmental study in an overall analysis of the ancient human ecology.

THE TEHUACÁN VALLEY

An archeological project undertaken by R. S. MacNeish, with such a strategy in mind, has been located since 1961 in the dry Tehuacán Valley of southern Puebla, Mexico (MacNeish 1964a; Mangelsdorf, MacNeish, Galinat 1964).[7] The valley is fringed with bone-dry caves in which the food remains of early peoples have been preserved to a remarkable degree in stratified deposits. For a number of reasons, including the results of his past archeological work in Mesoamerica, MacNeish believed that he would find here the origins of maize agriculture in the New World, and he has been proved right. It now seems certain that the wild ancestor of maize was domesticated in the Tehuacán area some time around the beginning of the 5th millennium B.C.

While the Tehuacán environment is in general a desert, the natural scientists of the project have defined within it four microenvironments (Fig. 1).

---

6 For a general article on the analysis of food remains in archeological deposits see R. F. Heizer (1960:93–157).

7 We thank Dr. MacNeish for permission to use unpublished data of the Tehuacán Archaeological-Botanical Project in this article.

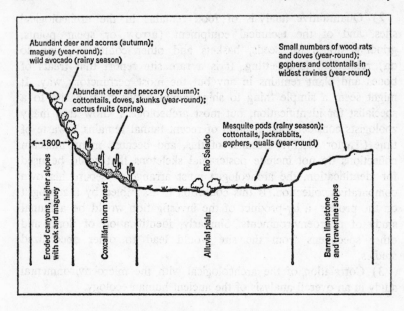

FIGURE 1 An idealized east-west transection of the central part of the
Tehuacán Valley, Puebla, Mexico, showing microenvironments and the
seasons in which the food resources are exploited. East is to the left.
The length of the area represented is about 20 kilometers.

1) *Alluvial valley floor,* a level plain sparsely covered with
mesquite, grasses, and cacti, offering fairly good possibilities, especially along the Río Salado, for primitive maize agriculture dependent on rainfall.

2) *Travertine slopes,* on the west side of the valley. This would
have been a niche useful for growing maize and tomatoes and
for trapping cottontail rabbits.

3) *Coxcatlán thorn forest,* with abundant seasonal crops of wild
fruits, such as various species of *Opuntia,* pitahaya, and so on.
There is also a seasonal abundance of whitetail deer, cottontail
rabbits, and skunks, and there are some peccaries.

4) *Eroded canyons,* unsuitable for exploitation except for limited
hunting of deer and as routes up to maguey fields for those peoples
who chewed the leaves of that plant.

The correlation of this study with the analysis, by specialists,
of the plant and animal remains (these include bones, maize cobs,

chewed quids, and even feces) found in cave deposits has shown that the way of life of the New World's first farmers was not very different from that of the Great Basin aborigines in the 19th century. Even the earliest inhabitants of the valley, prior to 6500 B.C., were more collectors of seasonally gathered wild plant foods than they were "big game hunters," and they traveled in microbands in an annual, wet-season-dry-season cycle (MacNeish 1962). While slightly more sedentary macrobands appeared with the adoption of simple maize cultivation after 5000 B.C., these people nevertheless still followed the old pattern of moving from microenvironment to microenvironment, separating into microbands during the dry season.

The invention and gradual improvement of agriculture seem to have made few profound alterations in the settlement pattern of the valley for many millennia. Significantly, by the Formative period (from about 1500 B.C. to A.D. 200), when agriculture based on a hybridized maize was far more important than it had been in earlier periods as a source of food energy, the pattern was still one of part-time nomadism.[8] In this part of the dry Mexican highlands, until the Classic period (about A.D. 200 to 900), when irrigation appears to have been introduced into Tehuacán, food production had still to be supplemented with extensive plant collecting and hunting.

Most of the peoples of the Formative period apparently lived in large villages on the alluvial valley floor during the wet season, from May through October of each year, for planting had to be done in May and June, and harvesting, in September and October. In the dry season, from November through February, when the trees and bushes had lost their leaves and the deer were easy to see and track, some of the population must have moved to hunting camps, principally in the Coxcatlán thorn forest. By February, hunting had become less rewarding as the now-wary deer moved as far as possible from human habitation; however, in April and May the thorn forest was still ripe for exploitation, as many kinds of wild fruit matured. In May it was again time to return to the villages on the valley floor for spring planting.

Now, in some other regions of Mesoamerica there were already, during the Formative period, fully sedentary village cultures in

---

[8] The research discussed in this and the following paragraph was carried out by Flannery as staff zoologist for the Tehuacán Project during the field seasons of 1962 and 1963; see Flannery (1964; 1967).

existence. It is clear that while the Tehuacán Valley was the locus of the first domestication of maize, the origins of full-blown village life lie elsewhere. Because of the constraining effects of the macroenvironment, the Tehuacán people were exploiting, until relatively late in Mesoamerican prehistory, as widely spaced and as large a number of microenvironments as the Great Basin aborigines were exploiting in the 19th century.

COASTAL GUATEMALA

Near the modern fishing port of Ocós, only a few kilometers from the Mexican border on the alluvial plain of the Pacific coast of Guatemala, we have found evidence for some of the oldest permanently occupied villages in Mesoamerica (Coe 1961). We have also made an extensive study of the ecology and ethnology of the Ocós area.

From this study[9] we have defined no less than eight distinct microenvironments within an area of only about 90 square kilometers. These are as follows:

1) *Beach sand and low scrub.* A narrow, infertile strip from which the present-day villagers collect occasional mollusks, a beach crab called *chichimeco* and one known as *nazareño,* and the sea turtle and its eggs.

2) *The marine estuary-and-lagoon system,* in places extending considerably inland and ultimately connecting with streams or rivers coming down from the Sierra Madre. The estuaries, with their mangrove-lined banks, make up the microenvironment richest in wild foods in the entire area. The brackish waters abound in catfish (*Arius* sp. and *Galeichthys* sp.), red snapper (*Lutjanus colorado*), several species of snook (*Centropomus* sp.), and many other kinds of fish. Within living memory, crocodiles (*Crocodylus astutus*) were common, but they have by now been hunted almost to extinction. The muddy banks of the estuaries are the habitat of many kinds of mollusks, including marsh clams (*Polymesoda radiata*), mussels (*Mytella falcata*), and oysters (*Ostrea columbiensis*), and they also support an extensive population of fiddler and mud crabs.

3) *Mangrove forest,* consisting mainly of stilt-rooted red mangrove, which slowly gives way to white mangrove as one moves

---

[9] The study was carried out largely by Flannery.

away from the estuary. We noted high populations of collared anteater (*Tamandua tetradactyla*) and arboreal porcupine (*Coendu mexicanus*). A large number of crabs (we did not determine the species) inhabit this microenvironment; these include, especially, one known locally as the *azul* (blue) crab, on which a large population of raccoons feeds.

4) *Riverine,* comprising the channels and banks of the sluggish Suchiate and Naranjo rivers, which connect with the lagoon-estuary system not far from their mouths. Freshwater turtles, catfish, snook, red snapper, and mojarra (*Cichlasoma* sp.) are found in these waters; the most common animal along the banks is the green iguana (*Iguana iguana*).

5) *Salt playas,* the dried remnants of ancient lagoon-and-estuary systems which are still subject to inundation during the wet season, with localized stands of a tree known as *madresal* ("mother of salt"). Here there is an abundance of game, including whitetail deer and the black iguana (*Ctenosaura similis*), as well as a rich supply of salt.

6) *Mixed tropical forest,* found a few kilometers inland, in slightly higher and better drained situations than the salt *playas.* This forest includes mostly tropical evergreens like the ceiba, as well as various zapote and fan palms, on the fruit of which a great variety of mammals thrive—the kinkajou, the spotted cavy, the coatimundi, the raccoon, and even the gray fox. The soils here are highly suitable for maize agriculture.

7) *Tropical savannah,* occupying poorly drained patches along the upper stream and estuary systems of the area. This is the major habitat in the area for cottontail rabbits and gray foxes. Other common mammals are the coatimundi and armadillo.

8) *Cleared fields and second growth,* habitats which have been created by agriculturists, and which are generally confined to areas that were formerly mixed tropical forest.

Among the earliest Formative cultures known thus far for the Ocós area is the Cuadros phase, dated by radiocarbon analysis at about 1000 to 850 B.C. and well represented in the site of Salinas La Blanca, which we excavated in 1962 (Coe, Flannery 1967).[10] The site is on the banks of the Naranjo River among a

---

[10] The research was supported by the National Science Foundation under a grant to the Institute of Andean Research, as part of the program "Interrelation-

variety of microenvironments; it consists of two flattish mounds built up from deeply stratified refuse layers representing house foundations of a succession of hamlets or small villages.

From our analysis of this refuse we have a good idea of the way in which the Cuadros people lived. Much of the refuse consists of potsherds from large, neckless jars, but very few of the clay figurines that abound in other Formative cultures of Mesoamerica were found. We discovered many plant remains; luckily these had been preserved or "fossilized" through replacement of the tissues by carbonates. From these we know that the people grew and ate a nonhybridized maize considerably more advanced than the maize which was then being grown in Tehuacán.[11] The many impressions of leaves in clay floors in the site will, we hope, eventually make it possible to reconstruct the flora that immediately surrounded the village.

The identification of animal remains (Fig. 2), together with our ecological study and with the knowledge that the people had a well-developed maize agriculture, gives a great deal of information on the subsistence activities of these early coastal villagers. First of all, we believe they had no interest whatever in hunting, a conclusion reinforced by our failure to find a single projectile point in the site. The few deer bones that have been recovered are all from immature individuals that could have been encountered by chance and clubbed to death. Most of the other remains are of animals that could have been collected in the environs of the village, specifically in the lagoon-estuary system and the flanking mangrove forest, where the people fished, dug for marsh clams, and, above all, caught crabs (primarily the *azul* crab, which is trapped at night). Entirely missing are many edible species found in other microenvironments, such as raccoon, cottontail rabbit, peccary, spotted cavy, and nine-banded armadillo.

There is no evidence at all that occupation of Salinas La Blanca was seasonal. An effective food production carried out on the rich, deep soils of the mixed tropical forest zone, together with the

---

ships of New World Cultures." The oldest culture in the area is the Ocós phase, which has complex ceramics and figurines; the paleoecology of Ocós is less well known than that of Cuadros, which directly follows it in time.

[11] P. C. Mangelsdorf, who has very kindly examined these maize specimens, informs us that they are uncontaminated with *Tripsacum* and that probably all belong to the primitive lowland race, Nal-Tel.

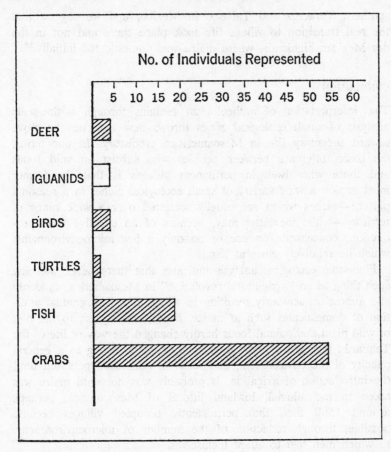

FIGURE 2 Animal remains, exclusive of mollusks, found in Cuadros phase levels at Salinas la Blanca.

food resources of the lagoon-estuary system, made a permanently settled life possible. Looked at another way, developed maize agriculture had so reduced the number and spacing of the niches which had to be exploited that villages could be occupied the year round.[12]

Conditions similar to those of the Ocós area are found all along the Pacific Coast of Guatemala and along the Gulf Coast of

[12] To paraphrase the concept of "primary forest efficiency," developed by J. R. Caldwell (1958), we might think of the Cuadros Phase as leaning to a "primary lagoon-estuary efficiency." We might think the same of the Ocós phase of the same region, which may date back to 1500 B.C.

southern Veracruz and Tabasco in Mexico, and we suggest that the real transition to village life took place there and not in the dry Mexican highlands, where maize was domesticated initially.[13]

CONCLUSION

The interpretation of archeological remains through a fine-scale analysis of small ecological zones throws new light on the move toward sedentary life in Mesoamerican prehistory. In our terms, the basic difference between peoples who subsist on wild foods and those who dwell in permanent villages is that the former must exploit a wide variety of small ecological niches in a seasonal pattern—niches which are usually scattered over a wide range of territory—while the latter may, because of an effective food production, concentrate on one or on only a few microenvironments which lie relatively close at hand.

Fine-scale ecological analysis indicates that there never was any such thing as an "agricultural revolution" in Mesoamerica, suddenly and almost miraculously resulting in village life. The gradual addition of domesticates such as maize, beans, and squash to the diet of wild plant and animal foods hardly changed the way of life of the Tehuacán people for many thousands of years, owing to a general paucity of the environment, and seasonal nomadism persisted until the introduction of irrigation. It probably was not until maize was taken to the alluvial, lowland littoral of Mesoamerica, perhaps around 1500 B.C., that permanently occupied villages became possible, through reduction of the number of microenvironments to which men had to adapt themselves.

---

[13] An additional factor which may in part account for the priority of coastal Guatemala over Tehuacán in the achievement of a sedentary mode of life is the presence of an extensive system of waterways in the former region, which might have made it less necessary for local communities to move to productive sources of food. By means of canoes, a few persons could have brought the products of other niches to the village. However, our evidence indicates that the Cuadros people largely ignored the possibilities of exploiting distant niches.

9 ANCIENT MESOAMERICAN CIVILIZATION

Richard S. MacNeish

A PROBLEM that has long interested the layman, the scientist, and the philosopher has to do with how and why civilizations arose. Any hypothesis or generalization about this social phenomenon must be based on broad comparative historical data. Specifically, one must compare long archeological sequences, from savagery to civilization, which have been uncovered in relatively independent areas. The ancient high cultures of Mexico and Central America (termed Mesoamerica) have always represented an interesting facet of this problem, for here were prehistoric civilizations which apparently arose independently of any of those in the Old World.

It is generally accepted that the development of agriculture is basic to the rise of village and urban life. And so, in our work in Mesoamerica, it was assumed that if we could but find the origins of agriculture—and in the New World this meant maize or corn—then we would be well on the way to finding out where and how civilization evolved in America.

After a number of years of investigation, it became apparent that the desert valley of Tehuacán (about 150 miles south of Mexico City) was the region in which evidence could most likely be uncovered about the beginnings of the domestication of corn (MacNeish 1961). Precisely why we decided on this area is explained in an article by Mangelsdorf and others (1964), so I confine my discussion to the archeological researches recently undertaken in this southern Puebla valley.[1]

Reprinted by permission of *Science*, from Vol. 143, No. 3606, 1964, pp. 531–37, and by permission of the author. Copyright 1964 by the American Association for the Advancement of Science.

[1] The actual investigations were organized under the auspices of the Robert S. Peabody Foundation for Archaeology, Andover, Mass., and were financially

In attacking such an all-inclusive problem, the project was most fortunate in having the cooperation of a number of scientists from a wide variety of fields. Obviously, I am extremely grateful to these various specialists, but I must confess that I say this with a sigh of relief, for at the beginning of the first field season we were far from convinced that the much-vaunted interdisciplinary approach was practicable. We know now that it can and does work, and thanks to our experts' endeavors we have gathered and interrelated specialized studies in botany, corn, beans, squash, human feces, pollen, zoology, geology, geography, physical anthropology, prehistoric textiles, ethnohistory, and ethnography.[2] These investigations, of course, were in addition to the usual archeological researches carried out so ably by my field staff.[3]

---

supported by generous grants-in-aid from the National Science Foundation and the Rockefeller Foundation. The Tehuacán Project also received support and assistance from the Instituto de Antropologia e Historia of the Government of Mexico.

[2] Drs. P. C. Mangelsdorf and W. C. Galinat of the Harvard Botanical Museum and E. J. Wellhausen and R. Hathaway of the Rockefeller Foundation studied the corn remains; Drs. T. Whitaker, senior geneticist of the U. S. Department of Agriculture, and H. Cutler, executive director of the Missouri Botanical Gardens, investigated the prehistoric cucurbits, and Dr. L. Kaplan of Roosevelt University studied the prehistoric beans. Dr. C. E. Smith of the U. S. Department of Agriculture made botanical studies in the Tehuacán Valley; Dr. R. Drake, at the University of British Columbia, identified the shells; and Dr. Eric C. Callen, of McDonald College of McGill University, analyzed the human feces found in the caves. Miss Monica Bopp, and later Dr. James Shoenwetter of the University of Southern Illinois, studied various pollen profiles in the valley to determine ancient changes in climate and vegetation. Dr. Carmen Cook De Leonard of the Centro de Investigaciones Antropologicas of Mexico aided us with her knowledge of the ethnohistory and ethnobotany of the Tehuacán Valley, and Mrs. I. Johnson of the National Museum of Mexico examined the textiles we found in the excavations. Kent Flannery, a student at the University of Chicago, identified the 12,000 archeological bones we uncovered; Dr. J. L. Lorenzo, chief of the Prehistoric Section of the Instituto de Antropologia of Mexico, and Dr. J. Moser of the Federal Department of Geology of Mexico surveyed the geology, and Dr. R. Woodbury of the U. S. National Museum, Dr. J. Anderson of the University of Buffalo, and D. Byers of the R. S. Peabody Foundation investigated, respectively, the ancient irrigation systems, the human skeletal remains, and the geography of the Valley. F. Johnson, also of the R. S. Peabody Foundation, carried out a program of dating the archeological remains by the carbon-14 method.

[3] The Tehuacán field staff included Mr. Peterson, assistant director; Dr. M. Fowler of the University of Southern Illinois; F. Johnson of the R. S. Peabody

Before discussing what our diverse group accomplished in the Tehuacán Valley, let me briefly describe the valley itself. It is located in the southern part of the state of Puebla, and in the northernmost section of the state of Oaxaca, in the central highlands of Mexico. Efforts were concentrated in a relatively small area, about 70 miles long and 20 miles wide. Although the valley is considerably longer than it is wide, it has a basinlike appearance, for it is ringed by high mountains, the Sierra Madre Oriental is to the south and east, while to the north and west are the Mixteca Hills. Both rise considerably above the Tehuacán Valley floor, which is 1500 meters above sea level. Because of these precipitous mountains the valley is in a rain shadow and extremely dry. Most parts of the valley floor receive less than 600 millimeters of rainfall a year, and some parts receive less than 500 millimeters. Moreover, most of this rain falls during a 2-month period. Needless to say, the resultant vegetation is xerophytic. Thus, the Tehuacán Valley has all the characteristics of a desert.

Intensive archeological investigation in this region has now been under way for 3 consecutive years; in addition, I spent a brief 10 weeks in the area in 1960. Archeological reconnaissance has resulted in the discovery of 392 new sites or prehistoric habitations. These range from small temporary camps to large ruins of cities. At about 30 of these sites test trenches were dug. These were superficial, but even so, one sounding yielded stratified remains with five occupational floors, one above the other. Twelve test trenches in other sites revealed deep stratified remains. Excavations in these particular sites were expanded into major digs and became the basis for establishing a long prehistoric sequence of culture.

In these 12 sites of major excavation (selected from the original 392 sample sites), 140 stratified floors and occupational zones were unearthed. Five of these were open sites or middens, while seven were caves or rock shelters, or both.

Because of the extreme dryness of the area, in over 55 of the floors in the five caves everything had been preserved: foodstuffs, feces, and other normally perishable human remains and artifacts. This type of refuse not only allows one to make an unusually com-

Foundation; K. Flannery of the University of Chicago; R. L. Chadwick of Mexico City College; Angel Garcia Cook and A. Arbide of the School of Anthropology of Mexico; and Miss A. Nelken, a student of the Sorbonne in Paris, and her two "Tehuacánero" assistants in the laboratory, N. Tejeda and F. Molina.

plete reconstruction of the way of life of the ancient inhabitants, but gives considerable information about subsistence, food habits, diet, climatic changes, and, in many cases, even indicates which months of the year the floors were occupied.

Although our studies are a long way from completion (it has taken much time to even count and catalog the 750,000 specimens so far uncovered), preliminary results have been most encouraging. Some of these I summarize briefly in the following paragraphs.

AJUEREADO PHASE

The earliest assemblage of artifacts is called the Ajuereado phase.[4] In the caves, we uncovered evidence of seven different occupations, while surface collections have yielded four more sites of this cultural complex. As yet we have only three dates, obtained by the carbon-14 technique, on the final stages of this phase, but another five are being processed. The phase seems to have ended by at least 7200 B.C., and it may have come into being 3 or 4 millennia earlier. Examination of these floors indicates that in this period the inhabitants were grouped together into small, nomadic families or microbands who changed their camps three or four times a year with the seasons. As means of subsistence they collected wild plants and they hunted and trapped. Although they hunted such animals as horses and antelope of now-extinct species during the earliest part of the phase, even then most of their meat came from smaller game, such as jackrabbits, gophers, rats, turtles, birds, and other small mammals. In the later part of the phase they trapped only species that exist today. These people, in the so-called "big game hunting stage" (Willey 1960a) or "mammoth-hunting period," were far from being the great hunters they are supposed to have been. As one of my colleagues said: "They probably found one mammoth in a lifetime and never got over talking about it."

Preliminary studies of the pollen and animal bones seem to show that, in this region, the climate of the terminal Pleistocene was only very slightly cooler and wetter than the climate today. The vegetation was probably xerophytic, but not like the present-day desert vegetation in the Tehuacán Valley—it probably was more like the mesquite grasslands of western Texas.

---

[4] The names of the various phases were taken from the name of the site or cave where these cultural complexes were first unearthed.

The manufactured tools of this group were not numerous, and all were made by chipping flint. They include a series of bifacially leaf-shaped knives and projectile points, keeled and ovoid end scrapers, flake and bifacial choppers, side scrapers, gravers, and crude prismatic blades struck from even cruder polyhedral cores. No ground stone was utilized, and the floors held few perishable remains, hence we know nothing about the weaving industry or the traps and perishable tools of these peoples. No burials have been found, though there is one fragment of a charred human bone.

This complex (represented by many more artifacts than have been previously found for this time period) seems to be related to the earliest remains found elsewhere in Central America. It must be noted, however, that even at the earliest stage these peoples were not primarily dependent upon hunting and should be called plant and animal collectors rather than hunters. Further, the material culture of the Ajuereado phase continued unchanged even though the Pleistocene fauna became extinct and gave way to modern fauna.

EL RIEGO PHASE

Gradually the Ajuereado phase developed into one which we call the El Riego cultural phase. This is extremely well known, for we have dug up 24 floors and have found 14 open camp sites. Ten dates, obtained by the carbon-14 method, allow us to estimate the time of this cultural phase fairly accurately. It seems to fall between 7200 and 5200 B.C. These peoples were seasonally nomadic like their predecessors, but there had been a definite increase in population and some changes in the settlement pattern seem to have taken place. The sites are almost equally divided between very small camps, which obviously represent the family groups or microbands of the dry seasons, and much larger sites, representing camps of related families or macrobands which gathered together in the spring and wet seasons. The means of subsistence was basically plant and animal collecting, supplemented by some hunting—not very different from the previous period, although these peoples seem to have hunted deer instead of horse and antelope, and the cottontail rabbit instead of the jackrabbit.

As for their hunting and trapping activities, there were no fundamental changes; nor do they seem to have been "forced by the changing climatic conditions that followed the end of the Wisconsin Glaciation to make readjustments" (Willey 1960a). The preserved plant remains, however, seem to show that plant collecting was even more important than it had been in the previous culture. Nevertheless, it was only a seasonal affair. During the dry season, apparently, people still hunted and trapped in small groups and probably nearly starved, but when the spring came, and later the rains, a number of microbands seem to have gathered together in larger groups to live off the lusher vegetation. There is evidence that they were collecting a large variety of plants, and I would guess that this was the period when they finally conceived the idea that if you drop a seed in the ground a plant comes up. This concept is, of course, basic to any beginnings of agriculture. Further, these people were eating some plants which later became domesticated. These included one variety of squash (*Cucurbita mixta*), chili, and avocados. It is also possible that they were gathering and consuming wild corn as well as utilizing cotton.

The development of such a subsistence and settlement pattern undoubtedly caused some changes in their social organization. From comparative ethnological data one might guess that these groups were patrilineal bands with some sort of weak temporary leadership in the hands of a male, and perhaps some sort of concept of territoriality (Steward 1938). Further, there apparently were shamans, or witch doctors, who had considerable power in both the medicinal and the ceremonial fields. These, of course, would not have been full-time specialists.

The tools we dug up gave considerable evidence about the industrial activities of these peoples. For example, they manufactured a number of varieties of contracting-stemmed and concave-based projectile points which were very neatly chipped and were probably used to tip atlatl darts used in the chase. The most prevalent artifacts were, however, the large plano-convex scrapers and choppers chipped from pebbles or nodules of flint. These could have been used for preparing skins, but it seems more probable that they were used for pulping various plant remains. Some blades, burins, and end scrapers of types found in the previous horizon were still made and utilized. The most noticeable change in the material culture was the use of ground-stone and pecked-stone implements. Mortars and pestles were particularly numerous, and there were many milling stones and pebble manos. Tools of both types were probably used to grind up plant and animal remains into some sort of palatable (or unpalatable) stew.

In addition, it is in this period that we found the first evidence of weaving and woodworking—knotted nets, a few small fragments of twined blankets and coiled baskets, fragments of dart shafts, and pieces of traps.

To me, one of the most surprising findings for the El Riego cultural phase was evidence of relatively elaborate burials, which indicate the possibility of complex beliefs and ceremonies. We uncovered two groups of multiple burials. In the first were the skeletons of two children; one child had been ceremonially cremated. The head of the other child had been severed and roasted, the brains had been removed, and the head had been placed in a basket on the child's chest. The other multiple burial included an elderly man, an adolescent woman, and a child of less than 1 year. There was evidence that the elderly man had been intentionally burned, and the heads of both the woman and the child had been smashed, perhaps intentionally. These findings could certainly be interpreted as some sort of human sacrifice, but the correctness of such an interpretation is difficult to prove. In both these burials the bodies were wrapped in blankets and nets and were richly furnished with basketry. Is it not possible that the ceremonialism that is so characteristic of the later Mexican periods began at this time?

In terms of wider implications, the El Riego phase seems to be related to early cultures occurring in Northern Mexico, the U. S. Southwest, and the Great Basin areas which have been classified as being of the "Desert Culture Tradition." The later preceramic phases that follow the El Riego phase in the Tehuacán Valley are difficult to classify in this tradition because they have incipient agriculture and the numerous large choppers, scrapers, and milling stones decrease in importance. In addition, these Mesoamerican cultures developed their own distinctive types of grinding tools, baskets, nets, projectile points, blades, and other implements—all unlike artifacts found in the Desert Cultural manifestations.

COXCATLAN PHASE

The phase developing out of the El Riego phase was termed Coxcatlan. About 12 radiocarbon determinations indicate that it existed from 5200 to 3400 B.C. Twelve components of the phase were uncovered in cave excavations, and four open camps were also found. Although fewer occupations were found than in the El Riego phase, most of them were larger. However, the way of life may have been much the same, with nomadic microbands in the dry season and macrobands in the wet season. The macrobands seem to have been larger than those of the earlier phase, and they seem to have stayed in one place for longer periods. Perhaps this was due to their rather different subsistence pattern.

While the Coxcatlan people were still basically plant collectors who did a little animal trapping and hunting, all through this period they acquired more and more domesticated plants. Early in the period they began using wild corn, chili, avocados, and gourds. By the middle of the phase they had acquired amaranth, tepary beans, yellow zapotes, and squash (*Cucurbita moschata*), and by the end of the phase perhaps they had black and white zapotes. It seems that microbands still came together at some favorite collecting spot in the spring, and it may be that while they were there they planted some of their domesticates. This would have given them food to continue living at that camp after they had consumed their wild foods. As the numbers of domesticates increased, the group could, of course, have stayed together as a macroband for longer and longer periods. But with the onset of the dry season and the depletion of their agricultural "surpluses" they would have broken up again into nomadic microbands.

The changing subsistence and settlement pattern may have been connected with changes in social organization. The bands may still have been patrilineal. But one wonders whether the use of gardens and the more sedentary way of life might not have resulted in bands having definite collecting territories and ideas about property "garden rights." Moreover, a greater dependence upon agriculture (and rainfall) may have made the shaman even more powerful, not only in medicine and in birth and death ceremonies but also in regard to rituals connected with plantings and harvestings. In addition, the more sedentary life involving larger numbers of people may have resulted in some kind of macroband leadership, more stable than just that vested in the oldest or most powerful male in a family.

The industrial activities of the group were not vastly different from those of their predecessors, although different types of tanged projectile points were manufactured. Blades were more delicately made, scrapers and choppers were of new types, and true metates, with manos, were replacing the mortars, pestles, and milling stones. Some minor improvements were also made in the manufacture of nets, coiled baskets, bags, and blankets.

The most distinctive aspect of the Coxcatlan phase is its incipient agriculture. However, I do not want to give the impression that Tehuacán was the only early center of plant domestication or agriculture. In fact, our accruing archeological data having to do with the beginning of New World plant domestication seem to indicate that there was no single center, but, instead, that domesticates had multiple origins over a wide area of Nuclear America and the southern United States. For example, while tepary beans and corn may have been first domesticated near or in the Tehuacán Valley, pumpkins seem to have been domesticated in northeastern Mexico, sunflowers in the southwestern United States, potatoes and lima beans in the highlands of South America, common beans in still another region, and so on (Mangelsdorf, MacNeish, Willey 1964).

ABEJAS PHASE

The Abejas phase follows the Coxcatlan phase, and we estimate, on the basis of eight carbon-14 determinations, that it existed from 3400 to 2300 B.C. Thirteen occupations have now been uncovered, and eight sites were found in reconnaissance. We are now making plans to excavate what seems to be a pit-house village of the Abejas phase.

The settlement pattern seems to have changed significantly during this period. Ten of the cave occupations were hunting (dry-season) camps of macrobands, while eight of the macroband settlements were on river terraces in the Valley. The latter appear to have been larger settlements (of five to ten pit houses), and some of them may have been occupied all year round. This even more sedentary way of life was made possible by more efficient food production. This was accomplished with plants already known and, in addition, with domesticated canavalia and perhaps pumpkins (pepo) and common beans, as well as some varieties of hybrid corn with teosinte introgression. The people also used cotton and had dogs. However, even with this increase in domesticates, botanical studies and studies of feces reveal that more than 70 percent of their foods still came from wild plants and animals.

Again, many of the older techniques of artifact manufacture continued, though the types are a little different. Some of the types which carry over into much later times originated during this period. These include: split-stitch basketry and the manufacture of stone bowls and ollas, oval metates and large plano-convex manos, obsidian blades made from long cylindrical cores, and other objects.

If this phase provides evidence of a Marxian "Neolithic revolution," the revolution came long after the first plant domestications; the population showed no sudden increase in size, and the artifacts were little better than those of the preceding phase (Childe 1951a).

PURRON PHASE

The next phase, Purron is dated by six carbon-14 determinations which place it between 2300 and 1500 B.C. It is the least clearly understood phase in the sequence and was represented by only two floors in excavation. The excavated materials include a few plant remains, early tripsacoid corn cobs, manos, metates, scrapers, fine obsidian blades, and a number of very crude, crumbly pieces of broken pottery. The pottery, the earliest so far found in Mesoamerica, has the same vessel forms as the stone bowls and ollas of the previous period. This pottery may not be the first modeled in Mexico but only an imitation of still earlier pottery (as yet unfound) in some other area. One might surmise that the subsistence and settlement pattern and social organization of the Purron phase was much the same as that of the Abejas phase.

AJALPAN PHASE

The following phase, Ajalpan, dated by 18 carbon-14 determinations, is much better understood. It is placed between 1500 and 900 B.C. Seventeen floors were found in the diggings, and two open sites were found during survey. These Ajalpan people were full-time agriculturists; they planted early hybrid corn, mixta, moschata and pepo squashes, gourds, amaranths, beans, chili, avocado, zapotes, and cotton. They seem to have lived in small wattle-and-daub villages of from 100 to 300 inhabitants. Whether they built religious structures is not yet known, but their figurines, mainly female, attest to a complex religious life. Male priests and chiefs certainly must have had considerable power, although the rich female burials and the figurines hint that kinship and property ownership may have had a matrilineal emphasis.

Many stone tools of the older types were still made, but one of the more notable industries of this period was pottery making. The pottery, though well made, is usually unpainted, although a few examples of monochrome specular-hemitite red ware are found. A limited number of forms were modeled; the tecomate, or small-mouthed seed jar, is the dominant type of receptacle.

In terms of cultural relationships, the pottery, large figurines, and rocker-dentate stamp decoration are like those found in the earliest cultural manifestations in lowland Mesoamerica—that is, Veracruz, Chiapas, Pacific-lowland Guatemala, and the Pacific cost of Oaxaca (McNeish 1954; Lowe 1959b; Coe 1961). This does not, however, mean there was a migration, diffusion, or relationship only from the coast to the highlands, for remains from periods of comparable age have not yet been found in highland Mexico. In fact, Ajalpan could well be but a local manifestation of an early widespread horizon in Mesoamerica. Spinden, many years ago, concluded that such a horizon existed, and he called it the Archaic. More and more evidence confirming his original hypothesis is being accumulated (Spinden 1928; Coe 1962).

SANTA MARIA PHASE

In the subsequent Santa Maria period the pottery still shows resemblances to pottery of the Veracruz coast. But in addition to these resemblances it shows resemblances to the earliest pottery remains in Monte Alban (Caso 1952), the Valley of Mexico (Vaillant 1935a), and other highland regions.

Thus, we have good evidence for correlating a number of sequences from a number of areas, not only with Santa Maria but also with each other. Twenty-three carbon-14 determinations indicated that the Santa Maria period lasted from just before 900 to about 200 B.C. The culture is well known, for we have excavated 38 components and have found about 15 surface sites. The settlement pattern reveals that the people lived in small wattle-and-daub houses in villages which were oriented around a single, larger village having ceremonial structures.

These people were full-time farmers, using all of the plants previously known, although many of these plants had been developed into much more productive hybrids. This may be the period in which irrigation was first used.

Although a few new types of chipped stone tools, woven cotton fabrics, and new kinds of ground-stone tools appear, the great majority of the materials we uncovered consisted of pieces of broken pottery. These vessels were well made. They were mainly monochrome (white or grey), though there were a few bichromes. About half of all the vessels found were flat-bottomed bowls; the rest were ollas, water-bottles, composite silhouette bowls, and other forms. Decoration was usually achieved by incising on the interior bottoms of bowls or on the rims or lips, but a few of the vessels have plain rocker stamping, negative painting, and engraving.

Perhaps it was during this period that Mesoamerica became divided into two units, each with a distinctive cultural development (MacNeish 1954). One development, in the lowlands, may have been based on milpa (slash-and-burn) agriculture and have culminated in the development of ceremonial centers, run by a priestly hierarchy. The other development may have been based on irrigation agriculture and have culminated in the rise of secular cities. The Tehaucán sequence would be an example of this second type.

PALO BLANCO PHASE

This Santa Maria phase developed into the Palo Blanco period, dated between 200 B.C. and A.D. 700 by eight radiocarbon determinations. On the basis of information and materials from 17 excavated components and from about 150 sites found in survey, we are able to make the following reconstruction about the way of life of the people of this phase. They, too, were full-time agriculturists, and they systematically used irrigation. Besides the previously known domesticates, they had acquired tomatoes, peanuts, lima beans, guavas, and turkeys. They lived in wattle-and-daub villages or hamlets either oriented toward or adjacent to large hilltop ceremonial centers having elaborate stone pyramids, plazas, ball courts, and other structures. Some of these ruins covered whole mountain tops and, in terms of population, might be considered cities, albeit sacred cities. Perhaps these centers were under the authority of priest-kings; if so, the priest-kings certainly must have been assisted by full-time specialists and a hierarchy of bureaucrats, at least to run the irrigation works.

The manufactured products were varied and more elaborate than those of previous phases. The fine grey and orange pottery, the obsidian working, the bark cloth, and the elaborately woven cotton fabrics are particularly distinctive.

In terms of relationships, Palo Blanco seems to be an extension of the Monte Alban III (and IV?) cultures of Central Oaxaca and shows similarities to cultures in the so-called "Classic Period" of Mesoamerica (Willey 1960a). Why this period in the highlands is considered more "classic" than the later periods has never been satisfactorily explained.

VENTA SALADA PHASE

The final period, Venta Salada, is placed, on the basis of five carbon-14 determinations, between A.D. 700 and 1540. Study of the records of early Spanish conquerors of the Tehuacán Valley should shed further light on this phase. Studies made so far reveal that these people were full-time agriculturists who had irrigation. Further, their economy was greatly supplemented by commerce with other regions. Local salt-making and cotton-processing industries made products for exportation. Politically, the Valley seems to have been divided up into a series of little kingdoms each of which had urban centers with surrounding hamlets. Among the manufactured articles were such distinctive artifacts as polychrome pottery, a wide variety of cotton fabrics, bark cloth, chipped stone tools, and arrow points. Since we have excavated over 15 occupations of this final phase and have found about 200 sites in surface surveys, and also have excellent ethnohistorical records available, it will eventually be possible to reconstruct a fairly clear picture of the culture of the final preconquest phase. So far this has not been done.

CONCLUSION

Obviously, our studies are far from complete, even though some tentative conclusions have been expressed in this article. As more of our data are analyzed and the results are correlated, the total history of the Tehuacán Valley will become better understood. At present, some 30 authors, including myself, are in the process of getting six volumes about our work in Tehuacán ready for publication.

Richard S. MacNeish

Certainly these final volumes will contain information which will permit more perceptive and specific comparisons to be made with other prehistoric cultural developments in Mexico and South America, as well as with sequences in the Old World. Such analysis should lead to more cogent and better documented generalizations about the how's and why's of the rise of civilization than have been expressed heretofore.

10 FARMING SYSTEMS
AND POLITICAL GROWTH
IN ANCIENT OAXACA

Kent V. Flannery, Anne V. T. Kirkby,
Michael J. Kirkby, Aubrey W. Williams, Jr.

DURING the last 15 years an increasing number of anthropologists and geographers have turned their attention to the pre-Hispanic civilizations of Mexico and Guatemala. The evolution of these ancient complex societies is of general theoretical interest because it seems to have taken place independently of the early Old World civilizations. Given the limitations of the archeological data, there has been considerable latitude for varied and competing theories about the origins of the early New World states.

Some authors have theorized that Mesoamerican civilization arose in the arid highlands, because of the need for a strong centralized government to control large-scale irrigation projects (Wittfogel 1957). Others have argued that civilization began first in the humid tropical lowlands, where irrigation is not necessary (Coe 1963a).

Still others have sought a middle ground between these positions, maintaining that Mesoamerican civilization began through the "intertwining of many regional strands," both highland and lowland (Willey, Phillips 1958:151).

One of the most intriguing hypotheses of the evolution of early Mesoamerican civilization was that of Palerm and Wolf (1957: 1–37), who over a 10-year period in the 1950's sought to find correlations between social systems, agricultural systems, and their environmental settings. A major process they observed at work in ancient Mesoamerica was the formation and dissolution of "key areas" or "regional nuclei." These they defined as "areas of massed

Reprinted from *Science,* October 27, 1967, Vol. 158, No. 3800, pp. 445–53, and by permission of the authors. Copyright 1967 by the American Association for the Advancement of Science.

power in both economic and demographic terms" (Palerm, Wolf 1957:9), which at various points in Mesoamerican prehistory had acted as "nodal points of growth" or as nuclei for "symbiotic areas"; these nuclei were instrumental in stimulating cultural evolution over wide geographic regions (Wolf 1959:18).[1]

Each time Mesoamerica moved up to a higher level of social and political complexity, this move seems to have been accompanied by a shift of power and influence from one area to another. Some regions were nuclear only in the early (Formative) and middle (Classic) periods; other areas were nuclear only in the late (Post-Classic) periods. Only five regions in Mesoamerica were listed by Palerm and Wolf (1957:30) as having "maintained their key importance from Archaic times right up to the time of the Spanish Conquest." These areas are the Valley of Mexico, the region of Cholula-Puebla, the Mixteca Alta, the Valley of Oaxaca, and the region of Guatemala City (see Fig. 1).

Why had these five regions attained early nuclearity and retained it throughout the sequence? Palerm and Wolf (1957) presented a corollary hypothesis which they felt should be checked by future investigators. They pointed out that all the areas which were nuclear only in the *early* part of the sequence had predominantly slash-and-burn agriculture of lowland (*roza*) type. All areas which rose to prominence only *late* in the sequence were arid regions demanding very efficient irrigation systems. The five *perennially nuclear* regions are ones in which, today at least, virtually every farming technique known in Mesoamerica is applicable. They hypothesized that farming had begun in Mesoamerica as slash-and-burn, and that through time a series of new techniques had been worked out: irrigation, flood-water farming, chinampas, and so on. As such technological innovations appeared, they were "applicable to an ever-decreasing number of areas" (Palerm, Wolf 1957:36). The areas in which the greatest variety of techniques could be assimilated remained nuclear; those in which only the older techniques could be applied gradually lost their influence and assumed a marginal role.

None of Palerm and Wolf's (1957) "perennially nuclear" areas has ever been investigated with their hypothesis in mind, though a number of related theories have now been tested in the Valley of

---

[1] For the original statement of the "symbiotic area" concept, see W. T. Sanders (1956).

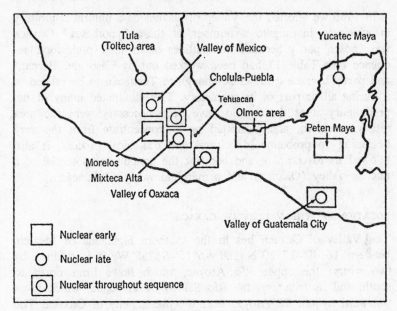

FIGURE 1   Outline map of Mexico and Guatemala, showing regions mentioned in the text. "Nuclear" areas listed by Palerm and Wolf are indicated by squares or large black circles; Tehuacán, a "marginal" area, is indicated by the small black dot. For the sake of brevity we have adhered to Palerm and Wolf's original classification, although recent archeological data indicate that it needs to be revised and updated.

Mexico (Sanders 1965). However, excavations in a few of Meso-america's "fringe" or "marginal" areas—ones which *never* became nuclear—have been carried back to the very beginnings of agriculture by MacNeish (1958; 1962). One of these, in the Valley of Tehuacán, Mexico, has now yielded the longest single stratified sequence in all of Mesoamerica. Publication of the Tehuacán sequence (MacNeish 1964a) places Mesoamerica in a better position than ever before for the testing of theories about the processes involved in the establishment of village life, and about the evolution of chiefdoms and early states.[2]

---

[2] For the definition of the terms *band, tribe, chiefdom,* and *state* as used in this article, as well as the characteristics of each type of social grouping, see E. R. Service (1962).

In 1966 we selected the Valley of Oaxaca as a natural laboratory in which to investigate a number of these hypotheses.[3] Oaxaca was chosen partly because the outlines of its later prehistoric sequence (see Table 1) had been worked out by Caso and Bernal,[4] and partly because it lay close enough to Tehuacán to be related to it during all or part of its prehistory. This eliminated many of the preliminary steps that would have been necessary were the area totally unknown, and permitted us to concentrate from the very beginning on problems of cultural and ecological process. It also allowed us to compare and contrast the agricultural potential of a nuclear valley (Oaxaca) and a marginal valley (Tehuacán).

LOCATION OF THE VALLEY OF OAXACA

The Valley of Oaxaca lies in the southern highlands of Mexico, between 16°40′–17°20′ N and 96°15′–96°55′ W. It is drained by two rivers: the upper Río Atoyac, which flows from north to south, and its tributary, the Río Salado or Tlacolula, which flows westward to join the Atoyac near the present city of Oaxaca. The valley is shaped like a Y or three-pointed star, whose center is Oaxaca City and whose southern limit is defined by the Ayoquesco gorge, where the Atoyac River leaves the valley on its way to the

[3] The first field season of the project (1966), entitled "The Prehistoric Cultural Ecology of the Valley of Oaxaca," was sponsored by the Smithsonian Institution. The second field season (1967) was sponsored by National Science Foundation grant No. GS-1616 to the University of Maryland. The staff included K. V. Flannery (archeologist); M. J. Kirkby and A. V. Kirkby (geomorphologists); A. W. Williams, Jr. (ethnologist); J. Schoenwetter, Museum of New Mexico (palynologist); C. Earle Smith, U. S. Department of Agriculture, and W. Ernst, Smithsonian Institution (botanists); J. A. Neely, University of Arizona, and F. Hole, Rice University (archeologists); M. E. King, Howard University (prehistoric textiles); and C. Moser, R. Orlandini, S. Maranca, M. Winter, S. Lees, K. Vaughn, J. James, S. Kitchen, and E. Martinez (field assistants). We are indebted to J. L. Lorenzo, Departmento de Monumentos Prehispánicos, Instituto Nacional de Antropología e Historia (Mexico City), and L. Gamio, representative of the I.N.A.H. in the Oaxaca archeological area, for official permission and good advice. Special thanks go to I. Bernal, J. Paddock, D. Quero, C. R. Welte, R. B. Woodbury, E. Salzberger, and W. T. Sanders for their help. Nancy H. Flannery drafted Figs. 1, 2, 4, and 5.

[4] On the basis of their stratigraphic work at the site of Monte Albán during the 1930's and 1940's, Alfonso Caso and Ignacio Bernal established a five-period sequence for the time span between 600 B.C. and A.D. 1500.

TABLE 1   Pre-Hispanic cultural periods in the Valley of Oaxaca, compared with those of adjacent regions, as determined by radiocarbon dating and interregional similarities in artifacts.

TES	TEHUACÁN VALLEY	VALLEY OF OAXACA	CENTRAL CHIAPAS	OLMEC REGION
. 1500		Monte Albán V		
1400				
1300	Venta Salada			
1200				
1100		Monte Albán IV		
1000				
900				
800				
700				
600		Monte Albán III		
500	Palo Blanco		Laguna	
400				Upper Tres
300			Jiquipilas	Zapotes
200				
100		Monte Albán II	Istmo	
0			Horcones	Middle Tres
B.C. 100				Zapotes
200				
300		Monte Albán I	Guanacaste	Lower Tres
400	Santa María		Francesa	Zapotes
500			Escalera	
600				
700		Guadalupe	Dili	La Venta
800				
900				
1000		San José	Cotorra	San Lorenzo
1100	Ajalpan			
1200				
1300				
1400		?	?	
1500				
2000	Purrón			
3000	Abejas			
4000	Coxcatlán	Coxcatlán		
5000				
6000				
7000	El Riego	Guilá Naquitz	Santa Marta	
8000				

Pacific Ocean. The climate is semiarid, with 500 to 700 millimeters of annual rainfall, confined largely to the summer months. The valley-floor elevation averages 1550 meters.

Situated in the mountainous central part of the state of Oaxaca, the region is surrounded by valleys with steep sides, narrow floors, and perennially flowing streams. In contrast, the Valley of Oaxaca is a wide, open plain with abundant flat land and streams which are dry most of the year. Yet it was this valley, where moisture is scarce and man must devise means to control it, which became the most powerful nuclear area in the southern highlands. It is generally believed that this development was the work of the Zapotec Indians, who now inhabit the valley and whose history can be traced back many thousands of years in that region (Bernal 1965:788; Paddock 1966).

PHYSIOGRAPHY AND VEGETATION

A typical cross section of the valley shows four distinct physiographic zones: (i) the "low alluvium," or present river flood plain; (ii) a zone of "high alluvium," which is mainly an abandoned flood plain of Pleistocene-to-Recent age, formed by the Atoyac River and its tributaries when they flowed at a higher elevation; (iii) a piedmont zone flanking the high alluvium; and (iv) the surrounding mountains.

The river channel is incised no more than 1 to 2 meters into its present floodplain, which is only locally present and nowhere more than 600 meters wide. The main part of the flat valley floor, which varies from 1 to 15 kilometers in width, is formed by the high alluvium; this zone is separated from the low alluvium by a 1- to 3-meter rise in elevation. Between the high alluvium and the mountains lies the piedmont zone, where the land has a slope of 1 to 2 degrees and has been dissected by tributary streams to form low rounded spurs and isolated hills with up to 30 meters of relief. The piedmont was originally formed as a series of coalescing alluvial fans, and remnants of this deposited material remain as fan gravels of probably Pleistocene age. Later stream dissection has exposed underlying rocks which are pre-Jurassic to Miocene. The piedmont zone grades eventually into the true mountain zone, where valleys have up to 1000 meters of relief and slopes are steep. The mountains are formed mainly of pre-Jurassic metamorphic rocks, Cretaceous limestones, and

Miocene ignimbrite tuffs. The tuffs are most extensive in the extreme eastern end of the valley, between Mitla and Tlacolula, where they abound in small caves and rock-shelters which were occupied during the earliest periods of Oaxaca prehistory. In the extreme western part of the valley, where rocks of the basal metamorphic complex are most widely exposed, there are deposits of magnetite and mica which were used and traded by the later occupants of the valley as exotic raw materials.

Originally, each of these physiographic provinces would have had its own distinct vegetational cover. Today, after thousands of years of intensive cultivation, so little remains of the original valley-floor vegetation that it can only be hypothetically reconstructed from pollen grains and carbonized seeds in archeological sites of that zone.[5] The present Atoyac floodplain may have had phreatophytic species like bald cypress (*Taxodium*), willow (*Salix*), and wild fig (*Ficus*), while the high alluvium was probably characterized by a more open cover of grasses and woody legumes like mesquite (*Prosopis*). The piedmont is still one of the most complex vegetation zones, with varying communities of tree legumes, prickly pear (*Opuntia*), organ cactus (*Lemaireocereus*), maguey (*Agave*), *Dodonaea,* and—at elevations of 1800 meters and above —scattered oaks (*Quercus* spp.). The high mountains have forests of oak, pine, and manzanita (*Arctostaphylos*). It is to be hoped that future work in Oaxaca will greatly enrich this tentative and oversimplified reconstruction.

AGRICULTURAL POTENTIAL

We feel there are several environmental aspects of the Valley of Oaxaca which make it a better place for agriculture—and especially for primitive, pre-Hispanic types of agriculture—than many adjacent parts of highland Mexico, including some of the other areas described by Palerm and Wolf (1957) as nuclear. Second, some of the agricultural techniques worked out by the Zapotec Indian inhabitants of the valley gave them an early advantage over their neighbors. Finally, there are various additional factors, only

---

[5] The pollen is being analyzed by J. Schoenwetter; the modern flora, by W. Ernst; and the ancient plants preserved in dry caves, by C. E. Smith. We acknowledge their generosity with the botanical data, but they should not be held responsible for any errors in our reconstruction.

indirectly related to agriculture, which contributed to the rise of stratified societies in Oaxaca.

In the sections which follow we outline some of the environmental features of the Valley of Oaxaca which may be considered advantageous. We then attempt to show their relevance to the periods of food-collecting and incipient cultivation (8000 to 1500 B.C.), early village farming (1500 to 600 B.C.), and the rise of towns and ceremonial centers (600 to 200 B.C.).

The Valley of Oaxaca has 700 square kilometers of relatively flat land, the largest such expanse in the Mexican highlands south of Cholula-Puebla. Until recently, it was generally believed that the valley was the bed of a former lake, which had dried up prior to 600 B.C. This lake was mentioned in Zapotec legends, and casual inspection of the valley revealed supposed "shorelines" or old "lake terraces," as well as seasonally inundated areas which were reputed to be remnants of the lake (Bernal 1965; Paddock 1966). In 1960, Lorenzo (Lorenzo 1960) presented geological evidence to the contrary. Similarly, our study reveals no evidence of a lake.

The supposed lake "shoreline" is not horizontal but varies in elevation by over 200 meters within a distance of some 40 kilometers. What it really consists of is the break in slope formed where the steeper fan gravels meet the valley alluvium. The fan gravels are clearly fluvial in origin, and no lacustrine deposits or fossils have been found, so the hypothesis of a permanent lake in the valley during the last 10,000 years must be rejected. The seasonally flooded localities reputed to be "lake remnants" are in reality low-lying areas where the water table is close to the ground surface. Many of these occur in clay areas of low permeability, which further tend to maintain standing bodies of water for long periods.

With the rejection of the lake hypothesis, other explanations should be suggested for the Valley of Oaxaca's unusually wide and flat floor. It is known that relatively arid climates favor alluvial-fan deposition, and this tendency toward alluviation in combination with the inability of the upper Río Atoyac to downcut (because of the high resistance of rocks in the Ayoquesco gorge) could explain the great width of the valley. Furthermore, this extensive deposition could have been initiated by downfaulting, for local deformation of Miocene (but not later) sediments shows that some late-Miocene/

Pliocene dislocations have occurred in the valley. Thus three factors —aridity, downfaulting, and a low rate of stream degradation— all may have contributed to the alluvial expanses which make the Valley of Oaxaca unique among its neighbors.

LESS SEVERE SOIL EROSION

In the mid-1940's Cook studied a number of the higher valleys just to the north of the Valley of Oaxaca—Tamazulapan, Yan- huitlán, and Nochistlán, in the Mixteca Alta. All these valleys have suffered extremely destructive soil erosion, which Cook traced to agricultural activities extending far back into the pre-Hispanic era (Cook 1949b).

By comparison, soil erosion is not a severe problem in the Valley of Oaxaca, although there is some local gullying of hill- slopes. One reason is that, relatively speaking, little land has so far been cleared in the higher mountains. In the Valley of Oaxaca, accelerated erosion due to clearing of the natural vegeta- tion for agriculture is most severe not only on the steepest slopes but also where the vegetation is densest. This is strikingly shown by our erosion measurements on steep slopes near Mitla, made in 1966 over a period of 2 months during which 237 millimeters of rain fell. Table 2 gives the ratios of the rate of erosion on cleared land and the rate of erosion on land with natural vegetation.

It would appear that agricultural land clearance in the oak-pine forest zone results in an accelerated erosion of 45 times the natural rate, whereas in the cactus-scrub zone, where slopes are already in equilibrium with a sparse vegetation cover, clearing of land does not appreciably increase erosion. The gentle slopes of the valley floor further discourage erosion, and the presence of an extensive flat area lessens the incentive to clear land higher in the mountains. All these factors combine to keep soil erosion to a minimum in the Valley of Oaxaca. It is perhaps worth noting that the most badly eroded valleys of the Mixteca, like Yan- huitlán, occur at elevations of 2000 meters in the pine-oak zone, where the ratio of acceleration on cleared land is highest.

SOILS AND WATER TABLE

The flat valley floor and the thick alluvial deposits offer clear advantages as a site for early agriculturalists, but these factors

TABLE 2. Comparison of erosion ratios in three different vegetation zones near Mitla, in the Valley of Oaxaca. [Erosion ratio=C/N, where C=erosion rate on cleared land and N=erosion rate on land with undisturbed natural vegetation. Both C and N were calculated, for slopes of comparable steepness during the same rainy season (1966), by measuring the percentage of surface material moved downslope from a previously established 50-meter line.]

Erosion sites	Elevation (meters)	Natural vegetation	Ratio for rate of erosion: cleared land/land with natural vegetation cover
No. 1	1750	Cactus-scrub	1.0
No. 2	2000	Oak-*Dodonaea*	3.8
No. 3	2300	Pine-oak	45.4

are partially offset by the relative aridity, which limits both available water and soil fertility. Soil profiles are poorly developed, and the alluvial structure is retained almost unaltered below the A horizon. Prismatic structure and some salt accumulation is found in the B horizon. Most valley-floor soils belong to the Brown Soils group, but they tend toward Gray Desert soils in the most arid areas, such as the Mitla end of the valley.

Humus and nutrient concentrations in the soils are so low that it is the differences in water availability which constitute the most important determinant of the usefulness of the soils for man. The finest grained soils with the best water-holding characteristics occur on the high alluvium, in a band running parallel to the river, but at distances of 500 to 1500 meters away from it. Except where the high alluvium is more than 2 kilometers wide, this band of fine-grained soils extends to the outer edge of the alluvium, where it meets the piedmont zone.

Soil-grain size influences water retention and is thus important both for (i) dry farming and (ii) commercial crops with high irrigation requirements. In between these two extremes, in cases where more limited types of irrigation are practiced, the depth to water table and the yields from wells are more important than soil texture in determining the value of the soil for farming. This brings to mind recent comments by Stevens (1965:289–90) on Indian farming in general: it is not necessarily the best soils which are the most intensively used, because factors of technology and water table may be the primary ones.

Within the present flood plain of the Atoyac River, well water is within 3 meters of the surface; within the zone of high alluvium, it lies between 2 and 10 meters down. In both these zones, water yields are usually adequate for small-scale irrigation of the specialized types described below. In the fan gravels of the piedmont zone, water is generally more than 10 meters below the surface, and well yields are only sufficient for immediate household needs.

A RELATIVELY FROST-FREE CLIMATE

At elevations of 2000 to 2800 meters, in areas like the Valley of Mexico or Cholula-Puebla, winter frosts may have been a real deterrent to year-round cultivation of maize until frost-resistant strains were developed, some time after the Middle Formative period. For example, Sanders' (1965:20, 23) figures for the Valley of Mexico indicate that between October and February the area may have temperatures which are detrimental to maize. In contrast, temperatures on the floor of the Valley of Oaxaca are well suited to year-round growing of maize, even the primitive strains of the Early Formative.

At the level of the valley floor (1420 to 1740 meters, with an average of about 1550), the mean annual temperature is 20° C, with an annual range of 6° C and a daily range of 15° C. *Extreme* minimum temperatures over a recent 12-year period are close to 0° C. In any one year there is only slight probability of frost, and this largely in the higher parts of the valley. In the main Atoyac River floodplain south of Oaxaca City, all of which lies below 1550 meters, frosts are virtually nonexistent, and the present-day Zapotec of this area cultivate sugarcane, which requires an 18-month frost-free period.

These favorable conditions deteriorate rapidly as one ascends the hills to either side of the Valley of Oaxaca. Above altitudes of about 2300 meters, summer temperatures are low enough to inhibit cultivation of maize, and wheat is at present a more reliable crop. At elevations of 3000 meters, mean daily minima in January are about 0° C, and the dominant cultivar is the potato.

The two ancient indigenous races of maize known so far for the Early Formative period in Mesoamerica—Nal-Tel and Chapalote—do poorly in cold conditions and are sensitive to highland rusts (Wellhausen *et al.* 1952:54–62). The essentially frost-free nature of the southern Valley of Oaxaca probably gave it considerable advantage over the higher valleys of the nearby Mixteca at this early period (1500 to 900 B.C.), when only those primitive races of maize were known. In later periods, with frost-resistant strains of maize, this difference was probably less crucial, as high population densities in the Mixteca and the Valley of Mexico suggest.

PRECIPITATION AND HYDROLOGY

Mean annual rainfall on the floor of the Valley of Oaxaca varies from 490 millimeters at Tlacolula to 740 millimeters at Ocotlán. There is a general rise in precipitation with increasing altitude, so that the surrounding mountains at elevations of 3000 meters may receive almost 1000 millimeters annually. Open-water evaporation depends principally on temperature, and decreases with elevation. On the valley floor it averages 2000 millimeters annually (three to five times the precipitation), while at 3000-meter elevations it is only 340 millimeters (one-third the precipitation). Hence the growth of permanent pine forest on the high mountains, and the sparser cactus and mesquite-grassland cover of the lower slopes.

For the growth of annual crops without irrigation, the ratio of rainfall to open-water evaporation must remain close to 1.0 throughout the summer months, with June to August the most critical period. On the floor of the Valley of Oaxaca this ratio ranges from 0.50 near Tlacolula to 0.93 near Ocotlán. This range may be contrasted with similar figures obtained for the floor of the Valley of Tehuacán, which vary between 0.45 and 0.56.[6] Thus conditions in the western part of the Valley of Oaxaca are somewhat more favorable for dry farming than are those in Tehuacán, a fact which was probably important during the early stages of agriculture.

Even more striking contrasts between Oaxaca and Tehuacán may be seen, however, when one examines their irrigation potential.

---

[6] M. J. Kirkby and A. V. Kirkby, unpublished studies; meteorological data courtesy of the State of Oaxaca and the Comisión del Papaloapan.

The Tehuacán Valley has an extremely low water table (about 20 meters), but the valley lies just to the south and east of a block of limestone-travertine mountains which constitute a major aquifer. Very large quantities of subsurface water emerge from springs at the base of this range, near the western outskirts of the city of Tehuacán (Smith 1965a). Thus, shallow-well irrigation is impossible; much more feasible is a large-scale canal-irrigation system to carry water from the prolific springs out to the central and southern parts of the valley. Such a canal system was indeed developed at Tehuacán during later periods of its prehistory, when the population of the valley was already high (MacNeish 1962; 1964b; Woodbury, personal communication).

Canal irrigation on a large scale is nowhere practical in the Valley of Oaxaca, where springs are small and surface flows are insufficient for irrigating more than a small area. However, because of the unusually high water table, shallow-well irrigation is widely practiced, and this technique, which requires relatively little effort and can be performed on an individual family basis, can be traced back to at least 700 B.C. and probably earlier.

FOOD-COLLECTING, INCIPIENT-CULTIVATION
PERIODS: 8000 TO 1500 B.C.

The oldest archeological materials recovered in 1966 came from a series of caves and rock shelters near Mitla. These shelters occur in volcanic-tuff cliff faces at elevations of 1900 meters, near the transition from the piedmont to the higher mountains.

For years it had been known that this elevated region, 200 meters or more above the valley floor, was richer in surface finds of the food-collecting era than any other; when a recent lake on the valley floor was still considered a possibility, the hypothetical lake was often used to explain the restriction of these early cultures to the upper piedmont (Jewell 1966). The real reason why this zone was so consistently used in early times is that it has the richest and most varied assemblage of edible wild plants of the entire region. For the most part, shelters immediately overlooking the valley floor were used infrequently or not at all before 1500 B.C.; it was full-time agriculture, with its need for flat land and fine-grained soil, which eventually diverted attention from the upper piedmont and allowed the high alluvium to emerge as the zone of major utilization.

Between 7840 and 6910 B.C. (as estimated on the basis of radiocarbon determinations), the Indians who camped seasonally in Guilá Naquitz Cave collected acorns, pinyon nuts, mesquite beans, prickly pear and organ-cactus fruits, wild onion bulbs, hackberry, maguey (*Agave* sp.), *nanche* (*Malpighia* sp.), *susí* (*Jatropha* sp.), and a dozen other species, all of which were preserved within the cave by desiccation.[7]

Toward the end of this period, small black beans (*Phaseolus* sp.) and squash seeds (*Cucurbita* sp.) appear in the refuse; thus Guilá Naquitz is added to the list of sites known to belong to the "incipient cultivation" period in ancient Mexico (MacNeish 1964b:413–26).

A nearby cave, Cueva Blanca, dated at about 3295 B.C. by the radiocarbon technique, yielded a later food-collecting, incipient-cultivation horizon which is in most respects identical to the Cox-catlán phase (5000 to 3000 B.C.) defined by MacNeish (1964a) at Tehuacán. It would appear that at this period the whole of the southern Mexican highlands was occupied by a series of related, seminomadic bands who moved seasonally from resource area to resource area and engaged in increasingly effective experiments with the growing of maize, beans, and squash.

Not only is it impossible to speak of "key" or "nuclear" regions at this time, it is also virtually impossible to define individual "culture areas" within the southern highlands. This suggests that, while cultures were still primarily food-collecting, the individual peculiarities of the various valleys were not especially significant. It was full-time agriculture which brought about specialized adaptations to local peculiarities of soil, rainfall, and water table and gave each valley its regional character. At this point, even slight differences in agricultural potential may have started certain valleys, like Oaxaca, on the path to nuclearity.

EARLY VILLAGE FARMING PERIOD: 1500 TO 600 B.C.

Several parts of the valley were selected as "pilot areas" in which to survey for early village farming communities, with subsequent test excavations. Chief among these was a 10-kilometer strip in

---

[7] Plant identifications by C. Earle Smith, U. S. Department of Agriculture, personal communication.

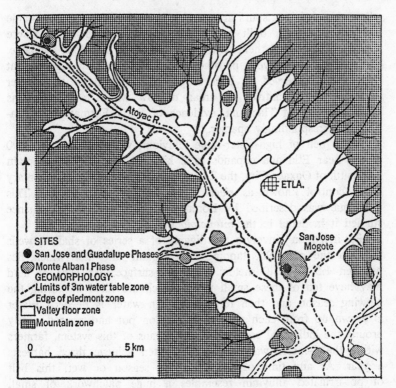

FIGURE 2 "Pilot" survey area in the northwestern part of the Oaxaca Valley, showing the distribution of Formative archeological sites with regard to physiographic areas and water resources (see text).

the extreme northwest corner of the valley, near Etla. We concentrated on the Early Formative San José phase (1200 to 900 B.C.) and the Middle Formative Guadalupe (900 to 600 B.C.) and Monte Albán I (600 to 200 B.C.) phases (Table 1).

In the Etla region, the most favorable agricultural land is that part of the high alluvium where the water table is within 3 meters of the surface. As shown in Fig. 2, most Formative sites thus far located (including all the Early Formative sites) are concentrated in or adjacent to this zone. In the narrow parts of the valley, prime localities were the tips of piedmont spurs, which raised the villages just high enough above the alluvium so they would not flood in the rainy season. In wider parts of the valley, where the piedmont spurs are too far from the 3-meter water-table belt, villages were built on the high alluvium in areas where sandy soils provided them with the best-drained locations available. Our preliminary surveys in other parts of the valley suggest that the pattern observed at Etla is probably typical of the earlier part of the Formative. In areas of low water table, such as north and east of Tlacolula, evidence of Early Formative occupation is correspondingly sparser.

In this belt of high-water-table alluvium, which narrows to 500 meters near Etla and expands to 2 kilometers in the broad plain just south of Oaxaca City, the Zapotec practice a kind of rudimentary water control known as *riego a brazo* or "pot-irrigation." This technique was described by Lorenzo (1960), and we have since studied it in detail in the *municipio* of Zaachila.

"Pot-irrigation" involves the digging of a series of shallow wells right in the cornfield, tapping the stratum of water which lies between 1.5 and 3.0 meters from the surface. An acre of land may have ten of these small wells, which are filled in during the plowing season and then reopened when water is needed. Water is drawn up from each well in a 3-gallon pot and poured gently around the individual corn plants. By means of this system, farmers within the 3-meter water-table zone often achieve three harvests a year. At any time of the year, dry season or wet, this belt of pot-irrigated alluvium resembles a huge patchwork of small but highly productive gardens. *Riego a brazo* requires no large labor force or centralized control; it is carried out on an individual-household basis. However, the zone where this technique can be used constitutes a very small percentage of the valley-floor area in Oaxaca, and, as mentioned above, it cannot be used at all in low-water-table areas like the Valley of Tehuacán.

The association of San José and Guadalupe phase villages with this zone of pot-irrigation was very suggestive, but until recently no actual well to demonstrate the existence of the technique in the earlier part of the Formative had been found. In August of 1966, Richard Orlandini and James Schoenwetter of the Oaxaca Project discovered a Formative well which had been exposed by adobe-brickmakers in a bank some 50 meters back from the river at Mitla. Associated pottery dated the well to the Guadalupe phase, considerably strengthening our evidence for water control in the early village farming period.

Agriculture within this high-water-table zone supported villages of large size and material wealth. The best-known site of the San José and Guadalupe phases in San José Mogote, which we tested in 1966 (see Fig. 2). Here Early Formative artifacts can be picked up over 40 acres of a piedmont spur surrounded on three sides by alluvium. Rows of post molds and burned wall fragments suggest that houses were large and rectangular, with partial stone foundations and wattle-and-daub walls which were plastered with mud and whitewashed. Besides the usual internal features, like hearths and bell-shaped sub-floor cooking pits, one San José phase house had a recessed circular area a meter and a half in diameter, which had been plastered and painted red. Around this circle were scattered fragments of figurines, exotically decorated pottery, fragments of black and white mica, raw chunks and small polished mirrors of magnetite, and ornaments and discarded fragments of imported marine shell.[8] In levels belonging to the early Guadalupe phase, such scatters gave way to an artificial platform of earthen fill with stone retaining walls oriented almost due north-south, and presumably having had a ceremonial function. Such orientations characterize later ceremonial structures in the valley as well (Acosta 1965:814–36).

The evidence of long-distance trade in the San José phase (which is lacking in earlier periods) reflects two things: an increasing interest in status differentiation (with artifacts of imported materials serving as insignia of status) and formalized contacts with other Indian groups in differing environmental zones of Mesoamerica. Marine pearl oyster and *Spondylus* shell were imported from the Pacific, while *Neritina* and pearly freshwater mussels came from the Gulf Coast. *Anomalocardia subrugosa,* a mollusk eaten by Formative villagers in the estuary zone of the distant Chiapas-Guatemala coast (Coe 1961; Coe, Flannery 1967), was also imported.

---

[8] The magnetite, probably from one of the known Etla or Zimatlán sources, was identified by Dr. P. Desautels, Division of Mineralogy, Smithsonian Institution. Identification of marine and freshwater mollusks was made by Dr. J. Morrison, Division of Mollusks, Smithsonian Institution. The "exotically decorated pottery" referred to would be technically described by Mesoamerican archeologists as zoned punctate and zoned rocker-stamped neckless jars (*tecomates*), white-rim black ware, and bowls and cylinders with excised (*raspada*) designs in the "Olmec" tradition.

Most important are the chunks and mirrors of magnetite, a raw material native to the Valley of Oaxaca, for nodules of this metal are known to have been polished into concave mirrors and buried in ceremonial caches by the "Olmec" peoples of the southern Gulf Coast (Drucker *et al.* 1959). At present, the Valley of Oaxaca must be considered a possible source for the Olmec magnetite.

RISE OF TOWNS AND CEREMONIAL CENTERS: 600 TO 200 B.C.

During the later stages of the Middle Formative period, villages within the 3-meter water-table zone increased in size and number. Coupled with this population increase, which we attribute to the success of dry farming and pot-irrigation in that part of the high alluvium, came the first sizable spread of settlement up the more permanent tributaries of the Atoyac into the piedmont (Fig. 2). These latter sites are of two types: "habitation" sites on the first terrace of the stream or a low ridge near it, and "ceremonial" centers on hilltops nearby.

We doubt that this pattern of settlement was random. Most sites outside the high alluvium at this period are on perennial streams, and, like the present villages of the piedmont zone, they are located not downstream, at the point where most water is available, but upstream, where the water can be most effectively diverted for irrigation. Today, these villages divert the water into canals which follow the natural contour of one of the piedmont spurs downstream until they come to the crest of the spur. Here the village and the "master canal" are located, and water is distributed to fields on both sides of the spur.

This technique of small-scale canal irrigation is only feasible along the upper edges of the piedmont zone, where streams have good perennial flows. Moreover, the actual area irrigated is relatively small, and it is the communities upstream that get most of the water. For this reason, villages both in the piedmont and in the pot-irrigation zone augment their water-control farming by cultivating the nearby hillsides. The technique used is simple dry farming with fallowing, called variously *tlacolol* or *barbecho* in different parts of Mexico (Palerm, Wolf 1957), and it profits from the low erosion rate of the lower piedmont zone. Such an agricultural pattern, combining an intensively cultivated (often irrigated) core area with a less intensively cultivated hinterland, has been called the "infield-outfield" system (Wolf 1966:21).

The piedmont areas into which these later Formative farmers expanded have been cultivated for so long that traces of early irrigation canals are virtually eradicated. They remain only in instances where the water used for irrigation was so rich in dissolved travertine that the canals themselves have actually been "fossilized" through deposition of this calcareous material. In 1966, James Neely of the Oaxaca Project investigated one such area in the mountain zone near Mitla.

This site, called Hierve el Agua, is a complex of "fossilized" ancient irrigation canals covering a square kilometer of hillside below a spring particularly rich in travertine. A series of dry-laid stone terraces had been irrigated by means of small canals which carried the water down to the fields and along the tops of the terrace walls. Neely's 40 test pits dug into these terraces reveal an occupation beginning before 300 B.C. and expanding through all subsequent periods of Oaxaca prehistory. It is probably no accident that this evidence of small-scale canal irrigation begins during the first sizable expansion out of the 3-meter water-table zone and up the perennial tributaries.

With at least four agricultural systems operating—dry farming and pot-irrigation in the high-water-table zone, canal irrigation and hillside fallowing systems in the piedmont—the Valley of Oaxaca reached another plateau on its climb toward civilization. San José Mogote grew to more than 100 acres, and in the process it differentiated internally into ceremonial and secular precincts, cemetery areas, and probably precincts of craft specialization as well. Similar developments took place throughout the valley, where there were now more than 30 ceremonial mound groups in operation (Bernal 1965:797). The most impressive of these was the mountaintop elite center of Monte Albán, which (although still in its initial building stages) already had, according to archeological evidence, monumental construction, bas-relief carving, a stela-altar complex, calendrics, and hieroglyphic writing (Bernal 1965:788; Paddock 1966).

By now, this area of "massed power" had begun to extend its influence into the surrounding valleys, bringing them rapidly into its sphere. This influence can be seen over an area of tens of thousands of square kilometers, from the Pacific Coast

to the Tehuacán Valley. In fact, techniques of pottery design in
Tehuacán and adjacent regions swung quickly away from previous
traditions and featured, during this and subsequent periods, provincial
imitations of the Valley of Oaxaca styles (MacNeish 1964a).

While much of the surrounding area may willingly have entered
into a symbiotic relationship with the Valley of Oaxaca for the
economic advantages it offered—such as a ready market for their
surplus and their locally specialized products—there are hints that
not all the marginal valleys joined peacefully. Caso (1965:937)
believes that at least one set of glyphs carved in stone at Monte
Albán represent conquered neighboring towns, and Coe (1962:
95–6) had recently suggested that an even earlier series of bas-
reliefs, the so-called *danzantes* of Monte Albán I, depict slain
and mutilated captives. While these warlike interpretations remain
to be proved, they are in no way inconsistent with what is known
ethnographically of groups of a chiefdom stage of organization
(Service 1962).

EVALUATION OF HYPOTHESES

With these data in mind, we can now tentatively evaluate the
relevance of various developmental hypotheses to what happened
in the Valley of Oaxaca. First of all, it no longer seems likely that
slash-and-burn was the sole early farming technique in Mesoamerica; in fact, given the locations of the cave areas where farming began, such as the moist barrancas of the arid Tehuacán Valley,
it is even possible that some kinds of water control (like the terracing of wet arroyos) are as old as agriculture itself.[9] However, our
work in Oaxaca strongly supports Palerm and Wolf's (1957) view
that the ability to assimilate new agricultural techniques through time
is a key factor in retaining nuclearity.

Furthermore, the four systems we postulate for the Monte Albán I
period did not represent the final stage of Zapotec agriculture. In
later periods (A.D. 100 to 900), large mound groups and habitation

---

[9] There are some indications that moist barrancas in the arid highlands of
Mexico were the original habitat of wild maize; it is caves in such settings
which have produced the earliest evidence of cultivated maize. C. E. Smith
(1965a) suspects that maize cultivation began in such barrancas and only later
spread to the alluvial fans at the mouth of the barranca and from there out
onto the valley floor.

sites cover areas of the high alluvium where only dry farming or flood-water farming is possible; by A.D. 1300 the area farmed included not only the entire valley floor but also the lower slopes of the mountains, which were frequently terraced. The terraces apparently depended on rainfall and on the lower evaporation rate of the north- and east-facing slopes. These data suggest that the assimilation of new farming techniques was also a way of bringing into cultivation more and more of the previously unproductive physiographic units of the valley: the greater the number of systems used, the greater the acreage producing at top capacity.

Our evidence for early irrigation in the Valley of Oaxaca will undoubtedly please advocates of the "hydraulic theory" of state formation (Wittfogel 1957). However, we see no evidence in Oaxaca for irrigation systems so large that they would necessitate a strong centralized authority. In fact, we fear that the hydraulic theory—at least, in its purest form—may at times obscure the real effects of irrigation in ancient society, which are as varied as the techniques themselves. In Oaxaca, canal irrigation of the Hierve el Agua type is applicable to a very tiny portion of the valley, and it is no more productive (in terms of labor input relative to crop yield) than pot-irrigation. Moreover, many canal-irrigating villages are so high in the piedmont that only summer crops can be grown. What canal irrigation *did* do was to open up an additional niche within the valley which had not previously been agriculturally productive.

Perhaps most significantly, in canal-irrigation communities there tends to be less equitable distribution of land and property rights than in pot-irrigating communities. As past writers have observed, irrigated land is "improved" land; it represents an investment which makes it a more scarce and competed-for resource than it previously was, and leads to problems of inheritance of property and differential access to good land. If a developing society has tendencies toward status differentiation already, which the Formative peoples of Oaxaca did have, these tendencies can be aggravated by control and inheritance of irrigation systems. It may be that early irrigation in Oaxaca can be most profitably viewed in these terms.

SUMMARY AND CONCLUSIONS

The Valley of Oaxaca's large flat floor, high water table, low erosion rate, and frost-free floodplain give it a higher agricultural potential than that of most surrounding areas. The development of the pot-irrigation system early in the Formative period gave it a head start over other valleys, where the low water table did not permit such farming; Oaxaca maintained its advantage by assimilating canal irrigation, *barbecho,* infield-outfield systems, flood-water farming, and hillside terracing as these methods arose. With the expansion of population in the high-water-table zone of the high alluvium, competition for highly productive land and manipulation of surpluses may have led to initial disparities in wealth and status; competition probably increased when canal-irrigation systems were added during the Middle Formative, improving some localities to the point where one residential group owned land more valuable than that of its neighbors.

Trade in exotic raw materials, which appear to have served as the insignia for status over much of Formative Mesoamerica, increased the wealth of the Oaxaca communities, and their elite made contact with the elite of other cultures, such as the Olmec. Such contact probably stimulated exchanges of the "lore" known only to the elite—calendrics, hieroglyphic systems, and symbolic art—thus widening the gap between farmer and chief. Through cooperation or coercion, the Oaxaca Valley chiefdom drew together a symbiotic area of 50,000 square kilometers, commemorating its accessions with stone monuments carved in bas-relief. By the start of the Christian Era it was the dominant political entity in the southern highlands of Mexico, and had become a true state.

The Oaxaca Project has only begun, and our reconstruction must remain a tentative one. We are especially aware that we cannot as yet integrate into this scheme the botanical and palynological materials from Oaxaca which are currently undergoing study. They will make the story still more complex, but civilization is a complex process; single-cause theories, no matter how attractive, are inadequate to explain it.

11 THE EMERGENCE
OF FOOD PRODUCTION IN CENTRAL PERU

Thomas C. Patterson

QUESTIONS CONCERNING the emergence of food production and its consequences have long interested archaeologists, but our answers to them have been something less than convincing in the past. A traditional answer to such questions—one that came into vogue about twenty years ago and has been popular ever since—postulates a close relationship between the emergence of agriculture, on the one hand, and the beginnings of such things as permanent settlement, population growth, and cultural diversification, on the other. This answer is actually a theoretical model that contains several distinct parts and is based on a number of assumptions which are usually left unstated. The reasoning behind the model—which might be called the agricultural origins of civilization theory—goes something like this.

Hunting and gathering is a difficult, time-consuming way to make a living that requires the inhabitants of an area to move seasonally from place to place as the resources of each locality become available. Semi-nomadic bands of hunters and gatherers wandering in the same biome shared many of the same cultural patterns, because their livelihood was so dependent on the natural environment and because they were exploiting the same set of natural resources. These wanderers occasionally may have planted a few seeds here and there and harvested the plants when they matured, but such activities were minor ones and did not yield enough food to sustain the population throughout the year. This situation continued until certain genetic changes occurred in the species they were cultivating. Once these changes took place, however, the productivity of the plants increased substantially, and the people produce more food than they could collect from the surrounding environment. Their food supply

Unpublished manuscript reprinted by permission of the author.

was now independent of environmental constraints, because they controlled its production; consequently, they were able to settle in permanent villages close to their fields and devote their time and energy to caring for domesticated plants and animals instead of foraging about the countryside. Since they were able to get more food for less work, they could divert their excess time and energy into other activities—such as having more babies or elaborating and diversifying their cultural patterns.

This model has a number of attractive features, such as the emphasis it places on the interrelationships between economic production, population growth, and settlement patterns. It is undoubtedly qualities like this that account for much of the popularity that the model has enjoyed among archaeologists. It not only accounts for a great deal of what we think should be in the archaeological record of an area but also provides a concise, logical explanation of why these features appear in the sequence. Recent investigations in Mesoamerica and Peru, however, have begun to cast a shadow of doubt over the agricultural origins theory, and, as these investigations progress, it is becoming increasingly apparent that the model has a number of severe limitations and that its continued use will actually retard, rather than enhance, our understanding of how food production emerged in the past and what consequences it had. The major difficulties with the model are that it is too simple and too general. It does not take into account the relevance of variation, either within a single region or between different regions, and it does not adequately explain how and why the changes from one economic orientation to another actually occurred.

Many of the difficulties with the agricultural origins theory stem from the fact that it is framed largely in terms of a pair of stereotypes and the contrasts that exist between them. Thus, a hunting and gathering economy or society is seen as something very different from an agricultural economy or society. Each type is an ideal one, formulated in such a way that it emphasizes the similarities of the economies or societies assigned to it rather than their distinctive features. The important feature of agrarian societies, for example, is that their members practice agriculture, and it makes little difference whether the agriculture they practice involves shifting cultivation or intensive irrigation. It is clear from archaeological, historical, and ethnographic information that a great deal of variation exists in each of the stereotypes. It is easy to find examples of hunters and gatherers who spend very little time and energy acquiring the food they need to sustain themselves or of agriculturalists who devote a great deal of time and energy to farming and still barely make a living at it. It is also easy to find examples of hunters and gatherers who live in permanent settlements or of agriculturalists who move from one place to another during the year. It has been argued that these stereotypes represent what are general rules and that the examples of variation are unimportant because they are merely exceptions to the general rules; however, such a view of the relevance of cultural variation avoids the inescapable fact that people do not live in general but rather in specific times and places. They do not adapt their behavior to general conditions but rather to the particular ones that prevail when and where they live.

Explanations of change or process are also limited by the use of the hunter-gatherer and agriculturalist stereotypes. In the agricultural origins theory, these stereotypes become stages of economic development in a transformational sequence, and answers to the questions of how food production emerged and what consequences it had involve comparing and contrasting one stereotype with the other. This technique does not allow us to show the step-by-step ways in which hunting and gathering economies eventually became agricultural economies in many parts of the world. It does not even show us how one ideal type can be transformed into another. What it does show, however, is that there was a difference between the stereotypes that were used to organize the evidence. When the technique is applied to archaeological data from different areas, it is not surprising that food production is often said to have emerged in much the same way everywhere. Answers to the question of why these changes occurred are even less convincing than those dealing with how the changes took place. The mechanisms underlying these economic transformations are frequently single-factor causal explanations; they are often vaguely specified—e.g., diffusion from a nuclear area or cultural evolution—and they often involve circular reasoning—e.g., agriculture appears because people started farming. These single-factor explanations are neither particularly adequate nor particularly satisfying. Furthermore, they probably are not correct, especially when we consider them in the light of a number of recent archaeological investigations and studies of agricultural land use systems.

During the past few years, archaeologists have begun to talk about contemporary intersite variation within a region, not so much in terms of "this site is a ceremonial center and that one is a city," but rather in terms of the economic activities that occurred at each. They have recognized from artifacts and food remains, for instance, that a particular site may have been a hunting camp occupied in the late spring while another one in a different locality may have been a station from which food plants were collected in the late summer and early fall (MacNeish 1964a). They have also recognized that more than one economic activity may have taken place at a particular site and have considered the implications of the time and labor allocations required by the various activities (Flannery 1968b).

What I want to do in the next few pages is to examine how and why an agricultural economy emerged in the coastal valleys of central Peru and to consider some of the wider implications of this process. Instead of wrenching agriculture from its environmental and economic context by trying to trace the sequence in which cultivated plants appeared in the area and to determine the places where they originated, I want to consider agriculture as merely one part of a broader economic system that is composed of many different patterns of land use and resource exploitation, each of which may have had its own peculiar set of time and labor requirements. Such an approach focuses attention on the environmental diversity of an area, the availability of resources, and the ways in which different peoples exploited them.

THE ENVIRONMENT

The coastal valleys of central Peru and their environs are characterized by an amazing variety and number of ecological habitats, the distribution and composition of which have been affected by both nature and man. There have been climatic fluctuations in postglacial times that undoubtedly produced changes in the size and configuration of many of the habitats in the area but not in their composition and number. Man has also played a prominent role in altering the ecology of the area by displacing the natural vegetation of the valley floors and coastal plain so that only small remnants of it survive today and by replacing large portions of the original ground cover with cultivated plants, roads, and buildings. The ecological patterns we see today in the area bear little resemblance to the conditions that prevailed five or six thousand years ago;

however, we can reconstruct the ancient environments in considerable detail, as well as their distribution, by studying the meteorological patterns that prevail over the area and how these would have been different in the past and by examining where the remnants of natural plant formations occur and what conditions are needed to sustain them.

An important feature of the environmental diversity of central Peru is that much of it is patterned because of the topography and prevailing climatic conditions. The most prominent topographic features of the area are the western slopes of the Andes that rise from an elevation of a few hundred meters near the shore to heights of more than five thousand meters about a hundred kilometers inland and the series of small rivers that begin in a zone of regular seasonal rainfall near the crest of the Cordillera Occidental and flow in a generally westerly direction before they empty into the sea. These rivers are separated from each other by ridges and hills that decrease in elevation toward the sea. The upper and middle parts of the valleys are narrow canyons, and the rivers that created them may cover the entire floor of the gorge in some places and be flanked by narrow terraces in others. The gradients of the rivers diminish noticeably below about the five hundred meter contour, and they have deposited wide alluvial fans along their lower courses. The alluvial deposits of the Rímac and Chillón Rivers have merged to form a single broad expanse of land on the coastal plain, while those of the Lurín and Chilca Rivers are narrower and separated from each other and the one to the north by ranges of low hills (Dollfus 1965:212–365). The amount of water that flows in the rivers varies substantially, not only from one river to another but also from one season to another in the same river. They are highest in March and generally high from about January to April, while the smallest amount of water flows in them between about July and October (Dirección de Irrigación 1964:86–91).

The amount of water in the rivers reflects the pattern of seasonal precipitation above about three thousand meters, where the rains may begin any time from September onward, are generally heaviest in January, and are usually over by March. The height of the highland dry season falls during the months of June and July. This pattern contrasts markedly with that of the coastal plain and the lower slopes of the Andes, where the fogs and drizzle that characterize the wet season begin about June, are heaviest in August, and end by October. The precipitation patterns of the coast and high-lands, as well as the period when the rivers are swollen with water, have a number of interesting and important consequences regarding the times when wild plants mature or when planting and harvesting activities are carried out in the two areas.

Two other patterns can also be recognized in the environmental diversity of central Peru. One pattern parallels the coastline, and the other extends from the shore up the coastal valleys to the crest of the mountains. The pattern paralleling the coastline is essentially a repetitive one, consisting of a series of habitats that are repeated every fifteen or twenty kilometers. These habitats will vary some-what, depending on the elevation at which the cross section is made; however, on the coastal plain, for example, the series consists of a zone of desert that is virtually devoid of plants throughout the year, an area of lomas that is covered with plants during the wet season, the valley floor with several different kinds of habitats, and another zone of desert and lomas. The variety of habitats is rel-atively limited, and it is necessary to travel only a relatively short distance before the pattern repeats itself.

The pattern we see when we look up the coastal valleys from the ocean is markedly different. It also consists of a series of habitats, but these are never repeated in the same coastal valley. The series begins with the dense salt grass formations of the beach and passes through successive habitats composed of mixed bushes and shrubs, cactus and rainy-green shrubs, rainy-green grasses, and scattered shrubs, and finally ends in the bunch grass dwarf shrub formations of the puna. The arrangement of the habitats in this pattern is essentially linear.

The distinction that I have drawn between the repetitive and linear arrangements of habitats in central Peru may seem trivial. But it is not. It has important implications for where people went and how far they went to obtain certain resources. If, for example, they lived on the coastal plain near the mouth of a river, the re-

FIGURE 1 Lower Lurin Valley. C, cactus and bush habitat; CD, coastal desert habitat; L, lomas habitat; SG, salt grass habitat; VH, valley floor and riverine habitats; RH, rocky headland littoral habitat; SB, sandy beach littoral habitat; 1, Canario Phase sites (5200–4200 B.C.); 4, Gaviota Phase sites (1900–1750 B.C.); 5, early Initial Period sites (1750–c. 1500 B.C.).

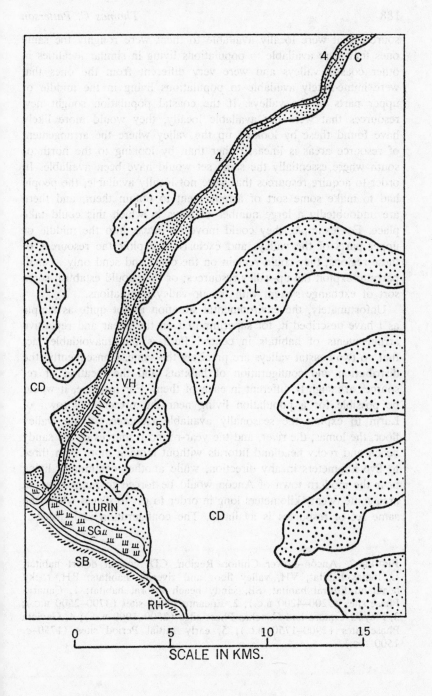

SCALE IN KMS.

sources that were locally available to them were roughly the same
ones that were available to populations living in similar localities in
other coastal valleys and were very different from the ones that
were immediately available to populations living in the middle or
upper parts of the valleys. If the coastal population sought new
resources that were not available locally, they would more likely
have found these by looking up the valley where the arrangement
of resource areas is linear, rather than by looking to the north or
south where essentially the same set would have been available. In
order to acquire resources that were not locally available, the people
had to make some sort of arrangement to obtain them, and there
are undoubtedly a large number of ways in which this could take
place. For example, they could move *en masse* into the middle or
upper parts of the valleys and exclusively exploit the resources of
these regions; they could remain on the coast and send only a small
party to exploit the up-valley resources; or they could establish some
sort of exchange system with the up-valley populations.

Unfortunately, the environmental situation is not quite as simple
as I have described it, for superimposed on the linear and repetitive
arrangements of habitats in central Peru is the unavoidable fact
that no two coastal valleys are precisely the same. Consequently, the
distribution and configuration of habitats and the location of resources are slightly different in each of them. For instance, it would
be possible for a population living near the present-day town of
Lurín to exploit the seasonally available resources of the valley
floor, the lomas, the river, and the year-round resources of the sandy
beach and rocky headland littorals without moving more than three
to five kilometers in any direction, while another community living
near the modern town of Ancón would be forced to range over an
area some twenty kilometers long in order to get to places where the
same set of resources is available. The configuration and distribu-

FIGURE 2 Ancón–Lower Chillon Region. CD, coastal desert habitat;
L, lomas habitat; VH, valley floor and riverine habitats; RH, rocky
headland littoral habitat; SB, sandy beach littoral habitat; 1, Canario
Phase sites (5200–4200 B.C.); 2, Encanto Phase sites (3700–2500 B.C.);
3, Playa Hermosa and Conchas Phase sites (2500–1900 B.C.); 4, Gaviota
Phase sites (1900–1750 B.C.); 5, early Initial Period sites (1750–*c.*
1500 B.C.).

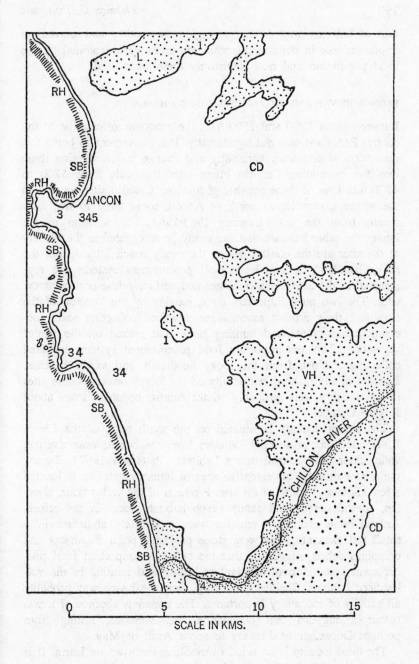

SCALE IN KMS.

tion of habitats vary from one region to another and played an important role in determining what resources were exploited by the local population and how intensively these were used.

ECONOMIC VARIABILITY AND ECONOMIC CHANGE

Between about 5200 and 1500 B.C., the economic orientation of the central Peruvians changed significantly. It is convenient to begin this discussion of economic variability and change by considering three localities containing Canario Phase sites that date from 5200 to 4200 B.C. One of these consists of fourteen Canario sites located in the winter season lomas north of Ancón, some three to five kilometers from the sea (Lanning 1963;1967). In addition to the lomas, the other habitats that can easily be recognized in the vicinity of the sites are the coastal desert, the sandy beach littoral, and the rocky headland littoral. Four food procurement systems are represented in the artifact assemblages and surface refuse scatter at the sites. The two most important ones, judging by the location of the sites and their artifact assemblages, involved collecting and processing lomas plants and hunting game that grazed on the winter vegetation. The less important food procurement systems involved collecting shellfish from the rocky headlands and sandy beaches. Because of the marked seasonality of the lomas resources, the sites in this locality were probably winter camps, occupied from about July to October.

The second locality is situated on the south bank of the Chilca River about six or seven kilometers from the ocean, near riverine, valley floor, and coastal desert habitats (Patterson 1967). During the winter months, an extensive area of lomas vegetation is located a few kilometers south of the site. Products of the valley floor, riverine, coastal desert, and sandy beach habitats occur in the refuse. Animal bone and plant remains were moderately abundant in a small test excavation, as were stone projectile point fragments and chippings debris, suggesting that the two most important food procurement systems involved plant collecting and hunting in the valley floor habitats. Shellfish collecting along the beach was probably an activity of secondary importance. The apparent absence of lomas resources suggests that occupation was seasonal, lasting from perhaps December or January to about April or May.

The third locality is on a hill overlooking the town on Lurín. It is situated about three kilometers from the ocean and is surrounded by a series of habitats. Products of the marine, sandy beach, rocky headland, valley floor, riverine, coastal desert, and lomas habitats appear in the habitation refuse at the site; some of the resources in the refuse—such as *Cucurbita* sp., the cultivated bottle gourd (*Lagenaria siceraria*), riverine crustaceans, or lomas snails—are available at different times of the year and suggest that the site was occupied continuously throughout the year rather than for just a few months. The refuse contents also suggest that fishing and shellfish collecting were the most important food procurement systems; these were undoubtedly followed by collecting plants from the valley floor and lomas habitats and crustaceans. Plant cultivation was a minor activity, and the only plants involved were apparently bottle gourds and an unidentified variety of squash. Hunting seems to have been the least important activity, judging by the absence of animal bone and the discovery of only one projectile point and two stone chips at the site.

The three Canario populations shared virtually the same set of food procurement systems, but their economic orientations were very different, as were the kinds of settlements in which they lived. The Lurín population relied extensively on year-round resources and supplemented these with ones that became available at different times. Permanent settlement was feasible for them because of the proximity of so many resource areas. The contemporary populations in Ancón and Chilca relied most extensively on seasonally available resources and supplemented them with permanent ones. Year-round settlements were not feasible for these populations as long as they exploited seasonal resources in areas with slight or only modest environmental diversity. The Ancón and Chilca localities probably represent the remains of two parts of an annual cycle of transhumance. Populations exploiting seasonal resources lived in the coastal valleys during the summer months and in the lomas areas during the winter. Another pattern that may have occurred in central Peru—at least the possibility of it cannot definitely be excluded yet—is one where a population lived in the puna grasslands from about December to May and in the coastal lomas from about July to October.[1]

---

[1] The evidence for this pattern consists mainly of some similarities between Canario Phase artifact assemblages and those of the Lauricocha III occupation in Lauricocha Cave U-1 in the north central highlands (Cardich 1958; Lanning 1963).

Two Encanto Phase localities, dating from about 3700 to 2500
B.C., show conditions that contrast somewhat with those of the
Canario Phase but are clearly developments of them. One locality is
the Loma Encanto near Ancón, and the environmental setting of the
thirteen Encanto Phase sites on it was identical to that of the Canario
locality situated a few kilometers to the north (Lanning 1963; 1967;
Patterson, Moseley n.d.). Virtually the same patterns of resource exploitation occur; only fishing seems to have been added as a food
procurement system. But the emphasis placed on the different procurement systems has changed significantly. The marine and littoral
habitats—both the rocky headland and sandy beach littoral zones—
provided the bulk of the protein consumed; lomas plants were collected and processed in much the same manner and quantity as in
the preceding period, while the importance of hunting land animals
had diminished considerably, judging by the relative paucity of bone
in the refuse. The location of the sites, as well as the large quantities
of lomas resources in the habitation refuse, suggests that they were
occupied seasonally during the winter months.

The other locality is Chilca Village 1, situated on the bank of
the Chilca River about four kilometers from the ocean and midway
between it and a large lomas (Donnan 1964; Patterson, Moseley
n.d.). Marine, sandy beach and rocky headland littorals, riverine,
valley floor, coastal desert, and lomas habitats occur within five or six
kilometers of the site, and the resources of nearly all of them have
been reported or observed in the habitation refuse. The most important food procurement systems were apparently marine or littoral-oriented—such as fishing, collecting shellfish from the two littoral habitats, hunting marine mammals and shore birds, and carving
up whales that were stranded on the beach. Plant remains and
projectile points also occur in the refuse, but it is not clear how important plant and animal foods were in the diet of the population,
although it is evident that plants from the lomas, riverine, and valley
floor habitats were used.

The contrast between the conditions that prevailed during this
period and those of the preceding one is most striking in the Ancón
area. Although the Ancón population still relied to a considerable
extent on the seasonally available resources of the terrestrial habitats, particularly the lomas, it is clear that they were exploiting the
year-round resources of the ocean in a much more efficient and intensive manner than their predecessors. It is likely that the increased

reliance on protein-rich marine resources fostered some population growth in the Ancón area—probably the kind of increase in which the nutritional level of the population as a whole rose. Such an increase in population could easily lead to over-exploitation of some lomas resources, and, when combined with other factors such as shrinkage resulting from desiccation, could lead to a significant reduction in the size of this habitat.

Another feature of the Encanto Phase economies of central Peru is that the economic orientations of the different localities were much more similar to each other in emphasis and intensity than those represented at the various Canario Phase localities. The resources of the marine and littoral habitats were everywhere more important than they had been earlier. This is not to say that other patterns did not persist from the preceding phase. They did. Cultivated plants—such as the bottle gourd and perhaps squash—were still being grown in the valley floor habitats. The transhumance cycles that prevailed during the Canario Phase—one between the lomas and the lower parts of the coastal valleys and perhaps another between the puna and coastal grasslands—may also have been practiced by some of the Encanto Phase populations of central Peru.[2]

The third period that I want to consider extends from 2500 to 1900 B.C. and includes sites of both the Playa Hermosa and Conchas Phases (Moseley 1968; Patterson, Moseley n.d.). Unfortunately, the only sites that can be assigned with certainty to this period are coastal ones located near Ancón and Ventanilla—regions where the kinds of habitats that occur, as well as their configurations, are very similar. Refuse deposits are extensive at the sites, particularly those of the later Conchas Phase, and suggest that fishing was the most important food procurement system, followed closely by shellfish collecting in the two littoral habitats and by hunting sea mammals and shore birds. The other food procurement systems were secondary and involved plant collecting and plant cultivation, both of which had to have taken place in the valley floor habitats. Thus, the inhabitants of these coastal-oriented villages

---

[2] The evidence for transhumance between the coastal and puna highlands during the Encanto Phase consists of artifact similarities between Encanto Phase sites on the coast and the Lauricocha III artifacts from Lauricocha Cave L-2 (Cardich 1964; Lanning 1963).

used resources that were available locally and ones that were available in distant localities.

There is an inland site that may date to this period. It is a small one located at the edge of the valley floor about three kilometers from the Chillón River and probably represents the refuse accumulation of no more than two or three families over a fairly short period of time. The refuse contains large quantities of fish, shellfish, and several fishhooks, indicating that this inland population also exploited the marine and littoral habitats; however, the presence of a number of grinding implements, more than were found in the coastal sites, suggests that plant processing was also important. The presence of a continually increasing variety and quantity of cultivated plants in the refuse deposits at the coastal villages also indicates that plant cultivation, which presumably took place along the banks of the Chillón River, was also an important activity. Whether or not this particular site does, in fact, date to the time of the Playa Hermosa and Conchas Phases, it is informative with respect to what we might expect to find when we do locate inland occupations that can be assigned with certainty to this period.

What occurred at the beginning of this period was the emergence of a new economic orientation in central Peru, even though virtually all of the patterns of resource exploitation had been present in the area for more than a thousand years. The new orientation involved the intensive and efficient exploitation of only a limited number of resources—those found in the marine and littoral habitats. The exploitation of these zones became so efficient and intensive that the resources of several of them were completely depleted by the end of the period, while the productivity of several others was substantially diminished. This new economic orientation had a number of consequences. First, the patterns of resource exploitation represented at the different sites were less varied than they had been during the preceding period. What distinguished one coastal site from another was often nothing more than the intensity with which a particular food procurement system was employed; for example, populations living near sandy beaches collected the resources of this habitat more frequently and intensively than those of the rocky headlands. Another consequence was the rise of a new kind of settlement, one that was focused on the resources of a single habitat and located as close to it as possible. The permanent villages of this period were located where they were, not because of the proximity of many different habitants, but rather because of the proximity of one or two economically important ones. The locations of these settlements actually facilitated the exploitation of resources that were concentrated in relatively small areas, because they brought together large numbers of people in the immediate vicinity of the habitat that was being used and therefore reduced the amount of economically unprofitable time spent in traveling between the resource and residential localities.

Plant cultivation was another food procurement system that become much more important during this period than it had been previously, particularly after a substantial population increase at about the beginning of the Conchas Phase. This activity was apparently carried on by small inland populations living within a few kilometers of places where the rivers flooded seasonally. The most important land use system in the agricultural system of this period involved the fairly intensive use of floodlands in places where the rivers had not cut deep channels or where their gradients were slight. Consequently, agricultural production involved a single crop each year, with the times of planting and harvesting being almost entirely dependent on the level of the rivers.

Cultivated plant foods became much more important during the Gaviota Phase, which lasted from 1900 to 1750 B.C. (Moseley 1968; Patterson, Moseley n.d.). The evidence for this consists partly of a substantial increase in the quantity and variety of cultivated food plants in habitation refuse deposits at coastal-oriented villages and partly in the establishment of settlements in the inland areas of the valleys. There were more coastal villages during this period than in the preceding one; in fact, settlements were located near virtually all of the productive shellfish beds in the Ancón and Ventanilla areas and presumably near productive beds in other parts of central Peru, as well. The food procurement systems represented in the coastal villages at Ancón and Ventanilla were not significantly different from those of the preceding period. Although shore birds and mammals were occasionally hunted, fishing and shellfish gathering in the two littoral habitats still provided the bulk of the protein that was consumed by the coastal populations. What distinguished one coastal site from another was the fact that those located near the rocky headland habitats have high proportions of rock-dwelling shellfish in their refuse, while the refuse deposits at those located near sandy beaches contain high proportions of sand-dwelling molluscs.

There are two kinds of inland settlements during this period. One kind is located on the coastal plain, and the other is located in the middle parts of the coastal valleys. Settlements on the coastal plain, like Chuquitanta or Chira-Villa, which are located in areas where arable land and permanent water supplies are found within a kilometer or so of the sea, show slightly different economic orientations than the coastal villages. Plant cultivation in the nearby habitats of the valley floor or in the flood plains along the edges of the rivers may have been as important as either fishing or shellfish collecting for these inland-oriented populations. Nearly all of the cultivated plants that have been reported from the Gaviota Phase sites could, for example, have been grown in the two areas of flood plain located near Chuquitanta or adjacent to the marshy lands near Chira-Villa.

Both the coastal populations which were primarily, if not entirely, marine and littoral-oriented and the inland populations of the coastal plain with their mixed economies contrast with the inland populations living in the middle parts of the coastal valleys. The up-valley sites are generally much smaller than the coastal and lower valley ones and are located at varying distances from the sea. Traveling time on foot between the shore and up-valley sites ranges from about four hours to about two and a half days. Even though marine shellfish occur in small quantities at nearly all of the up-valley sites, littoral harvesting or fishing must have been unimportant activities for their inhabitants because of the distances and traveling times involved; they certainly would have been economically unprofitable activities. Another feature of the up-valley sites is that they are systematically located in places where river water, fuel, building materials, and arable land are available throughout the year. The kind of valley floor habitat in which the arable land is situated is the distinctive feature of these sites. Three of them are located in habitats dominated by columnar cacti, and three are in habitats composed of cacti and shrubs.

The sites were occupied by people who may have spent a little time collecting crustaceans from the rivers but who were primarily engaged in agriculture, growing a variety of plants. Some plants that are adapted to a wide range of environmental conditions—like chili peppers (*Capsicum* spp.)—were undoubtedly grown at most, if not all, of the up-valley localities, while others— like avocados (*Persea americana*) or coca (*Erythroxylon coca*)—

that are most productive when particular sets of environmental conditions prevail may have been grown at only one or two localities. If this was in fact the situation, then each of the up-valley populations was producing a different combination of food plants and, consequently, had an economic orientation and set of activities that were slightly different from those of the other up-valley groups.

Agriculture based on seasonal rainfall would have been impractical or impossible at the up-valley sites, because rainfall is either highly irregular or absent altogether in areas where they are located. Near all of the sites, however, the rivers have cut fairly deep channels, and flood plains either do not exist or are exceedingly small. Consequently, any kind of intensive agricultural land use in these localities, almost by necessity, meant that a water management system was used. Such a water management system probably involved no more than a few short irrigation canals that brought water from the rivers to the lands above the riverbanks. Since the source of water was more or less constant, the lands could have been watered throughout the year, and more than one crop could have been harvested.

A number of changes with important economic consequences occurred during this period. The size of the population increased substantially, which led to the establishment of a number of coastal fishing villages and settlements in the inland portions of the coastal valleys. Judging by the relative size of the sites, the majority of the inhabitants in central Peru resided in inland settlements, mostly on the coastal plain, and, to a much smaller extent, in the middle parts of the river valleys. The establishment of settlements in the middle parts of the valleys probably involved a redefinition of the ecology of these regions—one that no longer emphasized the availability of certain natural resources but stressed instead the agricultural potential of particular inland habitats and locations. It is also clear that cultivated plants became much more important in the daily diet of the central Peruvians than they had been previously. These plants were grown under a variety of fairly intensive agricultural land use systems, ranging from flood-water farming along the banks of the rivers in the lower parts of the valleys to irrigation farming in the middle parts. It was also a period in which populations were becoming increasingly specialized economically. Fishermen and shellfish collectors lived in the coastal villages, while farmers resided in the inland settlements in the middle parts of the coastal valleys.

Perhaps the most important feature of the new economic orientation in the Gaviota Phase was the exchange or redistribution of goods between different localities. Coastal products, like shellfish, were consumed by inhabitants of the up-valley localities, while up-valley products, such as coca, were used by the peoples living in the lower parts of the valleys or along the coast. The occurrence of cultivated plants in refuse deposits at coastal villages during the preceding period suggests that some sort of exchange or redistribution system already existed between the coastal populations and those living in the lower parts of the river valleys. What distinguishes the Gaviota Phase redistribution or exchange system from the earlier network are the size of the area in which it worked, the number of populations that participated in it, and the larger proportion of goods from distant habitats that appear in habitation refuse deposits.

A number of changes that eventually had important economic consequences for the inhabitants of central Peru occurred between about 1750 and 1500 B.C. Several of the coastal-oriented villages of the preceding period were completely abandoned before the beginning of this period, while others were apparently occupied on a much-reduced scale by peoples who visited the localities only intermittently. A few coastal-oriented settlements, like the one at Ancón, continued to be occupied throughout the year by populations that were still primarily engaged in fishing and shellfish gathering. Still, the coastal population in Ancón, at least, was consuming an increasing variety and quantity of cultivated plant foods that could not conceivably have been grown locally because of the prevailing environmental conditions.

The large inland settlement at Chuquitanta was also abandoned shortly before 1750 B.C. A few families from the settlement may have moved to a small alluvial fan about three kilometers north of the Chillón River and continued to farm the larger of the two flood-plain areas, producing a single mixed crop each year. The remainder of the Chuquitanta population and possibly those from the abandoned fishing villages around Ventanilla presumably resettled at the Huaca la Florida, which is located a kilometer and a half north of the Rimac River and eleven kilometers from its mouth. This site consists of a large pyramidal structure surrounded by an extensive area of habitation refuse and wall foundations. The extent of the surrounding area suggests that a substantial number of people resided at the site after 1750 B.C. La Florida is situated in a place where both flood-water and irrigation farming could have been practiced. The amount of land that could have been brought under cultivation by flood-water farming techniques alone was substantially smaller than that in the vicinity of Chuquitanta; however, several hundred hectares could have been brought under cultivation in the area by using a small water management system, consisting of a single irrigation canal about six kilometers long with smaller ditches branching off it. This is roughly twice the amount of land that was farmed by the inhabitants of Chuquitanta during the preceding period, even under optimal conditions. Furthermore, the irrigated lands would have been more productive ones since the land use system was more intensive. The combination of the year-round availability of water in the Rimac River and the use of a relatively simple water management system meant that more than one crop could have been harvested each year.

A similar argument can probably be made for changes that occurred in the lower part of the Lurín Valley during this period. The points are clear, however. There was still a great deal of economic variation in the area, but agriculture was becoming more important in the economy of central Peru, agricultural produce was becoming more important in the diet of the central Peruvians, and agricultural activities were occupying a greater part of their time and energy.

DISCUSSION

In the preceding pages, I have presented a set of pictures describing certain aspects of the economic organization of the ancient peoples who lived in central Peru at different periods between 5200 and 1500 B.C. Each picture is essentially a synchronic description of the various economic patterns that prevailed during one of the periods; however, I still have not answered the questions posed at the beginning of the paper. Rephrasing them slightly, they become: why was one set of activities and opportunities—those associated with agricultural production—continually selected out of an array of possibilities and emphasized so that it became progressively more important through time, and what consequences did this selection process have on the daily lives of the ancient peoples of central Peru? It is clear from the pictures of central Peruvian society that more than just genetic changes, diffusion, and cultural evolution were involved in the emergence of the agrarian economy. Cultural variability, environmental diversity, and economic change—to name only a few—played important roles and must be taken into account if we are going to explain what happened in this area. Since no single-factor causal explanation adequately accounts for even a small portion of the events that took place, it is convenient to use a different approach in attempting to answer these questions. A systems analysis approach is one way of answering them. An adequate, though admittedly incomplete, explanation of the changes that occurred in central Peru can be formulated in terms of a dynamic, four-factor model. Each factor accounts for a slightly different set of variables that were operative during the period when agricultural production was transformed from a relatively unimportant activity to one that had far-reaching consequences. These factors interacted with each other in such a way that a relatively insignificant change in one of them produced changes in the others and had enormous ramifications that completely altered the appearance of the cultural system as a whole.

Population change is the first factor in the model, and it may well have been the most important one involved in the transformation (Boserup 1965). It is possible to construct a very simplistic demographic model that adequately accounts for the population expansion that occurred in central Peru between 5200 and 1500 B.C.[3] This model is based on several premises. First, changes in the nutritional level of a society may radically alter the size of its population. Second, the food supply of a society is relatively elastic when technological changes related to subsistence are taking place or when what constitutes usable food resources are being redefined. Third, population growth may not be uniform throughout the society as a whole but may be greatest among those sectors or groups which experience the largest increases in nutrition. Fourth, population growth can lead to the over-exploitation of resources that are not replenished annually and eventually to a decline in the nutritional level of the society. Fifth, this situation can lead to a search for new sources of food or to the more intensive and/or efficient utilization

---

[3] Wrigley (1967) provides a useful discussion of demographic models.

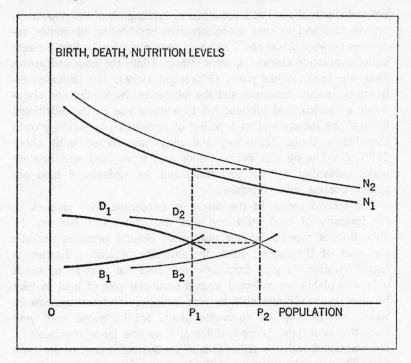

FIGURE 3 Demographic Change. The relationship between the maximum population of a society and its nutritional level. B_1, D_1, and N_1 reflect the birth, death, and nutritional levels of population P_1 at time t_1. An increase in the nutritional level to N_2 leads to an increase in the size of the maximum population to P_2, while the birth and death levels remain unchanged.

of already established resources. Sixth, under these conditions, the nutritional level of the society may return to its former level or even increase somewhat.

The population expansion in central Peru can be programmed in the following way. The nutritional level of the society as a whole rose slightly during the Encanto Phase when there was more intensive and efficient utilization of marine resources. The size of the population increased slightly as a consequence of the higher nutritional level, and, subsequently, the society overexploited some of the resources of the terrestrial habitats, like the lomas at Ancón. This over-exploitation may have reduced the nutritional level of the society and eventually led to a reduction or leveling off of the population growth rate and to even more intensive exploitation of marine resources between 2500 and 2250 B.C. New plant foods, first brought under cultivation elsewhere, were imported into the area and grown along the banks of the rivers (Pickersgill 1969). The increased reliance on marine resources and the increasing availability and abundance of agricultural produce led to another rise in the nutritional level of the society and to a period of sustained population growth that began about 2250 B.C. and may have lasted until about 1500 B.C. During this period, more and more land was brought under cultivation for the first time, and the agricultural land use system became more intensive.

The second factor in the model is concerned with changes in the intensity of land utilization and the effects this had on the allocation of time and labor resources.[4] Several premises underlie this part of the model. First, the intensity of land utilization is highly variable, ranging from extensive land use systems in which only wild plants are collected from a particular plot of land as they become seasonally available to very intensive land use systems in which several crops of cultivated plants are harvested each year from the same plot. Second, different time and labor requirements are associated with the different land use systems found in the same area. Third, as the intensity of the land use system increases, more hours of work are required to produce a given quantity of food. Fourth, there is a shift from relatively extensive land use systems to more intensive ones as the population of an area increases. Fifth, the shift from less intensive to more intensive land use systems does not occur simultaneously in all parts of an area.

There were at least three major land use systems in central Peru between 5200 and 1500 B.C. The earliest was a system of extensive land utilization that involved collecting wild plant resources as they became available in the different habitats. No preparation of the land was necessary either before or after the plants were harvested. Once the harvest season was over in a particular habitat, the area was not exploited until the resources became available again in the following year. The second system was somewhat more intensive and involved mixed crop farming in the seasonally flooded

---

[4] Boserup (1965) has developed this aspect of the model in considerable detail, and my argument follows her presentation very closely.

lands along the sides of the rivers. One crop of cultivated plants was probably produced each year. It was a seasonal system that required a considerable input of labor at certain times and virtually none at other times. The soil had to be cleared and prepared, the seeds planted, and weeds removed before the crop was harvested. Once this occurred, no agricultural labor was necessary until the following year. The third system involved irrigation farming and yielded more than one crop each year. In addition to clearing and preparing the soil, planting seeds, removing weeds, and harvesting the crop, the land had to be watered and fertilized and the irrigation ditches had to be kept in constant repair.

The kind of land use system that is employed in an area has a number of implications concerning the amount of labor that is necessary. If a plot of land is planted more frequently, it is necessary to devote an increasing amount of agricultural labor to each given amount of land; however, the output resulting from every man-hour devoted to agricultural labor in a multi-cropping system may actually be less than that in an annual cropping system, even though the amount of farm produce and land under cultivation may be greater (Boserup 1965; Geertz 1963).

Moderately intensive land utilization becomes apparent in central Peru about 2500 B.C. This pattern continues on the coastal plain until at least 1500 B.C. Intensive land use, involving irrigation agriculture, appears in the middle parts of the coastal valleys about 1900 B.C., where it persists in substantially modified form until the present day. Multi-crop, irrigation agricultural systems were apparently first used on the coastal plains of central Peru about 1750 B.C. in conjunction with less intensive methods of land use. The consequence of this pattern was that a continually increasing amount of time and labor was allocated to agricultural activities after 2500 B.C.

The third factor involved in the model is concerned with the movement of people and/or goods from one place to another in an area (Haggett 1965:40–55). Several premises underlie this part of the model as well. First, central Peru was inhabited by more than one population, each of which potentially had access to the same set of resources, even though these were often not exploited in the same way or with the same intensity. Second, each population had its own particular field of movement defined by the resources it exploited and the seasonality of these products. Third, the nature and shape of these fields changed through time. They began as continuous fields where the movement of people was more important than the movement of goods. Subsequently, the fields became distorted as the products of a particular resource area increased in importance and were exploited more intensively. Finally, the fields became fragmented, and the movement of goods from one fragment to another became more important economically than the movement of people.

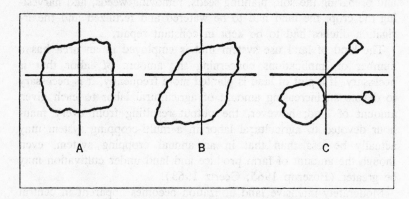

FIGURE 4 Fields of Movement. A, Continuous Field in which there is approximately equal activity and opportunity in each of the quadrants; B, Distorted Field in which there is increased activity and opportunity in the lower left quadrant and diminished activity and opportunity in the upper left quadrant; C, Fragmented Field in which there is maximal activity and opportunity in the lower left quadrant with outliers of fairly high activity and opportunity in the upper and lower right quadrants.

Between 5200 and 1500 B.C., the fields of movement of the central Peruvian populations were continuous, because the members of each group exploited the resources of different habitats in terms of regular annual cycles. What distinguished one population from another during this period was the size of their fields of movement. These ranged from relatively small, amoeba-shaped fields of the populations that exploited the resources of various contiguous habitats to the long, linear fields of the populations that exploited the resources of non-contiguous habitats. Continuous fields of movement became distorted or fragmented between 2500 and 1900 B.C.

as the populations spent more and more time exploiting the resources of single habitats or sets of closely related contiguous ones and only occasionally utilized the products of distant localities. In order to obtain resources from the distant habitats that their predecessors had once exploited, they began to engage increasingly in exchange or redistribution networks, in which the transference of goods was economically more important than the movement of people. The fragmentation of the fields became more apparent after 1900 B.C., with the appearance of the up-valley hamlets that were producing crops adapted to the environmental conditions of the region and exchanging these goods for ones that they could not obtain locally.

The fourth factor in the model is concerned with the location and permanency of settlement. This part of the model is based on two premises. The first is that the location and permanency of settlement is closely related to the location and configuration of resource areas and to the seasonality of their products. The second is that changes in the location of settlements reflect changes in the ways in which significant resources are being defined and exploited. Permanent settlements occurred in central Peru when one of two conditions prevailed. During the period from 5200 to 2500 B.C., they occurred in areas where many habitats were contiguous and could be exploited from a single residential locality. The resources of these habitats were either plentiful throughout the year or became available at slightly different times. The maximum travel distance between the residential and resources localities under these conditions seems to have been about five or six kilometers. When travel distances greater than this were involved, a pattern of seasonally shifting settlements prevailed, and these were usually located near habitats with available resources. After 2500 B.C., permanent settlements occurred in areas where the resources of a single habitat or a small set of closely related contiguous ones were intensively and efficiently exploited throughout the year. This resource may have been a natural one, like shellfish, or partly under the control of man, like cultivated plants.

CONCLUSIONS

Agricultural production emerged in various ways in different parts of the world. The particular process that took place in central Peru was very different, apparently, from the one that occurred in the

Tehuacán Valley of Mexico, for example, and it may have been quite different from the processes of change on the north coast or in the central highlands of Peru. Consequently, we cannot take the process I have discussed here as *the exact model* of what happened in other parts of the central Andes where evidence is not yet available or soon forthcoming. The peoples living in these regions were faced with different problems and opportunities than the central Peruvians, and they undoubtedly dealt with them in different ways. This does not mean that we should not attempt to generalize about the emergence of food-producing economies in other parts of Peru or in other areas. We should. It does imply, however, that we should consider carefully the research strategies that we have used in the past and the ways in which we have traditionally interpreted archaeological evidence.

Instead of writing so much about a topic we know so little about, perhaps we should undertake detailed historical studies in various parts of the world in order to get more adequate and reliable information about what happened in the past. Instead of searching for a single model that accounts for the appearance of agriculture everywhere, perhaps we should be studying the range of variation that exists among these processes. Instead of searching for vague similarities among the ways in which agriculture emerged in different areas, perhaps we should determine whether the same variables or factors were operating in every situation and whether these were operating and interacting in the same manner. Instead of searching for the origins of agricultural systems, perhaps we should place food production in the context of the broader economic system of which it was but a part!

ACKNOWLEDGMENTS

An earlier version of this paper entitled "Cultural Variation During the Later Preceramic Periods" was presented at the annual meeting of the Society for American Archaeology that was held in Milwaukee, Wisconsin, in May 1969. Both this version and the earlier draft have profited considerably from the comments of Michael D. Coe, Alex Georgiadis, R. Bruce Grove, Karen W. Spalding, James Schoenwetter, and the students enrolled in Archeology 37b, a course that I taught at Yale University during the spring of 1969. I want to thank these people for their constructive criticism and to absolve them of any responsibility for errors of fact or interpretation that appear herein. I also want to thank Frédéric Engel, Edward P. Lanning, Richard S. MacNeish, Michael E. Moseley, and Harry G. Scheele for providing me with information about their unpublished research. The archaeological field investigations on which this paper is based have been generously supported by the National Science Foundation, the Wenner-Gren Foundation for Anthropological Research, and the Comisión de Intercambio Educativo del Perú, Mrs. Gertrude M. Connor, and Mr. Landon T. Clay. It has been carried out under the auspices of the Patronato Nacional de Arqueología, the Museo Nacional de Antropología y Arqueología, and the Unversidad Nacional Mayor de San Marcos. I wish to thank them for their support and patience.

THE NEAR EAST

12 AGRICULTURAL ORIGINS IN THE NEAR EAST AS A GEOGRAPHICAL PROBLEM

Karl W. Butzer

INTRODUCTION

THE PREVIOUS CHAPTERS attempted to appraise man-land relationships during the slow process of cultural innovation characterizing the Paleolithic and "Mesolithic." These hunter-gatherer populations had all been very sparsely settled and technologically simple, with a limited or even negligible impact on the natural environment. However, the same transition of Pleistocene and Holocene that left Europe at the cultural level of advanced food-collecting, witnessed the dramatic beginnings of agriculture in the Near East.

The culture groups of the Near Eastern late Pleistocene were specialized hunter-gatherers (Hole, Flannery 1967; Flannery 1965). But, at least as far as their tool inventory is concerned, these Upper Paleolithic people were comparatively uninteresting and not remarkably progressive or specialized. Then about 11,000 years ago two cultures appear in the Levant and northeastern Iraq: the Natufian and Karim Shahirian. Both assemblages were characterized by so-called agricultural implements such as sickle-blades, grinding stones, and polished stone axes known as celts and presumed to have been used as hoes in many cases. None of these tools as such necessarily indicate agricultural activity, but the combination suggests partial subsistence on either wild grains or cultivated cereals. And at Zawi Chemi Shanidar, one site of the Karim Shahirian assemblage, there is fairly good proof of the presence of domesticated this part of the model. First, the intensity of land utilization is

Reprinted from Karl W. Butzer, *Environment and Archeology: An Introduction to Pleistocene Geography* (Chicago: Aldine Publishing Company, 1964); revised by author especially for this edition.

sheep (Perkins 1964), *ca.* 8900 B.C.[1] By 7000 B.C. subsistence-farming had become a common economic trait in parts of the Near East.

A focus of agricultural origins in this particular area and at this particular time is of environmental and geographical interest. Firstly, localization of early domestication is to some extent circumscribed by environmental factors. Suitable biological resources must be present if local domestication is to be possible. A second problem concerns possible environmental influences on the cultural processes implied by agricultural origins. And thirdly, the invention of agriculture is of great physical import, marking a drastic change in man-land relationships. The following chapter attempts to outline some of these environmental problems in relation to the hearth of domestication in the Near East. Beyond doubt the environmental problems related to first domestication in other culture areas, for example in the New World, are quite distinct. But their consideration lies beyond the scope of a selective survey of man-land relationships at different cultural and technological levels.

THE NEAR EAST AS A HEARTH OF DOMESTICATION

There have been several hearth areas in which domestication of specific associations of plants and animals was apparently first carried out. Basically such areas are habitats with a number of wild plants and animals suitable for domestication, and presumably where such species could first be domesticated in the habitat of their wild ancestors (Braidwood 1958). There were at least two independent hearths of domestication (in the Old and New World) and probably three, specifically (*a*) Mesoamerica and the Andean Highlands, (*b*) the Near East, particularly the hill country of south-western Asia, and (*c*) southeastern Asia, probably along the margins of the Bay of Bengal and in Burma (Sauer 1952; Gorman 1969). At least the first two hearths had no obvious cultural intercommunications; in the case of areas (b) and (c), one in a subhumid winter rainfall belt, the other in the humid tropics, techniques and cultural backgrounds are so different that any *initial* contact would be rather difficult to establish. Lastly there *may* be minor hearths of domestication in which single species were first domesticated

---

[1] C[14] dates 8910±300 B.C. and 8640±300 B.C., W-681, W-667 (Solecki and Rubin, 1958).

before an agricultural economy had been introduced from without. North China (Watson 1969), Ethiopia, and West Africa (Alexander, Coursey 1969) provide possibilities of this kind.

The Near Eastern hearth region provided the biological materials, intellectual achievements, and cultural associations that underlie the civilizations of western Asia, northern Africa, and Europe. The basic biological inventory includes seed plants (cereals) and herd (as opposed to household) animals. More specifically, the food-producing cultures of these areas have from the very beginning depended primarily on the cultivation of wheat and barley for subsistence (Helbaek 1959).

THE NATURAL HABITAT OF THE CEREALS

According to Helbaek (1959) the locus of domestication of a wild plant would presumably be within its area of original distribution in the wild state. Consequently, a prehistoric group dependent upon wild wheat as its main food should have developed its subsistence pattern within the original area of natural distribution of that species. The same should apply to a culture primarily dependent upon barley.

The wild ancestor of domesticated barley (*Hordeum spontaneum*) is now distributed across the Near East and in several parts of southern Europe and northern Africa.[2] On the other hand the two wild wheats, from which all domestic wheats have been derived directly or by complex hybridization, are more restricted in range. The large-grained *Triticum dicoccoides,* direct ancestor of emmer wheat (*T. dicoccum*), has its natural distribution in the Zagros Mountains of Iraq and Iran, the Taurus of southeastern Turkey, and much of the Levant. The wild small-grained *T. aegilopoides,* straight-line ancestor of einkorn (*T. monococcum*), occurs through much of Turkey and the Zagros (Harlan, Zohary 1966). If one can assume that the distribution of wild wheat and barley was 12,000 years ago as it is today,[3] it would seem that the cradle

---

[2] Harlan and Zohary (1966) feel that the wild barley of northern Iran and Afghanistan on the one hand and of Cyrenaica and the Aegean area on the other have spread as a result of the disturbances of agricultural settlement.

[3] Different climatic conditions during the terminal Würm may have modified the natural distribution, while man may since have eradicated the wild species in some areas. Barley, in particular, is cold-sensitive (Harlan, Zohary 1966).

of the "western" plant husbandry cultures lies in the winter rainfall zone of the Near East (Helbaek 1959).

Helbaek (1959) considers that cereal domestication proceeded in several stages. The first essential change from reaping of wild cereals to planting may have included concentration of the desired plant by sowing, improvement of growth by tilling, exclusion or removal of unwanted plants from the tilled plot, and protection of the crop against animals and birds.

Another major step was to select particular types of grain and thus begin the process of selection, specialization, and ultimately adaptation to peculiar environments outside of the limited natural range of distribution. In the case of wheat it meant moving down the domesticant to (a) the plains or, later on, into the artificial ecology of the irrigated flood plains, and (b) into more northerly zones or higher altitudes (Helbaek 1960b; Flannery 1965).

The last major step was the hybridization of the wheats into more advanced, specialized types such as club wheat, bread wheat, spelt, and naked wheat and the apparent evolution of barley into another, six-rowed type (Helbaek 1966a).

Besides conscious "primary" domestication, Helbaek distinguishes a "secondary" domestication, namely the segregation, for intentional cultivation, of a weed growing in cultivated soil which already unintentionally was subjected to selection through being reaped along with the intended crop. Either wheat or barley was probably so introduced, and rye and oats are typical examples. Both of the latter were introduced as weeds in wheat fields, rye from west-central Asia and oats from the Near East or eastern Europe. Both "appear" very late in the archeological record and were probably never primarily planted anywhere but in cooler latitudes where they proved to be particularly hardy plants. They play no role whatever in the Near East.

Regarding other plants, the various millets have an obscure history (Von Wissmann 1957). These are summer rainfall plants, so it is unlikely that they were first cultivated in the Near East with its Mediterranean-type climate. Of further note is the wild flax plant, *Linum bienne,* used for fiber and oil, which has the same habitat and cultural context as wheat and barley. Together with starchy vegetables of Near Eastern origin, the wine grape, olive, date, fig, apple, pear, cherry, etc., also seem to originate somewhere in the Near East. In overview, winter-rainfall *cereal cultiva-*

tion, orchard husbandry, and viticulture are characteristic of early plant domestication in the Near Eastern hearth (Helbaek 1959, 1960a).

THE NATURAL HABITAT OF THE HERD ANIMALS OF THE NEAR EAST

Present knowledge on the locus of first domestication of the herd animals is far less satisfactory than that of the "western" cereals. The former range of the wild ancestors is usually extensive; the wild progenitor(s) is frequently a matter of strong controversy, often due to rather muddled taxonomic situations; and the archeologic-osteologic material is far less complete. The most up-to-date surveys of the problem have been made by Zeuner (1963), Reed (1960; 1969), and Higgs and Jarman (1969).

The dog (*Canis familiaris*) is generally considered to be descended from the wolf, although later interbreeding with jackals may have taken place in the semiarid subtropics. The natural habitat of the wolf includes the greater part of the forest zone of Eurasia and North America. As the domestication of the dog took place rather early among European Mesolithic groups during the Pre-boreal or Boreal, the dog has no necessary association with agriculturists. There is, however, evidence of domesticated dogs in the Near East by 7000 B.C. (Reed 1969).

The goat (*Capra hircus*) is most generally thought to be descended from the bezoar goat (*C. aegagrus*), ranging from Palestine to the Caucasus, from Greece to the Indus. Fossil bezoar goats are also known from the late Pleistocene of the Levant. The actual habitat of the wild goat is somewhat more limited as a result of the ecological niche to which the goat is adapted, i.e., rough ground with rocky slopes which enable this agile climber to escape possible predators.

The sheep (*O. aries*) is probably mainly descended from the urial (*O. orientalis*), although other species of wild sheep may have contributed to certain breeds of domesticated sheep. The urial occurs in northern Iran, Afghanistan, northwestern India, and adjacent parts of Central Asia. Another possible wild ancestor, the eastern mouflon (*O. musimon* ssp.) inhabited Anatolia, Caucasia, and western Iran. Yet another, the argali (*O. ammon*), is found in Central Asia. Sheep are adapted to open, rolling country, avoiding open plains or dense forest.

Cattle (*Bos taurus*) are in all probability descended from the large, long-horned, wild *B. primigenius,* or aurochs, once distributed throughout the forested regions of Europe, southwestern Asia, and northern Africa. A short-horned species called *B. longifrons* or *B. brachyceros* has been postulated, but these animals were probably females of *B. primigenius.* Wild cattle favored woodland or forest as a habitat.

Originally there were several subspecies of wild pig (*Sus scrofa*) native to the woodlands of Eurasia and North Africa. The European domesticated pigs are essentially descendants of the wild boar (*S. scrofa scrofa*), and the Chinese ones of the banded pig (*S. vittatus*) native to southeastern Asia.

Domestication of horse, reindeer, and camel came relatively late and played no role in the original transition to food production, so that these genera are of peripheral interest in this discussion.

The natural habitats of the western Asiatic herd animals in a broad way overlap with the native distribution of the wild wheats and barley in the Near Eastern highlands. The range of the wild ancestors of the herd animals is very much greater than that of the wild wheats and barley however. Although the boar, aurochs, and possibly also barley were native to the alluvial flood plains of Mesopotamia and Egypt, sheep, goat, and wild wheats were absent. The Syrian, Iranian, and Central Asian deserts fall outside of this natural habitat zone.

THE NATURAL HABITAT ZONE

If there was sound reason to believe that cereal domestication preceded animal domestication, the Near Eastern hearth of agricultural origins could be more or less localized into a zone of preference —the Near Eastern highlands, and possibly a more peripheral zone, the alluvial flood plains of the Nile and Tigris-Euphrates. So far archeological evidence of animal domestication predates the earliest proven domesticated grains by as much as two millennia. It is only as a matter of convenience that the zone of overlap of the wild cereals and wild herd animals is emphasized here, even though the available archeological evidence suggests that the evidence may not be fortuitous.

A brief examination of the physical geography of the modern natural habitat of the wild wheats can be rather informative. The areas involved are characterized by irregular and diversified terrain and a minimum annual precipitation of 300–500 mm., and they coincide with the subtropical Mediterranean-type woodlands of the Fertile Crescent and the temperate forests of Anatolia (Fig. 1). Significant is the exclusion of this particular habitat from the steppe or semi-desert areas. Equally interesting is the location of known agricultural communities predating *ca.* 5000 B.C. These were all found within or at the peripheries of the woodland belt.

The alluvial valleys enjoy somewhat different environmental conditions. Apart from the peculiar terrain features of flood plains, neither the lower Nile Valley nor the Tigris-Euphrates lowlands have sufficient rainfall for non-irrigated agriculture. But crops could be planted as the annual floods receded (October in Egypt, June in Mesopotamia), and the moisture retained in the soil would normally be sufficient to bring one crop to maturity. The ecologic patterns of these alluvial flood plains were generally quite distinct from those of the highlands, even though a winter growing season would be common both to Egypt and the wooded hill country.

The geographical traits and subsistence economy of the earliest known Near Eastern farming communities speak for agricultural origins in the winter rainfall belt. This region corresponds closely to that ideal physical environment envisaged for first agriculture by C. O. Sauer (1952). From a different premise, Sauer argued that agriculture began in wooded lands rather than in grasslands with deep and continuous sod. This argument is based on the difficulty of cultivating heavy sod with primeval agricultural tools. Rather, a varied, open woodland could be more easily cleared by deadening the trees, so providing open spaces with looser topsoil for easy sowing. Dense forests were also inimical to primitive hoe agriculture. Sauer (1952:5–6) emphasizes that diversity of terrain is optimal in providing numerous ecologic niches—"a land of hills and valleys, of streams and springs, with alluvial reaches and rock shelters in cliffs." For it is here that the greatest diversity of plants and animals and suitable genetic reservoirs are to be found.

POSSIBLE ENVIRONMENTAL CHANGES IN THE NEAR EASTERN AREA AT THE CLOSE OF THE PLEISTOCENE

Climatic conditions in western Asia during the late Pleistocene have been discussed by Butzer (1970). Any specific changes that

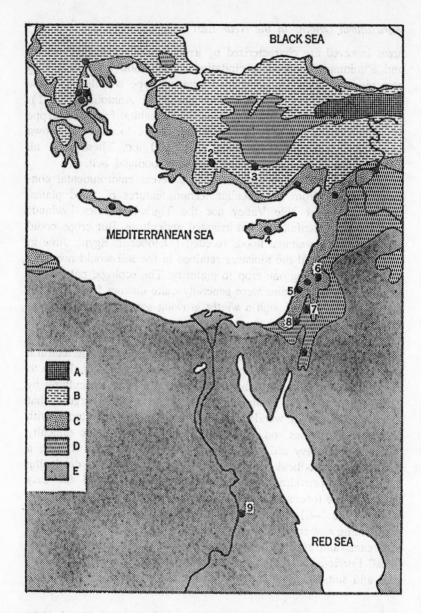

FIGURE 1 Natural postglacial vegetation of the Near East and location of early agricultural and proto-agricultural sites (*ca.* 9000–5750 B.C.). A, coniferous forests; B, deciduous and mixed forests; C, subtropical woodlands; D, grassland, E, desert-grassland, semidesert and desert. The galeria woodlands of the major rivers are not shown. Sites: 1, Sesklo; 2, Haçilar; 3, Çatal Hüyük; 4, Khirokitia; 5, Mount Carmel

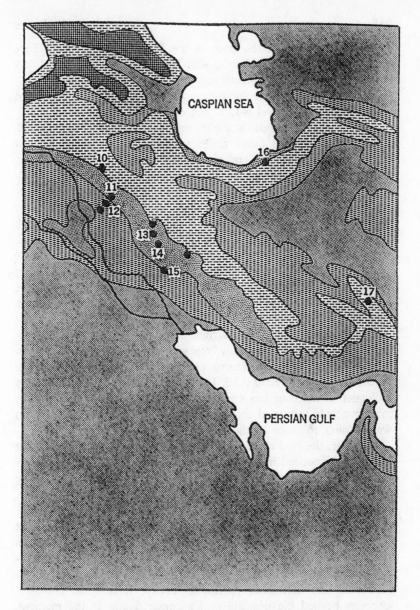

caves; 6, Ain Mallaha; 7, Jericho; 8 Judean Desert Caves; 9, Gebel
Silsila and Sebil; 10, Shanidar and Zawi Chemi; 11, Karim Shahir;
12, Jarmo; 13, Asiab; 14, Sarab; 15, Ali Kosh; 16, Hotu Cave;
17, Kerman. Only sites mentioned in text are labelled. (Note: new sites
have been added to map at points indicated by unnumbered circles.
Original map taken from 1964 edition.)

may have occurred at the close of the Pleistocene appear to have been confined to the highlands, with little evidence for ecologically significant change in the more mesic low country.

The fauna of the Mesolithic-type Zarzian culture of Iraq, dated 12,400±400 B.P. (W-179), is not considered indicative of a different climate than today's according to Braidwood, Howe *et al.* (1960:167–70). The fauna at Palegawra (965 m. elevation) includes gazelle, wild goat and sheep, wild cattle, red and roe deer, boar, onager (?), red fox, wolf, lynx (?) and a hedgehog (Braidwood, Howe *et al.* 1960:58–59), while the fauna of the corresponding Shanidar level B-2 (730 m. elevation) is dominated by wild goat (60 per cent) and red deer (20 per cent), together with bear, wild sheep, and boar (Perkins 1964). Pollen studies from Lake Zeribar, near Marivan (1300 m.) in the Zagros, indicate a change from almost 100 per cent NAP to about 15 per cent oak *ca.* 10,000 B.C. Oak then increases in an irregular fashion, while Chenopodiaceae decrease from 70 to 50 per cent, with Artemisia fluctuating around 10 per cent (Zeist 1967). An open, oak parkland is postulated (Wright *et al.* 1967). Northern microfaunal elements are gradually replaced by southern ones, documenting a rise in temperatures (Megard 1967). The late Upper Paleolithic fauna of Ksar Akil, Lebanon (Hooijer 1961), is equally indicative of more or less contemporary conditions. From this, one must conclude that local ecological conditions during the late Würm were similar to those of the present.

However, the cold relapse of the Younger Dryas possibly did not pass quite unnoticed in this part of the world. *Éboulis secs* horizons are found in contemporary horizons of Ksar Akil, Lebanon (Ewing 1951) and the Haua Fteah cave, Cyrenaica (McBurney 1967), offer possible suggestions but no proof for a cooler and moister climate at the close of the Pleistocene. Similarly there is evidence for recessional stages of the Würm glaciers of the Caucasus, eastern Anatolia, and northwestern Iran, some of which have been compared with the final Würm oscillations of the Alpine glaciers (see references and discussion in Butzer 1970). It is quite probable, although beyond the possibility of accurate dating at the moment, that a small glacial readvance occurred in the highlands at this time. Seen in this perspective it would, therefore, be unjustified to say that ecologic conditions were truly "modern" prior to *ca.* 8000 B.C.

Although the rather modest temperature changes suggested for the Younger Dryas cannot have been significant for human habitation, a possible depression of 1° to 3° C. would have had an effect on the distribution of the wild cereals. Wild wheats are now found to over 2000 m. in southeastern Turkey and Iran, while wild barley is rarely found above 1500 m. (Harlan, Zohary 1966; Helbaek 1959). Colder late glacial climates may therefore have excluded these species from parts of the Near Eastern highlands during the late Würm.

Locally, in Palestine and the Sinai, conditions may have been somewhat moister during a part or all of the Natufian period (*ca.* 9000–7000 B.C.). The gazelle, a characteristic open-country biotype, is comparatively infrequent at this level in the Mt. Carmel caves of Palestine, and a half dozen species of this genus disappeared at the time (Bate 1940). Complementing the faunal record is archeological evidence of fishing in the dry wadis of the arid south Judean highlands. This suggests permanent pools of water available throughout the year. The presence of hunting populations in the Negeb and Sinai deserts, as indicated by plentiful distribution of Natufian flints, also seems relevant. Corroboration is provided by contemporary spring deposits and alluvia in the Jordan Valley (Picard 1963; Vita-Finzi 1969; Nir, Ben-Arieh 1965). And in Egypt there is good evidence of local wadi alluviation during the terminal late Pleistocene (Butzer, Hansen 1968). These seem to be the available indications of greater moisture during the last millennium or so of the Pleistocene. The evidence appears to be limited to the lowland areas peripheral to the subtropical deserts. Such a "moist spell" probably did not have ecological significance in the mesic woodlands or cool high country.

ARCHEOLOGICAL EVIDENCE OF EARLY AGRICULTURE AND LIVESTOCK RAISING

In reviewing the archeological record it is often difficult to determine whether a particular community practiced food production or whether agriculture and livestock herding were entirely unknown. Smolla (1960) has devoted considerable attention to this problem of archeological evidence for early agriculture and animal domestication.

The stone artifacts commonly associated with agricultural operations are not unequivocal.

Sickle blades, consisting of rectangular flint blades, were designed to be mounted into a wooden or bone haft. Such bone hafts have been found on numerous occasions. However the sickles need not have been used to reap cereal crops, but may just as well have been employed on certain wild grasses or on reeds used for matting and hut construction. The sheen or luster frequently developed on such blades may be a silicon deposit derived from straw or grasses (Smolla 1960:109 ff., with references). Since wild cereals "shatter" upon touch, it is questionable whether sickle reaping would be possible at all. In fact the ethnological record shows that the simplest primitive reaping of wild cereals is performed by plucking the ears or by beating the plants and catching the grain or seeds in a basket (Smolla 1960:110). Sickle harvesting in the unripe state would not produce sickle sheen, while the seeds may not be reproductive.

Mortars, consisting of hollowed stone vessels, and querns or pestles used as handstones, are pre-eminently effective as grinding stones for grain or seed crushing to make flour. However *some* Natufian mortars were used to grind pigment (Garrod 1958), while mortars and pestles are sometimes used for meat grinding today (L. Binford, R. J. Braidwood, personal communication), and could also be employed for grinding acorns, wild grains, or bone grease.

Stone celts, resembling polished axes or hoes, may have been used as axes or hoes. There are, however, no good ethnological parallels for stone hoes (Smolla 1960:53).

All in all, the so-called agricultural tools are difficult to interpret, although when found in association and in large numbers they strongly suggest the intensive use and preparation of vegetable foods and probably of domesticated crops. Unfortunately there is no archeological record of more meaningful items such as digging sticks.

Botanical evidence of plant domestication can be recognized, but many of the morphological changes resulting from domestication take place very slowly. Theoretically, a single mutation will produce a "non-shattering" grain, so that selection of "non-shattering" mutants could rapidly produce a new domesticated stock with new morphological characteristics (J. D. Sauer, personal communication).

Osteological evidence for earliest domestication would be difficult or impossible to demonstrate by bone anatomy alone. An interesting example of circumventing this problem has been made by Perkins (1964) at Zawi Chemi Shanidar, the site of the earliest evidence of animal domestication to date. Here the faunal compositions of the Middle and Upper Paleolithic strata were quite uniform with wild goat outnumbering wild sheep by 3 to 1, and constituting about 60 per cent of the fauna. About 25 per cent of the animals were juveniles under a year of age. Suddenly, in the Zawi Chemi horizon, sheep bones jumped to 75 per cent, of which 60 per cent were immature. Goat dropped down to 10 per cent, still with 25 per cent juveniles. It is concluded that the sheep must have been domesticated at this stage, and that the larger part of each year's young was killed for food and skins before the end of the year. The hunting of wild goats had consequently become relatively unimportant.

As a result of these difficulties in accurate assessment of the archeological record, the absence of evidently domesticated cereals or animals from many sites need not prove that agriculture was unknown. Equally so, the presence of so-called agricultural implements does not necessarily prove knowledge of crop planting.

THE NEAR EASTERN ARCHEOLOGICAL RECORD PERTAINING TO EARLY AGRICULTURE

The Near Eastern tool inventory of various Upper Paleolithic cultures, culminating with the Kebaran assemblage in Palestine, the Nebekian in Syria, and the Zarzian in northeastern Iraq (Howell 1959; Hole, Flannery 1967), is broadly comparable with the European counterparts, although showing early microlithic traits. Settlement was largely concentrated in caves, although some Zarzian open-air sites have been tentatively identified (Braidwood, Howe *et al*. 1960:155–57). The only contemporary cultural group that falls out of this framework is the Sebilian complex of the Egyptian Nile Valley. The Sebilian groups are of particular interest since they were semisedentary, occupying campsites on the banks of the Nile, where they intensively used the aquatic and riverine food resources of their localized environment (Butzer, Hansen 1968:Chapter 4). Modest kitchen middens on the Kom Ombo area of Upper Egypt testify to considerable use of fresh-water molluscs, fish, and, more rarely, turtle and crocodile; in addition, a wide range of woodland and steppe mammals was hunted. Grinding stones are already present, often in great numbers. Geologically, the Sebilian and other contemporary industries in the Kom Ombo area have been dated *ca.* 15,000–10,500 B.C. (Butzer, Hansen 1968), i.e., no later in time than the Kebaran or Zarzian.[4]

Rather abruptly, archeological indications of agriculture appear in the Levant and Iraq *ca.* 9000 B.C., suggesting a very early diffusion of agriculture in the Near Eastern highlands. Sickle blades and pounding and milling stones appear more or less simultaneously in both the Natufian assemblage of Palestine, Lebanon, and Syria (Garrod 1958) and the Karim Shahirian of Iraqi Kurdistan (Braidwood, Howe *et al.* 1960). The contemporary Asiab assemblage of northwestern Iran (Braidwood, Howe, Reed 1961) does not yet appear to have sickles, grinding stones, or celts. An analogous culture with microliths, sickle blades, and grinding stones has also been discovered at Kerman, in southeastern Iran (Hückriede 1962). No evidence of cereals is available yet from either the Natufian or Karim Shahirian, but it is very probable that plant domestication was at least well under way. Domesticated sheep are present in the Karim Shahirian. These two cultures, which possibly extend through most of the ninth and eighth millennia precede a bona fide agricultural economy, certainly established in parts of western Asia by 7000 B.C. Both assemblages are essentially found within the natural habitats of wild wheat, barley, sheep, and goat. This may be the elusive stage of "incipient agriculture and animal domestication"—which Braidwood (1960a) describes as experimental manipulation of potential domesticates within a dominant food-collecting economy, at first still within the ecological niche to which the wild ancestor of the domesticate was adapted. However, successful adaptation to the lowland steppes began very early, as is shown by the Bus Mordeh assemblage of Ali Kosh in the Khuzistan foothills (Hole, Flannery 1967). Emmer and barley were cultivated and both goats and sheep were kept.

By 7000 B.C. agriculture had become the primary subsistence of village farmers found in the Levant, the Zagros area, and southwestern Anatolia. These people grew einkorn, emmer, and barley,

[4] A full ecological interpretation of the Sebilian complex will contribute to understanding agricultural origins in the Near East. However, this will only be possible after detailed publication of the archeological results by P. E. L. Smith and M. A. Baumhoff.

and kept domesticated goats and sheep. The domesticated pig also appears in the archeological context somewhere in the seventh millennium in the pottery levels of Jarmo, northeastern Iraq. For the sixth millennium village-farming communities are varied in Thessaly (Renfrew 1969), Crete (Higgs, Jarman 1969), Cyprus (Dikaios 1953), Anatolia (Mellaart 1965; Renfrew 1969; Reed 1969), a good range of sites in the Levant, northern Iraq, and adjacent parts of Iran as well as in the Belt Cave on the Caspian shores of Iran (Ralph 1955).

The regional appearance of the various achievements of cultural innovation and evolution in the Near East is summarized in Table 1. The major expansion of food-producing populations of the Neolithic level into the cooler environments of temperate Europe and into the different environment of the Tigris-Euphrates and Nile flood plains appears to postdate 5000 B.C.

THE ECOLOGY OF THE NATUFIAN IN PALESTINE

Remains of the Natufian cultural assemblage, dating from approximately 9500–7000 B.C., are widely distributed in the southern Levant.[5]

One of the best published and culturally important sites of the Natufian is found in the Mugharet el-Wad cave of Mt. Carmel, at base of the cave is 12.5 m. above the wadi floor, and extends for some 85 m. with an average height of 10 m. The Natufian strata underlie 0.3–1.2 m. of a consolidated brown earth and limestone rubble with early Bronze Age and later remains. About 0.2–3.0 m. thick, these beds consist of unconsolidated, stony red earth with an elevation of 45 m. on the southern face of a small wadi.[6] The

---

[5] Sites have been found in the Jabrud cave of Syria (Rust 1950), at Beirut, in three caves of the Mt. Carmel area of Palestine (Garrod, Bate 1937; Garrod 1958), at the base of Jericho (Kenyon 1959a), at Ain Mallaha near Lake Huleh (Perrot 1957, 1962, 1966), as well as in a number of caves in the wadis of the Judean hills, both northwest and southeast of Jerusalem (Neuville 1951). Surface finds have been made east of the Jordan River, in the Negeb and Sinai deserts, and at el-Omari and Helwan, near Cairo.

[6] The present-day climate has a January mean temperature of 13° C., a July mean of 27° C., and an annual precipitation of 625 mm. falling almost exclusively during the three winter months. The natural vegetation of the area is Mediterranean woodland.

TABLE 1 Archeological Evidence of Early Cereal Cultivation
and Animal Herding in the Near East

(Based on Hole, Flannery, 1967; Mellaart, 1965; Reed, 1959, 1961, 1969; Renfrew, 1969; and others)

SITES AND STRATIGRAPHY	APPROXIMATE DATES B.C.	BARLEY	EINKORN	EMMER	BREAD WHEAT	SHEEP	GOAT	CATTLE	PIG	DOG
Aegean Area										
Argissa (Thessaly), Aceramic	6500	X	X	X		X	X	X	X	?
Nea Nikomedeia (Macedonia)	6200	X	X	X		X	X	X	X	?
Knossos (Crete), stratum X	6100	X			X					
Khirokitia (Cyprus), Aceramic	6000					X	X			
Sesklo (Thessaly), Aceramic	6000–5000	X		X						
Ghediki (Thessaly), Aceramic	6000–5000	X	X	X						
Anatolia										
Haçilar, Aceramic	7000			X						?
Haçilar, Ceramic	5800–5000	X	X	X	X					?
Çayönü	7000					X			X	X
Çatal Hüyük, VI–II	7000	X	X	X	X	X		?	X	X
Levant										
Tell Ramad (Syria)	7000	X	X	X	X					
Jericho, Prepottery Neol. A	7000–6500	X		X						
Jericho, Prepottery Neol. B	6500–5500		X	X						
Beidha (Jordan), Prepottery	5850–5600	X		X						

Amouq (Antioch), A.	5750
Mesopotamia-Khuzistan	
Ali Kosh, Bus Mordeh	7500–6750
Ali Kosh, Ali Kosh	6750–6000
Ali Kosh, M. Jaffar	6000–5600
Tepe Sabz, Sabz	5500–5000
Tell es-Sawwan (Samarra)	5800–5600
Hassuna	5800
Kurdistan-Luristan	
Zawi Chemi, Karim Shahir	8900
Jarmo	6750–6500
Tepe Sarab	? 6500
Tepe Guran	6200–5500
Matarrah	5800

limestone talus in the sections located in front of the cave entrance. The underlying deposits of the interior cave contain Upper and Middle Paleolithic industries. Interpretive geomorphological work has not yet been carried out, so that the implications of the beds are obscure.

In the further absence of known botanical remains, the rich faunal collection of the Mugharet el-Wad is ecologically important. It includes rodents and insectivores with two species of hedgehog, mole rat (*Spalax*), a vole, squirrel, hare, the gerbil, and hyrax (*Procavia*). Spotted hyena, red fox, wolf (not dog, Clutton-Brock 1963), badger, marten, musteline, the Syrian bear (?), wildcat, and leopard number among the carnivores, while the bulk of the animals represented is composed of various ungulates: fallow deer (*Dama mesopotamica*), gazelle, wild goat, wild cattle, onager, and boar. Ecologically these species are partly woodland, partly open country, and partly even desert or cliff forms (the gerbil and hyrax). They corroborate the local situation of wooded upland to the northeast and perennial streams or ponds with fringing forests and widespread open country on the Pleistocene dunes of the coastal plain to the south. They also show that diversified hunting played an important role in the Natufian economy.

The cave floor included a mass of flint implements, waste materials, broken and occasionally charred animal bones, burials, and some crude stonework, possibly associated with the interments. Although architecture is lacking at this site, house foundations have been uncovered at Ain Mallaha (Perrot 1966). Some thirty-nine burials have been found, the dentition of which shows excessive wear and a very high frequency of abscesses of the premolars. Dahlberg (1960 and personal communication) believes this indicates a gritty diet, probably with a dominance of cereals or other coarse vegetable foods.

The technological inventory contains, in part, a number of implements common to the Upper Paleolithic: backed blades, burins, massive scrapers, rough picks, together with naturalistic carving in bone and stone. Great numbers of microliths, and at certain other sites also bone spear points, harpoons, fishhooks, pins, needles, and awls recall certain Mesolithic innovations. Novel for the Natufian in general, however, are lustrous sickle blades (saw-toothed varieties appearing in the Upper Natufian), some blades with bone hafts, as well as celts, mortars, and pestles. Flint arrowheads figure among the few innovations of the Upper Natufian. However the total assemblage shows a distinct shift of relative proportions between a dominance of Paleolithic artifacts in the Lower, of more characteristically Neolithic artifacts in the Upper, Natufian.

The Natufian culture represents one of the most interesting transitional assemblages of the Near East. Partly dated at 8840 B.C. (GL-70, Zeuner 1963:31; see also Mellaart 1965; Kenyon 1959a) from the Middle Natufian underlying Jericho, the populations in question were at least semisedentary judging by cave occupancy or house habitation in the open. Intensive exploitation of the different ecologic niches of the natural environment is a well-established characteristic, recalling both the earlier, Middle Sebilian, and the later European Mesolithic. Simultaneously, cereal agriculture was very probably known, judging by the abundant presence of all so-called agricultural implements and the dietary value of gritty foods as suggested by the dentition. Unfortunately no plant foods have been found so far, and the suggested domestication of pig, goat, and cattle at one of the Judean cave sites is unverified (Reed 1959). But the beginnings of plant and animal domestication must be conceived of at a stage and in a setting such as that of the Natufian or the broadly contemporary Karim Shahirian of Iraq.

ECOLOGY OF A VILLAGE-FARMING COMMUNITY: JARMO, NORTHEASTERN IRAQ

The townsite of prehistoric Jarmo is located on a bluff at some 770 m. above sea level in the rolling hill country of the Kurdish foothills of northeastern Iraq.[7] The village appears to have been occupied more or less continuously for about a quarter of a millennium shortly after 7000 B.C., judging by a wide scatter of radiocarbon dates (Braidwood, Howe *et al.* 1960; see also the ecological synthesis of Braidwood, Reed 1957).

The irregular terrain is a consequence of dissection of late Pleistocene silts by steep-sided stream valleys and gullies. An intermittent stream, probably perennial before the destruction of the natural vegetation, has partially destroyed the western end of the site by

---

[7] By extrapolation from other climatic stations in the area the January mean temperature is about 6.5° C., the July mean 29° C., the annual precipitation about 630 mm., falling predominantly in winter. The natural vegetation is that of a Mediterranean woodland.

undercutting. During the period of settlement (Wright 1952), the site was located at about 36 m. above this stream bed, which probably formed the major water supply of the village.

Botanical remains at Jarmo include both domesticated and wild emmer and einkorn wheat, domesticated two-row barley as well as acorns, pistachio nuts, lentils, the field pea, and blue vetchling.

Faunal materials include the remains of domesticated goat and pig (the latter in the upper strata of the site only, Reed 1961), as well as a fair number of wild animals representing the hunting booty of the community. Species listed are red fox, wolf, gazelle, wild cattle, red and roe deer, wild sheep, boar, and onager (?).[8] Great masses of terrestrial snails (*Helix salomonica*) are present together with some fresh-water crabs and fish. The faunal selection suggests a woodland environment with some areas of open plain or rough country.

The village covered a total area of about 12,500 sq. m., and the cultural materials attain about 7 m. in depth. A good third of this area was never occupied by houses, and a total of 25 houses is estimated as the maximum size of Jarmo. This includes a guess on how much of the site has been destroyed by gullying. Each house presumably represented a family unit. Assuming a family-household size of 5 to 7 people, 25 houses would indicate a population of 125 to 175 people. The lower figure is probably closer to the truth. This is, incidentally, the average size of villages in the area today.

The architecture itself, although well-defined, was not pretentious. Sun-dried mud was employed, being laid in successive 10 to 15 cm. tiers often set on foundations of unmortared stone. The resulting mud-walled house had several rectangular rooms and was not unlike the local houses of today. The village had no regular plan, and consisted of simple houses, animal shelters, and storage buildings, without evidence of community buildings or social structure.

The technological inventory of Jarmo contains various flint implements, among which great quantities of sickle blades and microliths made of a glassy volcanic rock, obsidian, are of most interest. The obsidian was quarried some 500 km. to the north in the Lake Van area, indicating commercial contacts. Together with the celts are various grinding stones and bowls. Pottery only appears in the upper third of the settlement strata. Other items include bone needles,

---

[8] Statistical analyses were apparently not carried out.

awls and the like, as well as evidence of reed matting. The technology is then a complex of domestic, of hunting, and of agricultural equipment. The dentitions of seven skeletons show signs of only moderate wear (Dahlberg 1960), implying a less coarse diet than was common for the Natufian population. This probably points toward better preparation of vegetable foods, and possibly also to a fair proportion of meat in the dietary economy.

All in all, the farmers of the village of Jarmo appear to have established a well-balanced economy which, even at the stage of primitive subsistence agriculture, insured adequate local food resources for permanent habitation over two centuries. The absence of the plow, or for that matter plow animals, means that some form of hoe agriculture was practiced. Although cereals dominated in the sown fields, a number of vegetable crops may also have been grown. Domesticated animals, apparently present in good numbers after the local introduction of the pig, supplied a dependable and possibly appreciable meat fraction to the diet. Hunting was still an important economic trait, while gathering of wild plant and animal foods is substantiated by finds of acorns, pistachio nuts, and snails. Jarmo is indeed the prototype of agricultural villages which already dotted the moister hill country of the Near East by the close of the seventh millennium. The origins of the cultural landscape and the expression of man-land relationships at the food-producing level will be considered in the subsequent chapters.

THE DESICCATION THEORY OF AGRICULTURAL ORIGINS

Although the cultural and intellectual processes basic to the economic transition from food-collecting to food-producing are of no direct concern to the natural scientist, the abundant environmentalist theories on that topic certainly are. These theories are based on the belief that late glacial or early Holocene desiccation affected wide areas of the subtropics that had enjoyed pluvial conditions earlier during the Pleistocene. As a result, the former hunting populations of the deserts of northern Africa, Arabia, Iran, India, and Central Asia were allegedly expelled or forced to concentrate along sources of permanent water at springs or along permanent streams.

The oldest of these hypotheses can be associated with R. Pumpelly (1908:65–66), who excavated at the Neolithic site of Anau, southern Turkmenistan:

With the gradual shrinking in dimensions of habitable areas and the disappearance of herds of wild animals, man, concentrating on the oases and forced to conquer new means of support, began to utilize the native plants; and from among these he learned to use seeds of different grasses growing on the dry land and in marshes at the mouths of larger streams on the desert. With the increase of population and its necessities, he learned to plant the seeds, thus making, by conscious or unconscious selection, the first step in the evolution of the whole series of cereals.

In the same sense Peake and Fleure (1927:14) write:

. . . men naturally turned their attention back to the old habit of collecting food as their hunting became less successful. In certain regions however, men were led towards a new idea; it occurred to them to produce food by the cultivation of edible plants.

Or as Childe (1929:42) describes the same process in more detail:

Enforced concentration in oases or by the banks of ever more pre- carious springs and streams would require an intensified search for means of nourishment. Animals and man would be herded together round pools and wadis that were growing increasingly isolated by desert tracts and such enforced juxtaposition might almost of itself promote that sort of symbiosis between man and beast signified in the word domestication.

For Childe, the resulting "emancipation from dependence on the whims of the environment" (1929:46) was *the* impetus for the economic revolution ("Neolithic revolution") heralded by the in- vention of food-production. Toynbee (1935:Vol. I, pp. 304–5) adopted the same economic revolution and the same impetus as the "physical challenge" at the root of ancient Egyptian and Meso- potamian civilization, as well as for the origin of nomadic pastoralism (Toynbee 1935:Vol. III, pp. 10–12). Similar ideas persist in more recent revisions of both Childe and Toynbee.

There is no doubt today that the simple patterns envisaged by the theories of Pumpelly, Peake and Fleure, Childe, and Toynbee are archeologically not tenable, since the food-producing revolution does not seem to have taken place in the deserts. In the hill country of western Asia, where the decisive steps of local agricul- tural invention were probably undertaken, the desiccation theory loses all meaning. These are well-watered regions where pluvial-in- terpluvial oscillations would not seriously reduce wild game resources. The native vegetation of the Near Eastern highlands is a subtropical or warm-temperate woodland under modern climatic conditions.

Streams from the higher country provide abundant, perennial waters or at least did so before the catastrophic impact of deforestation and soil erosion in historical times. Even if rainfall changes had occurred, they would only have carried limited ecological implications in an area of varied topography and with numerous local ecological niches. Instead, temperature changes may have had greater importance, particularly, in late glacial times when the cold highlands once more became habitable. Such changes would therefore have enlarged the area of suitable lands at about the time of agricultural origins.

In conclusion, the previous review of paleoclimatic information does not suggest any incisive changes in the late glacial and early Holocene record of western Asia, and the climatic changes that did take place certainly did not follow a simple pattern of progressive desiccation. It seems unlikely that the cultural innovation of the Near Eastern hearth of domestication was associated with any dramatic ecological changes at the close of the Pleistocene. Instead, a bountiful natural environment with a fortuitous assembly of suitable domesticates presumably favored the geographic location of the Near Eastern hearth.

POSTSCRIPT 1969

It is becoming apparent that the concept of a Near Eastern "nuclear area" requires modification. During the late 1940's and early 1950's, the literature dealing with agricultural origins in the Old World was highly speculative. Little factual material was available and wide-ranging hypotheses were formulated on the basis of limited evidence. Today, some fifteen years later, the wealth of available archeological and biological data favors a more empirical approach. There is no lack of speculative writing, but serious attempts to interpret the evidence have become unduly restricted. New finds are often categorized within the increasingly rigid framework of a single "nuclear area" and a single cultural-ecological association. In fact, some workers have adopted a new form of environmentalism that obscures the fact that the origin of agriculture is, in the first place, a cultural phenomenon.

The archeological record remains very incomplete, despite the increasing number of excellent sites that span a long range of time, and appear to reflect on different stages in the development of food-producing economies. Anatolia has already brought many surprises, and wider exploration is bound to reveal further evidence that the warm-temperate environments of modern Turkey were far from being a cultural hinterland of the Taurus-Zagros area. The amazing Neolithic sites of Macedonia and Thessaly now show that southeastern Europe was one of the core areas of early agriculture, and studies further afield in Iran and Transcaucasia are bound to extend the concept of a "nuclear area."

Patterns of sedentary or semisedentary settlement—believed by some to be vital for the earliest agricultural innovations—were common in late Pleistocene and early post-Pleistocene times. They must already be inferred for some Acheulian populations, and both the open-air and cave sites of Upper Paleolithic groups in the tundra-steppes of Europe frequently indicate seasonal if not semipermanent occupation of suitable localities. A similar record of semisedentary settlement is suggested for the Sebilians and other groups that were settled along the Nile River as early as 15,000 B.C. Long-term residence at one or several closely adjacent sites may reflect availability and reliability of food sources more clearly than technology. Such prerequisites were present at many times and at many places during the course of the Pleistocene; they were not unique to the Near Eastern "nuclear area" at the close of the Pleistocene.

Given suitable food resources, intensified food collecting provided the basis for large settlements of considerable permanence. Recent excavations have adequately demonstrated this proposition for the Tehuacán Valley in south-central Mexico and for the Tennessee and Wabash valleys in the central United States. At Tehuacán, intensified food collecting permitted a significant increase of population over several millennia, at a time when cultigens provided less than 10 per cent of the food intake. In the case of the eastern woodlands of North America, efficient exploitation of riverine environments permitted large and stable villages for some 3000 years prior to the local adoption of agriculture. The Sebilians and other folk of Egypt and Nubia are another case to point, with some large cemeteries speaking for populations of at least moderate size. Here intensive utilization of a river-oasis remained practical or preferable for ten millennia, until agriculture first penetrated the Nile Valley—presumably with fresh populations—at a surprisingly late date. Much more recently, certain Indian populations of California and the Pacific Northwest provide examples of the same process.

These examples should serve to remind that farming and livestock raising were not the only means of supporting relatively large populations in suitable meso-environments. Situations of this kind were the exception rather than the rule, but they are almost certainly relevant to agricultural origins and diffusions.

The first steps to agriculture marked no sharp break in subsistence patterns or population level among semisedentary groups with an intensive food-collecting economy. When agricultural traits spread and were adapted by preference or necessity, there probably were few discontinuities between the subsistence forms of adjacent agricultural and non-agricultural populations. The strong distinction made between farmers and hunters today reflects western cultural attitudes that have intensified over millennia, reinforced by an increasing technological gap. Initially, however, the convergence of unlike economies would not have been considerable within any one meso-environment. On the other hand, regional specializations must have been conspicuous. Each environment provided an individual set of potential resources that were managed and exploited distinctively, before the introduction of agriculture as well as after. Consequently, the early stages of agricultural innovation must have been marked by strong regional contrasts, reflecting both different resources and traditions. Barring violent conquest or displacement, traditional methods, attitudes, and preferences may have persisted over centuries or millennia, long after the introduction of agricultural traits.

Viewed within this perspective, wheat-and-barley farming can reflect but a part of the spectrum of advanced subsistence patterns in the Near Eastern area before 5000 B.C. One set of questions that can be raised concerns the variable role played by one or more domesticated animals in different areas. Were there food collectors who herded animals? Were there herders who cultivated some grains during part of the year? Did or did not herding precede farming initially—at the very beginning, or locally—in certain areas? Did herding and farming originally have different roots among regionally specialized food collectors or did they spring from a single, regional tradition? Did herding and farming traits diffuse at similar or different rates? In their entirety or selectively? Another group of questions could be formulated about the relative role of legumes and certain other vegetables. Such plants were cultivated in Mexico for almost 3000 years before the first domestication of maize, and grains may also have been preceded by other cultigens such as peas and lentils in the Near East. Our cultural bias has favored an overemphasis of grain farming in the current Near Eastern literature, possibly obscuring the significance of other domesticates.

In retrospect, it appears that archeological research must be directed at a wider range of problems. Present understanding of the "terminal food-collecting stage" in North America shows how much more we need to know about the intensive food-collecting economies of a broader area in northern Africa, southeastern Europe, and western Asia. We have learned little new about the "stage of incipient agriculture" in the Near East during the past decade, despite ongoing excavations. Perhaps there has been too much attention to house structures, burials, and the identification of habitation residues—with only rudimentary analysis of total archeological associations. Only conscious effort will serve to demonstrate dietary and subsistence patterns, and allow inferences on different regional traditions. On presently available evidence, the nuclear area of the Near East must be extended into southeastern Europe, to account for evidence there of advanced, domesticated cattle a millennium earlier than anywhere in western Asia. Future excavations will probably reveal that the "nuclear area" included parts of Transcaucasia and Iran, beyond the Zagros ranges to Turkmenistan.

The basic environmental requisites for the complex of agricultural traditions of the Near Eastern hearth area are fairly simple: a winter growing season with sufficient moisture for dry farming. This submediterranean environment now extends through Anatolia into the Aegean world and certain uplands of the central and western Mediterranean Basin. The essential restricting factor would seem to have been the availability of suitable domesticates. In the case of potential herd animals, the situation is still rather fluid, with few limitations. In fact, it now seems probable that cattle were first domesticated in the Aegean area and possibly also in some part of Africa; the progenitors of sheep and goats remain a puzzle, and the last word has not yet been said on the locus of domestication of the first farmyard pigs. If, indeed, wheat was the original cultigen in the Near East, the locus of first domestication was more restricted. But the abundance of wild wheats in natural habitats may be exaggerated, for wild wheats now thrive in deforested areas made available by human interference in historical times. In undisturbed woodlands wild wheat would hardly be so abundant as to permit a subsistence based primarily on the harvesting of such primitive stands.

In concluding, we make a plea for the primary relevance of cultural traditions in agricultural origins. The Near Eastern-Aegean "nuclear area" must have contributed a number of local subsistence patterns that were ultimately adapted and fused to a hybrid, food-producing economy with exchange and competition between neighboring groups. Just as the subtropical forests of Transcaucasia may have provided orchard trees and the temperate woodlands of Macedonia the domesticated cow, other meso-environments may have contributed not only to the array of cultigens but to other facets such as manipulation, preparation, patterns of complementary cultivation, and, above all, dietary preferences. Hopefully, renewed archeological search will extend beyond the established village farmers to those groups of more diversified food collectors who made the first steps to agriculture possible in the Near East, and who each put their stamp upon the subsistence economy that subsequently diffused through mid-latitude Eurasia.

13 THE EARLIEST VILLAGE COMMUNITIES OF SOUTHWESTERN ASIA RECONSIDERED

Robert J. Braidwood

FOREWORD

IN THE SEVEN YEARS since this paper was written for a prehistoric congress in Rome, new evidence has appeared to change the picture I gave. Were the paper to be rewritten, several points would need reconsideration; a sample of these are indicated in footnotes throughout the text.

In retrospect, it seems likely that this paper will stand as a sort of summary of the original exploratory years of research focus on the appearance of food production in southwestern Asia. Following *ca.* 1962, both the evidence and speculation upon it began to open up in a variety of new directions.

Robert J. Braidwood
July 1969

In 1952, my wife and I finished the manuscript of a paper called "The Earliest Village Communities of Southwestern Asia" (Braidwood, Braidwood 1953). I propose here to attempt to bring our personal understanding and interpretation of the available evidence on the subject up-to-date in summary form, without duplicating the descriptions and bibliography already available in that earlier paper. Already in 1952, we had found the terms "mesolithic" and "neolithic" uncongenial to communicate our understandings of the pertinent culture-historical events in southwestern Asia; we hold the same position if anything more firmly now, and I shall not use these terms. What this paper is concerned with is simply our under-

Reprinted by permission of G. C. Sansoni, editor, *Atti del VI Congresso Internazionale delle Scienze Preistoriche e Protostoriche*, Vol. I, *Relazioni generali*, pp. 115–26, and by permission of the author.

standing of the available evidence as to how the cultural level of effective village-farming communities appeared in southwestern Asia, and the background for it.

ENVIRONMENT

The detailed study of the climatological and environmental history of end-Pleistocene and early post-Pleistocene times in southwestern Asia is only now being undertaken by qualified natural scientists (cf. in Braidwood, Howe, Reed 1961; Braidwood, Howe, Negahban 1960; Helbaek 1959; Reed 1959; Wright and others in Braidwood, Howe *et al.* 1960; Wright 1961a; 1961b). It is becoming reasonably clear, however, that suggestions concerning both the scale of environmental differences from those of the present, and of the marked displacement of life-zones—sometimes offered for the pre- and protohistoric ranges of time in southwestern Asia—have been considerably exaggerated (cf. also Butzer, n.d.). In brief, we have no evidence available at the moment (admittedly in a still incomplete but growing complexity of understandable developments)[1] which demands interpretation in the direction that environmental change *caused* the appearance of plant and animal domestication or *impelled* the rise of effective village-farming communities. It is readily granted that the environments of the natural habitat zone of the potential plant and animal domesticates were necessarily *permissive,* but the achievement of effective food-production resulted from the human cultural manipulation of these potential domesticates. Thus the plant and animal domesticates and the socio-cultural complexity which followed the establishment of an effective village-farming level are to be seen as the artifacts of human activity.

There is also, however, some reason to suspect that the natural habitat zone of the potential domesticates[2]—long the scene of previous and continual occupation by food-collectors, with increasing degrees of intensified adaptiveness to localized niches as time went

---

[1] Wright (1968:334) shows reason to suspect more paleo-environmental change than we had expected (RJB, July 1969).

[2] From Wright's (1968) evidence for paleo-environmental change, it follows that wild plant and animal distribution 12,000 years ago may have been quite different from that of now, thereby increasing the difficulty of defining the natural habitat zone of the potential domesticates (RJB, July 1969).

on—was itself a zone of considerable sub-regional diversity, and in this it parallels a similar situation in Mesoamerica (Braidwood and Willey 1962a). The natural habitat zone appears to have included the western and southwestern facing flanks of the Zagros from as far southeast as Shiraz in Iran; thence the zone bore north and westwards about the southern and southwestern flanks of the high Anatolian plateau, while a southern arm fronted upon the Mediterranean along the flanks of the Lebanon and the Judean hills and parts of their trans-Jordanian extensions. The western and northwestern boundary of the natural habitat zone is not yet delimited (Thrace? the Caucasus?), in fact its delimitation is still very imprecise anywhere. The point is, however, that the zone included a complex system of relatively well watered and adjoining higher piedmonts and intermontane valleys, and that minor degrees of fluctuation in precipitation and temperature (to the degree in which they occurred) would have been compensated for by nature in modest up slope or down slope movements, with little inconvenience to plant, animal or human ecologies.

Further, it is not supposed that in their natural wild states all elements of the familiar constellation of plants and animals (wheat, barley, certain legumes, sheep, goat, dog, pig, cattle, certain equids) inhabited exactly the same niches all at once. It is now, and may always remain, fruitless to ask exactly where the first plant and animal domestication took place as a full complex. It appears, rather, that the human manipulation of one or two elements of the constellation may have begun in one niche, that of other elements in other niches. It is visualized that this situation obtained in the general time range of *ca.* 11,000 to 9,000 years ago, probably at all points along the general natural habitat zone. From a culture-historical point of view, this is the level we would label that of "incipient cultivation and domestication." From an environmental point of view, it is (we believe) important to visualize that this level probably *only* obtained within the natural habitat zone; a zone of general environmental permissiveness but of sub-regional diversity, of relatively easy access from intermontane valley to intermontane valley and upper piedmont, and within which minor climatic fluctuations (if they really existed) were readily compensated for.

It is probably still too soon to completely eliminate the now arid and semi-arid stretches of Arabia, and of the higher central plateau steppes of Anatolia and Iran from further consideration. These have, naturally, not yet been areas of very intensive prehistoric archeological survey. They have not so far yielded evidence which is reasonably pertinent to the problem of the appearance of an effective food-production, however, and we very much doubt that they still hold many surprises. The relatively lush environments of the southern littorals of the Black and Caspian Seas, with such summer rainfall as would have inhibited the maturation of wild wheat, for example, appear to us to have been regions within which an intensified level of food-collecting would have persisted long after the rise of incipience and perhaps even of early village-farming communities in the natural habitat zone. This does not, of course, mean that the intensified food-collectors of these lush littorals may not, on occasion, have borrowed odd traits from the more nuclear area. It might even be possible to raise the same question with regard to certain portions of the Levant littoral, but the effect of lushness cannot have been so great there, and in any case, the matter would demand further study. Interpretations such as those of Perrot (1962), who very suggestively considers the Palestinian environments in terms of the contrasts between the Mediterranean coastal zone and an inland semi-arid zone, will stimulate further useful environmental studies. Adams (1960:25) has made the interesting suggestion that there may already have been riverine-oriented food-collectors along the lower reaches of the Euphrates and Tigris, before the introduction of agriculture into lower alluvial Mesopotamia from the hill flanks to the east and north. As the case stands at the moment, however, the locale within which the levels of [1] incipient cultivation and domestication, and of [2] the succeeding earliest phases of effective village-farming communities developed was the so-called natural habitat zone of the higher piedmonts and intermontane valleys suggested above (cf. Braidwood, Howe *et al.* 1960:9 and maps; Helbaek 1959: and map).

THE CULTURE-HISTORICAL SEQUENCE

[1]. *The terminal level of the food-collecting era,* in southwestern Asia, was one in which increasing phases of intensified adjustment to regional environmental situations is manifested to us archeologically by an increasing variety of localized blade-tool industries.

Locally variant industries of the general Zarzian inventory are now
to be accounted for along the flanks of the Zagros (Braidwood,
Howe *et al.* 1960; Braidwood, Howe, Reed 1961; Solecki 1955;
1957a). As the Zarzian development proceeded, the microblade and
geometric component in the general inventory increased, very modest
quantities of obsidian (not available locally, however) were utilized,
there is also the suggestion of a few artifacts in ground stone, and
there are certainly hints of Zarzian settlements in the open as
well as in rock shelters. Preliminary studies on the animal bones
(by Reed, Perkins, Flannery) point towards "niche adaptation,"
with high frequencies of onager bones for sites on or overlooking
valley floors but with high sheep/goat bone frequencies for sites on
the ridges.

In Palestine, the final phases of the blade-tool sequence (cf.
Howell 1959), as seen in Atlitian the Kebaran and in el-Khiam
D-E are not so well represented by excavated materials as are the
earlier phases (Perrot 1962), and the depths of deposits at this
general range in Yabrud and in the still unpublished Ksar Akil
suggest a degree of complexity which is not yet clear. Again the
use of microblades and geometrics was on the increase, and again
open air sites became more common. Perrot suggests the association
of the microliths with composite weapons and more intensified
hunting. We know, as yet, very little of these phases of the terminal
level of food-collecting north of Lebanon, although at least three
separate varieties of generalized blade-tool industries have been
noted in Turkey (Bostanci 1959; Kökten 1955; 1958; Senyürek
1956; Senyürek, Bostanci 1958a; 1958b). These have been given
names such as "Aurignacian" or "upper paleolithic," but their respective sequential order is not yet known, and it is probable that
they do not represent all that went on during the final phases
of the Pleistocene or earliest post-Pleistocene in Turkey.[3] It seems
reasonable, however, to expect that the flint industries of the
terminal food-collectors of the littoral zone of southern and southwestern Turkey will (when we have detailed knowledge of them)
probably bear some typological-technological linkage to their contemporary counterparts along the Syro-Palestinian littoral. Certainly

---

[3] I am much indebted to Dr. Ufuk Esin, Fulbright visitor to the University
of Chicago in 1961–62, for the opportunity to learn many details of Turkish
prehistory.

the generalized little groups of Turkish "Aurignacian" we now know do not run contrary to this notion.

It would appear then, on the basis of still very incomplete evidence, that for latest Pleistocene (and perhaps earliest post-Pleistocene) times, roughly from 15,000 to 9,000 B.C., there was over-all occupation of the region described above in general terms as the natural habitat zone. The peoples of this region all produced their flint tool kits within the complex of habits we know as the blade-tool tradition, an onset of the use of microblades and geometrics took place, but there were *at least* two general sub-regional variants. One of these was the Zarzian of the Zagros flanks in Iran and Iraq, and Howe (Braidwood, Howe *et al.* 1960) following a much earlier suggestion of Garrod, has wondered whether this sub-tradition may have had trans-Caucasian typological linkages. The other sub-tradition, including such industries as the Atlitian and Kebaran in Palestine, perhaps the Nebekian and its antecedents at Yabrud, and even some of the extant Turkish "Aurignacian" material, appears to have been a manifestation of the littoral strip of the eastern Mediterranean and its immediate hinterland. There may have been other such sub-traditions, but we do not yet know of them.

[2]. *The level of incipient cultivation and domestication.* It is not yet possible to see a smooth technological-typological transition from the above two sub-traditions into the known phases of the level of incipient cultivation and domestication.[4] There does not appear to have been continuity from the latest phases of the Zarzian into the Karim Shahirian along the Zagros (Braidwood, Howe *et al.* 1960:157); neither is there continuity from the Kebaran into the Natufian along the littoral (Garrod 1958; Perrot 1962). How the Karim Shahirian may yet be divided into sub-phases, depending on the type site, Zawi Chemi Shanidar and Asiab is not yet clear (Braidwood, Howe *et al.* 1960; Braidwood, Howe, Reed 1961), nor is Perrot yet satisfied concerning the proper subdivision of the Natufian. Probably, both in the littoral and along the Zagros,

---

[4] About 1964, Perrot (in privileged reports and public lectures) proposed the existence of well-settled "villages" but without produced food, and several examples of such "hunters' villages" have since been excavated (e.g., Van Loon 1968:265), thus suggesting that a distinction between terminal intensified food collecting and incipience may be more semantics than reality (RJB, July 1969).

still other phases pertinent to the general level of incipience will still
be discovered. M'lefaat, near Mosul, may show of one of these, but
our sondage there did not yield enough material to clinch the matter;
the same may be true of the post-Natufian levels of Nahal Oren
(Wadi Fallah), el-Khiam and perhaps some of the deeper levels of
Tell es-Sultan (Jericho), but this—the so-called "Tahunian" material, to which term Perrot rightly takes exception—is also still an
unclear range.

In each instance where we know the generalized Karim Shahirian
type of material along the Zagros, the sites were outdoor settlements, each with some modest suggestion that simple structures
were being built. So far, for the rather many rock shelters examined,
there is little beyond a scatter of Karim Shahirian materials in
the uppermost layer in the Shanidar cave alone (and the pertinent
material is seen much better nearby at the Zawi Chemi Shanidar
open site). Thus, in Kurdistan, a positive shift to open air settlements appears to have obtained. Both coarse and fine ground stone
artifacts were made (e.g., querns, boulder-mortars, coarse stone
bowls; beads, bracelets, pendants, etc.), and there are hints of
simple clay figurine modeling at Asiab and at Karim Shahir itself.
The flint industry was in the blade-tool tradition, had fine microblades, but rather few geometrics and lacked other elements of the
Zarzian as well. Chipped celts with polished bits appeared. Obsidian
was rare or virtually non-existent on some of the sites; blades
with sickle sheen were also very rare. There is not yet primary
evidence of plant foods from any of the sites (although the study of
the Asiab coprolites might yet yield indications of such), but
Perkins and Solecki (personal communication) report evidence of
the domestication of sheep at Zawi Chemi Shanidar. The Karim
Shahirian fauna was all essentially modern, and the animal bone
frequencies reflect the setting of the individual sites. Most Karim
Shahirian sites yield land snails in some quantity; Asiab, overlooking a river, had many freshwater clams. The general complexion
of the Karim Shahirian suggests some hunting but also quite intensified collecting. The lack of many geometrics (for composite
weapons?) or of normal-sized projectile points is noteworthy, and
this element of contrast with the Natufian continues into the next
level and beyond, setting the Zagros and the Mediterranean littoral
apart.

The Natufian of the rock shelters is well described in the general literature (Garrod 1958), but the newer exposures of important open-air sites are perhaps less well known (Perrot 1962; 1960). Round stone-founded structures of about 6.0 m. in diameter are now known, with their hearths, boulder-mortars, bins and storage pits. Several artifacts, reportedly of Natufian type, are said to have come in the basal layer of Tell es-Sultan. The complexion of the Natufian assemblage in general suggests some high degree of intensification of hunting and fishing practices, although normal-sized projectile points (as distinguished from the probable composite weapons suggested by many of the geometric microliths) probably pertain to the next phase. Although no primary and positive evidence of either animal or plant domestication is yet available, Perrot follows the usual assumption that the Natufian sickle blades imply at least the collection of wild wheat and barley and that the various milling artifacts also pertain to cereal food processing activities. We ourselves are still confused as to what may be inferred from "sickle sheen" alone, and wonder about its possible occurrence in the cutting of reeds for use in the structures; the milling stones could have pertained to the preparation of many types of wild food. At least, in contrast to the Karim Shahirian, the general complexion of the Natufian would appear to suggest greater emphasis on the chase and on fishing.

Until recently, our knowledge of the Natufian was almost confined to Palestine, but a short preliminary report (Bostanci 1959) indicates a flint industry with a microlithic component at Beldibi, near Antalya on the southern coast of Turkey, which appears to have strong general typological similarity to the Natufian industry. Such a general distribution of variants of the Natufian along the Syrian and Turkish stretches of the littoral was to be anticipated (Braidwood, Braidwood 1960:449; Perrot 1962), and again the matter of sub-traditional differences—Karim Shahirian along the Zagros and Natufian along the Mediterranean littoral and its immediate hinterland—seems indicated. As in the instance of the previous terminal food-collecting level, however, we have as yet no idea of what may have been going on in other portions of the natural habitat zone.

There are, as yet, little beyond a few hints of a phase (or phases) following that of the Karim Shahirian, and still within the level of incipience, along the Zagros flanks. As indicated above, M'lefaat may yet prove to exhibit such a post-Karim Shahirian phase, and we had surface indications of several others (Braidwood, Howe *et al.* 1960), but the matter is not yet satisfactorily understood. There does appear to have been an immediately post-Natufian phase (or phases) in Palestine, as exhibited by the variety of materials generally classified as "Tahunian," but this situation also remains confused. It is at this point in the Palestinian development (if not even slightly earlier) that Perrot usefully proposes consideration of two sequences; one in his semi-arid inland zone, and one along the Mediterranean littoral itself. The contrast Perrot (1962) suggests would be such as may be seen between Nahal Oren (Wadi Fallah) and the so-called "Pre-Pottery Neolithic A" (="PPNA") of Tell es-Sultan. From what has been reported so far from either of these groups of materials, we know little of the subsistence basis they imply, but it is of interest that Perrot suggests a "mixed economy" at best, that Zeuner (1958) remarks on the generally very high proportion of game at Tell es-Sultan, and that normal-sized projectile points now begin to appear in earnest. So far, there appears to be no primary evidence of cereals from this range in Palestine, nor completely acceptable evidence for animal domestication (Reed 1959), and the implications of the sickles and milling stones are open to the same qualifications which obtained for them in the Natufian.

Nevertheless, Perrot, impressed by the well-known massiveness of the ring-wall at Tell es-Sultan, and by the relative size and apparent complexity of the settlement itself (Kenyon 1959a; 1959b), cannot conceive of the "Jericho PPNA" assemblage except as it may have been based upon cereal cultivation and animal domestication, for which he fully realizes there is yet no direct evidence reported. Perrot may be right; Tell es-Sultan may have had the role of a frontier "factory" or trading establishment (cf. Troy, in later times), dependent upon as yet undiscovered previous developments in the Judean hill-country environment, and serving as an outpost for these in their dealings with the peoples of the semi-arid hinterland. This suggestion implies a surprising degree of socio-cultural complexity for what we might have expected of this time range, but we have hitherto had no yardstick against which to measure such things. The only other possibility which comes to our minds (assuming always that the Tell es-Sultan radiocarbon determinations have not suffered due to some "geobiochemical" contamination of the samples) is that the Tell es-Sultan settlement represents an establishment of highly intensified food-collectors adjacent to the fine Jericho spring. Highly intensified levels of food-collection did sometimes result in large and spectacular sites (e.g., Poverty Point, Louisiana, cf. Caldwell 1962), but a major trouble with this alternative is that we do not yet know the food element (or elements) at Tell es-Sultan upon which such a high level of collecting intensification might have been based. In sum, a reasonable explanation for the complexity of Tell es-Sultan, in the place and at the time suggested for it, still eludes us, in lieu of further evidence.[5]

There is no other available material in southwestern Asia (with the possible exception hinted at by level B of Beldibi; cf. Bostanci 1959) which would appear likely to fall within the level of incipient cultivation and domestication. This of course implies that we retain our earlier judgment concerning the Belt and Hotu materials as primarily representing extended intensifications of food-collection in a specialized environmental niche (Braidwood 1958; 1960c:304). The conception of such a level of incipience is admittedly a difficult one to maintain, in the present state of knowledge (cf. Braidwood, Willey 1962a), but we nevertheless insist on its potential usefulness as part of a working model against which to plan field research, if nothing else. It appears to have commenced by *ca.* 9000 B.C. or even earlier, it appears to have been restricted to a natural habitat zone of certain potential domesticates, it *does not* (as did the "mesolithic" of northwestern Europe) appear to have resulted from a cultural readaptation to climatic amelioration and environmental change at the end of the Pleistocene for we have no clear indications that such amelioration and change is evidenced. Thus, in the sense that it is to be viewed primarily as a cultural event, it is perhaps also fair to apply *post-facto* judgment in our conception of it (Braidwood 1960b); the contrast between the levels of sociocultural complexity implied by the terminal food-collecting materials (e.g., the Zarzian) and of the earliest now known effective food-producers (e.g., Jarmo) calls for such an intermediate level. Its explication is at the same time the most fascinating and the most exasperating of the problems which face us in the prehistory of southwestern Asia today. So far, the only *primary* evidence we

---

[5] More recently, Perrot is in fact willing to conceive of food collectors' settlements, cf. footnote 4, above (RJB, July 1969).

have that the level included incipient domesticates is the instance of the sheep at Zawi Chemi Shanidar.

[3]. *The level of primary effective village-farming communities.* Regardless of whatever full socio-cultural implications the usage "pre-pottery" or "pre-ceramic" may have (as contrasted with purely classificatory implications, for the convenience of archeologists!), there are now an ever growing number of instances of pre-ceramic village materials. The "Jericho PPNB" levels of Tell es-Sultan and one or two other Palestinian instances are reasonably well known, the basal horizons of Ras Shamra V (Schaeffer 1961) and of Khirokitia on Cyprus (Dikaios 1961) indicate essentially the same horizon, as do Mellaart's (1961a) "aceramic" layers in Hacilar in the hills of southern Turkey. And to these instances, Milojčić's (1959) and Theocharis' (1958) Thessalian sites would be added if our considerations were to reach outside of southwestern Asia. A restricted exposure in Baluchistan suggested a comparable level to Fairservis (1956), although the single radiocarbon determination available is rather late. The first comprehensible exposure of such a general horizon appeared in the lower levels of Jarmo in Kurdistan (Braidwood, Howe, *et al.* 1960), and it is from this site that the primary evidence for cultigens and domesticates is so far most impressive in the direction of a settled and effective village-farming community way of life. It is this notion of a level of settled and effective village-farming communities, and the evidence for such a level which we turn to next.

We have asserted that the level of incipient cultivation and domestication was probably only viable within the general natural habitat zone.[6] The same was possibly true also for the very first phase or phases of the primary village-farming community level. Unfortunately, from no place in the materials now available to us do we yet see direct technological-typological continuity between the two levels. There is an apparent discontinuity between the Karim Shahirian and the Jarmoan along the Zagros flanks (Braidwood, Howe *et al.* 1960:182–3, fig. 8), it is not at all certain that M'lefaat will fill this gap, and the same discontinuity exists in what

---

[6] New excavations have clearly shown my original conception of the limits of the natural habitat zone to be too restricted, e.g., Ali Kosh at a low elevation on the Zagros, Ganj Dareh at a much higher elevation, Beidha in southeastern Jordan, etc. (RJB, July 1969).

we now know of the Kermanshah plain between Asiab and Sarab (Braidwood, Howe, Reed 1961). Neither is a smooth and single technological-typological flow observable in Palestine between any material of the so-called "Tahunian" phase (e.g., the Tell es-Sultan "PPNA") and what follows next (e.g., "Jericho PPNB," Abu Ghosh, basal Ras Shamra, etc.), although Perrot (1962) hints that there may be still unpublished materials which will bear on the point. At Hacilar (Mellaart 1961a), there is a discontinuity between the "aceramic" and the later fully food-producing layers, although Mellaart (in private correspondence) anticipates that he may be able to link the two in still untested deeper layers at Catal Hüyük. On the basis of a general assessment of available radiocarbon determinations (Braidwood 1959), it seemed not unreasonable to suggest that the level was under way by *ca.* 7000 B.C., and further determinations—if treated with proper respect for the range of statistical errors—have not changed this generalization.

Were all of these instances fully and effectively food-producing on a year-around permanently settled basis? The question is not yet easy to answer. Jarmo yielded two varieties of wheat, a barley, certain legumes, the goat, probably the sheep and dog and (in the uppermost and ceramic yielding horizons) the pig (Helbaek 1959; Reed 1959; the same in Braidwood, Howe *et al.* 1960; further studies by Reed, Flannery, personal communication). But, to a degree, Jarmo will eventually have to be understood in terms of the implications of Sarab, which may yet prove to have been an up-country temporary seasonal settlement of shepherds, for which a site of Jarmo type was probably the parent and "home base" in a lower intermontane valley. There are acceptable claims for the goat, dog and possibly cat in the "PPNB" horizons of Tell es-Sultan (Zeuner 1958). Otherwise, we know of no other verified claims for primary evidence of cultigens or domesticates[7] at this time range in southwestern Asia. Nevertheless, it seems fairly likely that most of the sites and sub-regions in question did support a primary and effectively settled village-farming community level of economy. This is not, of course, to say that food-collection did not remain a large element in the subsistence economy. The great bulks of land

[7] What is at issue here is that few archeologists (or their workmen!) are competent to make proper identifications of plant or animal traces; cf. the story of Ur royal tombs "onager team" which were in fact oxen (Dyson 1960).

snails at Jarmo, and its traces of pistachio nuts and acorns, as well as the bones of some certainly wild animals, hint in this direction, and parallel Zeuner's (1958) observations regarding Tell es-Sultan. To a degree, our first conception of the early primary village-farming community corresponded to a theoretical "ideal type"; the accident of the prior discovery of Jarmo appeared to confirm this theoretical picture. But as more of the Jarmo materials have been processed, and as the implications of Sarab and of Tell es-Sultan are considered (both in their own variant directions) it is clear that the actual socio-cultural dimensions of the level were already complicated and far from uniform.

At the moment, our own particular interests focus on what the "area co-traditions" (Willey, Phillips 1958:35) of the earliest village-farming communities may prove to have been, both along the Zagros sub-region and along the Mediterranean littoral. Unfortunately, much of the pertinent material which is known to have been recently excavated and which would bear on these matters, has yet to be processed in detail and reported upon. For the Zagros region, we still have no other excavated occurrence of basal Jarmo type (i.e., without pottery), but the upper ceramic-bearing sub-phase of Jarmo is approximately paralled at the nearby Shimshara, at Sarab near Kermanshah, and perhaps also at Haji Firuz near Lake Urmia (Dyson, Young, personal communication) and at Djari B and Mushki near Persepolis (Braidwood 1960d), insofar as ceramic analogies may be trusted alone. Perrot (1962) tends to see the new Palestinian assemblage (e.g., Jericho PPNB) as of Syrian origin and to this one might add Mellaart's (1961a) suggestion that Hacilar exhibits linkages with Palestine as well. Much may become clearer when the basal Ras Shamra V materials and those of Mellaart's Catal Hüyük are reported in detail. Nevertheless—and amorphous as this picture still is—it would appear that the subregional dichotomy, on the Zagros flanks vs. Mediterranean littoral, which we noted in our two earlier levels, persisted well into the primary village-farming community level. To what degree, in either of these sub-regions, there was a longer and more important persistence of intensified food-collecting procedures, we have as yet no basis upon which to make a judgment.

As developments in the level of the primary village-farming communities proceeded, it appears that the elements of the cultivated or domesticated portions of the food pattern were freed from their original natural habitat zone. Expansion down-slope to the lower stretches of the piedmonts and to the alluvial valleys now seems indicated, although Adams' (1960) suggestion that this movement did not take place into a vacuum bears consideration. There is not much information to add for this range since the time of our *Journal of World History* paper. At the moment, however, we would not tend to see evidence for any great degree of dependence and flow, on a technological-typological basis, of the Hassunan, Samarran or Halafian assemblages out of antecedents in either the Zagros flanks or the Mediterranean littoral "area co-traditions." It will be noted that our knowledge of Turkish and high Syrian Mesopotamia in the level of the terminal food-collectors, in the level of incipient cultivation and domestication, and of the earliest village-farming communities, is almost a complete and utter blank. Our hunch is that another "area co-tradition" will yet be recovered in this general sub-region, and that we shall understand the developments up to, and the distinctions between, the Hassunan, Halafian and perhaps also the Samarran better when we know this postulated high Mesopotamian sequence.[8]

It is perfectly clear that the level of primary village-farming communities—which we said made its start about 7000 B.C.—was well established throughout the environmentally possible stretches of southwestern Asia by about 5000 B.C. Even before this latter date, the new economy had appeared on Cyprus, without doubt sea-born, and several determinations for the earliest ceramic horizons in central Greece at about 5500 B.C. (Weinberg, personal communication) hint that the pre-ceramic horizons of Thessaly must have been earlier still.[9] How early may the outward spread of the new food-producing economy have begun, if it did—as we believe

---

[8] Up to now, the rigid interpretation of the Turkish antiquities law (quite understandable in terms of the excesses of museum-oriented archeologists in the days of the Ottoman Empire), has tended to discourage modern prehistoric research. It is simply impractical to attempt to process bulk categories of objects demanding statistical treatment and to make laboratory-bound non-artifactual studies under field conditions alone.

[9] Although we are still very uncomfortable about single radiocarbon determinations, or of groups taken from one site alone, the general over-all clustering of the available determinations on a master-chart increasingly makes archeological sense. The "spooks" stand out by their very inconsistency with the rest of the pattern. Thus, while we are certainly not prepared to enter arguments as to the physical-chemical validity of radiocarbon age determination itself, we are impressed with the pattern which appears as we keep adding to our own master chart (cf. Braidwood 1959:259).

(cf. Pittioni 1962b; in Braidwood, Willey 1962b)—spread out from southwestern Asia? Not during the level of incipience or of the earliest phases of the level of the primary villages, if we are right that these were only viable within the natural habitat zone. Bearing upon this point also, however, is the proposition that we do not yet know the boundaries of the natural habitat zone, especially towards the northwest. But mutations and hybridizations which allowed the new domesticates to flourish outside their original natural habitat had probably set in by *ca.* 6000 B.C. For example, emmer wheat was recovered in the Amouq A horizons (Helbaek 1960c:540), and the Amouq is a rather too low and humid environment in which to expect wild emmer to flourish, if we understand its habits correctly. Now the Amouq A materials parallel those of basal Mersin, for which a single radiocarbon determination is available at *ca.* 6000 B.C.; a determination which, however, appears to us to fit the general trend of the master chart in a comfortable fashion. Hence, we might suggest 6000 B.C. as a very rough approximation of the time when at least emmer may have been freed from its original habitat zone.

If the proposition for the spread of the new economy towards Europe must be pondered either in the above terms, or in terms of a more exact delimitation of the natural habitat zone itself (e.g., was Thrace, at least, included?), how are we to understand the apparently very retarded spread of the new economy to Egypt? Even if we allow an outer limit of tolerance on the early side for the available determinations for the Fayum and Merimdeh, a date of *ca.* 5000 B.C. would be about as early as the determinations would encourage. This could mean one of several things, for example [1], that food-production reached the lower Nile valley from some point further south, west, or through the Horn of Africa, or [2], that both of these series of determinations are "spooks" and have been contaminated in some way not yet understood, or [3], that in fact food-production did reach Egypt from the Mediterranean at a rather late date, probably due to the rather late appearance of strains of domesticates which would tolerate the Egyptian environment. Our own tendency is to favor the latter suggestion; from the point of view of the cultural mechanics involved, this makes Egypt the more interesting. In this view, Egypt's rate of cultural acceleration, up to the appearance of the early dynastic complex, would more fully parallel that of lower alluvial Mesopotamia, which also seems to have received the new economy about as late as 5000 B.C. If the date of the establishment of food-production in Egypt were to have been much earlier, the rate of its subsequent development—*vis-à-vis* Mesopotamia—might have seemed curiously slow-footed.

Since this paper ends on a diffusionary note, we should like to quote again a favorite line from the preface of Gordon Childe's first edition (repeated in each subsequent edition) of *The Dawn of European Civilization,* ". . . the peoples of the West were not slavish imitators; they adapted the gifts of the East and united the contributions made by Africa and Asia into a new and organic whole capable of developing on its own original lines." We would not be so sure now of Africa's role, if the proposition concerned the original spread of primary food-production, but the spirit of Childe's observation remains completely valid. Jarmo and its inhabitants were never transplanted to Europe on a magic carpet (or as an American supermarket is sent to a Moscow trade fair), and a great amount of cultural adaptation and readaptation happened all along the way, as ideas and a few basic elements of the new way of life spread from southwest Asia into Europe.

As to the developments which led to the appearance of an effective food-production in southwestern Asia itself, the picture appears increasingly to have become a very complicated one. We feel that the conception of sub-regional diversities is an important one, and also the idea that there may have been significant hold-overs—into the level of the village-farming communities—of intensified food-collecting procedures. As the village-farming community level came into being, however, the long trend towards ever more localized regional adaptations tended to reverse itself, perhaps in only some categories, at first. Obsidian was sought, and raw bitumen began to become available at longer distances from its natural flows. A new trend towards dispersion and an increasing commonalty of ideas set in, and the stage was set for even longer range diffusionary impulses to follow.

14 PREHISTORY AND HUMAN ECOLOGY OF THE DEH LURAN PLAIN (EXCERPTS)

Frank Hole, Kent V. Flannery, James A. Neely

THE ENVIRONMENTAL SETTING

ONE OF THE KEY environmental zones in the prehistory of the Near East is a belt of low piedmont and alluvial plain which stretches from the east bank of the Tigris River to the base of the distant Zagros Mountains. Within this zone of rolling, semi-arid steppe, at elevations of 100 to 500 meters above sea level, occur some of the highest densities of prehistoric archeological sites in the world.

Southwest of the piedmont lie the arid plains of southern alluvial Mesopotamia. To the northeast rise the wooded mountains of Kurdistan and Luristan, where the wild ancestors of all the early plant and animal domesticates in the Near East are at home. The piedmont is the zone of transition between Mesopotamia and the mountains, but it is also more than that: it combines many of the best features of both of the latter two regions.

Like the mountains, the piedmont has sufficient rainfall for dry farming. Like Mesopotamia, it has large rivers which can be used for irrigation. It is superb winter grazing land. Its summers are hot and dry, but not as hot and dry as Mesopotamia's. Its winters are cool, but not as cold as Kurdistan's. Once, before the advent of motorized hunting techniques, it supported enormous herds of wild herbivores. Perhaps most importantly, it was an environment where the cultivation techniques necessary in Southern Mesopotamia could be learned at slight risk to the farmer, because of the adequate rainfall. It was in this zone, as pointed out by Adams (1962:112), that

Reprinted by permission of the Museum of Anthropology, University of Michigan, from *Prehistory and Human Ecology of the Deh Luran Plain*, 1969, Memoirs 1, pp. 10–22 and 342–71, and by permission of the authors.

the crucial transition from dry-farming to irrigation was probably made.

Four-fifths of the piedmont zone occurs within the political boundaries of modern Iraq, where it is known as the Assyrian Steppe. One-fifth lies in Iran, where it is known as Northern Khuzistan.

For thousands of years the plains of Northern Khuzistan have been, developmentally and politically, one of the nuclear areas of Iran. In ancient times, Khuzistan was the heartland of the Elamite empire, one of the great "first generation" civilizations of the Near East. Here lay the walled city of Susa—"Shushan the Palace" —where Esther was crowned queen, and where Darius and Xerxes made their winter capital. Among the hundreds of other archeological mounds which cover the Northern Khuzistan plain are the ziggurat of Chogha Zambil, now reconstructed by the French; the large prehistoric town of Chogha Mish, currently undergoing excavation by a University of Chicago expedition; and the sprawling ruin of Jundi Shapur, site of one of the world's great pre-Islamic universities.

Khuzistan's prehistory is no less impressive than her history. In 1961, a survey by Robert M. Adams of the University of Chicago revealed no fewer than 130 prehistoric sites in the vicinity of Susa (Adams 1962:110). Four of these—Jaffarabad, Jowi, Bendi-bal, and Bouhallan, already excavated by the French in the 1930's —had yielded a five-period sequence which antedated the lowest levels of Susa (see Fig. 1). To these, the present report adds three antecedent periods which carry the Khuzistan sequence back to before 7000 B.C.

Most of the great prehistoric developments in Northern Khuzistan took place in this "heartland" between the Karkheh, Shaur, Diz, and Karun rivers. This sub-region of Khuzistan was called "Susiana" by the French archeologist, after the type site of Susa. Yet development in "Susiana proper" are echoed in the region of Ram Hormuz, 90 km. east of the Karun, and in Deh Luran, 60 km. west of the Karkheh. In terms of settlement patterns, architecture, ceramics, and artifact styles, the whole of Northern Khuzistan is a single coherent culture area.

One purpose of our excavations at Deh Luran was to determine how man had adapted to the Khuzistan steppe, and how dry farming, animal herding, and irrigation had begun there. Because of

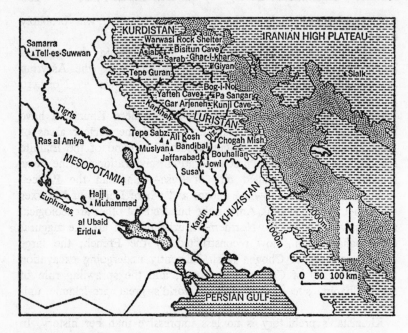

FIGURE 1 Map of southwestern Iran and adjacent Mesopotamia, showing some of the archeological sites mentioned in the text. (Small, isolated mountain ranges of over 2000 meters not shown.)

the general unity of the Northern Khuzistan environment, we feel that the Deh Luran evidence probably is relevant for an understanding of the early sequence in Susiana as well, and parallels between the two sub-regions will be drawn throughout this report. In this chapter, we will consider first of all the environment of Khuzistan in general, and finally the environment of the Deh Luran plain in particular.

The geology of Khuzistan

In considering the geology of Khuzistan, it is necessary to consider the genesis of the whole Mesopotamian Depression, as summarized most recently by Lees and Falcon (1952). The entire area is an unstable geosyncline, which was produced late in the Pliocene by movements of the earth's crust, forcing the Iranian Plateau closer to the central massif of Arabia. The more mobile strip of land between these plateaus was compressed and pleated like an accordion. The effects of this pleating can still be seen in aerial photographs of the Zagros Mountains, which take the form of parallel ridges running in a generally northwest-southeast direction, at right angles to the lines of pressure from the two plateaus.

The center of this pleated area was depressed, subsided, and began to fill with the erosion products of the parallel mountain ridges. In this still-subsiding geosyncline, thousands of feet of sediment have accumulated. The rivers draining the Zagros Mountains—Tigris, Euphrates, Karun, and Karkheh—annually carry several million tons of silt down to the Depression. The result is that many parallel ridges lie buried in central Mesopotamia, giving the illusion of a relatively level plain. As one travels northeast toward the Zagros, gradually the parallel ridges begin to rise out of the plain: first as low hummocks, then ranges of fifty or a hundred meters, then as true mountains (see Fig. 2).

The first truly substantial range is a series of sandstone hills called the Jebel Hamrin, which forms the border between Iran and Iraq for part of its course. Broken in many areas by tributaries of the Tigris, it forms no barrier to travel between the piedmont and Mesopotamia.

The next range to the northeast is considerably higher, and constitutes the first tier of the Zagros Mountains. In Northwestern Khuzistan (near Deh Luran), this series of mountains is known as the Kuh-i-Siah ("Black Mountain"), and rises to elevations of 1450 meters, forming the northeast frontier of the plain. In north-central Khuzistan ("Susiana"), this same range is known as the boundary between the piedmont and the Zagros.

These first parallel ridges are composed of Cenozoic sandstones, conglomerates, and gypsiferous marls. Their erosion products, which form the Khuzistan plain, are therefore sands and clays of various types. Many of the springs which originate in these hills are so full of dissolved gypsum salts as to be undrinkable and of little use for irrigation. In this case, intensive use is made of streams which have come from farther away, in the higher limestone mountains of Luristan and Kurdistan.

Wind and water have sculptured the face of Khuzistan with these raw materials. In some areas, long lines of stabilized sand dunes follow the Jebel Hamrin; in others, water stands in low depressions of gypseous clays. In some areas, rivers have cut their way far below the surface of the plain and are useless for irrigation; in others, the rivers flow above the level of the plain, held in check

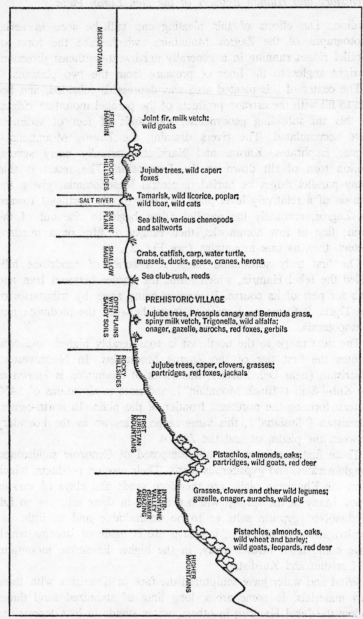

FIGURE 2 Idealized cross section of northern Khuzistan, between the Jebel Hamrin and the first Luristan mountains, showing "microenvironments" with some of their characteristic flora and fauna.

only by natural levees which, when breached, will open the way to extensive irrigation. Adams' (1962) survey in north-central Khuzistan makes clear how important such areas were in the prehistoric period. He also stresses one further point: in the northern part of Khuzistan, the belt of piedmont at the very base of the Zagros Mountains,

> . . . increased surface gradients and widespread underlying gravel deposits provide sufficient natural drainage over most of the area to minimize the problems of salinization and waterlogging that usually attend irrigation agriculture (Adams 1962:110).

The climate of Khuzistan

To the casual observer, the most striking aspect of the Khuzistan climate is the marked contrast between summer and winter. Throughout the summer months, dry air blows out of Eurasia and crosses Khuzistan on its way to the low-pressure areas in Arabia and India. Descending from a sub-tropical high-pressure area near latitude 30 degrees North, this air contains no moisture, and hence no rain can be expected. The evaporation rate is extremely high (Cressey 1960:99).

In addition, the area is scorched by local winds like the northwesterly *shamal*, which may blow hot and dry for nine days out of every ten, raising temperatures to 120 degrees Fahrenheit (de Morgan 1900, mentioned 138 degrees on one occasion). Still worse is the *simoon* or "poison wind," which is believed by villagers to have caused fatalities in the past. The *simoon* is a hot wind from the southeast which blows for three or four days with the intensity of a blast furnce, raising great clouds of dust which darken the sky for days.

The summers of Khuzistan appear to have left an indelible stamp on all who have experienced them. William Kenneth Loftus, first excavator of the site of Susa, on entering the area in the 1850's was struck by the fact that:

> It was now only the 19th of May, and yet the grass was scorched to a bright yellow, which . . . gave to the imagination a vivid idea of the intense heat reigning in that region three months later in the season. . . . During nine months in the year the whole country is burned up by the sun's heat, with an intensity which gives some credance to Strabo's report, that lizards and serpents could not crawl across the streets at mid-day without being burnt (Loftus 1857: 307, 346).

Late in the autumn the pattern begins to change. Westerly winds circulate irregularly across the middle latitudes, and where the polar and tropical air masses meet, weak cyclonic storms are produced. Some cyclonics traverse the entire Mediterranean, pass through the gap between the Taurus and Labanon mountains, and move southeast across the Syrian desert. Reaching the Zagros Mountains —the series of parallel ridges which separate Mesopotamia from the Iranian plateau—they rise, cool and condense. Some of these storms may be quite violent, and although their pattern is erratic and unpredictable, such low pressure areas move into Khuzistan on an average of once every two weeks. Once they have passed, there is clear, cool weather as cold air from the plateau to the north and east breaks over the mountains and descends on Mesopotamia (see Wright 1961b:136; Cressey 1960:97–102).

The violent rains of the Mediterranean cyclonics are particularly typical of autumn and spring in Khuzistan. At times they are preceded by a wall of red dust which only settles with the arrival of the rains. In mid-winter, more gentle and warmer rains may come to the area by means of anticyclonic storms from Arabia. Thus the winter passes in a succession of violent brief squalls, clear balmy days, cool drizzly nights, and occasional dust storms. When it is all over, an average of 350 mm. of rain have fallen on Northern Khuzistan.

The effect of this precipitation on the parched northern plains is frequently spectacular, as described by Loftus:

> At the beginning of January . . . the young grass, brought into existence by the heavy rains, makes its appearance, and increases with a truly tropical rapidity and luxuriance; nowhere have I ever seen such rich vegetation as that which clothes the verdant plains of Shush, interspersed with numerous plants of a sweet-scented and delicate iris (Loftus 1857:346).

An equally impressive description is that of Rawlinson, who wrote that in March of 1836 "it was difficult to ride along the Shapur (Shaur) for the luxuriant grass that clothed its banks, and all around, the plain was covered with a carpet of the richest verdure" (Rawlinson 1839:71).

The vegetation of Khuzistan

The Susiana that Loftus and Rawlinson explored was, like today's Northern Khuzistan, a pale shadow of its former self—overgrazed, overcultivated, and salinized for many thousands of years. We glimpse the original vegetation of Khuzistan only vaguely through the writings of botanist Henri Pabot (1960), who attempted to reconstruct it from the surviving vestiges of the ancient steppe flora. Helbaek's (1969) studies of the ancient plant remains from our Deh Luran sites contribute further data which was unknown to Pabot.

Pabot maintains that the original arborescent vegetation of Northern Khuzistan was sparse, with widely spaced jujube trees (*Zizyphus*) on the dry rolling plains. In the humid river bottoms grew forests of tamarisk (*Tamarix*), Euphrates poplar (*Populus euphratica*), and wild licorice (*Glycyrrhiza*). All these aborescent genera remain in the area today.

Because of the relatively low precipitation and the extremely high summer temperatures, few herbaceous perennials survived; but tough, hardy plants like camel thorn (*Alhagi*), *Prosopis* (a woody legume related to American mesquite), and bitter wild melon (*Citrullus*) grew all year. So did tough grasses like *Aristida* (needle grass), *Aeluropus* (cat's claw grass), *Hyparrhenia,* and *Cymbopogon* (oilgrass).

With the winter rains, the herbaceous vegetation of the plain grew richer from the addition of annual grasses, small legumes, and chenopods. Clovers and burnets, wild alfalfa (*Medicago*), spiny milk vetch (*Astragalus*), *Trigonella* (a member of the pea family), and plantain (*Plantago*) reached maturity by the end of March. Canary Grass (*Phalaris paradoxa*), Bermuda grass (*Cynodon dactylon*), meadow grass (*Poa*), and feather grass (*Stipa*) provided forage for herds of wild ungulates. Asphodels, iris, and wild narcissus added color to the "rich carpet of verdure" described by the early British explorers of Northern Khuzistan. However, Helbaek's (1969) study of the carbonized plants from Tepe Sabz indicate that some of the grasses and legumes may have been introduced as crop weeds during the sixth millennium B.C.

"Microenvironments" of Northern Khuzistan

The part of Khuzistan with which this report is concerned is the belt of northern plains receiving 200 to 350 mm. of annual precipitation, lying at elevations of 100 to 300 meters above sea level, and classified as semiarid steppe. This has been called the "dry zone" of Khuzistan by Pabot (1960); zoogeographically, it is the Iranian equivalent of Hatt's "Assyrian plains and foothills" biotic province (Hatt 1959). In this report we will refer to it simply as "Northern Khuzistan."

This belt is far from uniform; it can be divided into a number of biotopes or "microenvironments" (Coe, Flannery 1964) each of which is characterized by a particular plant community and certain species of animals. These biotopes are, in effect, "resource areas" which were exploited in different ways by the ancient inhabitants of Khuzistan. They include features as different as sand dunes, sandstone and gypsum hills, reed marshes, and saline and non-saline plains (both humid and dry). The data on Khuzistan suggest that, in the words of Adams (1962:109), "gross descriptive categories like 'semiarid steppeland' . . . may be as inadequate for a deeper historical understanding as they are for the contemporary planner."

In this section, we will present a brief description of Northern Khuzistan's major biotopes, emphasizing the potential resources of each from the standpoint of human exploitation. In our descriptions, we will draw heavily on the work of Hatt, Helbaek, and Pabot.

Open plains with sandy soils

This is one of the largest resource areas, and the one with the highest agricultural potential. These sandy soils are the best drained and allow better infiltration of rain; evaporation is lower than in silty soils, and the surface cannot form a compressed crust. Consequently, the sandy plains support the most varied plant complex of any soil area, and they were probably a more extensive habitat before cultivation began. Today, alluviation due to agriculture and deforestation have covered many previously sandy areas with silty alluvium, greatly decreasing permeability and reducing their potential for plant growth.

The dominant tree is the "christ's-thorn" or jujube (*Zizyphus*); perennial grasses include *Aristida* and *Poa*. Annual herbs include spiny milk vetch (*Astragalus*) and *Trigonella*, two small legumes eaten at 7000 B.C.; wild alfalfa or medick (*Medicago*), also eaten; and a variety of clovers, plantains, and annual grasses (*Schismus, Stipa*, etc.) which are useful for grazing. Bermuda grass and canary grass are also common.

These plains are grazed by the Persian gazelle (*Gazella subgutturosa*) and in prehistoric times also had herds of onager or wild ass (*Equus hemionus*). Red foxes (*Vulpes vulpes*) and jackals

(*Canis aureus*) are active nocturnally. The Karun desert gerbil (*Meriones crassus*) and the Indian gerbil (*Tatera indica*) burrow into well-drained areas or archeological mounds. Hyenas (*Hyaena hyaena*) make dens in the dry wadis cutting across the plain. Two large lizards, *Uromastix* and *Varanus,* are also residents.

The open plains had a high potential for gazelle and onager hunting, collecting of wild legumes, and cultivation of cereals. During the winter season, good pasturage was available for herds of domestic sheep and goats. This habitat was very heavily exploited in prehistoric times.

Shallow marshes

Many low areas of the Khuzistan plain are seasonally-flooded to permanent marshes. The more permanent sloughs have a border of reeds (*Phragmites communis*), cat's claw grass (*Aeleoropus*), club-rush (*Scirpus*), spike rush (*Eleocharis*), and common sedge (*Cyperus*). Most of these sloughs are shallow bodies of water with low oxygen content, inhabited by various genera of catfish and cyprinids (members of the carp family) who can tolerate such conditions. Water turtles (*Clemmys caspica*) and freshwater crabs (*Potamon*) are among the edible aquatic resources. Sloughs ultimately connected to the freshwater rivers of the alluvial plain may have various genera of mussels (*Unio, Leguminaea, Pseudodontopsis*). In this habitat, otter (*Lutra lutra*) and wild boar (*Sus scrofa*) abound.

During the winter, these marsh areas are visited by great quantities of water fowl. Ducks, geese, cranes, herons, and storks are among the birds which arrive in September and October and stay until March or April. These waterfowl were widely eaten in prehistoric times, as they are today.

The aquatic resources of the marshes and sloughs figured prominently in the ancient diet in Khuzistan. Fish, crabs, mussels, and water turtles were important to the first permanent settlers of the plain, and reeds and club-rushes are still used today in manufacturing mats and baskets.

Riverine

The sluggish rivers of Khuzistan meander across the plain, winding between sand bars and normally occupying only a small portion of their beds. The remainder of the bed is taken up by low forests of tamarisk (*Tamarix*), licorice (*Glycyrrhiza*), poplar (*Populus*), bramble bushes (*Rubus*) and other woody plants. There are carp, catfish, crabs, turtles, and freshwater mussels in the rivers, and along the banks live abundant small mammal populations—the Indian gerbil (*Tatera*), long-eared hedgehog (*Hemiechinus auritus*), otter, and various wild cats (*Felis chaus* and *F. libyca*). Until 1923, there were lions in the riverine thickets of Khuzistan (Hatt 1959:51).

In the tamarisk forests there are black partridges (*Francolinus francolinus*), marten (*Martes foina*), and wild boar. Such forests are today the last stronghold of the Mesopotamian fallow deer (Haltenorth 1961), an animal thought until recently to be extinct. In the Deh Luran plain, at least, there is no prehistoric evidence for fallow deer, and we are uncertain about its role in the diet of ancient Khuzistan.

The riverine habitat seems to have been used mainly for its aquatic resources. In addition, tamarisk was used for firewood; and (although we have no concrete evidence to this effect) it is possible that poplar, when present, was used prehistorically as a building material, just as it is today.

Rocky or gravelly hillsides

The rocky hillsides flanking the Northern Khuzistan plain have a distinct vegetation. At the northern margin of the steppe, where the talus rises toward the Luristan Mountains, chenopods and salt-resistant plants decrease and there is a substantial increase in perennial grasses, and arborescent and bushy species. Jujube trees (*Zizyphus*), *Prosopis,* and wild caper (*Capparis*) are among the woody plants with edible fruit. Plantains, clovers, burnets, mints, spurges, and small members of the mustard family are seasonally abundant. Good forage for domestic animals can be found on these slopes, including *Hyparrhenia, Cymbopogon* (oil grass), *Aristida, Aegilops,* and some varieties of wild *Hordeum* (including the ancestor of domestic barley).

These rocky hillsides are roamed by jackals and red foxes, porcupines (*Hystrix indicus*), gerbils and bandicoot-rats (*Nesokia indica*), and partridges (*Ammoperdix* and *Alectoris*). For the most part, the wild plant resources of this habitat outweigh the animals.

Habitats of little utility

Within the plains of Northern Khuzistan are localized habitats of low potential for human exploitation. These include areas of highly saline soils; sand dunes; eroded gypsum hills; and bare outcrops of sandstone.

Poorly-drained areas within the open plains biotope can be readily converted to saline conditions, and many areas have been so converted in the past. Such places then become agriculturally unproductive, featuring only a low cover of salt-tolerant chenopods or saltworts (*Salsola, Bassia, Halocharis* and others). *Aeluropus* and *Atriplex* also take over. The mammalian fauna of these areas is virtually nonexistent.

Sand dunes are seized and fixed by the sedge *Carex*. Once stabilized, they support a cover of needle grass (*Aristida*), bindweed (*Convolvulus*) and thistle (*Echinops*). Such stabilized dune areas are the haunt of the jerboa (*Jaculus jaculus*) who forages nocturnally for seeds and is able to go long priods without water.

The eroded gypsum hills at the north edge of the Khuzistan plain are an unpromising region of salt-tolerant chenopods, joint fir (*Ephedra*) and low perennial herbs. A few species of *Astragalus* colonize both these localities and the sandstone outcrops of the Jebel Hamrin. Partridges, foxes and jackals, and bandicoot rats are the dominant mammals. On the higher sandstone cliffs there are wild goats (*Capra hircus aegagrus*).

The higher mountains to the north

One other habitat must be considered. This is the zone of the Shaur anticline or Kuh-i-Siah range, which occurs at elevations of 600 to 800 meters, visible from the plain of Khuzistan but reached only after an all-day climb. This higher mountain area, which lies fully 300 meters above the steppe, receives somewhat more precipitation and has summer temperatures which are not so fatal to the vegetation as are those of the plain. Here stands of pistachio (*Pistacia atlantica*) and almond (*Amygdalus spartioides*) can be found, interspersed with good forage species like goat-face grass (*Aegilops*) sage (*Salvia*), wild members of the barley group (*Hordeum murinum* and *bulbosum*), brome grass (*Bromus*), *Hyparrhenia, Cymbopogon,* and clovers. Preserved pistachios and almonds in the prehistoric sites of the Deh Luran plain indicate that the ancient inhabitants of Khuzistan occasionally ascended to this zone, and it is reasonable to assume that they made use of this good forage by taking their sheep and goats up to the mountains. This habitat has a high potential for wild plant collecting and grazing, but is too steep and rocky for successful agriculture. Wild goats can also be hunted in this area.

Geography of the Deh Luran plain

The plain of Deh Luran is situated in the extreme northwest corner of Khuzistan, between 32 degrees 15 minutes and 32 degrees 30 minutes north latitude and 47 degrees 08 minutes and 47 degrees 24 minutes east longitude. It is bounded on the south by the Jebel Hamrin, the last landmark before the Iran-Iraq border. To the north, it is bounded by the Kuh-i-Siah, first of the high mountain ranges leading up to Luristan. Two shallow rivers, the Mehmeh and the Dawairij, constitute its western and eastern borders respectively. The occupied portion of the Deh Luran plain is about 300 square km.

The soils of the Deh Luran plain, like those of northern Khuzistan in general, are composed of sands and clays, which are the erosion products of the sandstones and gypseous marls which flank them. Today these soils range perilously close to the limits of cultivation because of salinity, and archeological evidence suggest they have always been in this situation—that the history of the plain has been one of localized worsening of the soil through agricultural activity, combined with the shifting of settlements to areas not previously cultivated and hence still fertile. The areas with the highest densities of prehistoric villages appear to be the localities with the worst salinity problem today.

In 1961 we took a series of soil samples from both fallow land and cultivated land in the vicinity of the site of Ali Kosh, in the southeast portion of the plain. The samples were analyzed for us by Dr. Charles Simkins of the Khuzistan Development Service, who has provided us with the following description:

Sample 06246:
Soil from a random series of points along a one-kilometer line in
   fallow land near Tepe Ali Kosh, in the Southeast Deh Luran
   plain pH 8.0 (mildly alkaline)
Conductivity 4.2 millimohs per cm. (very high salt content)
Oxidation value 0.44 (very low organic matter)
Phosphorus 3.0 parts per million (low available phosphorus)
Potassium 160 parts per million (relatively high potassium content)

Sample 06247:
Soil from a random series of points in a 200 meter square of planted
   field near Tepe Ali Kosh, in the southeast Deh Luran plain
   pH 8.1 (mildly alkaline)

Conductivity 5.6 (very high salt content)
Oxidation value 0.66 (very low in organic content)
Phosphorus 4.0 parts per million (low available phosphorus)
Potassium 290 parts per million (relatively high potassium)

Dr. Simkins' letter, evaluating these soil samples, reads: "Based on this analysis, we can be sure that the yields of most crops would be quite restricted in growth. A conductivity reading from 2 to 4 millimohs indicates that yields of very sensitive crops may be restricted due to salt content. Readings from 4 to 8 indicate yields of most crops restricted."

Soil salinity is not the only agricultural problem in the Deh Luran plain. Both the Dawairij and the Mehmeh rivers are brackish, so filled with dissolved salts from the gypsum beds north of the Deh Luran plain that they are virtually useless for irrigation. In 1961, Dr. Simkins also analyzed for us a sample of water from the Mehmeh River, and provided us with the following report:

Sample 1241:
Water from the Mehmeh River, near Deh Luran
Conductivity 7700 EC×10⁶
Per cent sodium 51.7
pH 7.31
total hardness 1852.0
Classification: "The above sample of water from the River Mehmeh comes under the classification of C4-S-4 water, possessing very high salinity and very high sodium hazard."

Of this sample, Simkins writes: "This water is not suitable for irrigation under ordinary conditions. It can only be used when the soils are very permeable; drainage must be adequate; irrigation water must be applied in excess to provide leaching, and only salt tolerant crops should be grown."

In spite of these limitations, it appears that the Deh Luran plain was a relatively favorable place for settlement during the period from 7500 to 3000 B.C. From this time span, we have thus far located at least thirteen mounds marking the eroded remains of prehistoric villages or towns. At their smallest, these mounds may be only a hectare in extent and a meter or two in height; the largest prehistoric site, Tepe Musiyan, is 1.5 km. in circumference and stands 17 meters high. To a very real extent, therefore, it would seem that the present barren and saline character of the Deh Luran plain is the result of misuse by man, who through intensive cultivation, overgrazing, and irrigation with brackish water, destroyed what may have been a reasonably fertile plain at 7500 B.C. We would guess that Deh Luran lay too close to the limits of tolerable salinity, and that once its natural equilibrium was destroyed it never recovered.

The prehistoric sites in the Deh Luran plain fall geographically into two clusters. Eight mounds occur in the northwestern part of the plain, on both sides of the Mehmeh River. The remaining five mounds lie west and east of the Dawairij River in the southeast part of the plain. These two clusters are separated by a low-lying depression which floods periodically during the winter rains, and has no evidence of prehistoric settlement. There are reasons to believe that in prehistoric times, before it filled in with silt, this depression was a shallow marsh or slough. Prehistoric agricultural activity seems to have centered on the higher and better drained areas to either side of this slough.

The northwestern cluster of sites lies in a region of rolling steppe cut by shallow, intermittent wadis. The northernmost site (Chagha Sefid) appears as a dull white mound on the outskirts of the village of Deh Luran, but all the remaining sites are in areas without permanent habitation. These areas, however, have local names ("Ashrafabad," "Chagha Dūzd," "Haft Tepe," etc.) and are used during the winter rainy season by Lurish nomads. These nomads descend from the mountains in October and set up black-tent encampments near shallow natural depressions where run-off from the rains tends to collect. They plow and plant these moist depressions with barley and wheat, obtaining one crop each winter. In addition, they graze their sheep and goats on the higher ground to either side of the depressions. Because of the extensive network of small stream courses and old silted-in irrigation canals in the Ashrafabad-Haft Tepe area, at least some of which are presumably prehistoric, a considerable amount of run-off is carried south to the vicinity of the prehistoric sites, where it accumulates in the depressions farmed by the nomads. Such was the case in the immediate area of Tepe Sabz, one of the prehistoric villages described in this report.

Today the vegetation of this area is meager. Camel-thorn (*Alhagi*), woody legumes (*Prosopis*), and bitter wild melon (*Citrullus*) are dominant on the high, flat steppe all year; in the winter, Bermuda grass (*Cynodon*) and canary grass (*Phalaris*) sprout in the moist depressions. In the deeper wadis and in the Mehmeh

River are stands of tamarisk (*Tamarix*). Many areas of the plain are today without any evidence of vegetation during the heart of the summer dry season.

The village of Deh Luran is the only permanent settlement in the vicinity of these sites. Deh Luran (which means, literally, "village of the Lurs") is a relatively recent enclave of exnomadic Kurds and Lurs who were resettled by the Reza Shah; there was no village there when Gautier and Lampre passed through in 1903. The unsuitability of the spot for a village of 1500 people is indicated by the fact that sweet water must be brought to the town daily by tank truck from a spring near Musiyan; the only springs at Deh Luran are either brackish or sulphurous. The majority of the villagers drink this water for lack of anything better, and irrigate a little barley and sesame. In the winter season, when rain water collects in small depressions and wadi bottoms near Ali Kosh, our Deh Lurani workmen eagerly filled their goatskin water bags from these mud puddles and carried the rain water home with them.

Northeast of Deh Luran, on the southern talus of the Kuh-i-Siah range, lies another series of springs; but these produce natural asphalt. Once commercially exploited by the British, these tar pits were eventually abandoned because of their small yield in proportion to the expense of transporting the asphalt. The Deh Luranis use the tar for waterproofing and minor roof repairs, and archeological evidence shows that it was used far back into prehistory for hafting tools and mending and waterproofing baskets. It is probable that asphalt from the Deh Luran springs (often incorrectly referred to in archeological reports as "bitumen")[1] was widely traded by the ancient villagers of the area.

The southeastern cluster of five prehistoric sites includes Ali Kosh, one of the sites we excavated, and Tepes Musiyan and Khazineh, excavated by the French in 1903. This area is somewhat less dissected by intermittent wadis, but the number of silted-in channels which may be ancient irrigation canals is very high. The village of Musiyan (from which many of our workmen came) farms many square kilometers of this region, using both naturally-flooded depressions[2] and drier areas which are irrigated with water pumped up from the Dawairij River. In addition, water from Ain Girzan, a

---

[1] True "bitumen" is free of impurities.

[2] Our workmen told us that in 1962, a winter of very heavy rains, water stood "as deep as a man's head" in fields surrounding Tepe Musiyan.

fresh water spring in the foothills leading up to the Jebel Hamrin, is channeled north toward Musiyan for irrigation. Ain Girzan is the only spring of any size in the entire Deh Luran plain which is not saline.

The Musiyan area produces barley, wheat, sorghum, and sesame, though not in excess of its needs. Each year many Musiyanis cross the Jebel Hamrin to find work at Amara or Baghdad in Iraq.

Only one other permanent settlement exists in the Deh Luran plain. This is the village of Bayat, a small hamlet near the police border post where the Mehmeh River leaves the plain and cuts through the Jebel Hamrin. The people of Bayat keep cattle and water buffalo, and trade milk and yoghurt to the village of Deh Luran. In addition, there seems to be some relationship between the people of Bayat and the seasonal nomads who settle the Ashrafabad-Haft Tepe area each winter. The region is one of low agricultural potential, where stabilized sand dunes flank the river and gravelly hills with jujube trees (*Zizyphus*) climb to the crest of the Jebel Hamrin.

We excavated or tested mounds in both the northwest and southeast site clusters in 1963. In addition, we observed many other localities in these cluster-areas where prehistoric sherds are strewn across the surface of the plain with no evidence of an archeological mound. These localities probably mark the site of villages of brief duration, and their number may be double that of the actual mounds. Because we know from our own excavations that the Deh Luran plain has received at least three meters of alluvium since 7000 B.C., it is probable that many small villages, occupied for only a generation or two, lie totally buried below the surface of the plain.

Our survey did not record sites occupied later than 3000 B.C., although many such sites can be found at Deh Luran. The most impressive of these is Tepe Garran, a high tower-shaped mound a kilometer north of Ali Kosh; and Tepe Musiyan, of course, has considerable material in its upper layers which postdates 3000 B.C. These materials were not germane to the problems of early food production, and we have left them for others to investigate.

SUMMARY AND CONCLUSIONS

In this chapter we will sum up the evidence for architecture, artifacts, way of life, and population density during each of the seven phases we have defined for the Deh Luran plain. These "capsule summaries" for each phase are based on the detailed descriptive material already presented in earlier chapters. We have, however, made an effort to present them in relatively nontechnical terms, and free of bibliographic references, feeling that in this way they may be of greater interest to the general reader. The Near Eastern specialist can find the technical data and references he wants in the appropriate previous chapter. The summaries which follow are intended as a culture history of the Deh Luran plain in particular, and Khuzistan in general.

But culture history is not the sole purpose of archeology. Archeology, we feel, should also be the study of long-term cultural and ecological processes. Therefore in this chapter we will also advance some hypotheses about the relationship of man to the steppe environment of Khuzistan: how he adapted his agriculture to it, how agriculture and grazing altered the vegetational cover, and how man re-adapted to a landscape that was now partly of his own making. At this stage we do not have easy answers to all that happened in Khuzistan, but we feel that one of our main purposes should be to present an explanatory model to be tested by future archeologists.

The Bus Mordeh phase
7500 to 6750 B.C.

Nine thousand years ago, much of the surface of the Deh Luran plain was an undulating expanse of sandy loam and reddish clays, derived in part from the sandstone hills of the Jebel Hamrin and the gypseous marls of the Kuh-i-Siah range. The center of the plain, a seasonally-inundated natural depression today, may at that time have been a semi-permanent slough bordered with sea club-rush, sedge, and feather grass. The villagers of the Bus Mordeh phase settled in the southeastern part of the plain, in a sandier and better-drained area only two kilometers from the Jebel Hamrin.

Out of a natural red clay deposit in the floor of the plain, the Bus Mordeh group cut slabs averaging 15 by 25 by 10 cm., which they used as unfired "bricks" in the construction of small houses or huts. The rooms they constructed were often no more than 2 by 2.5 meters, with walls 25 to 40 cm. thick and doorways a meter-and-a-half wide. As yet there are no certain indications—such as floor features and other architectural details—that prove these structures were dwellings rather than storage rooms. Size is not the critical factor here, for many prehistoric dwellings in the Southwestern United States are no more than 1.5 meters on a side.

The floors were of stamped mud or clay. No plaster of any kind is yet known from this period, but there is a suggestion of simple, over-one, under-one matting which may have been used as a floor covering or in roof construction (based on the way roofs are made in the area today). The clay-slab brick architecture is unlike anything known from the Zagros Mountains at this time (compare, for example, the "hut circles" of Zawi Chemi, the "pit houses" at Asiab, or the "wooden huts" of prepottery Tepe Guran). This suggests that it is a type of architecture native to the lowland steppe, where building materials other than mud or clay have always been scarce.

The subsistence pattern of the Bus Mordeh phase also shows a relative independence from the Zagros Mountains. The tens of thousands of carbonized seeds and broken animal bones left behind by these people show a high degree of orientation to the steppe environment. Nine-tenths of the seeds found in Bus Mordeh levels were from annual legumes and wild grasses native to northern Khuzistan. They systematically and intensively collected the seeds of medic or wild alfalfa, spiny milk vetch, *Trigonella* (a small plant of the pea family), canary grass, oat grass, and goosefoot, and ate the fruit of the wild caper. Since some of these plants have seeds no larger than clover seed, the amount of work involved in these harvests—which had to take place some time after the peak growing season in March—must have been considerable.

In addition, the Bus Mordeh folk planted emmer wheat and two-row hulled barley, two annual grasses which are not native to Khuzistan. Although constituting less than a tenth of the carbonized seeds left by these people, wheat and barley have significantly larger grains than most of the wild plants mentioned above, and were probably two of the preferred foods. They underscore the fact that the Bus Mordeh development, for all its peculiar architecture and its steppe collecting pattern, was not unrelated to developments in the highlands of the Near East, where the wild ancestors of wheat and barley are at home.

Wheat and barley were not the only "foreign" plants eaten by the people of the Bus Mordeh phase; three other grasses, which were probably weeds in the wheat fields, come from outside

Khuzistan. These were goat-face grass, ryegrass, and wild einkorn wheat, all of which were probably introduced into the Deh Luran area in imperfectly-cleaned batches of wheat seed. Once established, at least ryegrass and einkorn were probably eaten along with wheat and barley. We do not know from which area of the mountains all these seeds were first introduced into the Khuzistan diet, nor do we yet know at what time they first arrived. Harlan and Zohary (1966) have recently presented evidence suggesting that the large-seeded Palestinian race of wild emmer—and not the Zagros Mountain race—may be the ancestor of cultivated emmer wheat. If this proves to be the case, then the events antecedent to the Bus Mordeh phase may be even more complex than we suspected at first.

Carbonized seeds of club-rush (*Scirpus*) included with the grains indicate that the fields must have been very near the margins of our postulated marsh or slough. The cultivated cereals were harvested with flint sickles, roasted to render the glumes brittle, and then "threshed" by grinding with flat-topped or saddle-shaped grinding slabs of pitted limestone, a few of which were found in the rooms of this phase. "Groats," or coarsely-ground grits of wheat and barley, were recovered in some quantity.

Apart from their seed-gathering and wheat-harvesting in the late winter and spring, the people of the Bus Mordeh phase were herdsmen. A major aspect of their subsistence was the herding of goat, an animal not occurring normally on the plain (although wild goats inhabit the cliffs of the Kuh-i-Siah and Jebel Hamrin, not far away). North Khuzistan is excellent winter grazing land, a fact which may have had a great deal to do with the beginnings of food production there.

Most of the goats eaten during the Bus Mordeh phase were young; only a third of the flock reached the age of three years, and there were virtually no elderly goats represented in the bone remains. Judging by the discarded horn cores, mostly young males were eaten, presumably to conserve the females for breeding. Numbers of small, lightly-baked figurines resembling goats suggest that "magical" means may also have been resorted to in an effort to increase the herds. The goats of the Bus Mordeh phase differed barely, if at all, from the wild phenotype, having horns whose cross-sections were either quadrangular or lozenge-shaped; but the age-ratio of the herd differed strikingly from that of a wild goat population, not merely in terms of yearlings, but also in terms of the survivorship of two-year-olds, three-year-olds, and so on.

The Bus Mordeh villagers also herded sheep, but in much smaller numbers. One sheep skull from a basal Bus Mordeh phase house floor is hornless, indicating that sheep had been domestic for some time prior to the Bus Mordeh period. Our evidence tentatively suggests that horn loss by female sheep was one of the first osteological changes to follow domestication, and that male sheep underwent a change in horn core cross-section at a later date. There is no evidence that male sheep ever lost their horns at any time in our sequence. It is difficult to estimate the relative proportions of sheep to goat in the Bus Mordeh phase herds, but goats were certainly more than ten times as numerous. This would seem to be typical of the Southern Zagros. Similarly high proportions of goats (relative to sheep) characterized Tepe Guran (Flannery, unpublished data), Sarab (Bökönyi, personal communication), and Jarmo (Reed, personal communication).

Hunting and fishing constituted the fourth major component of Bus Mordeh subsistence. The common ungulate of the Khuzistan steppe is the Persian gazelle, which was brought down by the villagers in tremendous numbers. Onager, wild ox, and wild boar were also taken; small mammals, like the red fox, were a very small part of the diet. In particular, the Bus Mordeh phase stands out in the Deh Luran sequence for its use of aquatic resources like carp, catfish, mussel, and water turtle. Seasonal waterfowl, which visit the Deh Luran region between November and March, were also eaten, and, along with the harvested wild legumes, indicate the real importance of the winter resources of northern Khuzistan. On the basis of plants and animals recovered, we could not prove beyond a shadow of doubt that the Bus Mordeh folk were in the Deh Luran plain during the hot, dry summer months.

The flint tools manufactured by the Bus Mordeh villagers were varied and abundant, but for the most part it is impossible to separate those designed to deal with hunting and those designed to deal with domestic animals. Possibly the diagonal-ended-and-backed microliths served as parts of composite hunting tools, but the scores of endscrapers could have served as well for working the hides of domestic goats and sheep as for those of gazelles and onagers. Drills were also abundant, and the assemblage included reamers, burins, and retouched blades of various kinds.

From narrow, bullet-shaped cores, the Bus Mordeh people struck tens of thousands of flint blades, some of them only a few millimeters wide. A relatively small percentage of these were turned into other tools by means of bone pressure-flakers. Flint nodules from the bed of the Dawairij River served as raw material for the flint-knappers, and waste flakes were strewn through the rooms we found. About one per cent of the chipped stone was obsidian, identified through trace element analysis as native to the Lake Van region of eastern Turkey.

Other tools used by the Bus Mordeh villagers for dealing directly with problems of subsistence included pounders made from flint nodules or chunky, only partially-used flint cores; small abraders made from gritty slabs of sandstone; small "picks" of chipped flint; and bone awls made from the metapodials of goat or gazelle. The only evidence of containers so far recovered from this phase are three fragments of bowls ground from soft stone. Baskets may have been present, but our limited exposure did not reveal any evidence beyond the weaving of simple reed or club-rush mats. Compared with the phases which were to follow, the Bus Mordeh tool assemblage is lacking in variety, especially in the category of ground stone and heavy chipped-stone tools.

We have not yet recovered a burial that can with any assurance be assigned to the Bus Mordeh phase. We do know, however, that the villagers ornamented themselves with pendants of boar tusk, mussel shell, and polished flat pebbles; wore small "buttons" of tusk and mother-of-pearl which may have been sewn onto garments of some kind; and had necklaces of tubular stone beads, or flat disc beads which were red, white, and black. They also used cowrie shells which presumably came from the Persian Gulf.

On the basis of artifactual cross-ties and resemblances, the Bus Mordeh phase is probably broadly contemporary with sites like Zawi Chemi Shanidar, Karim Shahir, Asiab, and Tepe Ganj-i Dareh. Our chronological placement is supported by at least one of the Bus Mordeh radiocarbon dates, which was 7900 B.C. So far as we can tell from our excavations and surface survey, there is only one village of this phase in the Deh Luran plain; in fact, sites of this age are rare anywhere in western Iran, and no two of the sites known are exactly alike. That the Bus Mordeh folk had relations with people outside Deh Luran is evident from the occurrence of Turkish obsidian, and from the cultivated emmer wheat whose natural habitat lies elsewhere. Neither of these implies much in the way of systematic trade, but the Bus Mordeh villagers had at least a few local raw materials, like natural asphalt, which they could have exchanged for obsidian.

The relative scarcity of summer-season products in the refuse, plus the abundance of goats, suggests that the Bus Mordeh people may have been at least partially transhumant. Within a few days' travel from Deh Luran are mountain valleys like that of the Saimarreh River, which even today serve as summer pasture for Khuzistan herders. Transhumance would have been one mechanism for preventing total isolation of the Deh Luran villagers from happenings in the uplands, and it would have given them the opportunity to exchange new products or ideas with their neighbors. And yet, beyond the few items mentioned above, there is little tangible evidence to show an awareness, on the part of the Bus Mordeh folk, of the world beyond the plains of Khuzistan.

The Ali Kosh phase
6750 to 6000 B.C.

The Bus Mordeh adaptation was a successful one, and by comparing it with the Ali Kosh phase we can isolate those components which were most successful, for they were on the increase between 6500 and 6000 B.C. Cultivation of winter-grown cereals and hunting of large ungulates increased during the Ali Kosh phase, and there was a slight increase in numbers of domestic sheep. During the phase there seems to have been a real tapering-off in the collection of small-seeded wild legumes.

About 40 per cent of the carbonized seeds left behind in the hearths and middens of the Ali Kosh phase were grains of emmer wheat and two-row hulled barley. These were the same plants grown in the Bus Mordeh phase; only their amount had increased. Quite probably, in increasing the acreage under cultivation around Ali Kosh, the villagers had reduced the number of small wild legumes and useful wild grasses, since these have roughly the same growing season and compete for the same kind of soil as the cereals: sandy, well-drained loam with low salinity. We are uncertain to what extent grazing by goats and sheep also contributed to a reduction in the native wild flora. The effects of this land-use were to become apparent in later phases, but the Ali Kosh period was one of apparent prosperity.

Small legumes like those collected in the Bus Mordeh phase had dropped to just under twenty per cent of the seeds. Goat-face grass, ryegrass, and einkorn wheat, the crop weeds, were well established now; and the villagers collected wild oats, canary grass, goosefoot, caper, and others. A single lentil has so far been identified from this phase, suggesting that the Ali Kosh farmers were in contact with villagers in the mountains which, like Jarmo, had begun to cultivate some of the large-seeded annual legumes (Helbaek 1960a:115). Studies of the carbonized plants suggest that reeds or club-rushes may have been the most popular fuel for hearths.

The prosperity of the Ali Kosh phase is perhaps best reflected in its architecture. We do not know, because of our limited exposure, whether of not the village had grown larger, but the multiroomed houses evidently had. The rooms we found were larger than 3 by 3 meters, and the walls were up to a meter thick. The walls, built up of large, untempered, clay-slab bricks averaging 40 by 25 by 10 cm., were held together by mud mortar and often finished on both sides by a coat of smooth mud plaster. Where two walls came together, they simply "butted," with no interlocking of bricks. House floors were of stamped mud, often surfaced with a layer of clean clay, and apparently topped with over-two, under-two woven mats of reed or club-rush. There were apparent courtyards, which contained domed brick ovens and brick-lined roasting pits. No ovens were found inside rooms, and considering the heat of the Khuzistan summer, it would have been no advantage to have them inside. There were also doorways and small niches in walls, and narrow alleyways separating houses.

Domestic goats were the animals most commonly eaten by the villagers of the Ali Kosh phase. Showing clear osteological evidence of domestication, these goats had horn cores which might be quadrangular, lozenge-shaped, or plano-convex (medially flattened) in cross-section. Most were still eaten while quite young, though 40 per cent reached the age of three years—an increase over the Bus Mordeh phase. The few domestic sheep appearing in the Ali Kosh phase were still outnumbered heavily by goats; and male sheep horn cores still indicate no osteological deviation from the wild phenotype.

The Ali Kosh phase saw increased hunting of gazelle, onager, and wild cattle. To deal with the heavier ungulates, the villagers used a set of specialized butchering tools: flint pebble choppers for fracturing limb bones, small "slicing slabs" which could be inserted under tendons or ligaments to facilitate cutting with flint blades, and of course, blades and scrapers by the hundreds. Included in butchering areas are more enigmatic tools, like chipped limestone discs which (among other possible uses), may have been the "anvils" on which ungulate limbs were tapped to release their marrow. Chipping scars on the bones themselves suggest that this technique, common among some hunting peoples of the New World, was also used at Deh Luran. Scarred, chipped, fractured ox and onager bones were left in piles in the corners of the Ali Kosh phase rooms in association with such tools; gazelles and domestic goats were differently dealt with.

Use of aquatic resources went on in the Ali Kosh phase. Catfish, carp, water turtle, mussels, ducks, geese, cranes, herons, and river crabs were among the animals they collected. Their interest in small land mammals was relatively slight, although foxes were eaten.

The Ali Kosh villagers harvested their cereals with flint sickles, which were set into hafts by means of asphalt. They ground up wheat, barley, and crop weeds on saddle-shaped or shallow-basin grinding slabs, using simple discoidal handstones of pitted limestone. An innovation was the use of the stone mortar and pestle. Some grinding stones show traces of red ochre, an iron oxide pigment which was used in a variety of ways.

Besides chipping flint nodules into butchering choppers, the Ali Kosh folk produced tens of thousands of flint blades struck from narrow, conical, bullet-shaped polyhedral cores, and wider "tongue-shaped" cores. Some of the blades were secondarily retouched into diagonal-ended and backed bladelets for use in composite hunting tools, or into end-of-blade scrapers for hide-working. Chunkier cores were also used in the production of flakes, some of which eventually became scrapers. Drills, reamers, burins, and other tools were manufactured. Some of the finer retouching seems to have been done with small mussel-shell pressure flakers. Particularly characteristic of the phase were domed or keeled scrapers made from chunky cores, and resembling the "scraper planes" used in the prehistoric southwestern United States or Mexico for extracting the edible pulp from tough fiber plants. Obsidian from Lake Van constituted about two per cent of the chipped stone during Ali Kosh times.

The villagers used pounders made from flint nodules or crude flint blade cores (some of which were also used as pestles). We have already mentioned the flint pebble choppers and slicing slabs which were abundant in houses of this phase. Bone awls or bodkins and bone needles were manufactured, and at least some of them were sharpened on grooved rubbing stones made from gray, gritty sandstone. Chipped limestone discs, pecked balls of limestone which may have been light-duty pounders, and other heavy-duty ground-stone tools were common.

The use of containers is much clearer in the Ali Kosh phase than in the preceding levels of the Bus Mordeh period. In addition to over-two, under-two and over-one, under-one floor mats, the villagers made simple twined ("wicker") baskets with an over-one, under-one weave. Some of these seem to have been waterproofed with asphalt. A curious tool used (it would seem) in the stirring and spreading of asphalt resembles a limestone "sashweight." These roughly cigar-shaped stones, smeared at one end with asphalt and occasionally with red ochre as well, occurred by the hundreds.

Stone bowls greatly increased in number and variety during the Ali Kosh phase. Some were carved out of stone as soft as gypsum, while others were made with painstaking care from stone as hard as marble. Flat-based bowls with a simple rounded rim, or a "beaded" rim were commonest, but there were also shallow "trays" of limestone. None of these stone vessels were large enough to have served for storage; each would have held only a single meal for a single individual. Possibly they may once have held the gruel cooked up from the ground and roasted wheat and barley; it is worth noting that emmer wheat and hulled barley are largely unsuitable for bread-making, and that the ovens in the Ali Kosh phase courtyards were more likely for roasting or parching grain than for baking.

Lightly-baked, perhaps in the same ovens, were a variety of figurines. These included the small, goatlike figures already made in Bus Mordeh times, which may have functioned as charms connected with the increase of domestic herds. But the Ali Kosh villagers also made a few human figurines, preserved only in very frag-mentary condition. Clay cylinders of various kinds (some of which may have been parts of figurines) occurred in great quantity—some have pinched ends, some appliqué blobs, some show punctations that may depict tattooing such as that seem occasionally (when the opportunity presents itself) on the native women of Khuzistan even today.

These figurines are not complete or realistic enough to show us how the Ali Kosh villagers dressed; but the burials provided clues. The women of the phase practiced annular skull deformation and wore strings of beads composed of flat black or white stone discs, sea shells, or tubular stones. Men wore some sort of pubic covering, the imperishable part of which was a bell-shaped cover of polished stone, asphalt, or lightly-baked clay. Other ornaments, worn perhaps by either sex, included boar tusk or mussel-shell pendants, plummet-shaped or flat pebble pendants, and strings of disc beads with tubular bead spacers. Turquoise, imported from at least as far away as the Iranian Plateau, was made into small irregular beads. Native copper, perhaps from the Iranian Plateau as well, appeared in the form of a tubular bead which had been cold-hammered, cut with a chisel, and rolled into shape.

When an individual died during the Ali Kosh phase, his body (sometimes coated with red ochre) was tightly flexed and wrapped in a twilled, over-two, under-two reed or club-rush mat. An excavation was made under the floor of his house, and the bundled body placed (often in a sitting position) under the floor at no great depth, accompanied by articles of personal adornment. A few individuals, however, seem to have been reburied at a later date, after their flesh had decomposed. Perhaps in the case of a few persons of relative prestige, the bundled bodies were saved for a delayed, more elaborate burial (as in the case of a number of American Indian groups). Alternatively, certain individuals may have been disinterred and reburied at a later date, either purposefully or through accidental disturbance of a long-forgotten burial. Not all components of the skeleton were present in these secondary burials.

Ali Kosh is the only site in the Deh Luran plain which is definitely known to have been occupied during this period; the village was approximately a hectare in extent. Given the size and spacing of the Ali Kosh houses, it was probably not occupied by more than one hundred individuals. This would give us an estimated population density for the Deh Luran plain of perhaps 0.3 persons per square kilometer.

The network of exchange participated in by the people of the Ali Kosh phase, however, was greater than that of the preceding Bus Mordeh phase. Sea shells (from the Persian Gulf?), copper (from central Iran?), turquoise (from the Mashed region, near the Afghanistan border?), and obsidian from eastern Turkey, all reached Ali Kosh at this period. In addition, the domestic goats raised by these villagers were in contact with other herds, from whom they had presumably picked up some of the genes responsible for the medially-flattened horn core. It may be that this gene flow took place late in the summer, when the Deh Luran herds may have been taken up to the summer grazing lands of Luristan and came into proximity with other domestic herds.

Typologically, the Ali Kosh phase would seem to be contemporary with prepottery levels at Jarmo in Iraqi Kurdistan, and Tepe Guran in Iranian Luristan. Several radiocarbon dates in the 6500 B.C. time range would tend to support this placement.

The Mohammad Jaffar phase
6000 to 5600 B.C.

The Mohammad Jaffar phase saw innovations in subsistence, architecture, and artifacts. The villagers of this phase lived in houses whose foundations were built of river pebbles, with some use of larger cobbles and even river boulders. Above these foundations, the walls were of clay-slab bricks, plastered with mud; a few crumbled wall fragments indicate that in some cases this plaster was painted with red ochre. The walls were up to a meter thick, and floors were of stamped mud or clean clay, covered with over-two, under-two reed or club-rush mats.

More than a thousand years of agriculture had preceded this phase, and the carbonized plant remains reflect the changed land surface of this part of the Deh Luran plain. Emmer wheat and two-row hulled barley were still virtually the only crops known, although an occasional lentil indicates contact with mountain farming groups. But practices of fallowing and grazing had removed a great deal of the natural vegetational cover in the vicinity of the site, and its place was taken by pasture plants like plantain, mallow, vetch, oat grass, and canary grass. In particular, the area had seen an increase in the woody perennial legume *Prosopis,* a plant related to American mesquite and known to the Arabs as *shauk.* The fleshy pods of this plant are edible, and the discarded seeds (which are not eaten) appeared in carbonized form by the hundreds in Mohammad Jaffar phase middens. Adams (1965:5) points out that *shauk* tends to increase with cultivation because it matures so late in the year that it competes hardly at all with winter-sown crops, and hence does not suffer the fate of winter-maturing weeds.

This increase in *Prosopis,* which somewhat reduced the percentage of wheat and barley grains in the total assemblage of carbonized plants, was not the chance occurrence of a single bonfire: it characterized ash samples from outside houses, inside houses, in middens, in asphalt-coated baskets, everywhere. Other plants which seem to have been on the increase were fumitory (*Fumaria*) and goose-grass (*Galium*), both field weeds. Wild ryegrass, goatface grass, vetchling, and caper still appeared in the refuse.

In other words, farming in the Mohammad Jaffar phase, while obviously successful, required careful weeding and a reasonable fallowing system, which had altered the landscape to a noticeable degree. Similar problems must have beset the herdsman as he sought to find adequate pasture for his flocks in a region where the amount of land given over to cultivation was on the increase. For herding was also expanding, to judge by the animal bones, and sheep along with it. Sheep were outnumbered by goats at the start of the Mohammad Jaffar phase, but gaining on them rapidly by 5500 B.C. In later periods, they were to overtake and pass them by a wide margin, becoming the most common domestic animal of prehistoric and early historic Khuzistan (Adams 1962:115). Sheep, after all, have a panting mechanism which enables them to survive better than some domesticated animals under the hot climatic regime of the steppe (Schmidt-Nielsen 1964:99).

Osteologically, both the sheep and the goats of the Mohammad Jaffar phase can be considered as highly domesticated. Some goats had already begun to exhibit the helically-twisted or "corkscrew" horn core of modern Iranian domestic goats, although most individuals preserved the straight, medially-flattened, or quadrangular horn core cross-section. Male sheep of this period had the "goat-like" horn core cross-section typical of domesticates, and not the anteriorly-broad cross-section of wild Luristan sheep. The Mohammad Jaffar villagers still liked to eat their goats and sheep at the young stage, and only about forty per cent of the herd reached the age of three years.

Mohammad Jaffar phase hunters brought down gazelle, onager, aurochs, and wild pig, possibly using projectiles whose heads were barbed with backed and diagonal-ended microliths set in asphalt. As in earlier periods, piles of onager and aurochs bones are accompanied by the flint pebble choppers, flint blades, and scarred "slicing slabs" which were probably used in butchering. Broken limb-bone ends show chipping scars which may have been produced when the marrow was tapped out, perhaps on the chipped limestone discs abundant in the butchering refuse. Cut marks near tendon attachments show that limbs were disarticulated with flint blades; most bones show no evidence of burning, while a few are charred, as if some haunches had been roasted over hot coals. The villagers continued their use of winter water birds, and fished for catfish and some carp, as well as collecting crabs, water turtles, and freshwater mussels. As the grazing of domesticated animals increased, it would have reduced the amount of forage available for the wild ungulates; no real decrease in the number of such animals is noted until after the Mohammad Jaffar phase, but it may be significant that more small mammals seem to have been eaten in this period. Fox, hedgehog, and wild cat were included in the diet. Large canids were only rarely eaten, and there is no concrete evidence as yet for the domestic dog.

The hulled barley and emmer wheat were harvested with flint blades set in a haft, with asphalt as the principal mastic; grains were roasted before grinding up for use in gruel. The difficulty of removing the glumes of these early cereals had been countered by the Mohammad Jaffar people through an array of grinding implements which, in terms of variety and number, was never matched in later periods. Besides the saddle-shaped and shallow-basin grinding slabs inherited from the Ali Kosh phase, the Mohammad Jaffar folk made implements which were combination shallow-basin grinding slabs and mortars; these were used in conjunction with implements appearing to be combination handstones and pestles. They also used pebble mortars; boulder mortars; flat-topped boulder slabs; discoidal, loaf-shaped, or irregular elongate handstones; and stubby, bell-shaped mullers. The difficulty of processing in bulk cereals which were not yet genetically "free-threshing" is reflected in the lengths to which the Mohammad

Jaffar people had gone in evolving an adequate ground-stone industry for coping with the problem. In later periods, with free-threshing cereals, such variety of grinding implements rapidly dwindled.

The Mohammad Jaffar villagers continued to produce flint blades in the remarkable quantity as in preceding phases; more than a hundred sickle blades were recovered from levels of this period. An innovation was the practice of trimming sickle blades so that they would fit into a particular slot in the handle, a custom that was to become common in later phases. Drills, reamers, and end-scrapers made either on blades or on flakes were also tools typical of the period. It may be that many of the drills and reamers were for use in making wooden tools which have not been preserved; others, like some of the bone awls and needles, may have been for perforating hides. Nearly two per cent of the chipped stone from this phase was obsidian.

Bone awls, needles, and chisels may have been sharpened on grooved rubbing stones. Flat spatulas were ground out of ribs or flat slabs of animal bone. The villagers' kitchen areas were filled with discarded choppers, flint nodule pounders, "sashweight" asphalt stirrers, slicing slabs, chipped limestone discs, and pecked stone balls. They also ground up red ochre on pitted limestone slabs.

Twined baskets (either over-two, under-two or over-one, under-one) were coated with asphalt for waterproofing; some baskets had "floors" of plaited matting rather than twined centers, and most appeared to be shallow trays which may have served in seed-collecting. Many of the same stone-bowl types seen in the Ali Kosh phase continued, including flat-based bowls with a simple or beaded rim. The villagers also manufactured oval bowls and a few highly polished miniature vessels.

The most striking innovation in the field of containers was pottery, which made its first appearance in the Mohammad Jaffar phase. The pottery of this period was soft, friable, and straw-tempered, made of clay which differed but little from that used in previous periods to make figurines. The techniques used to finish and decorate the surface were not so far removed from those used in wall-surfacing: a smoothing or burnishing of the clay, followed by a coating of red ochre. The tempering material, straw, was a by-product of agriculture. Several of the vessel shapes are shared by stone bowls of the same period. The pots themselves could easily have been baked in an oven like that used for centuries previously to roast grain or bake figurines. In other words, although pottery appears rather abruptly in the Mohammad Jaffar phase, virtually all the concepts needed to manufacture it had already existed previously in southwestern Asia: clay working, smoothing and ochre-painting of clay, firing, and container forms. We do not know where this type of pottery, introduced into the Deh Luran plain early in the Mohammad Jaffar phase, was first manufactured. We simply point out that, like all innovations, it was simply a recombination of previously existing techniques.

The pottery of the Mohammad Jaffar phase was basically of three types, all of which were made with poorly cleaned clay tempered with chaff. First, there were plain buff bowls with pinkish or blackish firing clouds; these might be round and deep, with slightly everted lips, or else large and oval. Second, there was a variety of deep bowl whose surface was decorated with geometric motifs in fugitive red ochre paint; zig-zags, chevrons, or pendant triangles and lozenges. A few of these pots had small troughlike spouts at the lip. Third, there were small bowls, either hemispherical or carinated, some with beaded rims, covered with a soft, red ochre wash or slip which had been burnished. A few red globular jars with dimpled bases and constricted "hole-mouths" appeared later in the phase, but never in great frequency.

Lightly baked clay figurines were made in great numbers. Most appeared as fragmentary cylinders, broken limbs and torsos, but there was at least one recognizable human figure depicted in a squatting position with hands on knees—the kind frequently referred to as a "mother goddess." A number of stalk- or T-shaped figurines may have been highly stylized human figures also. Clay polishers (possibly for burnishing pottery) were manufactured, and in fact, far greater and more varied use of clay was made during the Mohammad Jaffar phase than in previous periods. The villagers even chipped broken sherds of pottery into small perforated discs, which may be crude spindle whorls, or fly wheels for pump-type drills. If they were truly spindle whorls, we do not know what their use implies, for it is not yet known when wool and flax first came to be spun in Khuzistan.

The Mohammad Jaffar folk wore pendants of flat polished pebbles, mussel shell, or crab claw, and bracelets of white, black, and red stone disc beads, interrupted by tubular stone spacers. They imported cowrie shells and turquoise nodules which were also used as ornaments, and they made smooth-surfaced stone bracelets of marblelike stone. Particularly characteristic were lip plugs of asphalt, clay, or polished stone, one of which was found *in situ* on the lower jaw of a burial. Men wore girdles or G-strings decorated with a fringe of flat black stone disc beads, and a pubic covering with a bell-shaped artifact of stone, asphalt, or lightly baked clay. No purposeful skull deformation is known from this phase so far, but our number of skeletons recovered is very small and consists mostly of males. In the realm of exotica, there were stone "phalli" made from limestone or alabaster, often carefully polished. Numerous similar highly polished alabaster "phalli" were found in graves of the earliest occupation as Tell as-Sawwan near Samarra in Iraq, apparently equivalent in time to the Sabz Phase (El-Wailly 1963; 1964). Their appearance during the Mohammad Jaffar phase in the Deh Luran plain gives us our first real evidence of interaction between the Khuzistan steppe and the Tigris River region—an interaction which is more strongly manifested during the Sabz phase, with the arrival of many new products and techniques of possible northeast Mesopotamian origin.

When an adult male died during the Mohammad Jaffar phase, his body was taken outside the house and buried in semiflexed position on its left side, facing west. No evidence of mat-wrapping was detected on the burials we found, but red ochre appeared in some graves and at least one individual seems to have had a basket (with perishable foodstuffs?) at the shoulder. The individual was accompanied by his articles of personal adornment, including as many as three or four turquoise beads. At the hips were traces of a beaded G-string and the usual bell-shaped artifact.

Ali Kosh was a village of approximately one hectare in extent during this period. On the basis of our surface collections, it is possible that there were two other small villages in the Deh Luran plain at that time, north of Tepe Sabz; this will, of course, have to be confirmed by future excavations. We might therefore tentatively estimate the population density of the plain as approximately 1.0 person per square kilometer.

The Mohammad Jaffar people participated in an ever-widening trade network at this time, although the amount of material exchanged was fairly small, and there is no evidence of a medium more sophisticated than balanced reciprocity. They had obsidian from eastern Turkey, turquoise possibly from northeastern Iran, specular hematite which may have come from Fars, and sea shells from the Persian Gulf. The designs on their pottery, made in red ochre, show some relationship to designs on the contemporary pottery at Tepe Guran in Luristan and Tepe Sarab in southern Kurdistan; some ties can also be seen with later pottery from the alluvial lowlands, namely Samarra and Matarrah in the Tigris drainage of Iraq. The dimple-based, hole-mouth vessels of red burnished pottery suggest later jars from Tepe Sialk, near the Anarak copper lode on the high Iranian Plateau, and the convex-walled bowls in plain buff and fugitive ochre-painted buff are reminiscent of Qalat Jarmo in northern Kurdistan and Hajji Firuz Tepe in Azarbaijan. Speaking generally about the Zagros Mountains and Khuzistan, this was a time of population increase and settlement into a variety of habitats. Surface surveys hint at transhumant herding patterns with summer and winter settlements, and active exchange which linked the peoples east of the Tigris and its tributaries into a loose network along which new ideas traveled rapidly.

The Sabz phase
5500 to 5000 B.C.

Midway through the sixth millennium, the Deh Luran plain (and perhaps Khuzistan in general) went through a rapid and crucial transition which was to set it clearly in the path toward population expansion and urban life. The two major innovations of that period were (1) the beginnings of competent irrigation, and (2) the first local evidence for the use of domestic cattle. Our evidence suggests that irrigation was still a small-scale affair, and that cattle were probably used mainly for food; but within the next two thousand years, more advanced irrigation and the cattle-drawn plow led the lowlands into civilization.

We do not know yet whether or not the Sabz phase was an indigenous development out of the Mohammad Jaffar phase. Numbers of artifact types bridge the gap between the two phases, but there are also striking differences. Certain pottery types, ornaments, and tools continued into the Sabz phase, but the whole aspect of the chipped-stone industry changed drastically, and new tools appeared in significant quantity. Were the tools which show continuity merely those which were of wide distribution throughout the steppe in the early sixth millennium, or do they really indicate a local origin for the Sabz phase?

In Susiana proper—the rolling plain drained by the Karkheh and Diz rivers, only a hundred km. to the east of Deh Luran—Robert Adams (1962:112) found at least thirty-four villages belonging to this general period of time. We find it hard to believe that this many farmers and herders suddenly descended on Khuzistan at about 5500 B.C. And since the environment in Susiana proper was at least as favorable for early village settlement as that of the Deh Luran plain, we suspect that Susiana must have been occupied during the Mohammad Jaffar phase, although sites of that age have yet to be found there.

Only future excavations will be able to solve the problem of whether the Sabz phase is indigenous to Khuzistan. If indeed it consists, in part, of an influx of new peoples, our guess would be that the area most likely to contain its origins is the adjacent Tigris River steppe of northeast Mesopotamia. In the latter region, sites like Tell as-Sawwan had already assumed unprecedented proportions and evidently included the residences of important persons whose status was expressed in the form of rich burial equipment. Our limited exposure of the Sabz phase revealed no high status graves, but the agricultural complex we recovered is identical to that of Tell as-Sawwan (Helbaek 1964), which suggests that both areas lie within the same farming province.

One aspect of the Sabz phase is clear. It cannot be derived from the highlands. Its tools, its pottery, its complex of domestic plants are already within the tradition which was to lead on to the Ubaid. Its ceramic ties are with Eridu I, Samarra, Matarrah, Jaffarabad, and the southern lowlands, and not with sites in the Zagros Mountains like Siabid, Dalma Tepe, Mushki, or Jari, nor with sites in far northern Mesopotamia like Hassuna or Halaf. In one sense, the Sabz phase is a redefinition of the period Le Breton (1957) called "Susiana *a*." Its new definition is based on more than pottery.

Because our 1963 trench hit only midden deposits of this phase, we know nothing about its architecture. A few traces of plaited reed or club-rush matting, and some possible "door pivot stones" like those of later phases, were our only clues. The middens were rich enough in carbonized sheep and goat dung, tamarisk firewood, carbonized seeds, and broken animal bones to tell us something about the village, however.

The people of the Sabz phase planted "free-threshing" hexaploid bread wheat as well as emmer. They had hulled six-row barley, which was to become with time the most successful cultivated cereal of the Mesopotamian lowlands. In addition, they raised two-row hulled barley, lentils, vetch, and vetchling. They left behind almonds which may have been cultivated, or else gathered wild on the upper slopes of the Kuh-i-Siah. And they grew linseed or flax (*Linum*) whose seeds are too large to have come from plants raised on rainfall alone; they are in the size range of irrigated flax seeds from lowland Mesopotamian sites (see Helbaek 1960b:192–93; 1969).

Accompanying this agricultural development came a shift in settlement pattern. Instead of occupying well-drained, low rises near the margins of the seasonally-flooded central depression of the Deh Luran plain, many sites of the Sabz phase (including Tepe Sabz itself) are located where they could have taken advantage of the many small stream channels coming down off the mountains to the north of the plain. These natural drainages could have been used as sources of irrigation water during the winter rainy season, and enlarged or diverted with a minimum of effort. Many of them, even today, drain into small, low-lying areas of the plain, which are presently farmed by the nomads who visit the Deh Luran plain in the winter.

But not all Sabz phase villages used irrigation; as pointed out by Adams (1962), some villages of this period in Susiana proper were located in situations where irrigation could not have been practiced, from which he concludes that agriculture at this time must have been mainly dependent on rainfall. Artificial water control during the Sabz phase may have been principally an insurance policy against a bad year, a supplement to rainfall farming. Its implications for the future of lowland steppe agriculture, however, are obvious. Adams, for one, should not be surprised to learn of its inception by 5500 B.C., for he had already ventured that "the high early density of settlement in this region can perhaps be traced to the exceptionally favorable circumstances the region would have offered for the transition from dry farming to irrigation agriculture . . ." (Adams (1962).

Appearing in this phase for the first time is an implement known, for want of a better term, as a "polished celt". It is a flat, elongate limestone pebble which had been chipped into shape and ground until smooth. The upper end shows traces of the asphalt which held it in its handle; the lower end shows the kind of polish which accumulates on flint hoes used in regions of alluvial soil. From the Sabz phase on through the whole of the Tepe Sabz sequence, not only in Deh Luran but throughout the Khuzistan steppe, this was one of the most common tools recovered. It is a tool, to the best of our knowledge, unknown from the mountains at this time, although roughly chipped hoes are found in the contemporary Hassuna context in northern Mesopotamia. Its appearance, simultaneously with the first evidence of irrigation, is probably no coincidence, or else why would it be absent in the rain-fed uplands? Several possibilities for its use exist, and at present we have no way to decide between the alternatives. It could be, purely and simply, a hoe for breaking the surface of the alluvium. It could, on the other hand, be an instrument which functioned in the opening of breaches in stream levees and in the digging of small channels for water. Still another, more intriguing hypothesis has been advanced by a paleobotanist colleague, James Schoenwetter. Schoenwetter feels that perhaps, under conditions of digging-stick agriculture, weeds may not have constituted much of a problem; nor would they have been as much of a problem when cattle-drawn plows made large-scale cultivation a possibility. The time when weeds were most annoying might have been the period between the start of irrigation and the adoption of the plow. It is probably in that period of time that the so-called "polished celt" fits stratigraphically. Perhaps future investigations will make the role of this instrument more clear.

The villagers of the Sabz phase also raised goats, whose small, helically-twisted horn cores are indistinguishable from those of the modern Iranian domestic goat. In somewhat smaller numbers, they also raised domestic sheep with small, curled, and anteriorly-keeled horns. To these animals they had now added the domestic ox. The cattle of the Sabz phase were much smaller than the wild aurochs, and constituted only five per cent of the animal bones recovered from levels of that period, but they represent another landmark in the prehistory of Khuzistan.

Hunting continued during the Sabz phase, with gazelle still the most popular quarry; some onagers and wild boar were occasionally taken. The Sabz phase villagers continued the fishing and collecting of mussel and water turtle which had characterized the earlier periods at Deh Luran, perhaps an aspect of subsistence which indicates continuity from the Mohammad Jaffar phase. Birds, and small mammals like the fox and hedgehog, were also a part of their diet.

The domestic dog had now become a scavenger around the villages of the Deh Luran plain. Paintings on pottery vessels show that the Sabz phase dogs had erect ears and a long, fluffy tail which curled up over the back like that of the modern Kurdish shepherd's dog. Their bones show that they were nearly as large as the wolves of the Zargros Mountains, and the intact, semiarticulated condition of their remains indicates that they were not eaten.

Although they grew free-threshing wheat, the Sabz villagers dealt with their hulled barley and emmer wheat with many of the same grinding stone types as the folk of the Mohammad Jaffar phase: saddle-shaped slabs, combination mortar-and-shallow-basin slabs, simple discoidal handstones, and irregular sausage-shaped pestles. They used flint nodule pounders, or hammerstones made from crude flint cores, much as the Mohammad Jaffar villagers. They used similar slicing slabs in butchering sheep, goat, and gazelle, and other animals, but (perhaps due to reduced hunting of onager and wild ox) they seem not to have needed so many flint pebble choppers. They stirred asphalt with "sashweight"-shaped stones, and made bone awls, spatulas, and gouges not unlike those of the earlier phases in our sequence.

One of the most dramatic changes from the pattern of the Mohammad Jaffar phase is in the quantity and quality of flint tools. The Sabz phase villagers chose to use a new source of flint of uniformly low quality for most of their tools (although a few blades of good quality flint appear). Gone for the most part are the finely-chipped bladelet cores which are so characteristic of the preceding phases, and so clear an indication of the mastery of flint chipping. Where flint blades had been counted in the thousands during the Mahammad Jaffar phase, their numbers were reduced to less than one hundred in excavations of comparable magnitude in the Sabz phase. In neither this period nor the subsequent Khazineh phase did we recover obsidian.

The principal tools of the Sabz phase were plain blades, and sickle blades which had been trimmed to fit into particular slots in a handle. Equipment for composite hunting tools included crescent-shaped microliths, while use of items like drills, reamers, and scrapers had begun to taper off. We do not yet know whether or not this decrease in hide-working tools is related to the increase in spindle whorls and the growing of irrigated flax, a situation which suggests that woven wool or plant fiber may have been replacing leather for certain items. Generally speaking, the change in flint also suggests a shift away from a preoccupation with hunting, a trend which is further supported by the other evidence we have cited.

Although they made a few stone bowls with simple or "beaded" rims, like their Mohammad Jaffar predecessors, the villagers of the Sabz phase had entered into a tradition of pottery-making which, though changing gradually through time, was to characterize Khuzistan for the next two thousand years. In quality and complexity their ceramics far surpassed those of the Mohammad Jaffar phase. They still made oval bowls and hole-mouth jars of soft, chaff-tempered pinkish-tan pottery, but they had ceased to decorate it with fugitive red ochre paint. They still made red-slipped, burnished bowls with simple or beaded rims, but grit particles now constituted a greater part of the temper than previously. In addition, the Sabz potters had begun to make a hard, sand-tempered, yellowish-buff pottery which was far sturdier and less friable than anything seen in the Mohammad Jaffar phase. It appears to have been fired at a higher temperature than the soft, chaff-tempered wares of the Mohammad Jaffar phase—possibly even in a true kiln—and although still handmade, it was a clear technological advancement. Literally thousands of sherds appeared in excavations of this phase: it was the first point in our sequence during which fragments of pottery outnumbered fragments of flint.

In undecorated form, this sand-tempered buff ware was made into oval basins (not unlike the oval bowls in chaff-tempered pottery), convex-walled bowls (not unlike their chaff-tempered counterparts), small hemispherical bowls with simple or beaded rims (not unlike their stone counterparts), hole-mouth jars with dimple bases, and several new shapes—perhaps the most distinctive being a bowl supported by a short pedestal.

Appearing for the first time in this phase, however, were numbers of vessels of this same grit-tempered yellowish-buff ware to which designs had been added with paint. Most designs were geometric, and the paint used was an iron oxide or peroxide, like red ochre, but fired at such a temperature that it almost always turned tawny brown or grayish-black, rather than red. Moreover, it was far from fugitive, except in the case of a few reddish variants (possibly accidental). The paint was applied in a broad-line, free-hand manner, with a great deal of individualism, yet the vessels have a more professional quality about them than those of the Mohammad Jaffar phase. At the same time, they lack the standardization and extremely precise painting of later phases in the sequence.

Vessels in this type of pottery included large oval basins with black bands at rim and base, or convex-walled bowls whose exteriors were covered with painted designs: herringbones, chevrons, vertical panels of wiggly-line motifs, checkerboards, screens, or crosshatching. There were bowls on pedestal bases, some of which had little triangular or diamond-shaped "windows" cut in them. A few small bowls with incurved rims were covered with designs which resembled knotted cords or basketry; some of these were so densely painted that the design, instead of appearing in black on a buff background, appeared as buff designs in a black field—a technique known as "reserve" or "negative" decoration, and which was to increase with time.

The Sabz phase villagers made numerous items of clay and fired pottery. They continued the tradition of stylized, T-shaped or "stalk" figurines seen in the Mohammad Jaffar phase, and they made spindle whorls of a very distinctive kind, in the shape of a star or asterisk. They chipped or ground pot sherds into scrapers of various sizes; some may have been used to scrape the sides of pots that were being shaped from plastic clay, while others may possibly have replaced the flint scrapers of previous periods.

The people of this phase ornamented themselves with lip-plugs of lightly-baked clay, asphalt, or stone, as in the Mohammad Jaffar phase. They made stone bracelets or anklets, but not of the smooth polished kind seen in Mohammad Jaffar times. Their bracelets were flattened bands whose outer surface bore deeply-incised parallel lines which followed the circular course of the bracelet.

Materials of the Sabz phase are widespread in Khuzistan, but lie principally north of the isohyet indicating 300 mm. of rainfall. They were competent at irrigation, but they preferred to stay within the area where rainfall farming was possible, an area still sparsely-enough inhabited so that there was room for many villages. In the Deh Luran plain, there were at least six villages of this phase, each containing perhaps one hundred persons. This would give us an estimated population density of approximately two persons per square kilometer. As mentioned earlier, Adams' survey in Susiana proper found thirty-four villages which pertain to this period, of which only two (Jaffarabad and Chogha Mish) have been excavated. Most are in the neighborhood of one hectare in size, but a few may have been considerably larger—we have verbal reports that Chogha Mish, for example, may have been a sizeable settlement already in the Sabz phase. A conservative estimate for the population of Susiana proper at this time period would, therefore, be on the order of 3400 inhabitants.

The Sabz phase thus extended geographically from at least as far as Deh Luran in the northwest to perhaps as far as Ram Hormuz in the southeast. Nowhere in this entire region were sites as abundant as in the "Little Mesopotamia" between the Karkheh and Diz rivers, where sufficient rain and surface water plus good drainage provided the ideal situation for the transition to irrigation farming. To the southwest, the Eridu I culture—related but not identical—found its own environmental setting and had its own geographical distribution in the arid Tigris-Euphrates plain. To the northeast, Iranian mountain cultures—also related but different—seem to have been farming in the valley plains and perhaps sharing the mountain grazing lands with herders of the Sabz phase.

This was a crucial period of Iranian prehistory, about which we would like to know more. It has shown us the earliest clear evidence of irrigation, of cattle-herding, and possibly of kiln-fired pottery in southwestern Iran. With it we enter the Susiana sequence, heretofore defined on the basis of ceramics alone, which led on to the emergence of town life and civilization in the land between the Karkheh and the Diz. What eludes us still is a clear-cut picture of its origins.

The Khazineh phase
5000 to 4500 B.C.

Villagers of the Khazineh phase lived in houses of mud brick whose walls were sometimes founded on a single layer of pebbles or cobbles. On the floors were twilled mats of reed or club-rush, and the doors swung on pivots which fitted into stone sockets. Villages reaching two hectares in size are known from the Deh Luran plain, and much larger villages may well be buried under later deposits on some of the really big sites in the area—like Tepe Musiyan.

Khazineh phase farmers cultivated free-threshing wheat, two-row and six-row barley (both hulled and naked), lentils, vetch, vetchling and flax. Their herds consisted of sheep and goats in about equal numbers, with a few cattle as well. The horn cores and bones of these animals are indistinguishable from modern Iranian domestic breeds: goats had tightly twisted horns, and female sheep were probably mostly hornless. Domestic dogs scavenged on the village dumps, and there was a little hunting of gazelle and onager.

Ground stone was lacking in variety, possibly because the "naked" grains made mechanical husking unnecessary. There were saddle-shaped grinding slabs, boulder mortars, simple discoidal hand-stones, and irregular sausage-shaped pestles in use. Plain flint blades were chipped from cores (often from one side only, not using the whole periphery of the core), and some flakes and blades were retouched into other tools. Some sickle blades were both backed and truncated for fitting into hafts. No microlithic tools or obsidian appeared in the various building levels of the Khazineh phase we exposed. Polished celts, hafted with bitumen, continued as tools of considerable importance, and pounders made from flint nodules or from roughed out flint cores were also typical of the Khazineh phase.

In the Khazineh phase appeared the first evidence of coiled basketry we have seen in southwestern Iran. A larger exposure of Sabz phase levels might show that the manufacture of coiled basketry actually began in that period, but our earliest clear-cut impressions in asphalt date to about 5000 B.C. Coiled basketry occurs much earlier in the Anatolian region (Mellaart 1962:56), along with coiled pottery; apparently it took a millennium or more for the technique to reach the southern Zagros. We conclude that in early periods—about 6000 B.C.—there were two distinct vessel making traditions in the Near East, one involving coiled basketry and coiled pottery (in Antolia) and the other concentrating on twilled and twined basketry and pottery built up by lamination (in the Zagros). By 5000 B.C. the distribution of the two traditions overlapped.

The pottery of the Khazineh phase was related to that from Qala't Hajji Muhammad, near Warka (Ziegler 1953), and phase *b* of the Susiana sequence as defined by Le Breton. Decorative motifs were shared with a number of sites ranging over all of southern alluvial Mesopotamia and the Khuzistan steppe; ties with the mountains are much more tenuous, but some correspondences can be seen with Halaf, Banahilk, Siabid and other early fifth millenium sites.

Chaff-tempered red pottery continued in domestic usage. The predominant form was a hole-mouthed jar with dimple base, but there were also open bowls and carinated bowls in burnished red. Much of this type of pottery may have been made locally in the village households.

In the same levels occurred thousands of sherds of decorated buff pottery which may have been made by craft specialists. Included were large carinated bowls with complicated geometric patterns painted (primarily in black) on the inside of the base— "sundials," "flowers," and "wheels" were common motifs. There were also many small hemispherical bowls with exterior patterns resembling knotted cords or basketry designs. "Bow-ties," rows of lozenges, or diamonds were also favorite designs. The Khazineh phase potters made "sauce boats" with handles, and convex-walled bowls like those already seen in the Sabz phase. Many of the latter were covered with "close" patterns, "screens" or "checkerboards" so densely painted that the design appears "in reserve." In fact, the Khazineh phase represented a climax in "reserve" or "negative" geometric patterns; never again was such a large proportion of the vessel surface so densely covered with black, greenish-black, or reddish-black paint.

For the most part, plain buff pottery appeared in the same shapes as black-on-buff painted ware, but it was less common.

The Khazineh phase villagers still used star-shaped spindle whorls and wore nail-shaped and cuff-link-shaped labrets, as had their Sabz phase predecessors. They manufactured scrapers (and pot lids?) from chipped sherds, and made awls and pressure-flakers from bone. A few fragments of bone appear to have come from broken hafts for flint tools.

Most of the activities indicated in the "kitchen debris" are those still carried on by the small villages of Khuzistan: hoeing, harvesting, grinding grain, roasting and cooking cereals and legumes, spinning fiber, tending and butchering sheep and goats, and working their hides.

In the Deh Luran plain at this time there were six to eight villages; Adams' survey in Susiana proper located 102 contemporary sites, some of which appear to have covered many hectares. Some villages were in areas where irrigation is possible; others were not. Dry farming, small-scale irrigation, and herding, with probable transhumant movements to the valleys of mountainous Luristan and Fars, were the main subsistence activities.

The geographic range of the Khazineh phase includes all of Khuzistan; to the southwest lay the Hajji Mohammad culture area, which had related pottery, but not necessarily related economic and social activities, as we shall see when we discuss the subsequent Mehmeh phase.

At this point it is clear that Tepe Sabz was near the small end of a size continuum which must have included much larger and more important villages elsewhere in Khuzistan. The debris of the Khazineh phase yielded few of the exotic imported items and raw materials one might expect from this period. This suggests to us that differential access to these exotic raw materials was a real factor, and that these items are most likely to be found at the more important sites, where persons of somewhat higher status resided.

There are at least twelve sites of the Khazineh phase in the Deh Luran plain, giving us an estimated population density of four persons per square km. Adams' surveys in Susiana proper disclosed 102 sites, suggesting a total population for Khuzistan of more than 10,000.

The Mehmeh phase
4500 to 4100 B.C.

Through a series of accidents, we know more about the architecture of the Mehmeh phase than that of any other period. The house plans visible on the surface of Tepe Ashrafabad, and the architectural features recovered in the step trench at Tepe Sabz, tell essentially the same story. Houses were rectangular, reaching at least 5 by 10 in size, and with a door which pivoted on a perforated stone on one of the long sides. The outer walls were nearly a meter thick, founded on two parallel rows of cobbles separated by a band of closely-set river pebbles. Above this, the outer walls were of un-tempered sun-dried clay bricks perhaps 20 by 50 by 10 cm. in size; they were finished with a layer of mud plaster. Inside the houses were platforms with cobble foundations, possible storage areas, and a number of walls of tamped clay which probably were room dividers. The floors were covered with twilled (over-two, under-two) reed or club-rush mats. Three to five persons could have lived comfortably in such a house, to judge by present dwellings in the Deh Luran plain.

Villagers in the Mehmeh phase cultivated roughly the same crops as in Khazineh times: two-row and six-row barley, free-threshing wheat, lentils, vetch, vetchling, grass peas, and flax, with some evidence of irrigation reflected in the size of the flax seeds. Sheep and goats, in approximately equal numbers, were by far the most common domestic animals; some cattle were herded, and domestic dogs were present. Onager, wild pig, small mammals, birds, and turtles made up a small percentage of the diet.

Representations of bowmen, gazelles, and gazelle and wild goat tracks on pottery of the Mehmeh phase suggest that these villagers hunted gazelle with bow and arrow, probably by ambush hunting along known gazelle trails. Such trails are abundant near Tepe Sabz, and follow tamarisk-filled *wadis* where a bowman could crouch in wait for the gazelle.

Most grinding stones from Mehmeh phase levels were saddle-shaped slabs; a few of these also had "sockets" in them for use as mortars. They were used in conjunction with simple discoidal handstones or irregular, sausage-shaped handstones or pestles. Pounders made from flint nodules or roughed-out cores, and com-bination pounder-rubbing stones were also typical of the phase.

The Mehmeh phase flint knappers struck hundreds of plain blades from cores, using only one side of the striking platform rather than the whole periphery. Some of these blades were retouched, truncated, or backed, often for use in sickles; still others were made into drills. Obsidian, used for blades, was very rare, representing less than one per cent of the chipped stone. Polished and hafted limestone celts and heavy grooved mauls made up the remainder of the stone tools.

Coiled basketry had now become a normal part of the artifact assemblage, as indicated by impressions in asphalt. These baskets were typically made on a grass bundle foundation, laced together with split grass stems.

The pottery of the Mehmeh phase overlaps with phase *c* of the Susiana sequence as defined by Le Breton, and has strong ties with Oates' "early Ubaid" at Eridu, and the Ras al Amiya pottery as described by Stronach. Specifically, this period featured a new pottery type, Mehmeh Red-on-red, which appeared also at Ras al Amiya (though in smaller quantities). This straw-tempered ware, which looked "Iranian" to Stronach (1961:122) had a soft pale red slip and was painted with geometric designs in dark red or purplish paint. Surprisingly, affinities of this pottery type seem to be with sites like Tepe Hissar and others on the Iranian Plateau rather than with nearer sites in the Zagros. Typical shapes were hole-mouth jars with dimple bases, covered with net or screen patterns, rows of tally marks, or other designs. Some of these jars had small spouts at the lip. Wide, shallow bowls or dishes with stripes (both inside and out), and small painted cups were also present. The temper included both chaff and grit. This type of pottery is a real "index fossil" for the Mehmeh phase.

Utility wares, presumed to be locally made, continued in much the same form as in Khazineh times. Soft, red pottery with chaff and grit tempering appeared in the form of hole-mouth jars with dimple bases, open bowls, and carinated bowls. However, the use of this soft red pottery was on the decline and it was destined to be abandoned altogether in subsequent periods. Khazineh Red wares represented a link with the earliest pottery-making periods in Khuzistan, a tradition which took many millennia to run its course.

To judge by the painted, black-on-buff pottery of the Mehmeh phase, ties between the Iranian Plateau and the Khuzistan steppe had never been stronger. Many large open bowls had naturalistic motifs like "rows of wild goats" or "dancing men" which can be traced as far as Sialk III, Hissar I*a,* and Tepe Giyan; these were also common at Tepe Jowi in Susiana proper, but did not appear at Eridu or Ras al Amiya. However, ties with the latter site can be clearly seen in globular jars with interior ledges at the rim, and fine bell-shaped bowls with meander or "wavy ladder" designs. Some carinated bowls with closely-painted "Hajji Muhammad" motifs or "sundial" interior bases persisted into the Mehmeh phase (just as they did at Ras al Amiya) but they were on the wane. Such designs were clearly in the process of being replaced by more "open" patterns such as typified in the later Ubaid pottery. And lastly, the extremely fine quality of some of the deep bowls of the Mehmeh phase suggests not only professional craftsmanship but use of at least a "slow" wheel.

Other distinctive artifacts of the Mehmeh phase were the "bent ceramic nails" so common at sites like Tepe Gawra, Eridu and al Ubaid. Almost all of these implements (whose function is still unknown) appeared in Mehmeh phase levels.

Villagers manufactured bone awls and needles, and flat knives cut from cattle ribs. Sherds were chipped into scrapers or pot lids (some of which probably were used to cover the mouths of ledge-rim jars). They used spindle whorls which were either star-shaped, oval-discoidal, or (more commonly) shaped like a small "chariot wheel." The "chariot wheel" type was made from buff pottery and painted in a variety of individualistic designs, most of which were not common on the black-on-buff pottery.

Mehmeh phase farmers ornamented themselves with T-shaped labrets and rings made from buff ware sherds of lightly fired clay. They also had copper pins with slightly diamond-shaped heads, like those used at Tepe Sialk in period III.

At least nine villages of the Mehmeh phase are known from the Deh Luran plain. The smallest are one to two hectares in extent, but there are hints that a very large village of this phase may lie buried under the south half of Tepe Musiyan. Adams found more than one hundred sites of this age in Susiana proper, most in the 1 to 2 hectare size range but some (like Chogha Mish) considerably larger. We estimate the population density of the Deh Luran plain at five persons per square kilometer, and the total population of Susiana proper at over 12,000 inhabitants during the Mehmeh phase.

It is clear from excavations in Iraq that there were towns of this period already in existence, some of them with temples. It is just as clear that by the Mehmeh phase, Deh Luran was a provincial backwater and Tepe Sabz a relatively small site with little evidence of ceremonial activities or political importance. The dramatic developments of this age were taking place in the Diz-Karheh plain, near Susa, and on the lower Euphrates near Eridu and Ur where much larger concentrations of population could be maintained. The marginal location of the Deh Luran plain kept it out of the mainstream of these developments, although extensive excavations at Musiyan might show that there was at least one important town in the area during the Mehmeh phase.

The Bayat phase
4100 to 3700 B.C.

Architectural details were well-preserved in Bayat phase levels at Tepe Sabz, but our step trench was too narrow to recover a complete house plan. The houses were large, with exterior walls up to a meter in thickness, composed of clay slab bricks and coated with a layer of mud plaster. Corners, where two walls came together, were "bonded" by interlocking the bricks from both walls. Smaller interior walls, possibly room dividers, were of compacted clay. In some cases, rooms were 3 m. wide and over 3 m. long, and the floors had a covering of twilled (over-two, under-two) reed or club-rush mats. Doors pivoted on perforated stones.

As houses aged and collapsed, they were used as dumps for refuse from adjacent houses: ash, hearth sweepings, broken pottery, the bones of butchered animals, even carcasses of dead dogs. Open areas between houses were used for burials. The Bayat phase villagers buried their dead in the extended position, lying on the right side and oriented roughly east-west. The graves were covered by stone slabs, some of which were discarded worn-out grinding stones. No ornaments were observed in our limited sample, but women were accompanied by saddle-shaped grinding slabs and simple discoidal handstones.

At this same time period, at Eridu in southern alluvial Meso-potamia, there is considerable evidence for high-status burials in brick tombs, accompanied by offerings of well-made pottery. This suggests that the Bayat phase burials we found may be typical only of the persons of lowest status (and possibly only of females?).

Bayat phase middens were rich in carbonized grains, spikelet forks, and internodes of barley, both hulled and naked. Both the six-row and two-row strains were grown. Since barley was the dominant cereal of later times in southern Mesopotamia (Helbaek 1960a; 1960b) it is interesting to note that its rise to prominence may have begun in Ubaid times. Factors favoring barley over wheat are low rainfall and high soil salinity, as well as the salinity of the water used for irrigation. All these factors may have applied in the Deh Luran plain, where today the soil salinity in some areas is so high that only sesame can be grown.

Other crops grown in the Bayat phase were wheat, lentils, vetch, grass peas, and flax, the same complex which had characterized Khuzistan since the beginnings of the Sabz phase.

Tamarisk was used as firewood in preference to reeds and club-rushes.

Helbaek notes a curious aspect of later Bayat phase samples of carbonized seeds: just as in the uppermost strata at Ali Kosh, agricultural products show signs of a recession, and weedy or salt-resistant plants come to the fore. By the time of Tepe Sabz' abandonment at around 3700 B.C., almost the only plants left are those which would have survived in salty fallow land or abandoned irrigation canals. We conclude that during the course of their two thousand year occupation, the farmers of Tepe Sabz so modified the immediate vicinity of the village that equilibrium was destroyed and the balance tipped toward salinity. Decreased agricultural productivity made it necessary eventually to abandon Tepe Sabz and move to a new location—in this case, perhaps only 5 km. away, to some site like Tepe Farukhabad.

It is interesting that the total duration of occupation at Tepe Sabz was similar to that of Ali Kosh; this suggests to us that two thousand years may be roughly the length of time required to reduce soil productivity in the Deh Luran plain to such a level that shifting of settlement becomes necessary—at least in areas where the soil is tenuously balanced on the verge of pro-hibitive salinity. More favorable localities (like that of Tepe Musiyan?) may have had a longer cycle of productivity, although our modern soil samples taken in 1961 indicate that even that area is now dangerously saline (Hole, Flannery, Neely 1969:20).

Sheep (some hornless) and goats (of the modern twisted-horn type) were herded in large numbers. There is evidence that sheep were becoming the dominant herd animals of the area, as we know they were during later periods of Khuzistan's history (Adams

1962:113). Cattle herding continued as a relatively minor activity. A single maxilla of what is probably a domestic pig indicates that Bayat phase villagers were in contact with pig-raising peoples— possibly the village farmers of Zagros Mountains, who are known to have had domestic pigs at this time (Flannery 1965:1254). There is little evidence for pig raising on the Deh Luran plain during the Bayat phase, however, possibly because seasonal transhumance was still an important part of the subsistence pattern. Hunting of gazelle, onager, and small game continued.

Saddle-shaped grinding slabs and simple discoidal handstone were the common grinding implements. The Bayat phase villagers produced hundreds of flint blades, only a few of which were ever retouched by design, although many show chipping from use. They made sickles by hafting blades which were either unmodified, or backed, or backed and truncated, probably depending on where they were to fit in the haft. Cores were chipped only around part of the periphery of the striking platform. Drills, and—very rarely—geometric microliths appeared. Less than one per cent of the chipped stone was obsidian.

Polished and hafted limestone celts were no longer as common as they had been. The manufacture of bone awls and spatulas continued, for metal was still an extremely rare item, at least at villages as small as Tepe Sabz. As in previous periods, the Bayat folk chipped out sherd scrapers and pot lids and wove baskets and mats from grasses of various kinds.

The pottery of the Bayat phase was squarely within the Ubaid tradition, and corresponds roughly to phase *d* of the Susiana sequence as defined by Le Breton. Ties were overwhelmingly with southern alluvial Mesopotamia and the Susiana sites of the Diz-Karheh River area; the naturalistic motifs of the Mehmeh phase had vanished, along with most of the other "Iranian Plateau" ceramic characteristics. Chaff-tempered pottery reached its lowest frequency in our entire sequence, and the painting of buff ware swung away from the earlier densely-covered style and took on the more open, "cursive" look of later Ubaid ceramics.

As chaff-tempered, soft red pottery disappeared, it was replaced by the hard, grit-tempered salmon red ware common in period A at Susa. Carinated bowls, hole-mouth jars, and a few necked jars were the only shapes in which this utility ware appeared. At this point we began to doubt that *any* of the pottery used at Tepe Sabz during Bayat times was produced in village households; even the "cooking wares" had the mass-produced, standardized look of craft pottery. Sherds of this salmon-colored pottery from Tepe Sabz were literally indistinguishable from those at Chogha Mish, more than 100 km. away—they could easily have come from the same kiln in the same pottery-making town.

The black-on-buff painted pottery was no longer as common as unpainted buff. On the larger bowls, decoration was limited to a series of hanging loops painted around the rim, or a simple wavy line between two pairs of straight lines. Large ring-based bowls with a simple painted band at rim and base were common; so were deep plain bowls with only a very cursive horizontal band of tally marks at the rim, or a plain black band. "Reserve" decoration or dense screen patterns were no longer in vogue. Perhaps the most abundant reminder of earlier ceramic styles was the fine, egg-shell-thin, bell-shaped bowl, which actually reached maximum frequency in the Bavat phase. This is the type of bowl which Stronach (1961:112) called "the finest product of the Ras al'Amiya potter."

Plain buff ware—in the form of carinated bowls, ring base bowls, and deep plain bowls—was the type of ceramic most abundantly represented in the trash piles of the Bayat phase. Standardized, technically competent, and aesthetically uninteresting, it nevertheless provided us with many of the most useful "index fossils" of the period.

A few rare sherds from vessels obtained by trade appeared in Bayat phase levels. All were types known from Mesopotamia: painted bichromes, fine black-on-tan, and highly burnished black.

Villagers of the Bayat phase used spindle whorls which were oval-discoidal or "chariot wheel"-shaped. Some whorls had appliqué blobs or rows of punctation. T-shaped labrets and ceramic "rings" appeared in small numbers. An innovation of the Bayat phase were the small biconical objects of unfired clay which have generally been referred to as "sling missiles." These "missiles," which occurred by the hundreds at sites like Tepe Gawra (Tobler 1950:16) never really became common at Tepe Sabz, and we wonder about their true functions.

The Bayat folk had definite ideas about property, which were reflected in their sealing of jars. Throughout the upper levels of Tepe Sabz occurred clay plugs which had evidently once been used to stopper pottery vessels. All had been stamped with cylindrical seals, and no two designs were alike. A few cylindrical bead seals appeared in the trash, bearing incised patterns like stylized, branching trees, or rows of herringbones. Apparently, the wet clay was pushed into the mouth of the jar and then the bead pressed into it two or three times and rolled from side to side. Whether the designs were specific to individuals, lineages, or merchants is not clear, but the Bayat phase was the earliest point in our sequence when such property-marking became evident.

At least nine villages or towns (some reasonably large) are known from the Deh Luran plain at this time period. One of these has an apparent series of temples within it, but it is not known yet whether this series reaches back into the Bayat phase. Adams found 116 sites of all sizes in Susiana proper dating to the Bayat phase. Since this part of the "Ubaid" sequence includes everything from hamlets to towns with temples and high-status cemeteries, it is clear that Tepe Sabz throws very little light on the social and political complexity of the period.

The Ubaid "oikumene," of which the Bayat phase is just one regional variant, stretched from Syria and eastern Palestine to the Turkoman steppe. It represented some sort of plateau on the road toward urban civilization. This final phase of our Deh Luran excavations, while telling us little politically, makes it clear that by 4000 B.C. the basic "barley and sheep" economy of the early Mesopotamian-Khuzistan civilizations was in the process of formation. We estimate the population density of the Deh Luran plain at this time at possibly six persons per square kilometer. The total population of Susiana proper probably exceeded 15,000.

MAN'S PLACE IN THE KHUZISTAN ECOSYSTEM

A model for consideration of the evidence

Our data from the Deh Luran plain, combined with those of Adams (1962), suggest a model for the internal dynamics of prehistoric Khuzistan, which can be investigated and modified by future workers in the area. The model is as follows.

At 8000 B.C. the original post-Pleistocene environment of Khuzistan lay unmodified: a rolling steppeland with 300 mm. of rainfall concentrated in the winter months, and a growing season which climaxed in March. Physiographically, the region as a whole is an unstable geosyncline, but because it tends to fill with alluvium at approximately the same rate at which it settles, the general ecology remained stable for thousands of years. Khuzistan provides a number of biotopes which were exploited by early man: (1) open sandy plains, (2) reed-bordered marshes, (3) gypseous or saline depressions, (4) slow-moving streams and rivers, and (5) sandstone foothills. Each of these "microenvironments" had a complex of edible plants and animals which characterized it and which were available either year-round or at certain well-defined seasons.

Our hypothetical picture of life in Khuzistan during the food-collecting era is one of plains hunters who stalked gazelle, onager, and aurochs, and made use of the aquatic resources of the marshes and rivers, which were available year-round. If the onager herds moved up to the lower mountains during the heat of the summer (as they are known to do in Baluchistan), some hunter bands may have followed them. When winter rains reached the steppe, it turned into meadows of Bermuda and Canary grass, attracting the ungulate herds back down to lower elevations. The rich leguminous vegetation of late winter months—wild alfalfa, spiny milk vetch, *Trigonella,* and others—was intensively collected by early man. In those days human population was so scanty[3] and the effects of human predation so slight that the steppe was in equilibrium. Man was simply one species in a large and stable ecosystem.

We note, however, that the original Khuzistan environment included two different types of alluvial plain. One, because of its excellent natural drainage and underlying gravels, had only a mild tendency toward salinity; this was the type found in much of Susiana proper, between the Diz and Karkheh. The other, found at Deh Luran and elsewhere in Khuzistan, was balanced just at the threshold of salinity. This distinction was of little importance during the food-collecting era, but was to become critical at a later date.

The first change in the Khuzistan ecosystem came sometime before 7000 B.C., with the introduction of cereal cultivation and the herding of Caprines. What this process involved is rather interesting, in terms of man's capture of solar energy through environ-

---

[3] Braidwood and Reed (1957:21), for example, estimate the population density of Late Paleolithic hunter-gatherers in Iraq as 0.125 persons per square mile.

mental exploitation. The intense summer heat of southern Iran inhibits the growth of perennial vegetation; most plants there are annuals which come ripe after the cool winter rains. The annuals include most of the grasses and legumes edible by man; the perennials are often tough and thorny species of little direct human food value. What man did, before 7000 B.C., was to domesticate the annuals he could eat, and then domesticate the animals who lived on the perennials. This intensified his access to both energy sources, either directly or through an animal converter.

It is clear from the species involved—emmer wheat, two-row hulled barley, goats, and sheep—that the first food-production in Khuzistan involved plants and animals introduced from the mountains, not native to the steppe. Their success on the steppe, however, was such that a kind of "positive feedback" was established: the more wheat planted, the more mutants with a tough rachis were selected for; the greater the yield, the more farmers survived; the greater the population, the more wheat had to be planted. And so the system of cultivation was amplified, and between 7000 and 6000 B.C. cultivated grains grew from less than 5 per cent of the seeds consumed to roughly 40 per cent.

It may be that early farmers were first attracted to the steppe because of its great potential as winter grazing land, and that they stayed in the area only long enough to harvest a winter cereal crop before taking their herds up to summer pasture in the mountains. (There is little evidence that, at the outset, they exploited Khuzistan's summer-maturing plants.) But the productivity of the steppe, with its friable alluvium and its marshy areas of high water table, where grain could be planted in moist soils, led eventually to sedentary communities with permanent storage facilities. Helbaek's evidence suggests that they planted in areas so wet that carbonized club-rush (*Scirpus*) even showed up among the wheat and barley grains.

Once stabilized, however, this early domestic plant and animal complex allowed for only slow and limited population growth; as late as approximately 5800 B.C., population density in the Deh Luran plain was still probably no more than one person per square kilometer. We suggest that this early complex, which involved mainly emmer wheat and goats (augmented by barley and sheep, but in smaller numbers) was basically an upland-mountain adaptation, imposed, with limited success, on the lowland steppe.

Our preliminary surveys in the intermontane basins of western Iran—Luristan and southern Kurdistan—suggest that while some valleys were nearly unoccupied during the Mohammad Jaffar phase, others may have had a population double that of the Deh Luran plain (*cf.* Hole 1962). Such populations might well be expected in the well-watered uplands, where wheat and barley grow wild, and the returns of dry farming greater than in northern Khuzistan. Yet even if we postulate a density of two to three persons per square kilometer for certain of Kurdistan's intermontane plains during the Mohammad Jaffar phase, a rather sparse population is implied.[4] Moreover, neither Khuzistan nor Kurdistan at this time period exhibit much in the way of surpluses, social stratification, or craft specialization. We conclude that neither Kurdistan, nor Luristan, nor the upper plains of Khuzistan managed to support stratified societies on the basis of the early wheat-goat-dry farming complex. The difference was this: Kurdistan and Luristan had reached an equilibrium which was to change but little in the subsequent two millennia, while Khuzistan was to change drastically.

One thing the early complex did was to modify the vegetational pattern of Khuzistan. First, imperfectly cleaned batches of grain from the mountains introduced several new plants into the lowlands as field weeds; among these were goat-face grass, ryegrass, and wild oats. Second, land clearance and grazing removed the native grass cover in the vicinity of villages and replaced it with fallow-land and pasture plants like mallow, plantain, fumitory, goosegrass, and wild vetch. At least some of the field weeds and fallow-land plants were harvested and eaten. Their increase was at the expense of wild plants which would normally grow during the winter, and which competed for the very soils needed by the cultivated cereals: fine-grained alluvium. Ironically, it was the small legumes which had once figured in early man's diet (like milk vetch, *Trigonella,* and wild alfalfa) which suffered the most from land clearance; summer-maturing plants, like *Prosopis,* actually increased once their competition had been removed, because they did not conflict with the winter-maturing cereals. And with

---

[4] We find Braidwood and Reed's (1957:22) estimate of 25 persons per square mile for the Chemchemal Valley during the Jarmo phase much too high: note that it is based, not on the number of Jarmo-age sites in the valley, but on the present density of farming villages.

year-round occupation of villages, summer-available plants like *Prosopis* were eaten in much larger numbers. Thus man's food habits changed as the vegetation of the steppe was altered by the early agricultural regime.

In areas like Deh Luran, there were some deleterious aspects to early agriculture. After 1500 to 2000 years of farming, the site of Ali Kosh was abandoned—and there are hints in the plant remains from the terminal occupation that one reason was soil exhaustion. Two millennia of steady cultivation in an area delicately balanced at the limits of prohibitive salinity had eventually tipped the balance, and left the immediate vicinity a mildly saline waste of low productivity. However, there were still vast areas of the plain lying unoccupied, uncultivated, and in equilibrium; any over-cultivation problem could be solved by shifting settlement a few miles away.

During the early "wheat-goat" phase of Khuzistan agriculture, productivity was sufficiently low so that there were always virgin lands available, allowing disturbed and salinized areas time to re-cover. The social unit produced was the small (one by two hectare) multifamily community, which stayed at approximately the same size but shifted to new localities at intervals of perhaps two millennia. This pattern might have persisted for many centuries, except for another systemic change which took place between 5500 and 5000 B.C.

This second major change was a crucial one for Khuzistan. It may have been an outgrowth of the wheat-goat complex, but this could not be proved on the basis of our date from Deh Luran; too many intervening steps are missing.

The change involves the addition of some simple irrigation techniques to cereal cultivation. This innovation took advantage of Khuzistan's pattern of braided, aggrading stream channels (Adams 1962:113), many of which flow so close to the plain that water can easily be diverted from them without lifting devices. One of the immediate ecological results was the stabilizing of a hulled six-row strain of barley, which was destined to become the most important cereal of the lowlands. Irrigated six-row barley initiated another "positive feedback" situation which, once begun, continued to reinforce itself and increase the area under cultivation dramatically when compared with previous periods.

A second systemic change of this period was an increase in the relative proportions of sheep, slowly at first but growing with geometric rapidity toward the end of our sequence. The ability of sheep to withstand the high summer temperatures of the steppe probably had something to do with this—and if only we had concrete data on the start of wool-bearing in sheep, we might find that this was also a factor, for wool is known to act as a cooling device for sheep in desertic environments (Schmidt-Nielsen 1964: 96–98).

These innovations of the Sabz phase (5500–5000 B.C.) ultimately led to a basic change in the whole food-producing pattern of Khuzistan. Instead of a wheat-goat complex, more suitable to the uplands, one can see the beginnings of the "barley-sheep" complex which was to typify the later Elamite civilization.

Still another innovation of the Sabz phase—and one without apparent local antecedents—was the introduction of domestic cattle. Faunal remains from Ras al Amiya and Eridu (Flannery and Wright n.d.) suggest that cattle were more important in southern alluvial Mesopotamia than in Khuzistan. At our sites they seem never to have exceeded 5 per cent of the animal bone debris. Why cattle were not more numerous is not clear; for literally millennia they remained at the same frequency. But the potential for yet another "positive feedback" situation was there, and when finally cattle were harnessed to the plow, sometime prior to 2000 B.C., agriculture went through another geometric expansion which supported the growth of walled towns and cities (Adams 1962:114). The period of this climax is, however, outside the time limits of our Deh Luran sequence.

The expansion of the irrigation-barley-sheep complex was at the apparent expense of wild ungulate hunting and wild legume collecting. Each village must now have been surrounded by an intensively cultivated "infield" and a grazed and sporadically cultivated "outfield" (Wolf 1966:21). This extensive destruction of the habitat on which the wild steppe legumes and large herbivores had previously subsisted seems to have been associated with a decline, first of wild oxen, then of the other wild ungulates. Gazelle and onager survived, probably, because they could exploit the saline fallow lands which were of low farming and grazing potential; but the plants and animals of the sandy well-drained alluvium could not compete with the new agricultural complex, well-suited as it was to the lowlands.

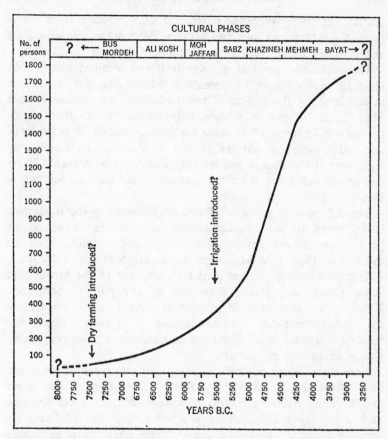

FIGURE 3   Theoretical population curve for the Deh Luran plain during the period 7500 to 3500 B.C. Based on number of village sites recovered per cultural phase, plus a rough estimate of 100 persons per one-hectare village (see text).

At this point, a population explosion is clearly reflected in our graph (Fig. 3) showing increase in occupancy of the Deh Luran plain through time. Although irrigation was introduced during the Sabz phase, its cumulative effects were really felt in the Khazineh and Mehmeh phases, when the number of occupied sites shot up to a dozen, and the estimated population went from 600 to 1500 persons. Similar trends can be seen in Adams' data from central Khuzistan, where the number of sites increased from thirty-four to one hundred and two between Sabz phase (=Susiana *a*) and Mehmeh phase (=Susiana *c*) times.

The population trend of the Khazineh and Mehmeh phases took the form, not so much of increase in village size, but of increase in numbers: by Bayat phase times (=Susiana *d*), Adams (1962: 110) notes "a grid of villages fully comparable to that of the present day in spacing." In other words, colonization of virgin lands and wide geographic distribution of 1 to 5 hectare multifamily villages over the landscape was the rule; and many of Adams' villages are strung out along the fossil courses of stream channels where simple irrigation was possible.

The difference in potential of this irrigation-barley-sheep complex is evidenced by our population density estimates of up to six persons per square km. at Deh Luran, and a total population estimate of 15,000 for Susiana in the Bayat phase (*ca.* 3750 B.C.). This represents a density at least six times that of the Mohammad Jaffar phase, and greater than that of any part of prehistoric Kurdistan we have seen. It may be that Kurdistan, committed to the rainfall-wheat-goat complex because of its early success, had reached a plateau which could not be exceeded without some basic change in agricultural pattern.

Here the differing potential of the plains soil types of Khuzistan began to make a difference, however. The plain of the Shaur and Karkheh rivers in central Khuzistan, with its good drainage and underlying gravels, stayed productive. The site of Susa, apparently founded late in the Bayat phase, grew to a metropolis within whose walls the density of population reached an estimated four hundred persons per hectare (Adams 1962:115). Here the agricultural complex supported social stratification, craft specialization, and urban life. At sites like Tepe Sabz, there is every reason to believe (on the basis of plant remains) that the "infield" surrounding the village had lost so much fertility that agriculture was no longer profitable. Many areas with too tenuous a balance and poor drainage remained fallow wasteland. The story of areas like Deh Luran is one of slowly shifting settlement which barely kept ahead of the destruction of the local environment.

Following the Bayat phase, Adams notes a decrease in number and an increase in size of sites. It appears that the population of Khuzistan had begun to concentrate itself behind the walls of a few very large towns or small cities. Adams (1962:114) suggests that this was a process of "the drawing together of the population into larger, more defensible political units." We wonder if there might not have been contributory processes at work here also: that is, the concentration of agricultural populations in those areas where salinization was less of a problem, and the intensified cultivation of those key areas by means of irrigation and the plow, leaving the worst salinized areas open for grazing land.

Ultimately, these pasture lands were to become "buffer zones" between the early city-states. Following the lead of Hickerson (1965), we might even postulate that competition between city-states was a regulatory mechanism which maintained these buffer zones, and counteracted deviations from the ecologically effective "walled-city" settlement system of the Early Dynastic period. Such competition effectively prevented a return to the dispersed settlement pattern of the Bayat phase, which may have reached the limits of its ecological potential by 3500 B.C.

CONCLUSION

The developmental model just presented cannot do justice to the complexity of ancient Khuzistan, but it is offered in the hope that future investigators, by testing it, will bring to light some of the processes which set the stage for urban civilization in southwestern Iran. We have collected a multitude of facts on prehistoric Deh Luran, but collection of facts in itself cannot lead on to understanding. As Coe (1963b) has recently reminded us, facts never speak for themselves; they must be cross-examined. Without a developmental model, all the artifacts and carbonized seeds in southwestern Iran could not explain how the Elamite empire evolved in the Khuzistan ecosystem, where only five or six thousand years previously man had lived by hunting onager and gazelle, and gathering wild legumes.

TEMPERATE EUROPE

15 THE SIGNIFICANCE
OF AGRICULTURAL DISPERSAL
INTO EUROPE AND NORTHERN AFRICA

Karl W. Butzer

ECONOMIC MOTIVES FOR AGRICULTURAL DISPERSAL

FOLLOWING the establishment of village farming communities in the Near Eastern woodlands during the seventh millennium, a rapid dispersal of agricultural techniques in the Old World began about 5000 B.C. Food-production had been introduced into much of Europe, the Mediterranean region, and northern Africa within a millennium after the Hassunan farmers of Iraq (*ca.* 5900–5200 B.C.) had begun to colonize the grasslands fringing the Near Eastern woodlands. By that time also agricultural communities are archeologically verified for southern and eastern Asia, although their origins are not yet understood. Much of this dispersal of technological features may have been associated with some form of ethnic movement, at least on a local scale. Yet the archeological evidence does not substantiate direct relationships between the earliest European or North African farmers and their contemporaries in the Near East. Needless to say, the routes and rates of dispersal are imperfectly understood. But the evidence available does permit a tentative discussion of possible motives for cultural diffusion and of the new ecologic problems arising from introduction of agriculture into new environments.

The subsistence economy of primitive agriculture may be fundamental in explaining this obscure migration of races, peoples, economies, or ideas. Primitive agriculture today is largely confined to the tropical woodlands, and it would be unwarranted to equate

---

Reprinted from Karl W. Butzer, *Environment and Archeology: An Introduction to Pleistocene Geography* (Chicago: Aldine Publishing Company, 1964); revised by author especially for this edition.

prehistoric Near Eastern farmers with modern Bantu populations in Africa or Quechua peoples in South America. But in a very general way some of the traits of shifting agriculture (see Watters 1960, with references) may have been common to the prehistoric Near East as well. The very extensive use of land, left to fallow for periods of up to 30 years and more, may have led to periodic overpopulation in some areas occupied to the limit of their possibilities with existing technology. Colonization of fresh lands must have been an appealing economic solution for groups living near the margins of the *oikoumene*.

Another factor possibly associated with early agricultural dispersals was chronic overpopulation. The invention and adoption of new tools and a new economic subsistence would inevitably promote a great increase of population, made possible by the increased and more reliable food supply. Food production per unit area was much greater, and even during a bad crop year a certain amount of food would be available. There would not be complete dependence on the seemingly erratic movements and biological cycles of wild game. Life and death were no longer so precariously balanced; birth rates increased and infant mortality declined. However, when a settlement reached its new carrying-capacity at agricultural subsistence, the rate of increase had to level off, either by emigration of by higher mortality rates. As long as fresh lands remained such as could be cleared and planted by fire or wooden or stone tools, the agriculturists probably sent out daughter colonies that supplanted or absorbed the sparsely settled food-gathering populations.

It would seem that the practice of primitive agriculture as well as chronic overpopulation could account for agricultural dispersals. Non-economic motives are not necessarily excluded, but it is also unnecessary to resort to an environmental factor such as climatic change.

One major environmental theory does in fact attempt to explain agricultural dispersals through the agency of "Postglacial desiccation" in the Old World subtropics. In particular, Childe (1925; 1929) thought that progressive postglacial desiccation in the Near East continued after the first general and successful steps to plant and animal domestication. The food-producing peoples expanded rapidly in numbers but were faced with a deteriorating environment. Desiccation eventually caused or, as others have put it more cautiously, played a part in the rapid expansion of Neolithic peoples and cultures into the moister lands of Europe. So, for example, Coon (1939:60–65) suggested that the dispersal of the Mediterranean race from the Near East (partly associated with early agriculture) was a consequence of desiccation incident upon the close of the Pleistocene. Childe (1958b:54) still suggests that Postglacial desiccation of the Sahara promoted ethnic and cultural movements from North Africa into Spain in the fifth millennium. In practice these arguments have no foundation in fact. As discussed below, the period after *ca.* 5000 B.C. was on the moist side in many of the areas in question. Furthermore, agricultural expansion was not confined to Europe but also extended to the semiarid landscapes of western Asia and many arid regions of northern Africa.

SAUER'S THEORY OF AGRICULTURAL DIFFUSION
FROM SOUTHEAST ASIA

C. O. Sauer (1952) has suggested that the primary hearth of first domestication was found in Southeast Asia, while several minor or "derivative centers of additional domestications" are postulated for India, the Near East, Ethiopia, and West Africa. Following E. Hahn, Sauer believes that vegetative planting of tropical tuber plants may have been the easiest and earliest step to domestication, and that this abstract concept subsequently spread throughout the Old World. Characteristic of this southeast Asian hearth in Burma and adjacent areas were household animals such as dog, pig; fowl, duck, and goose; non-seed, vegetative root plants such as banana, aroids, yams, sago, pandans, bamboo, sugar cane, and breadfruits. Postulated for the derived Indian-Himalayan center are plants such as the millets, pulses, gourd, jute, and other fibre plants, as well as some herd animals: goat, sheep, zebu, buffalo, and yak. The only herd animals allotted to the Near East are cattle, together with seed plants such as the wheats, grape, olive, fig, and flax. For Ethiopia, these additional domesticants are thought to include teff, sorghum, cotton, and sesame; for West Africa, the guinea hen, yam, and bush pig.

Although Sauer's ideas are only presented as a suggestive sketch, the sequence of archeological events presently available from the Near East and India (Sankalia 1962) suggest that agricultural origins were an essentially independent innovation in the former area. Recent archeological work indicates strong possibilities that various leguminous plants were domesticated in North Thailand by 7000 B.C. (Gorman 1969), so lending support to Sauer's concept of advanced fishing and planting populations in southeastern Asia.

An elaboration of Sauer's dispersal concepts is due to H. von Wissmann (1957), who outlined several successive nuclei of cultural diffusion in their geographical characteristics: (*a*) the tropical forests along the rivers and coasts of the Bay of Bengal: fishers and planters; (*b*) the forest-steppe and savanna of India: seed-planters with millets and oil plants; (*c*) the subtropical highlands of Afghanistan: sheep and goat farmers; (*d*) the small oases of the highlands and deserts of western Iran and Armenia: wheat and barley farmers. From here the alleged wave of dissemination entered Mesopotamia, which is not considered a center of agricultural origins but rather of technological invention.

Several elements stressed by Wissmann are: (*a*) Each nucleus sent out waves of dissemination which may have caught up with each other or may have lost some cultural elements upon entering a different climatic region. Such waves were taken over, transformed, or rejected depending on physical or human factors. (*b*) Major movement of cultures is postulated in the wooded steppes where the soil is rich and supposedly easy to work. (*c*) The movements are compared with Postglacial climatic fluctuations: (1) the Holocene thermal maximum (*ca.* 5500–3000 B.C.) may have permitted the spread of food production over the cold Central Asian mountain zone; (2) a moist spell in the third millennium may have established agricultural contacts across the Central Asian deserts, possibly leading to the origins of horse nomadism. (*d*) The Postglacial rise in world sea level was responsible for "burying" the archeological remains of the presumed late Pleistocene fishers and shell gatherers of southeastern Asia through marine submergence or intensive alluviation in lower stream courses. Reduced flood-plain alluviation after 4000 B.C., when modern sea level was attained, may have been related to the beginnings of settlement and rapid technological advance in the lower valleys of the Tigris-Euphrates and Nile.

Although Wissmann's views are interesting and deserving of attention, they go far beyond the available archeological evidence and can therefore only be rated as a hypothesis.

EUROPEAN CLIMATE DURING THE ATLANTIC PHASE

The original dispersal of agricultural traits in Europe coincides with the warm, moist Atlantic phase (*ca.* 5500–3000 B.C.). The Scandinavian Glacier had completely disappeared, and many mountain glaciers of the Alps were smaller than they are today while others disappeared. The botanical evidence suggests a considerably warmer summer climate than today's (Firbas 1949–52; Frenzel 1966; Lüdi 1955; Iversen 1960). So for example the altitudinal tree-limit was 200–300 m. higher than today's in the Scandinavian highlands and in the Sudeten ranges, 300 m. higher in the northern and southern Alps. Various water plants and trees requiring considerable summer warmth occurred at higher elevations or at higher latitudes than is the case today. Tree pollen occurs in certain strata of bogs in the north European tundra, while plant fruits of now sterile perennials have been found on the Arctic islands. In fact a third of the 125 species of Spitsbergen do not reproduce under present climatic conditions. Massive oaks grew beyond the present limit of oak in northeastern Russia, while the hazel was found considerably north of its present distribution in Scandinavia, and even the submediterranean wild grape (*Vitis silvestris*) thrived in southern Sweden. Particularly illuminating is a comparison of growing season temperatures at the northern limits of hazel (*Corylus avellana*) distribution in Scandinavia (see accompanying tabulation):

Mean Temperature °C.	Apr.	May	June	July	Aug.	Sept.	Oct.
Former limit	0.3	5.5	11.7	13.7	11.8	7.8	1.7
Present limit	2.5	8.2	14.0	15.8	14.1	10.1	4.5
Difference	2.2	2.7	2.3	2.1	2.3	2.3	2.7

From this it may be concluded that summer temperatures in mid-latitude Europe were at least 2° C. warmer than they are today during the Postglacial thermal maximum. Evidence for warmer winter temperatures is contradictory and unconvincing so far. Maximum summer temperatures may only have been reached during the Subboreal (*ca.* 3000–800 B.C.), when the Alpine tree-line was at its highest, about 300–400 m. higher than the modern tree-limit (Lüdi

1955). A greater melting of the world's glaciers may have occurred during the fourth millennium and the first half of the second millennium B.C., judging by glacio-eustatic sea-level fluctuations (see Fairbridge 1961). Whether or not ocean surface waters were warmer than today (Emiliani 1955) is uncertain. Conditions were analogous to those of an interglacial maximum, although the time interval was comparatively brief.

The forest composition of temperate Europe during the Atlantic was largely that of a mixed oak forest, with oak, elm, lime, ivy, and alder dominant in the western half of the continent, while pine played an important role farther east. Colonization of the drier lowland basins of central Europe by alder, spruce, and fir suggests that the Atlantic was considerably moister than today in much of mid-latitude Europe (Firbas 1949–52:Vol. I, p. 290f.). An extension of the forest into the present tundras and steppes is shown by Frenzel's (1960) palynological reconstruction of the Atlantic vegetation of European Russia.

ENVIRONMENTAL FACTORS INFLUENCING THE LOCATION
OF EARLY AGRICULTURAL SETTLEMENT IN EUROPE

A key environmental problem for early agricultural settlement in mid-latitude Europe concerns the physical attributes of the settled land: Did early colonization coincide with open grasslands, woodlands, or forest? Which soils and terrain were favored? Knowledge of the particular ecologic niches selected by agricultural colonists is useful both for assessing cultural adaptation and for explaining the observed patterns of dispersal.

Among the areas first settled by farming populations, the contemporary physical environment of central Europe is probably best understood. The culture in question is known as the early Danubian (Buttler 1938; Narr 1956), and dates from the fifth and fourth millennia. The Danubians were village farmers with a subsistence economy based on shifting agriculture. Three species of wheat, as well as barley, lentils, flax, beans, and peas were cultivated and presumably formed the staple diet, judging by the quantity of milling and pounding stones. Stone adzes were probably used for felling trees, but no tilling tools are known. The cow was the common domesticated animal kept, with pig in second place. Sheep, goat, and dog were of minor importance. The refuse pits show evidence of hunting activity, with red and roe deer, boar, aurochs, and woodland bison as favored game. The Danubians occupied long rectangular, gabled houses of wood and wickerware, measuring 5 to 6 m. wide, and 15 to 40 m. long. Vertical posts supported the walls and roof. These structures suggest small clan dwellings, also serving the purpose of animal stalls. Various storage buildings were present. Individual villages, frequently abandoned and subsequently reoccupied, may have had 200 to 600 inhabitants. Animals were generally kept within a fenced enclosure surrounding the village.

The sites of the Danubian culture are very strictly limited to loess areas in the Low Countries, Germany, Poland, Austria, Czechoslovakia and Hungary. No sites occur north of the margins of the Würm till. For the most part the warm, dry lowland plains or river terraces were selected, and within these, the loess areas (Gradmann 1906; 1936). The natural vegetation of the central European loess lowlands has long been the subject of controversy. Gradmann (1933) argued that grasslands, parklands, or open woodlands were still widespread in late prehistoric times, and that such lands were optimal in terms of better soils, easier cultivation, good pasture, and more bountiful game. Others, including Nietsch (1939) and C. Schott (1939) have argued that more or less closed forests dominated even the drier basins, requiring clearance by felling or burning. Godwin (1944) was able to verify this second point of view in the case of England.

Palynological evidence (Firbas 1949–52:Vol. I, p. 356 ff.) does not support widespread grassland or parkland during the Atlantic, even though the mixed oak woodlands on comparatively dry loess soils may have been lightly stocked. On account of the gradual decrease of *Artemisia* in the pollen record, Firbas believes that exposed bedrock, talus slopes, and stoney gravel or sand surfaces were colonized by tree vegetation late in the Holocene. Such natural gaps in the forest cover would obviously not have attracted settlers. Firbas concludes that the moister loess lowlands (wherever annual precipitation exceeds 500 mm. today) were occupied by closed mixed oak forests during the Atlantic, although the drier basins probably had a parkland or open woodland vegetation. Areas qualifying as comparatively dry are the interior basin of Bohemia-Moravia, the Elbe-Saale plain, the Upper Rhine basin, and the Hungarian plain.

Soil studies appear to substantiate Firbas' conclusions. Loess sediments are highly permeable and evaporate more soil moisture than any other sediment, so that loess soils are comparatively dry in the edaphic sense and do not favor tree growth. The climatically drier loess lowlands commonly have soils of the "degraded" chernozem type. Such chernozems originally developed under grassy vegetation with dry, warm summers—presumably during the continental climate of the Preboreal and Boreal. Subsequent woodland invasion during the moist, maritime Atlantic led to carbonate solution, increased acidity, and chemical weathering, with oxidation and some leaching (Scheffer, Schachtshabel 1960:275 f.; Wilhelmy 1950). These soils prove the former existence of grasslands in certain dry basins, at least until the beginning of the Atlantic. Consequently, with local agricultural settlement well under way a millennium later (*ca.* 4500 B.C.), a fair amount of parkland or open woodland was available to the Danubian colonists in the south and east.

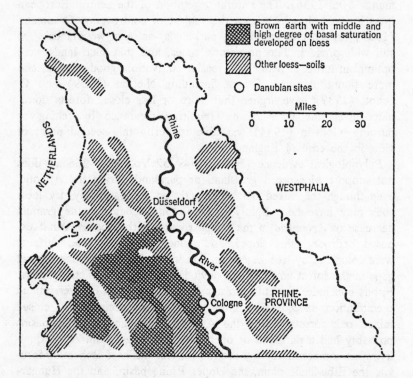

FIGURE 1 Danubian sites and soil types in the northern Rhineland (from K. J. Narr, 1956, copyright 1956 by the University of Chicago Press, with permission).

In overview, the earliest agricultural colonists entered the central European area during a period of optimal warmth and comparatively moist climate, increased rainfall more than compensating for increased evaporation. The settlements of the Danubian farmers are sharply restricted to loess sediments (Fig. 1), which obviously provided greater soil fertility. At the same time, these often were areas with parkland vegetation and calcareous, chernozemic soils, or otherwise they had base-saturated forest soils under closely stocked mixed oak woodland. It is no mere coincidence that primeval settlement, loess, calcareous or basic soils, dry lowland basins, and comparatively open, oak parklands or woodlands should provide a common denominator for the earliest agricultural lands of mid-latitude Europe. Only at a later date, when less demanding crops such as rye, oats, or spelt had been developed, was colonization extended to the more acidic and partly leached forest soils. Swampy terrain and heavy waterlogged soils were only occupied at a somewhat later date.

The new agricultural lands of mid-latitude Europe (Fig. 2) were not radically different from the subtropical or temperate woodlands of Asia Minor and Greece, particularly during the warm Atlantic and Sub-boreal phases. Despite an increase in winter cold and summer moisture, the landscape of the new environments was different in degree rather than in kind. It was probably not accidental that the pioneer farmers of Europe should select the environment most like that of their cultural antecedents: not the humid lands of the west, nor the cool, poorly drained till plains of the north, nor yet the snowy plains or open steppes of the east. Rather, the more intermediate environment of the Balkan peninsula and central Europe provided the most compatible solution in terms both of climate and edaphic factors. Just as open woodlands had probably witnessed the birth of agriculture in the Near East, they also provided the setting to the first agricultural venture into higher latitudes.

However, the change in crop ecology was important. Winters were cool rather than mild, whereas summers were decidedly moist. The winter cold may have eliminated some winter crops from the array of domesticated plants, although "winter" wheat and barley are still frequently planted in autumn in much of central Europe today. Somewhere, however, the idea of spring sowing of Mediterranean crops must have been experimented with and found to be expedient. Some of the evolution of new mutants and rapid hybridi-

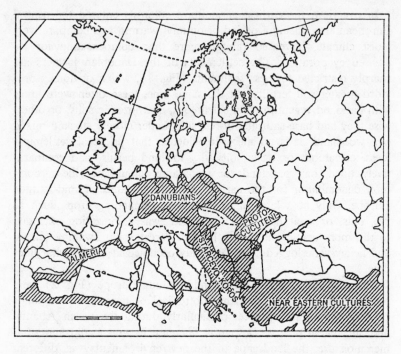

FIGURE 2 Early village farming cultures in Europe and adjacent areas
ca. 4200 B.C. Modified after Bengston and Milojčić (1958) and Waterbolk (1968).

zation of wheat species in temperate Europe may have resulted
from deliberate changes in plant ecology at the hands of man—
just like those accompanying the deliberate cultivation of oats and
rye on marginal soils and in cooler climates a few millennia later.

SAHARAN CLIMATE DURING THE MID-HOLOCENE

Agricultural colonization of the Mediterranean Basin, in particular of
the coasts of southern Europe and northwestern Africa, did not
encounter appreciable environmental differences anywhere in the
summer-dry subtropical woodland belt. The settlement of truly arid
lands, such as the Sahara, did however require considerable ecological adaptation. Fortunately for the early agricultural colonists, the
Saharan area enjoyed an abnormally moist climate during a time

interval roughly synchronous with the Atlantic phase in Europe. The evidence in favor of several moist intervals during the mid-Holocene may be subdivided into three categories: faunal evidence, chiefly on the basis of rock drawings; botanical evidence, both macrobotanical and palynological; and geological evidence, generally of a rather specific and detailed type.

A moister climate during late prehistoric times was first inferred from the widespread distribution of human artifacts and rock drawings in desert areas, often many miles from existing waterholes. The wild animals shown on the rock art included gazelles, antelopes, and ostrich as well as species associated with more luxuriant savanna vegetation: elephant, both the single- and two-horned rhino, hippo, and giraffe. Certain paleoclimatic inferences can be attempted on the basis of these animal representations and their distribution and frequency (Mauny 1956; Butzer 1958b), but indirect data of this kind is not conclusive. Consequently, it is fortunate that much geological and palynological data have been collected in recent years, often fixed by radiocarbon dating. As a result, the archeological evidence can now be seen from a new perspective.

The evidence for post-Pleistocene moist interludes is unsatisfactory and unconvincing along the Mediterranean borderlands, in Morocco, Tunisia, or the Cyrenaica. It is best developed in the Saharan highlands and along the major wadis systems or depressions that drain the higher country. So, for example, the Guirian terrace fill of the Saoura Valley includes evidence for accelerated fluvial activity and widespread lake or swamp formation, with one date of 4210±1700 B.C. (Chavaillon 1964; Beucher 1963). Pollen was examined from an exposure of gray sands, interdigited with organic horizons and capped by a travertine layer. The limited pollen includes pine (*halepensis* ?) and acacia (*raddiana* ?), but few grasses. The travertine, however, is dominated by pollen of xerophytic species (*Ephedra,* Chenopodiaceae) with some dubious traces of birch, elder, hornbeam, and pine.

In the Hoggar Mountains, silty-swampy fill accumulated in many of the valleys during Neolithic times, while pediment cutting proceeded in the uplands and organic swamp beds formed in some intradunal hollows of the lowland "sand seas" (Rognon 1967). Dating is generally insecure. The rock shelter at Meniet in the Hoggar contains strata from which 87 pollen grains were identified by Quézel and Martinez (1958). Of these pollen 56 per cent belong to arboreal species. In order of numerical importance they include cypress, Aleppo pine, evergreen oak, wild olive, hackberry (*Celtis australis*), the thorn bush *Ziziphus,* juniper, and tamarisk. Macroremains of *Ziziphus,* lotus, and hackberry help substantiate the pollen record, which further includes cereal, grass, sedge, and *Artemisia.* The uppermost stratum at Meniet has a C^{14} date of 3450±300 B.C. (Délibrias *et al.* 1959) and contains bones of an extinct buffalo. Similar results were obtained from a sample of hyrax dung from Taessa in the Hoggar, at some 2200 m. elevation. Pollen (3000 grains) included similar genera as at Meniet together with pistachio and walnut. A C^{14} date of 2730±300 B.C. was obtained for the dung. Limited numbers of pollen grains were also studied from sediments with cattle bones found below rock drawings in the Tassili Mountains (Quézel, Martinez 1961). These grains included Aleppo pine, evergreen oak, and cypress. A more impressive but incompletely published sequence is available from the nearby Acacus hill country, near Ghat (1370 m.). Here the rock shelter of Uan Muhuggiag (Mori 1965:218–41) indicates occupation *ca.* 3500–2500 B.C. by food-producing people with domesticated cattle and sheep. *Typha,* a swamp plant, accounts for over 50 per cent of four samples in the horizon, with the desert shrubs *Aristida* and *Artemisia herba-alba* accounting for about 10 per cent each. Macrobotanical remains include abundant *Typha,* together with acacia and some desert trees or shrubs. In the upper horizon there is little or no evidence of swamp plants, but *Artemisia herba-alba* attains over 50 per cent, *Aristida* 25 per cent, and *Artemisia campestris* up to 10 per cent.

Like many other parts of the Sahara, the Tibesti area has a wealth of naturalistic rock drawings pertaining to prehistoric hunting groups. Giraffe, elephant, and, to a lesser extent, rhinoceros are fairly common among these drawings, both in the highlands and in the Borkou foothills. Although geological evidence is not yet available, elephant fossils have been reported, and palynological data are available from "Neolithic" cave sediments at Mosséi (Quézel and Martinez 1958). The pollen count here was 60 per cent NAP and included 35 per cent *Acacia flava.* However, over 80 per cent of the macroremains pertained to pine and juniper.

Near the Djado Oasis, southwest of Tibesti, several lacustrine deposits with subfossil mollusca have been studied by Llabador (1962). All appear to have been laid down during the moister interval in "Neolithic" times. The Neolithic lacustrine beds of Adrar Bous, northeast of the Air Massiv, have yielded valuable paleo-ecological information concerning the local mid-Holocene environment. The fauna includes equids, cattle, antelope, wart hog, hippopotamus, tortoise, and crocodile. Two genera of fish, ostrich, and three species of gastropods complete the preliminary faunal inventory (Llabador 1962). Macrobotanical remains include the common reed and live oak. Two distinct palynological horizons are defined by Quézel and Martinez (1961). The lower consists of diatomite, attaining 3 m. in thickness, with 66 per cent of 251 identified pollen grains from NAP species. The upper horizon is a blackish swamp sediment of 10–30 cm. thickness, with 82 per cent of 192 grains NAP, almost exclusively chenopods. The arboreal species present in the diatomite include 13 per cent juniper, 12 per cent cypress, 5 per cent an extinct pine, 4 per cent myrtle, and 2 per cent pistachio. The limited arboreal species of the upper, swampy beds, dated 3180±300 B.C. (Délibrias and Hugot 1962), contain 12 per cent myrtle, 3 per cent cypress, and 2 per cent juniper. A severe degradation of the open Mediterranean-type vegetation is evident between the two horizons that mark the mid-Holocene moist interval.

Faure (1966) has studied the lacustrine deposits of the intradunal depressions of the Ténéré, phenomena having a wider distribution along the southern margins of the Sahara. Fresh-water lakes, probably interconnected with Lake Chad, were well developed *ca.* 7250–5000 B.C., and a last lake episode is dated *ca.* 3550–1150 B.C. In the Senegal Delta the earlier wet phase appears to have been contemporary with the development of the deep red paleosol, under moist, warm conditions, while the second wet phase coincided approximately with silt alluviation of the Senegal.

The Nile Valley provides further details and confirmation of several moist intervals (Butzer, Hansen 1968). A period of accelerated wadi activity that began 9200 B.C. terminated by 6000 B.C. Shell proliferations suggest rather more vegetation in the wadis. A little later, *ca.* 5000 B.C., a red paleosol suggests a mat of vegetation, and more frequent, gentle rains. Finally, after a second dry interlude, accelerated wadi activity and extensive sheet washing—in the wake of sporadic but heavy and protracted rains —are indicated *ca.* 4000–3000 B.C. Historical and archeological documents suggest that the desert wadi vegetation of northern and eastern Egypt was more abundant as late as 2350 B.C., when the prevailing aridity was established (Butzer 1959). At the same time, spring activity in the Kharga Oasis was greater, allowing agricultural subsistence by Neolithic settlers, while the static ground-water table was higher in much of the Libyan Desert, presumably facilitating cattle herding in now desolate areas (Murray 1951; also Knetsch *et al.* 1963, on the depletion of "fossil" water resources).

All in all the Saharan evidence indicates two or three moister interludes during the early and middle Holocene. Dates are slightly at variance from place to place, and since few of the local sequences are firmly dated, long-range correlations are difficult. Possibly three moisture peaks are indicated *ca.* 7000, 5000, and 3000 B.C., separated by dried interruptions, and followed—during the last three millennia—by conditions quite comparable to those of today. None of these changes in precipitation or effective moisture can be quantitatively estimated, and there is no evidence concerning possible changes of temperature. The impression obtains that the increase in moisture at the height of these moist intervals was ecologically significant, although not sufficient to gualify the "arid" or "hyperarid" nature of the climate. It appears that open woodland or parkland was present at edaphically favored localities in the high country, while fringing savanna-scrub and local swampy ground accompanied the major wadi lines and depressions. It is generally agreed that the paucity of modern vegetation in the Saharan highlands and wadis is due to human activity such as overgrazing and use of woody plants for fuel. However, the Sahara is exceptionally arid by standards of other world deserts, and this climatic aridity has not been accentuated by man. If left undisturbed over many generations, the plant life of the Sahara would indeed regenerate somewhat, but hardly in such a way as to permit wholesale faunal migrations or to provide resources for diverse agricultural and herding populations. The many categories of evidence for moist interludes during the early and mid-Holocene do provide evidence for real climatic variations.

PREHISTORIC CATTLE-NOMADS OF THE SAHARA

The rock paintings and engravings of the interior Sahara bear testimony to two amazing archeological complexes, an epi-Paleolithic hunting culture, and an early Neolithic food-producing culture with cattle, sheep, and local cultivation of cereals (see Rhotert 1952; Lhote 1959, 1965; Forde-Johnston 1959; Mori 1965; Clark 1967a, b; Hugot 1968, all with references). Unfortunately, it has not been possible to link conclusively the different groups responsible for the rock drawings with the various stone industries and pottery types vaguely labeled as "Saharan Neolithic." In fact, the standard archeological inventory offers no proof for the distinctiveness of the hunters and herders at any one site, nor does it support the concept of a general ethnic identity through the interior Sahara at any one time. Nonetheless, the bulk of the "Neolithic" inventory—ground and polished stone axes and adzes; large, bifacial tools; stone platters and dishes; different types or traditions of arrowheads and pottery; bone harpoons—can be assigned to late prehistoric populations with an economy based partly on livestock herding. Such associations have been established at critical sites in the Atlas, the Hoggar and Tassili, in the Fezzan and in the Nile Valley. However, in dealing with an area as vast as the Sahara and a time range of at least three and possibly as much as six millennia, it would be simplistic to assume cultural or economic uniformity, let alone ethnic continuity through space or time.

Despite the difficulties of resolving the broad patterns of the Saharan Neolithic with the available information, the Saharan data does provide the first verified example of nomadic pastoralism. The origins of the cattle-nomads of the central and eastern Sahara and of the cattle-and-sheep nomads of the western Sahara remain obscure. The earliest manifestation of food producing in Egypt, the Sudan, Cyrenaica, and Tunisia are all younger than 5000 B.C., so that the Uan Muhuggiag date of 5590 B.C. and its association with domesticated animals must be held in question. Consequently, whatever their origin, the early pastoralists of the western and central Sahara are probably dated with some accuracy by seven radiocarbon dates between 3450 and 2730 B.C. (in terms of corrected, calendar ages, *ca.* 4500–3500 B.C.).

The basic economic traits of the Saharan pastoralists have been discussed by Rhotert (1952), Lhote (1959) and Clark (1967b). Subsistence was primarily based on cattle herds derived from local domestication of *Bos primigenius* (=*africanus*)—possibly somewhere in the Nile Valley. Lack of emphasis of the animals' udders in the pictorial art suggests that meat rather than milk was the major form of exploitation. Domesticated sheep replace cattle in the Saharan Atlas, and an overlap of sheep and cattle-raising is indicated in the Tassili region. Much game was hunted, probably reflecting local fusion with autochthonous food-collecting groups. Possibly, although not necessarily, these cattle-nomads were the users of the occasional grinding stones reported from different parts of the Sahara. This may indicate that cereals were known locally, a point suggested also by the pollen from Meniet. The strong concentration of archeological sites in wadi valleys and at existing or former groundwater localities suggests that settlement was largely confined to areas with available water—both for human and for animal use. Caves were also occupied in some areas of the Tassili, Hoggar, and the Saharan Atlas.

No direct proof of nomadism is available for the Saharan cattle herders. However, significant cultural associations have been shown with nomadic Kushitic or Eastern Hamitic groups of the Red Sea coasts of Egypt, the Sudan, and Ethiopia (Rhotert 1952). The typical composite drawings of large cattle herds strongly suggest organized pastoralism. Also, the rapid dispersal of this culture through the Sahara may reflect a nomadic subsistence. With the erratic nature of the rainfall (even during the Holocene subpluvial) and the sporadic distribution of water and pasture, it is unlikely that permanent or semipermanent habitation *could* have been practiced in any one area. It seems necessary to assume that adequate water and fodder could only be guaranteed by periodic movements, possibly into the better watered highlands or to permanent waterholes during the dry season, to ephemeral pastures among the foothills and nearby alluvial plains during the episodic rains.

One may suspect that this very obvious case of adaptation of food production to an adverse environment had its origins in an agricultural community that gradually expanded or was displaced into marginal arid country where livestock raising was more economical than cereal agriculture. Or, these same people selectively acquired cultural traits from agricultural populations in nearby, better watered areas. At any rate, planting played a very small role in an economy based primarily on meat animals. This contrasts with the contemporary village farmers of the Near East and Europe, among whom subsistence was primarily based on cereals.

In retrospect, the diffusion of food-producing traits into the arid zone, and in particular into the Sahara, was a case of cultural or technological adaptation to a new environment. Yet this dispersal was only made possible by the temporary improvement

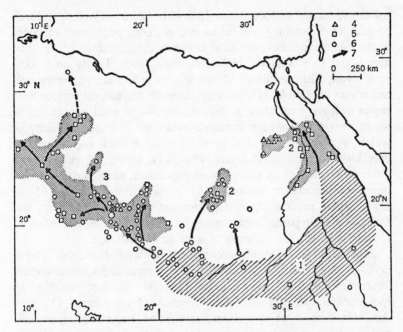

FIGURE 3 Hunters and cattle nomads in the Sahara *ca.* 5000–2000
B.C. 1, hypothetical cattle herding cultures *ca.* 4500 B.C.; 2, 3 domain of
hunting groups *ca.* 4500 B.C.; 4, rock drawings of the hunters; 5,
rock drawings of both hunters and cattle nomads; 6, rock drawings of
cattle nomads; 7, expansion routes of cattle nomads in the fifth millennium (from Butzer 1958b).

of the environment and resource base of the Saharan highlands
during the Holocene subpluvial. Not only did desiccation play no
role whatever in agricultural dispersals after 5000 B.C., but instead
the prevailing moister climate must have facilitated and perhaps
motivated man's expansion over the world's greatest desert. In fact
the spread of food-producing populations through the arid zone of
the Old World followed close upon the migration of the Ethiopian
faunas through the Sahara.

THE IMPACT OF FOOD PRODUCTION ON MAN-LAND RELATIONSHIPS

The impact of the new food-producing economies on the environment marks a rather significant change in man-land relationships. The

million years of Pleistocene time had witnessed a very gradual development of technology and economic patterns permitting existence of the human species under most environmental conditions. Man had also begun to modify the biological world, even if only on a local scale. Now, with the spread of ecologically potent farming communities across the Old World, transformation of the natural environment began to leave great scars in the landscape—the areal importance of which almost everywhere increased with time and the continuity of which was assured by the persistence of human populations at ever higher technological levels. The major aspects of geographical interest include (*a*) an explosion of population, made possible by an improved subsistence economy, (*b*) physical transformation of the environment, particularly through decimation of the native flora and fauna and their partial replacement by non-indigenous domesticated species, and (*c*) the creation of a cultural landscape.

Population is essentially controlled by available food. Rapid demographic expansion has ensued upon several major, technological improvements of the food supply: (1) after the first invention of tool-manufacture, (2) after the invention of agriculture, (3) with the intensification of agricultural production accompanying urbanization, and in more recent times, (4) with the industrial revolution. C. O. Sauer (1947) described the history of man as a succession of higher and higher levels, each one brought about by discovery of more food, either through occupation of new territory or through increase in food-producing skill. When the maximum possible population is reached, population must level off, either by gradual convergence of birth and death rates, or by draining off the surplus into daughter colonies.

The introduction of a subsistence based on farming and herding would provide a greater and more stable food supply. A much smaller economic area could provide sufficient food for much larger communities. Domestic animals could be used for meat at most times of the year, while the highly productive cereal crops could be stored for the whole year following the harvest. There was no longer any need to move when the local supply of wild plant foods or of game was exhausted. Starvation no longer ensued when biological cycles reduced the local game population. Above all, the food supply was far more reliable, both in the course of the seasons, as well as during the passing of the years, so maintaining a much higher population level. Of course, exceptionally cold winters, drought years, crop and animal plagues, etc. would still exert a noticeable influence on the population curve. But man was becoming conspicuously less dependent on the vagaries of the environment.

Braidwood and Reed (1957) have discussed subsistence levels and modern ethnographic parallels, and suggested typical population densities of approximately 1 person per 100 sq. km. at the unspecialized Pleistocene food-gathering level, 5 per 100 sq. km. at the specialized late Pleistocene-early Holocene food-gathering level, 1000 per 100 sq. km. at the early agricultural level, and 2000 per 100 sq. km. at the early urban level. Obviously these are only meant to be orders of approximation, but the values help illustrate the degree of change involved.

The physical transformation of the natural environment was primarily the result of man's agricultural activities. Changes were originally confined to the biological sphere. The natural woodland or grassland vegetation was partly replaced by fields of wheat, barley, and vegetables. Such crops, originally native to a restricted area of western Asia, were to spread through most of the world, into lands where their very existence was often possible only through the caring hand of man. Species, which in natural competition shared minute ecological niches with countless other plants, now dominated acre upon acre of monocultures. Unconsciously agricultural or grazing activities favored certain local herbaceous plants by creating open spaces in woodlands, so increasing the importance of fire-tolerant plants in the course of slash-and-burn clearance. Similarly, new ecological niches were provided for a rash of new weed plants, whose original habitats and specific niches had been as insignificant as those of the cereals or vegetables.

The same can be said for the animal world. The wild fauna, with some exceptions, was decimated through a reduction of the natural habitat by cultivation, disturbance of breeding haunts, as well as improved hunting techniques by ever larger populations. Instead, the new farming populations tended select domesticated animals, thus enabling dispersal of certain species on a continental scale and causing drastic changes in the composition of the fauna. Certainly these qualitative and quantitative changes of flora and fauna required millennia, and the face of the earth was at first only altered locally. The cumulative effect over several millennia has, however, been significant and sometimes catastrophic.

The cultural landscape reflects intensive settlement with effective transformation of the biological environment through agricultural land use. With the introduction of village farming into an area, cultivated fields and biologically altered grazing areas began to dot the landscape. Architectural skills had improved and shelter requirements were met by construction of houses, stables, and storage huts. Individual farmsteads coagulated to form villages dispersed over the countryside. With incipient urbanization these man-made structures increased in size, number, and importance as towns and cities, market places, roads, bridges, fences, and the like were added. Irrigation and drainage schemes were implemented in marginal environments. Forests were removed for land clearance and timber, and grasslands plowed up. These innovations were often followed by such unpleasant corollaries as soil deterioration and soil erosion.

Although the record of man's early transformation of the physical into a cultural landscape is poorly preserved in the Old World subtropics, the case of mid-latitude Europe is better understood. The significance of forest clearance and crop cultivation by village-farming communities was first recognized in Denmark from the pollen records of the Sub-boreal by Iversen (1949). The earliest appearance of cereal pollen was accompanied by a rapid increase or the appearance of weed colonists such as *Artemisia, Rumex, Plantago,* and chenopodiaceae, with a corresponding decrease in mixed oak forest. Such discontinuities were followed by temporary birch pollen maxima—common after forest fires—with subsequent increase of alder, hazel, and finally, oak. Evidence of burning is occasionally visible in the peat stratigraphy. Iversen explained these features through forest clearance by burning and felling, with subsequent livestock-grazing or crop-planting in the "opened" woodland. The fields were soon abandoned in the course of shifting cultivation, and so allowed to revert back to forest. Interestingly, open woodlands such as oak-birch forests on sandy soils showed little or no pollen discontinuity other than the presence of cereal and *Plantago* pollen. These show the existence of cultivation on plots available without recourse to intensive clearing.

This original picture of common, but not exclusive, slash-and-burn agriculture seems to be substantiated by the over-all archeological and palynological evidence in mid-latitude Europe (J. G. D. Clark 1945; Firbas 1949–52: Vol. I, p. 363 ff.). Fire was apparently not necessary in the more open landscapes. Tree-felling with stone axes was quite feasible, as recent experiments by Steensburg (1957) showed. Bark-peeling or girdling of trees was probably also an effective clearance method, particularly after brush and lighter growth had been removed through burning. An interesting form of semiagriculture preceded true agricultural colonization in Denmark (Iversen 1960, Troels-Smith 1960a). This Erteboelle culture may represent a contact culture, based largely upon stalled or tethered cattle. The animals were almost entirely fed with the foliage of elm, mistletoe, ivy, and ash. As a result there was a sharp reduction in elm pollen, formerly interpreted as a climatic change at the transition of the Atlantic to the Sub-boreal. A little wheat and barley was apparently grown, but there was no forest clearance worth speaking of. This example illustrates that the methods and significance of forest clearance by early agriculturists can hardly be generalized.

Prior to the first introduction of the ox-drawn plow from Mesopotamia into temperate Europe during the second half of the third millennium, soil preparation was made by hoe or digging stick. With such tools it is unlikely that most of the woodland soils yielded well for more than a year or two, requiring twenty or more years of fallow thereafter. Fertility must have been more enduring on the chernozemic soils, since recent plow agriculture without fertilization on the Ukrainian chernozems only required one fallow year in three. The exact nature of rapid soil depletion or yield reduction is complex, reflecting actual mineral depletion, rate of weed colonization, erosion resulting from soil structure changes, or humus destruction. The common symptom of sharply reduced yields probably results from a number of interacting factors.

Soil erosion was probably unimportant since cultivation was limited to the more productive lowland soils. Clearance and cultivation of hillsides was a late innovation in mid-latitude Europe. Deforestation or moderate grazing would not leave bare soil exposed for very long. Even in the Mediterranean region, in such an ancient land as the Lebanon, the commercial importance of lumber in historical times suggests that widespread deforestation was rather uncommon in prehistoric times. In fact Heichelheim (1956) and Darby (1956) emphasize that general deforestation and land deterioration even in the Mediterranean region fall largely within the two millennia of our own era. It would therefore seem that early agricultural land use did not yet provoke its more unpleasant side-effects such as accelerated runoff, seasonally accentuated stream discharge, soil erosion, gullying, and gradual loss of soil moisture attendant upon the destruction or removal of humus. At any rate, both archeological and geological evidence to this effect is absent.

The preceding discussion of man-land relationships assumed that human populations automatically expand to the limit of resources available within a given technological framework. Such an assumption is of course questionable. Unfortunately the archeological data is inadequate for such evaluation of the underlying cultural patterns. Although less significant at the food-collecting level, efficiency of exploitation among technologically equivalent groups assumes considerable importance at the food-producing level. Was there a fundamental stability in the relationships of man to the exploitable resources of his habitat? Or, did local over-exploitation of resources already lead to temporary or semipermanent environmental crises? At the early agricultural level it would seem that a basic stability persisted, and with so much new land to occupy, it is possible that local overexploitation was still uncommon. But the problem remains to be investigated more thoroughly.

16 FOOD PRODUCTION
IN PREHISTORIC EUROPE

H. T. Waterbolk

B Y ABOUT 300 B.C. all the plains south of the Scandinavian mountains were inhabited by people who lived together in villages
of a more or less permanent character. These settlers cut the deciduous forest with stone axes, cultivated a variety of crops, and raised
cattle, sheep, goats, and pigs. Hunting was of little importance.

The art of pottery was known everywhere. From highly varied
shape and ornamentation, archeologists have been able to distinguish
a number of cultures of limited geographical and chronological
occurrence and various degrees of relation.

How different is the picture if we go back in time another
5000 years, to about 8000 B.C. The last cold spell of the Ice Age
was then almost over. Hunting and gathering were the major means
of subsistence. Animal domestication and plant cultivation were
unknown. Camp sites were relatively impermanent, shifting from
one place to another.

NUCLEAR AND NONNUCLEAR CULTURES

From 8000 to 3000 B.C. in southwestern Asia there was a progression
from food collecting to urban civilization, through the levels of
incipient cultivation and domestication, of primary effective village
farming, and of developed village farming and town life (Braidwood,
Braidwood 1953; Braidwood 1962). For the purposes of this discussion, the nuclear development must be accepted as a given fact,
though in its later stages some parts of southeastern Europe also
participated (Rodden 1965; 1964).

Reprinted from *Science*, December 6, 1968, Vol. 162, No. 3858, pp. 1093–1102,
and by permission of the author. Copyright 1968 by the American Association
for the Advancement of Science.

In other parts of the Old World, cultures had, in principle, been developing along lines independent of those of nuclear development. According to Caldwell (1958), who treated eastern North America in its relation to nuclear Meso-America, a nonnuclear type of culture may attain a "primary forest efficiency"—the successful exploitation of the natural food resources that brought about residential stability, great material wealth, development of craftsmanship and art, disposal of goods with the dead, and the building of large earthworks. Forest efficiency could even lead to resistance to the introduction of food production. We shall see that this concept of forest efficiency can be usefully applied to Europe.

The terms Paleolithic, Mesolithic, and Neolithic have little meaning for the study of the introduction of food production. There are very different types of "Mesolithic" economies, and "Neolithic" elements like polished axes, pottery, and domesticated sheep are introduced quite independently; not even the additional presence of cattle and pig and of cultivated wheat and barley need result in full dependence on food production.

CLIMATE AND RELIEF

Any cultural development in Europe has to be seen against the background of two major natural factors, namely climate and relief. The most significant climatic event is the Ice Age.

The last cold stage had a much more intense effect in northern Europe than it did in southern latitudes. Correspondingly, the environmental fluctuations in the early postglacial were of much greater importance in the north than in the south, where the major climatic improvement had started long before and had not been interrupted by pauses and minor readvances.

As to the bearing of relief, mountain areas are less suitable for agriculture than are the plains, where soil conditions generally are good, and internal communications are easy. Not only the lowland plains, but also the higher plains, such as the south German plain, should be considered in this connection. An ordinary contour map gives a false picture of the size of the habitable areas.

The irregularities of coastlines and mountain chains differentiate coastal plains from the continental plains. Continental plains generally communicate with each other along the coast and overseas; the continental plains communicate with the coastal plains and with each other through river valleys or low passes. The major plains and their connections are indicated on Fig. 1.[1]

Low ridges or even watersheds can be important boundaries between cultural provinces by a combination of factors including soil, climate, and vegetation, as well as by the absence of waterways. For instance, in the hills between Bohemia and Moravia there are no geographically determined channels of communication.

FOOD COLLECTORS BEFORE ABOUT 6000 B.C.

Here I emphasize southeastern, central, and northwestern Europe; Iberia, North Africa, Russia, and Scandinavia get less attention.

For a rough chronological arrangement of the evidence, three periods can be distinguished. The appearance of the first village farmers in Greece (about 6000 B.C.) and the expansion of Bandkeramik farmers toward northwestern Europe (about 4500 B.C.) serve as boundaries to separate the three.[2]

In the period in which the first evidence of incipient food production in southwestern Asia is recorded (Braidwood 1965:57–67), reindeer hunters still roamed the plains of northern Europe from Belgium to Poland. In this area the Upper Dryas climatic deterioration had again opened up the forest cover which had earlier expanded northward during the preceding Alleröd-interstadial (10,000 to 9000 B.C.).

These reindeer hunters belong to the "Tanged Point" tradition, a

---

[1] The maps are based on the U. S. Air Force Operational Navigation Charts 1:1,000,000, which have a special tint for relatively level areas. For obvious reasons of unequality in the published basic information and the uncertainty of the age of many cultural stages, it was impossible to make anything but extremely tentative distribution maps. They should only be considered as serving the purpose of illustrating the main argument in this paper. Apart from the works mentioned in the other notes, the major sources were the following books and papers. Arnal and Burnez (1958), Bernabo Brea (1957), Bourdier and de Lumley (1954), Bronsted (1957), J. G. D. Clark (1952; 1955) Driehaus (1960), von Gonzenbach (1949), Hagen (1967), Jażdżewski (1965), Knöll (1959), Leisner and Leisner (1943; 1956), van Noten (1967), Obermaier (1924a), Piggott (1954; 1965), Pittioni (1954; 1962a), Preuss (1966), de Sonneville-Bordes (1960), Stenberger (1965), Tackenberg (1954), Tixier (1963), Vaufrey (1955), Wyss (1960).

[2] For radiocarbon dates used in this article see Ehrich (1965), and Deevey *et al.* (1966; 1967).

FIGURE 1 Major plains of Europe are indicated, irrespective of elevation. High mountain areas (above 1000 meters) are shaded. The inter-
connections of the plains are shown by a double-headed arrow. 1,
Vardar-Morava Gate; 2, Iron Gate; 3, Moravian Gate; 4, Linz Gate; 5,
Elbe Gate; 6, Burgundian Gate; 7, Aquitanian Gate.

late phase of which is known as the Ahrensburg culture. In the
deep tunnel-valley sediments adjacent to the Stellmoor (Clark 1936;
Rust 1962; Troels-Smith 1955:129–53) settlement, remains have
been found of at least 650 reindeer, whereas only a few specimens
of elk, bison, wild horse, lynx, beaver, fox, and wolf, and of such
fowl as ducks and geese have been uncovered. The flint industry
comprised tanged points, "Zonhoven" points, gravers, and scrapers.
Harpoon points have also been found. Ornamentation is rare:
simple geometrical designs are engraved on some reindeer ribs.
In the bog, a wooden post with a reindeer skull on its top was
found.

Cave sites from a late variety of the Ahrensburg culture with a
fauna comprising both tundra and forest animals are known (Schwa-

bedissen 1944; Gutmann, Taute 1964). These sites testify to the adaptation of the reindeer hunters to the forest environment.

Another tradition in the lowlands of western Europe is the Federmesser tradition, which included various local groups such as the Azilian, the Tjongerian, the Creswellian, and others (Schwabedissen 1954; Bohmers 1960; Taute 1963), and probably resulted from an adaptation of Magdalenian reindeer hunters to the forest. In the Alleröd period, a northward expansion of these Magdalenian survivals took place. Their sites occur along river valleys or lakes, but there is no indication of any means of subsistence other than the hunting of big game, such as red deer, elk, and aurochs.

Another development within the same tradition can be observed in the western Mediterranean where a number of coastal cave sites are known, the Romanellian (or Grimaldian) (Vaufrey 1928; Sauter 1948; Radmilli 1962), which have yielded remains not only of big game, but also of small animals such as hares and birds, and considerable quantities of land snails and of shells collected at the seashore. This is the earliest evidence in Europe for the exploitation of this important natural resource.

Soon after 8000 B.C., the final postglacial climatic improvement started. It caused changes in the environment that were particularly drastic in the northern parts of Europe. In the "Preboreal" the birch-pine woods regained the areas from which they had been pushed during the Upper Dryas period. Deciduous trees, beginning with hazel, moved northward. In Europe nearly everywhere outside the Mediterranean zone a pine-hazel period can be distinguished in the early postglacial ("Boreal"). Into these woods moved elm, oak, lime, and somewhat later ash and alder; after these deciduous trees had gained dominance ("Atlantic") beech, white pine, and hornbeam moved in ("Subboreal"). On the French Mediterranean coast the land snail fauna indicates a change toward a drier climate (Escalon de Fonton 1955; 1956; 1966).

It apparently took some time before man could efficiently adapt to the new environment. In many well-investigated areas, the frequency of sites that can be dated between 8000 and 7000 B.C. (Preboreal) seems to be significantly lower than those from the preceding and following millennia. It is therefore difficult to find a continuous series of intermediate assemblages between the Federmesser and Tanged Point traditions and their successors, and to localize the areas where the transition and readaptation took place.

Perhaps this is a general phenomenon—we may expect a rapid alteration in the environment to result in a change in the quantity of food that can be obtained with traditional methods, and in many cases to bring about diminution of population, or emigration. Only after adjusting the hunting and collecting methods to the new fauna and flora can the population expand again. A similar situation seems to be present in the early Atlantic period in the western Baltic.

In the early postglacial period at least three traditions can be distinguished in the human habitation (Fig. 2): Maglemosian, Sauveterrian-Tardenoisian, and Montadian. The center of the Maglemose tradition was in the western Baltic area. It also included parts of Britain and the present North Sea. We know of a seasonal settlement (Star Carr in England) (Clark 1954), as early as in the Preboreal period, in a river valley bog, where man lived as close to the water as possible during winter and early spring. People hunted red deer (dominant), roe deer, elk, aurochs, wild boar,

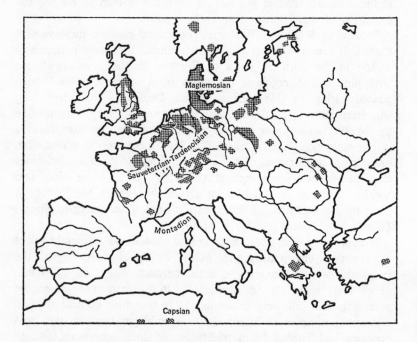

FIGURE 2 Distribution of farming cultures (cross-hatched) and hunting-collecting cultures about 6000 B.C.

and other furbearing animals such as fox, marten, and beaver. Birds were not numerous, and fish remains were conspicuously lacking. The preference for settling at the lakeside thus does not seem to have been determined by fishing or hunting of waterfowl. A wooden paddle is evidence of water transport.

Sites dating from the Boreal period are much more frequent. Seasonal culture layers, mainly known from the bogs of Denmark, Schleswig-Holstein, and Scania, now also contain large quantities of hazelnut shells and fish remains (Troels-Smith 1957:101–33).

In all stages of the Maglemosian tradition, macrolithic tools occur with microlithic flint types. Core and flake axes and adzes were made, which though still unpolished, could efficiently cut small trees to be used, for example, as substructures for huts. Other stone was also used for making tools, such as mace heads, hammers, and axes, some of them perforated and made by pecking. There was also some art: amber model animals and geometrical ornaments made by incision and pricking on bone and antler tools.

Much less specialized were the groups belonging to the Sauveterrian-Tardenoisian tradition of western Europe, from parts of Britain, the Low Countries, and France to inland Germany (Bohmers, Wouters 1956; Barrière 1954). The flint industry was predominantly microlithic.

People lived mainly on game hunting and their settlements were frequently shifted. They would certainly have taken advantage of the hazel, but it is doubtful that fishing was of any importance. In hilly countries cave sites occur rather frequently, and heavy soils are avoided.

Microlithic flint industries of Sauveterrian-Tardenoisian affinity, and therefore probably of Boreal age, occur as far eastward as lower Austria and Slovakia, where they seem, however, to be rare (Gulder 1953; Barta 1959; Kmoch 1966). Southeastern Europe has so far yielded very little that can be attributed with any certainty to this period. Some Rumanian and Moldavian sites may belong here.

Along the Mediterranean coast, habitation continued (Escalon de Fonton 1955; 1956; 1966). In the Rhône delta, a continuous sequence of industries has been established from the Romanellian to the food-producing Chasseen. It is probable that the first stage after the Romanellian, the Montadian, is to be dated from the Preboreal and Boreal periods. The settlements occur in rock shelters. The culture layers are very rich in mollusks, both terrestrial and marine.

Further, there are aurochs, red deer, wild boar, and large quantities of hare or rabbit. The flint industry has a degenerated character.

Flint industries of this type also occur elsewhere in the Mediterranean area, as for example, in Liguria, near Salerno (Radmilli, Tongiorgi 1958), and also along the Adriatic coast of Jugoslavia, in the cave Crvena Stijena (Brodar 1958–59; Benac 1962).

VILLAGE FARMERS APPEAR IN GREECE

Sometime around 9000 B.C., incipient food production had started locally within what Braidwood calls the natural habitat zone in southwestern Asia among cultures that have a microlithic component strongly reminiscent of that in the later cultures of western and northern Europe. Around 7000 B.C., the first village-farming settlements were present in that area. Pottery was still, however, lacking, and it did not become common for perhaps another 1000 years.

In the prepottery stage, the European continent was hardly influenced by the nuclear development. Only in Thessaly have preceramic levels with remains of a farming culture been reported. Here, people cultivated wheat, barley, millet, lentils, and other legumes. They raised mainly sheep, but also had goats, swine, and cattle. Hunting and collecting were of minor importance (Milojčić et al. 1962; Weinberg 1965).

Such sites have also been found on Crete and Cyprus. The sea apparently posed no more problems: it unites the sites—all in coastal plains—more than it separates them. There are various archeological connections with Anatolia, and it is probable that this area or its lowland flanks in Syro-Cilicia and in the prehistorically little-known western littoral of Turkey was the place of origin of the first colonists on European territory. Admittedly, there is evidence for the presence of hunting and collecting communities in Greece in late-glacial or early postglacial times,[3] but their persistence up to the time immediately preceding the first evidence of farming is still to be proven.

---

[3] R. Stampfuss (1942); described materials from the Seidi cave in Boeotia, which according to Escalon de Fonton (1955; 1956; 1966) could belong to an early stage of the Montadian. S. S. Weinberg (1965) mentions similar finds from other sites in Greece.

DRAMATIC ENVIRONMENT CHANGE

With the Boreal-Atlantic transition, about 5500 B.C., there was much environmental change north of the Alpine belt. Pine and hazel lost their prominent place to a mixed deciduous forest. Marine transgressions enlarged the North Sea and brought salt water into the Baltic.

Increase in precipitation promoted the vegetation on lakeshores and the filling up of basins. Raised bogs appeared in former lakes or marshes, which was disastrous to fish and waterfowl.

The mixed oak forest was more shady than the fairly open pine woodland, and there was less grazing for large animals. Big game such as aurochs and red deer decreased in number. All these changes required readaptation by man, who now faced a rapid decrease of the natural resources he had been relying on for two millennia.

Danish investigators have noticed an increase in the importance of waterfowl hunting, fishing, and collecting of wild fruits and berries in the Maglemose area, toward the end of the Boreal period, as evidence of elk and aurochs become rare. Only very few habitation sites from the early Atlantic period are known (Fig. 3). In contrast to those from the preceding period, these sites all seem to lie on the coast. At the site of Vedbaek, north of Copenhagen, remains were found not only of red deer, roe deer, and wild boar, but also of sea mammals such as grey seal, ring seal, porpoise, and fish such as cod and haddock. Sea hunting and fishing appear here as a new means of subsistence and compensate for the decrease in big game and inland fish. Shellfish, however, were not collected. Pottery was unknown, and there is no evidence for food production (Troels-Smith 1957).

As was the case in the Preboreal period, there seems to be a decrease in population during the adaptation to the new environment. In the Low Countries, one early Atlantic site is known, de Leijen. It is situated at the shore of a depression which was still open water at the time of habitation. People collected hazelnuts and also water nuts, and must have lived on fish as well (of the possible organic materials, only carbonized fruit remains were preserved at this site). Generally, however, higher grounds had become unsuitable for human habitation. But there is reason to

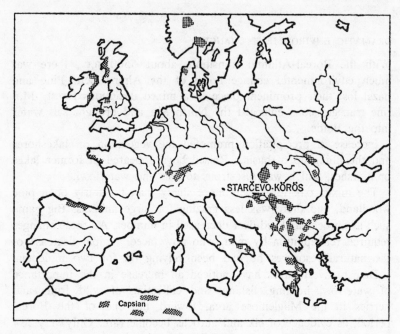

FIGURE 3 Distribution of farming cultures (cross-hatched) and hunt-ing-collecting cultures about 5000 B.C.

believe that parts of the Rhine delta in the North Sea that are now deeply sub-submerged were inhabited during the Atlantic period.[4]

Further south, in Belgium and France, there is as yet no proof of inland habitation during the Atlantic period.[5] But a few shell middens of this age are known from the coast of Brittany, and the rise of the sea level since about 3000 B.C. in that area makes it probable that their number had been much larger. At Téviec and

[4] The evidence is mostly of indirect nature, as, for example: (i) Maglemosian influences on the flint industry of de Leyen; (ii) the uniformity of the Ertebølle, Lower Halstow, and Campignian flint industries; (iii) the presence of a settlement site with Rössen influence on a bank of the IJssel River, at 5 m. below O.D. in a Zuiderzee polder; (iv) the presence of communities (Vlaardingen culture) on creek banks in the delta around the middle of the 3rd millennium B.C., which, although in the possession of cultivated grain and domesticated animals, still rely heavily on hunting, fishing, and collecting.

[5] The radiocarbon dates of about 2800 to 3100 B.C. recently reported from the Tardenoisian type area (Deevey et al. 1966:82) are evidently too recent.

Hoedic, interesting cemeteries have been excavated with graves containing one to three individuals and grave goods—antlers, bone tools, and shell necklaces (Giot 1960:24–26). Other shell middens of Atlantic age are known from Britain (Churchill 1965), Portugal (Roche 1965), and northwest Spain.[6]

As the Boreal-Atlantic transition set in, people everywhere in western, northwestern, and northern Europe moved toward the coast and added coastal hunting, fishing, and collecting as means of subsistence to the traditional hunting of big game and inland collecting and fishing. The Atlantic forest as such was an unfavorable environment for man, and European man could best survive by adapting himself to the coast. In making this adaptation, however, there was an important consequence. The coastal resources allowed a considerably higher degree of sedentary occupation, freeing man of the necessity of continuous wandering. One precondition for the acceptance of farming (Caldwell 1958)—residential stability—was thus automatically fulfilled.

In the narrow zone between Alps and Jura mountains there are many lakes and streams. Here we find a very varied environment, especially if the high mountains are included as suitable area for seasonal hunting. It is not surprising that in this area there is proof of human habitation during the Atlantic period, in caves (Wyss 1960; Bandi 1963) and open air sites, such as the Lautereck (Taute 1967), a rock shelter on the upper course of the Danube where people specialized in carp fishing. Elsewhere in central Europe there is no proof of human habitation between 5500 and 4500 B.C.

Along the western Mediterranean coast, adaptation had, as seen in the preceding section, taken place long before. Possibly it was the Alleröd climatic improvement which had here brought about the same necessity of movement toward the coast as the Boreal-Atlantic change was to bring about in the north.

SOUTHEASTERN EUROPE (6000 TO 4500 B.C.)

At about 5500 B.C., in the coastal plains of the Aegean area ceramic farming villages were present everywhere (Rodden 1965; 1964; Milojčić *et al.* 1962). Large rectangular buildings have been

---

[6] No C_{14} dates are as yet available, but the shell fauna in the middens should point to the time of the postglacial climatic optimum according to Obermaier (1924b).

excavated at Neo Nikomedeia. Early sites also occur in the inland valleys of Macedonia and Bulgaria.

At about 5000 B.C. the plains of southeastern Europe were inhabited by agricultural groups of the Starčevo-Körös tradition with their main distribution area in the southern part of the Hungarian plain. Here natural steppe conditions may have prevailed, but sites of this tradition also occur in areas such as Bosnia, which most probably had a forested character. The use of heavy wood in the house construction in Macedonia may be seen as a first adaptation to European forest conditions. This adaptation probably continued in the Hungarian plain, which certainly had gallery forests along the rivers, and was bordered everywhere by wooded hills.

Most of these settlements seem to be completely dependent on food production (Clason 1967). There is, however, some evidence for the persistence of a food-collecting economy. On an island in the flood plain of the river Theiss a site has been found (Bökönyi 1964) with remains of forest animals, many fish, many birds, and layers of shells up to 30 centimeters thick. There was evidence for the local domestication of cattle. At some sites in the Bug-Dnestr area, a "Mesolithic" level is reported below a series of "Neolithic" levels (Titov, private communication). The lowest Neolithic level contains many bones of wild animals alongside domesticated cattle, and many fish remains. There are sites on river banks. The flint industry is microlithic.

In both areas we must reckon with the possible persistence of communities which did not produce food and instead specialized in fishing and thereby attained sufficient residential stability to be receptive to new ideas on food production. In this connection, mention should also be made of the recently excavated site of Lepenski Vir situated on a bank of the river Danube in the Iron Gate. There were three main horizons. The lower horizon comprises five layers, with a total of 59 trapezoidal house foundations, each with an elaborate hearth. The most spectacular finds are large sandstone pebbles that are worked into human faces with a fishlike mouth. Agricultural tools are lacking. Bones of deer, boar, and various fish species have been found. Fishing and hunting thus seem to have been the major means of subsistence. Pottery appears only in the two uppermost layers of the lower horizon. Horizon III, separated by a sand deposit from the foregoing horizon, belongs to the Starčevo culture.

In large parts of the Hungarian plain, Bulgaria, and Rumania, which were inhabited by the Starčevo-Körös farmers, evidence for the presence of such food-collecting communities is lacking. We therefore assume that there was an actual colonization by people from the narrow coastal plains of the Aegean coast, through the Vardar-Morava gate and parallel valleys, and up the Marcia valley, and from there either westward toward Serbia or northward along the Black Sea coast into the Dobroucha and Walachia. There is also the possibility of migration over sea through the Dardanelles and the Bosporus. Unfortunately, there is little evidence from the coastal plains of western Anatolia and Thrace.

In the Thessalian standard sequence of cultures (Milojčić 1960), Milojčić is found below the Sesklo level, which should be parallel to Starčevo, a level characterized by a pottery that is ornamented by impressions of shells (Cardium). Related pottery occurs in many places along the Mediterranean coasts. It probably originated in the Levant (for example, Mersin) and spread westward (Evans 1958; Batović 1962; Arnal, Burnez 1958). It is found along the Dalmatian coast, in Apulia, Sicily, Liguria, south France, Spain, and even Portugal, always in areas (often at the same sites) that were already inhabited by coastal hunting-collecting communities (Arribas 1967). From the few radiocarbon dates available it is probable that this pottery had reached the western Mediterranean by 4500 B.C. It may have been preceded by the domesticated sheep and goat, or both. In the section of Châteauneuf-lez-Martigues in the Rhône valley, bones of these animals occur well below the first pottery (of Cardium type) (Ducos 1958). They are also reported in late Tardenoisian layers of Rouffignac and in aceramic shell middens of Portugal, Asturia, Brittany, and Ireland.

THE FINAL PHASE (4500 TO 300 B.C.)

By 4500 B.C., then, the foundations were laid for the final spread of food production throughout Europe. Evidence for this general moment of time suggests (i) that the Hungarian plain was a dominant center which had incorporated all the major achievements of the nuclear area in the Near East, and which had added to these an adaptation to the European deciduous forest; (ii) along the Mediterranean coast, a diffusion sphere connected with the Levant and the Aegean; (iii) along the Atlantic and Baltic coasts, popula-

348

H. T. Waterbolk

tions of hunters, fishermen, and collectors, who by a many-faceted exploitation of natural resources had attained a fair degree of residential stability; and (iv) finally, locally in inland Europe, small groups of people who had been increasing their economic potential by specializing in river and lake fishing and collecting.

One of the most remarkable events in European prehistory is the explosive spread of the Bandkeramik culture. From about 4400 B.C., large loess areas north and west of the Hungarian plain were colonized in a short time (Fig. 4).

Permanent settlements were founded everywhere. They consisted of some 10 to 20 wooden buildings up to 40 meters long and 5 to 6 meters wide, the roof of which was supported by three rows of posts inside the houses. In each village, one building is larger and of heavier construction than the others (Waterbolk, Modderman 1959; Waterbolk 1962:227–53). The people lived by agriculture and husbandry. Hunting was of minor importance; the

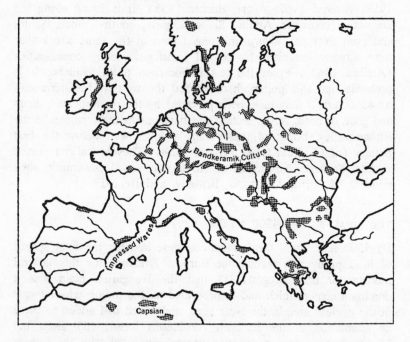

FIGURE 4 Distribution of farming cultures (cross-hatched) and hunting-collecting cultures about 4200 B.C.

percentage of wild animals never exceeds 10 percent of the total bone remains (Clason 1967).

The pottery is very homogeneous. In a period of several centuries a parallel development of form and ornament took place over the whole area of distribution. Toward the end, regional differentiation increased.

A possible center of this large-scale colonization is the northwestern part of the Hungarian plain. An early pottery stage with Starčevo influences has recently been distinguished in this area (Quitta 1960; 1964). It also occurs in Bohemia, South Germany, and Saxony-Thuringia.

Although the river valleys clearly directed the distribution of the Bandkeramik, it is by no means a riverine culture. Sites occur mainly on well drained loess plateaus, with no direct relation to rivers or streams. In this large area there is no conclusive evidence that earlier populations took over agriculture and husbandry and were assimilated into the Bandkeramik culture.

We mentioned the site of Lautereck. Here, Bandkeramik pottery appeared in the otherwise normal collecting inventory of a carp fishing settlement on the Upper Danube, outside the loess area. In a still later stage, Aichbühl pottery (about 3800 B.C.) also occurred at the same site in an inventory that was otherwise still unchanged. This is one of the few sure contacts between the Bandkeramik culture and an indigenous inland culture, and it certainly does not suggest a fast rate of assimilation.

Contacts of the same kind can be expected at all points where the Bandkeramik culture occurs far down the river valleys so that it meets the coastal communities. The results of such contacts are evident much later, when the Bandkeramik culture had been succeeded by regional cultures such as Rössen in the west, Stichbandkeramik in central regions, and Precucuteni in the east. For this level, dates of 3800 to 3500 B.C. are probable.

For northwestern Europe, the Rössen culture appears to be of great importance (Behrens 1959; Schwabedissen 1967). Rössen settlements with long houses are known from the same loess soils and the same areas as were occupied by the Bandkeramik farmers. But isolated finds of Rössen pottery occur at sites along lakes and rivers where the traditional means of subsistence are maintained with small-scale agriculture and husbandry.

In the western Mediterranean area, the communities of coastal collectors which, by way of diffusion, had learned to make pottery and to herd sheep and goat, or both, now also took over agriculture. They no longer lived exclusively on a narrow strip along the coast, but moved onto the coastal plains behind. Minor geographical barriers were crossed. Cardium pottery penetrated from Liguria to the Po plain, from the Provence into the Garonne plain through the Aquitanian gate, from the Catalonian coast into the Ebro valley. The new economy seems to have resulted in an increase of the population, and, with the coastal plains as the starting point, all available open spaces were occupied.

At the same time, the traditional communication lines along the Mediterranean and Atlantic coasts were maintained. A network of connections thus extended all over western Europe, including the British Isles. The coastal communities served as connecting points in this network and as nuclei of cultural innovation. They became starting points for the final spread of farming over the plains of western Europe. In this area a certain cultural uniformity prevailed —the "Western Neolithic" tradition. This tradition is characterized, for example, by certain pottery types, hilltop settlements ("causewayed camps"), and megalithic monuments (menhirs, alignments, collective tombs).

WESTERN AND DANUBIAN TRADITIONS MEET

So far in this account of the spread of food production into Europe, the new economy has moved into and developed in a succession of regions where food production was unknown. We now have the problem of what happened when the Western Neolithic tradition and the Danubian tradition (as evidenced by the regional successors of the Bandkeramik) met. Keeping in mind the maritime emphasis of the Western tradition and the predilection for loess soils shown by the Danubian tradition, the areas where both traditions can be expected to meet are: the western part of the Alpine foreland, Burgundy, the upper Rhine lowland, the Seine basin, and the coastal plains along the North Sea.

In the Alpine foreland (Vogt 1961), the Lautereck site shows that the first influence of local groups in this area could have taken place even before 4000 B.C., but probably it was half a millennium later, in Rössen times, that the reorientation became manifest. Here again, the actual transition from food collecting to food production is not observed; but this is a general phenomenon.

We see only the result of the adaptation, not the adapting process itself, because it concerned only a small number of people, and the chance of finding their settlements is small. Only where man used caves and rock shelters as settlements—as in Châteauneuf-lez-Martiques—may we expect to observe gradual transitions in the occupation layers. For them the choice of settlement sites was much more restricted; and furthermore, caves and rock shelters are obvious places for archeological exploration.

The first agricultural groups in the Alpine foreland preferred lakeshores or bogs as settlement sites. There are few early sites. The earliest may be those of the Aichbühl culture. Others show Rössen influences (for example, the Egolzwil culture). This level can be dated at about the middle of the 4th millennium B.C.

About 3000 B.C. (Fig. 5) the population had apparently increased considerably. There were many farming villages, all situated on the marshy shores of the lakes. The old familiar "Swiss lake dwelling" sites are now known to have been built on the shores of lakes or bogs, but not built out over the water. Cereal grains are

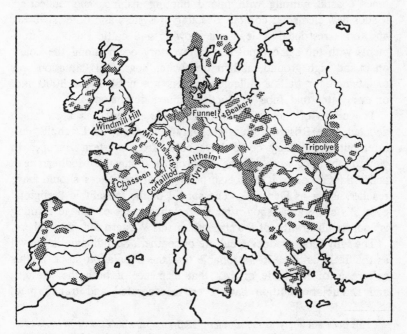

FIGURE 5 Distribution of farming cultures (cross-hatched) and hunting-collecting cultures about 3000 B.C.

common in most of the settlements, but collecting of wild fruits and berries was practiced as well. Locally, fishing remained important. Hunting was a major occupation; in some sites, bones of wild animals dominated over those of domesticated animals. The pottery shows a great diversity in form and ornament. West of Lake Zürich the Younger Cortaillod culture which belonged to the Western tradition developed; east of this lake the Pfyn culture of clearly Danubian affinity developed. This diversity can best be explained by assuming that the hunting and collecting communities in this area had undergone influences from both the west and the east. Two other groups further eastward have the same preference for lakeshores: Schussenried (South Germany) and Mondsee (Austria).

In the North German-Danish area the Ertebølle culture (Schwabedissen 1967; Troels-Smith 1960b:95; 1967; Lüttschwager 1967) originated at about 3800 B.C. as a successor of both the early Atlantic Vedbaek culture (on the Danish islands) and the Oldesloe culture (a lakeshore, inland hunting and collecting culture in Schleswig-Holstein of Atlantic age). The Ertebølle culture not only combines coastal hunting with inland hunting, fishing, and collecting, it adds new elements: coastal collecting of oysters and other shellfish, and, on a restricted scale, grain growing and cattle raising. Settlements with the same type of flint inventory occur along the coast, on inland high ground, and in freshwater bogs. This situation was maintained for half a millennium; it is not until about 3000 B.C. or even later that food production gained dominance.

The origin of the well-known Ertebølle pottery has been much debated. The Rössen culture certainly influenced the Ertebølle culture, but the pottery could have come from western Europe. In view of the long range of the connections along the Mediterranean and Atlantic coasts it is not surprising that influences should have reached as far as Denmark. The spread of the megalithic "religion" over this same area, soon after the establishment of village farming is another illustration of the strength of this Western diffusion sphere.

The fully food-producing culture of southern Scandinavia is known as the TRB culture. It is probable that the population stock of this culture is of Ertebølle origin,[7] that elements of both the Western and Danubian tradition have been incorporated and transformed,

---

[7] This does not apply to the southern TRB groups, which occur in loess areas which had been inhabited since Bandkeramik times, and which contributed much to the origin of the TRB culture.

and that an expansion of population had taken place after the establishment of food production. Expansion went northward to south Norway, westward to northwest Germany and Holland, and eastward to Poland. Just as the megaliths illustrate the persistence of the Western tradition in the TRB culture, copper imports from the Hungarian plain, knob-ended battle-axes (*Knaufhammeräxte*), and long houses illustrate the long-distance contacts with the Danubian tradition.

In France the main food-producing culture is the Chasseen, of which Bailloud distinguishes four regional varieties (Bailloud 1964). The southern variety could have developed out of the Cardial.[8] In Brittany the Chasseen is characterized by megalithic grave monuments of clearly Iberian affinity, and by polished axes made of locally quarried greenstone, which were exported over wide areas in France. One megalithic tomb was found on top of a shell midden with a carbon-14 date of 4000 B.C. (La Torche). The presence of goat in the shell middens of Téviec and Hoëdic is another indication that the coastal culture of Brittany could have played a part in the development of the western variety of the Chasseen. The eastern variety occurs in Savoy and Burgundy; it is hardly different from the younger Cortaillod culture of Switzerland, and has the same preference for lakeshores.

In the Paris basin, the Chasseen is preceded by the *Groupement de Cerny* which Bailloud thinks followed the late variety of Bandkeramik in this area, and thus belonged to the Danubian tradition. It occurs far to the west and seems to reach the coast of the North Sea. It should be a contemporary of the Rössen culture. In this area the western influences seem to have become more important than the Danubian. The northern variety of the Chasseen is the only one in which the polished flint axe, which it has in common with the Funnel Beaker culture, is known.

For their axes and adzes the Bandkeramik and Rössen cultures depended largely on an amphibolite which occurs naturally in Silesia (Schietzel 1965), Rössen-type adzes are lightly distributed over large parts of the plains of northwestern Europe. It is clear, however, that for a large-scale expansion of farming, a local source of material for axes and adzes would be essential. In the

---

[8] Escalon de Fonton (1967) sees the Chasseen of the Rhône valley as an intrusive culture, coming fully developed from the east.

western Baltic area, suitable unweathered flint occurs abundantly both as boulders in cliffs and in the chalk. Here large flint tools had been in use for many millennia and the step toward polishing was a small one.

In north France and Belgium crude macrolithic flint assemblages are known as the "Campignian." Most investigators now agree that it is the flint exploitation "facies" of food-producing cultures (Chasseen, Michelsberg). Both at Spiennes (Belgium) and at Rijckholt (Netherlands), flint mines were in operation before 3000 B.C. (de Laet 1967).

In the British Isles early carbon-14 dates for food-producing cultures have been obtained along the Irish Sea (Watts 1960; Clark 1965a). In this area coastal settlements of Atlantic age are present (Larnian, Obanian) which have yielded evidence for the gradual introduction of elements of food production (polished axes, sheep, or goat). Some of the major stone axe factories are situated in the same area (Tievebulliagh in Ulster, Langdale in the Lake District, Graig Lwyd in North Wales, and Cornwall), and these sent their products as far as Wessex (Clark 1965b), although flint was available there.

It is therefore possible that the Early Neolithic culture of southern Britain was not entirely due to an invasion from France (Clark 1966), but had its origin in the expansion of an Irish Sea population which had gradually acquired the elements of an agricultural economy through its coastal contacts.

In the transitional zone between the Western and Danubian spheres, there is another group whose origin has been much debated[9]—the Michelsberg culture, with its main distribution along the upper Rhine with some outliers as far as Bohemia and Belgium; its pottery occurs in the Spiennes flint-mining area. Radiocarbon dates from Spiennes, Ehrenstein, and Thayngen suggest an age between about 3400 and 2900 B.C. The Michelsberg culture is probably a local successor to the Rössen culture, and its population stock is therefore of ultimate Danubian origin, but it has incorporated various western elements. The relation of Michelsberg with TRB, Altheim, Baalberg, and other contemporary groups north of the Alps need not be explained by one common origin of these groups, but could be due to a phenomenon of acculturation of groups of heterogeneous origin.

---

[9] See various contributions in Böhm and de Laet (eds.) 1961.

By about 3000 B.C. the map of Europe had been filled with a complicated pattern of food-producing cultures of the village-farming type, each with a certain individuality. This individuality seems to have been the result of both environmental and historical factors. The environments called for adaptation to local circumstances of soil, relief, climate. But historical factors, such as migration, diffusion, acculturation, and local tradition were important in establishing boundaries and relations. It will take a long time to unravel the complicated processes which have led to the formation of these cultures.

FINAL CONSIDERATIONS

The major factors in the spread of food production over Europe seem to have been the following. (i) The presence of the nuclear area in southwestern Asia, from which the first fully food-producing groups migrated into Greece, and from which ideas were diffused along the Mediterranean and Atlantic coasts. (ii) The coastal adaptation of the descendants of the upper Paleolithic hunters and collectors. This adaptation was gradual and progressive, and the western Baltic area demonstrates that at least in that area it was provoked by successive environmental changes. Along the Mediterranean coasts such factors had probably been operating too, but at an earlier date. Coastal adaptation meant a greater variety in means of subsistence and, by its very nature, a greater residential stability —both preconditions for the acceptance of the farming way of life. (iii) The successive building up in southeastern Europe of potentials for the expansion of population over large areas. In this process adaptation to a fully forested environment was an essential element. The first wave of expansion comprised large parts of the Hungarian plain (Starčevo-Körös), the second, the loess areas northwest, north, and northeast of the Alpine and Carpathian mountain chains (Bandkeramik). (iv) The slowness in turning to food production exhibited by the sessile coastal and inland groups, doubtless because of the effectiveness of their mode of life. Mixed economies resulted in which agriculture and husbandry played a subordinate role (for example, Ertebølle). (v) The rapid colonization of the coastal plains after food production had gained dominance and a potential for population expansion had been built up. (vi) The interaction of the continental (Danubian) and coastal (Western) movements in a broad zone of contact between the Alps and the North Sea, where cultures with a mixed Danubian and Estern character originated.

There is no proof in Europe for the presence of a level of incipient food production in Braidwood's sense. Any domestication of indigenous cattle and pigs ensued after the introduction of domesticated animals in the area. It has been alleged that in the south of France (Arribas 1967) wild sheep was domesticated in the Atlantic period, but this is contradicted by the natural distribution of the species in Asia and by its absence among the animals that were hunted in earlier periods. Only the apparent strong specialization of the Ahrensburg people on the reindeer might have had aspects of domestication, in the same way as with some recent arctic peoples. But with the disappearance of tundra conditions this could not have had any lasting effect, and the successors of the Ahrensburgian were hunters.

There is also no botanical proof for food production before the introduction of wheat and barley from southwestern Asia. Still, there is the hazel, the fruits of which are extremely common in some culture layers, and the postglacial spread of which was so rapid that Firbas has suggested that man played a part in this spread (Firbas 1949). Of course, it would be easy to promote hazel growth by cutting down other shrubs. But man would only do so if he would be sure of coming back regularly. This might be the case in the Maglemosian area. Here seasonal lakeside settlements are known, where man specialized in fishing. In this rich environment, wanderings were certainly less necessary than in other areas. One might even see the core and flake axes as useful tools for such a purpose. It is doubtful, however, whether we shall ever be able to prove anything like the cultivation of hazel, and it must be said that such a contrivance had no decisive effect, for the addition of coastal collecting was necessary to overcome the effect of the Boreal-Atlantic environmental change.[10]

The development of prehistoric culture in Europe does indeed agree in broad outline and many details with the nonnuclear development in eastern North America. The increasing efficiency

---

[10] Another European plant of which the fruits have been collected and that one might think of as possibly being furthered by man is the water nut (*Trapa natans*).

in the exploitation of natural resources, the trend toward residential stability, the importance of the shellfish economies, the development of art, the disposal of goods to the dead in the later stages, are all features of the nonnuclear cultures of the eastern United States and southeastern Canada which we also find in northwestern Europe. Admittedly, we do not know a European counterpart for ceremonial centers and earthworks, as there were with the Hopewellian and Adena peoples before food production gained dominance. But the slowness to add animal husbandry and grain growing to an already effective food economy is again a feature which both areas have in common. This cultural slowness—Caldwell calls it resistance—is the main reason why it took as much as 3000 years for village farming to travel by way of diffusion from the Aegean to the North Sea along the coastal route.

The shorter continental route was not much faster, for the obvious reasons that it was barred by mountain chains and depended only on expansion of population and migration. But even so, by 4400 B.C. fully food-producing communities had reached the edge of the north German lowland plain at a distance of 300 kilometers from the heart of the Ertebølle area. A distance of 2000 kilometers—as the crow flies—had already been covered in the same time which thereafter was necessary to cover these last 300 lowland kilometers and to establish fully effective village farming in the Ertebølle area and its surroundings.

SUMMARY

Against the background of the postglacial climatic development and the major physiographic features of Europe, a description is given of the spread of food production over the continent. After the immigration of the first farmers into Greece from Anatolia, adaptation to European forest conditions took place and potentials for successive population expansions were built up. Large parts of continental Europe appear to have been uninhabited at the time immediately preceding the immigration of farmers. The reason was probably that the forest had become unsuitable for human occupation after the deciduous species had gained dominance. Along the Mediterranean and Atlantic coasts, hunting and collecting communities had been able to maintain themselves by adding sea

hunting and fishing and shore collecting of shells to the traditional
inland hunting, fishing, and collecting.

These communities were sufficiently sessile to be receptive to
new ideas on food production that arrived successively by way of
diffusion along the coasts. They became centers of population expansion and cultural innovation after food production in the course
of time had gained dominance. In a broad zone between the Alps
and the North Sea the coastal (Western) and continental (Danubian) traditions interacted.

Acknowledgments: For discussions and for reading the manuscript I thank
R. J. Braidwood, L. Braidwood, J. Caldwell, R. Hall, and my collaborators at
the Biological-Archaeological Institute, J. J. Butler, A. T. Clason, R. R. Newell,
J D. van der Waals, and W. van Zeist. J. J. Butler improved the English text,
M. Bierma prepared the typescript, T. Appelboom assisted in the preparation
of the distribution maps, which were drawn by H. Roelink.

THE EASTERN WOODLANDS OF NORTH AMERICA

17 EASTERN NORTH AMERICA

Joseph R. Caldwell

THE IDEA of diverse culture-historical pathways toward urban life has led me to repeat some previously published arguments about the prehistory of eastern North America (Caldwell 1958). The region from the Atlantic as far as the Plains can be considered a developmental unity differing in important respects from those sequences in Mesoamerica and southwest Asia reputed to have led more directly to cities and high civilizations. Here a long period of adaptation to forest existence, mostly completed by the end of the so-called "Archaic" stage of about 8000–1500 B.C., culminated south of the Great Lakes during the subsequent Hopewellian phase of roughly 400 B.C.–A.D. 500. This adaptive trend to the establishment of "primary forest efficiency"—represented by changes in hunting methods, emergence of economic cycles and food specializations, and achieving a kind of balanced reliance on almost all sources of natural foods—had a peculiar effect on the course of historical development. It apparently became possible in the forested East to get along very well without agriculture. There are indeed cultigens, probably antedating the beginning of the first millennium A.D. in the Hopewellian and related Adena manifestations, but there is no evidence that these were depended upon more than any single source of wild food. Perhaps it would be unwise to speak specifically of resistance to food production, but there was evidently some time lapse between first knowledge of cultivation and considerable reliance on it among most groups, with some later Hopewellians as a possible exception. Our first reliable indication of a dependence on food production sufficient to have had noticeable social effects is at the beginning of Mississippian times, around A.D. 800. A similar

Reprinted from Robert J. Braidwood and Gordon R. Willey, editors, *Courses Toward Urban Life* (Chicago: Aldine Publishing Company, 1962); copyright © 1962 by Wenner-Gren Foundation for Anthropological Research, Inc.

reluctance to depend greatly on food production, even long after its methods were known, has been described in other papers in this symposium dealing with regions outside the areas where the first nuclear civilizations arose. An ethnographic instance of a similar phenomenon may be represented in California, although a climatic reason has been suggested (Kroeber 1939:211).

Long before these events, both the Great Plains and the forested East shared with a vast region of the North American continent a common economic basis in the hunting of large mammals. At least, such is inferred from the occurrence in the East of fluted projectile points of Clovis type, persisting perhaps as late as 7000 B.C. But on the Plains arose a distinctive development of the bison-hunting specialization of Folsom-Plainview, from perhaps 9000 B.C. until after 6000 B.C., apparently coming to an end at just about the time some of the eastern societies were in the midst of their adaptation to a forest mode of life. We shall have something to say about the Plains in this paper. If some of its developments can be regarded as mainly autochthonous, Plains prehistory on the whole can hardly be intelligible without constant reference to events in the eastern forest area that supplied Plains societies with so much cultural material. For this reason, not lessened by my inability to handle Plains materials with the sagacity they deserve, we shall consider the Plains as an appendage of the forested East.

We said that primary forest efficiency was being reached toward the end of the Archaic stage. An important series of economic innovations took place during that interval. More stylistic elaboration occurred later. Style changes found particular expression in the ceramic and mortuary activities of some of the later societies. We shall refer to these successive expressions as the Hopewellian, Gulf, Mississippian, and Southern Cult "climaxes," using this term in the sense introduced by Kroeber (1939:223): regional situations of relatively greater cultural elaboration and organization from which a radiation of cultural material took place.

What may be an interesting feature of these climaxes is that only in the case of the Mississippian is there any good reason to conjecture an economic cause—that is, increased dependence on food production. And it is in this climax, incidentally, that we have our best evidence for the outward migrations of people from a presumed heartland in the central Mississippi Valley. For the others—Hopewellian, Gulf, and Southern Cult—there is less evidence of movements of peoples and more evidence for the spread of ideas ("cultural material") to peoples surrounding climax areas. These other climaxes, moreover, represent more noticeably at least in part, reworkings of the old eastern ideas of lavish mortuary procedures and the placing of valuable objects and regalia with selected individuals.

All the climaxes recognized here took place in a context of increasing influence from Mesoamerica. There are increasing numbers of discrete recognizable Mesoamerican elements as one moves chronologically from Hopewellian, through Gulf, through Mississippian, to Southern Cult. Yet we cannot guess at the nature of these Mesoamerican connections except to suggest, following Kelley (1955), that the intervening area of low cultural level in Texas and northeast Mexico had a certain effect on what could be transmitted to the East via this route. And it must be said that Mesoamerican elements in eastern North American assemblages are rarely identical with their analogues in Mesoamerica.

On the basis of the foregoing, we may now suggest a little more precisely how the prehistory of eastern North America can be contrasted with the prehistories of such regions of nuclear civilization as Mesoamerica and southwest Asia. The development of a forest efficiency may have slowed down further economic innovation, especially the adoption of agriculture as an economic basis, while offering a sufficient livelihood to permit stylistic elaborations, and such non-economic activity as the building of mounds and earthworks and the disposal of considerable wealth with the dead. Instead of the more direct progress to new levels of "sociocultural integration," such as we imagine to have occurred in regions of nuclear civilizations, there was a succession of little-understood cultural climaxes that to some degree represented reworkings of the old eastern idea of elaborate and lavish treatment of certain selected dead.

If we may now regard the East as one kind of culture-historical pathway and the Mesoamerican development that was influencing it as another, we have a framework within which we shall, in the final and most speculative part of this paper, engage the main questions asked in this seminar—whether effective food production and urbanism may have been emerging in eastern North America.

In a vast region east of the Mississippi River a series of forests extended from subtropical Florida to subarctic woodlands. Within this area can be distinguished certain variations in native subsistence.

In historic times small tribes of the Atlantic and Gulf coasts lived partly by hunting, partly on seafood, and raised a little maize. Other tribes in the interior put more reliance on maize, beans, and squash, but hunting and gathering were always important. In the upper Great Lakes area there were maize, hunting and gathering, and, where available, considerable reliance on wild rice (*Zizania aquatica*). In the northern forest of the eastern subarctic, where planting was impossible, there was still gathering and hunting, especially of the moose and caribou.

The archeological evidence is that there was once a time when there was no planting at all and that the acceptance of food production as a major economic basis was a long and difficult affair. Even in historic times, food production was only supplementary in many regions and was the sole economic basis in none. Aside from cultivation, subsistence practices seem to be variations on the common theme of hunting and gathering whatever was available. Even the corn-growing Choctaw and Illini might leave their towns deserted to go hunting, and some Illini claimed that they ate maize only when they could not get bison. The Cherokee, whose women annually raised thousands of bushels of maize, regarded themselves not only as warriors but more strictly as hunters, pleading economic necessity to claim several million square miles of land that they did not occupy.

In these eastern forests and somewhat beyond, a number of intergrading culture subareas have been distinguished by ethnologists working with historical data of the native tribes. This lightness of cultural contour, as Kroeber (1939:60) has said, has its parallels in the lack of sharp environmental differences. Again the archeological evidence comes to our aid in showing that this was probably always so—that the cultures of the entire region tended more toward uniformity at any particular time than toward subregional differences. The import of this is that we can consider the prehistory of the East as a great interrelated culture-historical structure.

The foundations of this historical structure are represented by the ancient hunting and gathering societies belonging to what is called the "Archaic" stage, a conception co-ordinate with the far-flung "Desert" culture of western North America and other regional manifestations in North and South America.

The interior grasslands were historically involved with the forested East. Tallgrass prairie extended eastward from the ninety-eighth meridian into a kind of prairie peninsula narrowing between the northern and southern hardwood zones of the forest. In the eastern prairies there is little evidence of a particular prairie subsistence until the occurrence of bison bones in assemblages of the historic periods. Settlements were on the rivers and streams. It has been argued that these offered forest environments within the prairie zone. On the western prairies and on the short grass of the High Plains extending to the slopes of the Rocky Mountains there was an early hunting specialization. The Folsom materials, from about 9000 to 7000 B.C., apparently represent societies subsisting mainly on large, and some now extinct, herbivores, especially bison (*taylori, antiquus,* and *occidentalis*). For our story, however, specialized plains hunting continued during the time of succeeding Yuma, Eden-Scottsbluff, and Plainview-like assemblages to about the time of the altithermal, perhaps about 4000 B.C. A possible climatic explanation for the disappearance of some of these hunters is supported by the observation that similar flint projectile-point forms persist until 2800 B.C. in Canada (MacNeish 1959a:12).

Succeeding Prairie materials, such as Signal Butte I in Nebraska at about 2400 B.C., imply greater emphasis on smaller game and hunting, but on the High Plains an impoverished bison-hunting economy was still present in Coronado's time (Eggan 1952:39).

Developments in the eastern forest area had the most serious consequences for later history in the grasslands. By Hopewellian times, at least, eastern settlements were fingering westward along the major rivers. But correlating cultural manifestations on the Plains with particular eastern contemporaries is a difficult task that has scarcely begun. When the introduction of the horse and gun made a new plains-hunting development possible, the eastern tribes thus attracted to the area provided much of the cultural basis for the famous specializations of historic Plains Indian life.

The plains-hunting Folsom specialization mentioned earlier may be a regional adaptation in an early context of hunting societies, including the slightly earlier Clovis materials of the southwestern United States. Unfortunately, with the exception of Bull Brook in Massachusetts, at about 7000 B.C., there are few early dated materials *in situ* from the eastern forest areas and no associated animal remains. Occupation sites with chipped-stone assemblages are beginning to be recognized, and thousands of characteristic fluted points, more usually resembling Clovis than Folsom, have occurred as surface finds. There is a significant lack of shell heaps representing forest and waterside adaptations; these evidently arose later. In the Great Lakes region during the final retreat of the Wisconsin Glaciation, 10,000–5000 B.C., there was a gradual change in the periglacial forests from spruce-fir to pine and gradual disappearance of such fauna as mastodon and giant beaver. The distribution of fluted points correlated with glacial, lake level, faunal, and vegetational evidence, has enabled Quimby (1960) to make a good circumstantial case that mastodon were hunted in the region, perhaps as a major basis for subsistence.

As the ice slowly retreated from the Great Lakes region, hunting peoples here, no less than on the Plains, found themselves in a changing world. How great were these changes is portrayed in Quimby's admirable little book. The assemblages in this region during 7000–5000 B.C., called "Aqua-Plano" to indicate the similarity of projectile-point forms to the post-Folsom "Plano" assemblages on the Plains, were hunters in a landscape dominated by spruce and pine, lake waters, and glacial ice. Deer, elk, and barren-ground caribou were there to be taken, but it is possible that the mastodon was already gone. By this time, however, the use of boats or canoes is inferable from the same evidence that indicates that, in the summertime, groups of people were probably fishing on lakeshores and islands that could not have supported them in winter months. In the succeeding "Archaic Boreal" period, 5000 to possibly 500 B.C., which witnessed the development of the deciduous forest in the region, there is evidence of continued adaptation to the land and the discovery of its resources. There is now, Quimby tells us, an emphasis on ground and polished woodworking tools, like the axes, adze, and gouge, and there is also the remarkable development of the Old Copper industry.

The record of technological development in the Great Lakes region may be expected to differ somewhat from that in the more southerly parts of the eastern forest, if only because it occurred in a setting dominated by striking postglacial changes. We shall describe the forest adaptation in the southerly regions in slightly different terms, but with an assurance that these events were taking place almost contemporaneously with those in the north and were influencing and/or being influenced by them.

During the general period of from about 8000 to 1500 B.C.— the Archaic stage, in which the Boreal Archaic is a regional development—there is evidence of the development of a forest-hunting pattern. The earlier chipped-stone spear points had been lanceolate, suitable as tips for thrusting-spears. The trend is to shouldered and barbed points better for javelins and ambush hunting (Caldwell 1958:13), with direct evidence for the spear-thrower (atlatl).

There is evidence for the development of seasonal cycles. Earlier levels going back to 8000 B.C. at the Modoc Rock Shelter in southern Illinois suggest year-round occupation (Fowler 1959b). Later levels of about 3000–2000 B.C. show a greater proportion of deer bones and more restricted artifact assemblages, which could be the debris left by hunting parties. A similar development occurs at a later time in Wisconsin farther north (Wittry 1959a). Various localities in Illinois and Kentucky suggest other specializations; one shows an abundance of acorn hulls, multiple pitted "nutting stones," extensive areas reddened by fire—presumably for roasting acorns —but no storage pits or other features (Fowler 1959b).

Archaic adaptions were not everywhere alike. On the Green River in Kentucky, the Tennessee River in northern Alabama, the upper Savannah River in Georgia, and on the Atlantic and Gulf coasts shell middens are large and numerous. A degree of reliance on shellfish—also an Archaic innovation—may have encouraged a greater degree of *sedentism:* the earliest southeastern pottery— fiber tempered—occurs most frequently on shell heaps.

In post-Archaic ranges of time there were some economic innovations that can be regarded as developments of the hunting-gathering pattern already established. Most later change, however, seems to have been in small things—in the form and decoration of artifacts, especially pottery, and in particularities of burial customs. Change usually represented not technical improvement but stylistic differentiation. As a result, we can discern the existence of several regional traditions: a Northern (Woodland), a Middle Eastern, a Southern Appalachian, and a Gulf.

In the *Middle Eastern Tradition* (Caldwell 1958:23–27) there is evidence of continued development of the hunting-gathering pattern. While some Middle Eastern pottery occurs on shell heaps, there is a dependence on acorns and underground storage greater than in earlier or later times, but no evidence of food production. The distinctive pottery of this tradition (cord-wrapped-stick decorated) is characteristic of such manifestations as the Late Eva Focus and "Round Grave" cultures in Tennessee and is spread throughout the acorn-rich central deciduous part of the eastern forest. It stops just beyond the area that includes the Crab Orchard Focus at the edge of the Prairie Peninsula in southern Illinois, at just beyond the edge of the Kellogg Focus in Georgia on the border of the southern pine forest, and includes the Badin Focus in North Carolina on the edge of the pine forest of the Atlantic coastal plain. Small circular storage pits are numerous, and a few show traces of fire. Large burned areas like those found at the Archaic Ferry site have not been noticed. If the bow and arrow was adopted early in the Middle Eastern region, as has been argued (Caldwell 1958:26–27), this would be a further development of hunting practices to a stage essentially as known in historic times.

The stylistic distinctiveness of the *Southern Appalachian Tradition* is represented by pottery decorated with impressions of carved wooden paddles. Economy was not dissimilar to that of preceding Archaic times. There is yet no evidence of food production until a relatively late date; carbonized maize has been found in the Woodstock period in northern Georgia—this ought to be roughly equivalent to early Mississippian times, about A.D. 800 (Caldwell 1958:48).

The *Northern Tradition* includes the Hopewellian assemblages; with less assurance, Adena; and most of the manifestations that have been called "Woodland" except in the south that do not have cord-marked pottery as the major decorated type.[1]

The Northern Tradition seems to be rooted in earlier Archaic manifestations of the region, including the proposed Boreal Archaic, where there are specific burial practices that showed greater elaboration in subsequent Adena and Hopewellian times (Ritchie 1955; Quimby 1960:49). The Adena Aspect of the upper Ohio Valley, from about 800 B.C. well into the first millennium A.D., is known

---

[1] For readers who are new to eastern archeology, it should be explained that most of the students of this region do use the term "Woodland." Specifically, it includes everything that is not Paleo-Indian, Archaic, or Mississippian. The thirty-five hundred years or so of eastern prehistory since Archaic times has been divided into three parts: Early, Middle, and Late Woodland. It is true, however, that all of us are interested in regional differences and more definite dating, and I suppose I differ from many of my colleagues in my inability to understand the additional necessity of using this great threefold scheme. In the present paper the focus is directly upon the developments of particular regions of the East; major regional continuities are regarded as cultural traditions, to be contrasted or examined in their interplay, and from which to infer certain events.

chiefly from the contents of conical burial mounds, but with other information from occupation sites. It is partly earlier and partly ancestral to the Hopewellian manifestations to be described in more detail below.

Mortuary practices show considerable similarity. Although the great majority of subsistence remains from Adena sites are products of hunting and gathering, at the Cowan Creek Mound, Ohio, A.D. 445, we find evidence of a cucurbit (pepo), probably pumpkin, associated with a mass of charred goosefoot (*Chenopodium*) seeds (Goslin 1957). Rock shelters in Kentucky, where plant remains are less certainly associated with Adena materials, have yielded such cultigens as gourd, pumpkin, squash, and sunflower; but no Adena site has yet shown evidence of maize or beans.

It may soon become possible to speak of an Adena cultural climax as distinct from Hopewellian. In addition to the mortuary elaborations of Adena, we find a number of distinctive Adena cultural elements, for example, tubular stone pipes and reel-shaped gorgets, widely diffused to the Northeast and Southeast (Webb, Baby 1957; Ritchie, Dragoo 1960).

We are still in the dark as to the kind of sociological reality represented by the Hopewellian assemblages. These date for the most part between 400 B.C. and A.D. 500. The Hopewellian "culture" was first defined in southern Ohio many years ago on the basis of its typical monuments—groups of burial mounds often with extensive earthen enclosures. Since most excavators have not been unmindful of the occurrence of fine museum specimens deposited in graves, most of our information concerns burial customs. Across the northern United States from western New York to Kansas City are other prehistoric sites called Hopewellian, evidently coordinate developments, related but not necessarily tributary to Ohio.

The Illinois Valley shows an enormous number of Hopewellian sites, some of which have yielded relatively older radiocarbon determinations. Sites still farther west are thought to have a particular connection with the Illinois Valley (Griffin 1958). Hopewellian influences appear in the Northeast and the Southeast. There are some specific connections with the Marksville period of the Gulf Tradition.

The culmination of this post-Archaic phenomenon of regional differentiation and stylistic change we shall describe as the Hopewellian climax, subsequently followed by a decline. While Hopewellian shows cultural elements ultimately derived from Mesoamerica—the rare finds of cultivated maize are the best example—the view taken in the present paper is that Hopewellian cultural elaborations were essentially a development of the older Archaic hunting-gathering economy and religious practices organized around the care of the dead in the hereafter.

Some will not agree that the economic pattern was basically hunting-gathering: it has usually been assumed that Adena and Hopewellian, to build large burial mounds and earthworks, must have had an agriculturally based surplus. It is risky, however, to argue from earthworks to agriculture. Preserved food remains are almost altogether mammalian, fish and bird bones, mollusk shells, and various kinds of nuts and acorns. Finds of maize, beans, and squash are more exceptional than for later times. The most we can say is that some Hopewellian societies were practicing mixed economies, with hunting-gathering having the best of it. This, in turn, leads to a view of gradual acceptance of food production in the East, with emphasis on the successive steps by which it may have come about and with separate consideration of the social consequences of food production of each degree.

We know some details of log tombs and round or oval houses made of poles. Relics of costume are occasionally found with the dead, and other details are known from small pottery figurines. Differential placement of burials and grave objects suggests variation in social status. The skill exhibited in fine objects placed with the dead implies full or part-time artisan specialists. A widespread trade supplied the raw materials for mortuary offerings. From the Lake Superior region came native copper, which was cold-hammered into ornaments. Mica from the southern Appalachians was cut in abstract and naturalistic forms and probably attached to costumes. From Florida came seashells for ornaments and, especially, the large *cassis* shells for cups. Obsidian was probably supplied from as far west as Wyoming.

The larger Hopewellian settlements, particularly in Ohio, lend themselves to interpretation as primarily religious or mortuary centers, especially when we contrast them with large sites of subsequent Mississippian times that have more of the character of secularized towns. According to this view, smaller dispersed settlements were occupied for most of the year. At a much later peripheral site in the Southeast, the Irene Mound site, Georgia—

which may reflect an older adjustment because it is peripheral—
there is a predominance of public over domestic buildings. It has
been suggested that such sites may have been occupied by care-
takers while the populations were away.

By A.D. 500, Hopewellian was being replaced in the extreme
northerly and westerly portions of its range by generalized Northern
assemblages not greatly different from those that had preceded it.
In the old regional centers of Ohio and the Illinois Valley the
decline of Hopewellian was probably more complex, and the spectacular features of Hopewellian burial practices were not all at once
replaced by simpler rites. In the lower Illinois Valley the Branden-
berg site shows late Hopewellian pottery and ceramic features inspired by the Gulf Tradition (Griffin 1952a), which had been
reaching its own climax during the Marksville period after A.D. 1.
Similar Gulf elements also occur farther south at the Twenhafel site.
Still later in southern Illinois we find smaller sites and simpler, less
specialized artifacts (Maxwell 1951).

The Hopewellian climax was the high point of cultural complexity
reached by the Northern Tradition. We regarded this as a largely
indigenous development of hunting-gathering and mortuary practices
first formulated in Archaic times. Subsequent major developments:
the Gulf, Mississippian, and the Southern Cult climaxes occurred
with increasing rapidity and show progressively stronger Mesoamerican features. The role of Mesoamerican influences in these developments may have been to broaden progressively the basis for innovation.

The Hopewellian decline in the North is paralleled by the rise of
the *Gulf Tradition* in the South. This occupied portions of the
Gulf Coastal Plain on both sides of the lower Mississippi Valley.
Here the appearance of ceramics had been slightly delayed, and
the regional Archaic is notable for some curious large earthworks
at Poverty Point, Louisiana, 1000–500 B.C. (?), evidently not
earlier than some of the mound-building developments in the North.
The stylistic distinctiveness of the Gulf Tradition becomes noticeable with the common occurrence of pottery in the Tchefuncte
period of about 500 B.C.–A.D. 1 in the lower valley. Burial mounds
are possibly derived from contemporary Hopewellian manifestations
of the Northern Tradition. During the succeeding Marksville period,
from about A.D. 1 to A.D. 500, Gulf features were spread into
northwest Florida. It is possible to infer from the presence of a

temple mound at Kolomoki in southwest Georgia that this feature may be present in the Gulf Tradition before A.D. 500, and here it is associated with a large village site. Other temple mounds in the central Mississippi Valley have been attributed to the somewhat later Middle Baytown period of that region but are said to resemble ceremonial centers rather than constantly occupied towns (Phillips, Ford, Griffin 1951:441). There was a considerable elaboration of mortuary practices, which reached a culmination in the Marksville and Troyville periods (and their equivalents in adjacent areas of this tradition), with a lavishness only slightly inferior to Hopewellian. Mortuary artifacts again suggest some degree of craft specialization. A trade in exotic materials for these could represent a partial continuation of the far-flung trade arrangements of the earlier Hopewellian climax, but which were now serving burial mounds distributed from Florida to Texas. Gulf pottery, in a variety of forms and decorations, shows great similarities from one end of a vast region to the other, arguing a high degree of interaction among Gulf peoples. Ceramic styles also document the eastward spread of the Gulf Tradition into Florida and the slighter diffusion of Gulf elements into Late Hopewellian of southern Illinois. There is evidence of maize cultivation at the Davis site, Texas, dated A.D. 398, but we do not know its importance in Gulf economies.

In the central Mississippi Valley on the border of the Gulf Tradition there somehow emerged a new tradition, the *Mississippian*. A date for early Mississippian at the Eveland site in Illinois is A.D. 939. There is no evidence of a corresponding decline in the Gulf Tradition, as there was earlier for the decline of Hopewellian. Mississippian continued to receive Gulf influences while at the same time surpassing Gulf in some respects. Mississippian shows greater reliance on food production, greater or at least more concentrated populations, and, if we are justified in considering most large Hopewellian and Gulf sites as primarily centers of religious ceremonial, we can say that the Mississippians had more secularized towns, maintaining larger populations for longer periods of time.

A central Mississippi River heartland suggested by geographical distribution of Mississippian sites has not provided evidence for a single origin of the Mississippian Tradition—which in any case would probably be a culture-historical impossibility (Phillips, Ford, Griffin 1951:451–54). Yet Northern [Bluff culture] and Gulf [Middle Baytown] assemblages in this region do provide better evidence of continuity with succeeding Mississippian features than one finds elsewhere. In this matter, the circumstance that the Mississippian Tradition seems to have arisen on the northern border of the Gulf Tradition is interesting in the light of the earlier appearance of Gulf ceramic features in late Hopewellian sites in southern Illinois.

It is the concurrence of temple mounds and plazas; emphasis on plain, painted, and sometimes modeled pottery; reliance on maize agriculture; and semisettled towns that give Mississippian assemblages their Mesoamerican character. All but the last two features are readily derived from earlier Gulf occurrences, perhaps ultimately from Mesoamerican sources. Other supposed Gulf "firsts"—rim-flange bowls, duck-effigy vessels, and elaborate incised decoration —seem to have reached Mississippian assemblages at a later time.

The steps in the development of the Mississippian economy are unknown, but food production assumed a new importance. Not only do we more frequently find carbonized maize, but the size and apparent permanence of settlements implies population aggregations larger than before. Yet, for all this, hunting and gathering are still greatly relied on. There never existed in prehistoric America that fruitful combination of plant-raising and animal husbandry that became the foundation of Old World agriculture.

We should not give the impression that all Mississippian sites were large, but it is probably true that we have more large Mississippian sites than we do of any other period. Regional situations differed. There are many small sites, and some of those in southern Illinois may have been hunting camps. Twenhafel in Illinois shows the unusual condition of a small Mississippian settlement superimposed upon a really large Hopewellian one. In western Georgia there are at least two Mississippian sites larger than anything found earlier or later in the region. Arkansas, Mississippi, western Tennessee, and southeastern Missouri are notable for scores of extensive Mississippian sites with moats or embankments and well provided with platform mounds. In northwestern Florida, Willey (1949:581) has contrasted the intrusive Fort Walton Mississippian with earlier sites of the Gulf Tradition, suggesting that there was a shift of ceremonialism to the temple mound and a disappearance of the old burial-mound ceremonialism. His population estimate for Mississippian there is no larger than that for the preceding Gulf period, but he thinks that communities were larger.

The details of the spread of the Mississippian Tradition include migration of peoples, acculturation situations, and the diffusion of ideas to more remote groups. In the early Mississippian range of time far-flung fortified sites like Aztalan, Wisconsin, and Macon Plateau in Georgia indicate outward movements of people. These arrivals interrupted previous cultural continuities, and their survivors, if any, must have participated in the succeeding mixed cultural balances representing the fusion of Mississippian with the older regional traditions. A wholesale acculturation of an original Northern population to semi-Mississippian ways can be suggested if the Fort Ancient Aspect—Shawnee (Central Algonkian) equivalence stands (Griffin 1952b:364). The Owasco Aspect farther east continued to represent the Northern Tradition, while probably adopting some Mississippian features secondhand from Fort Ancient. In the Southern Appalachian Tradition the north Georgia sequence of Etowah I-II-III-IV-Savannah-Wilbanks-Tumlin-and-Lamar suggest that original Southern Appalachian populations received repeated Mississippian influences. In the Gulf Tradition the Plaquemine period of the lower Mississippi Valley, and the Fulton Aspect of eastern Oklahoma show strong Mississippian diffusions. Fort Walton of northwestern Florida, however, may be involved with a migration of actual Mississippian peoples from central Alabama (Willey 1949). On the prairies and plains of Kansas and Nebraska an intensification of food production, somehow connected with the Mississippian development to the east, gave rise first to semisedentary small-village cultures. Later settlements were larger, fewer, and fortified. The descendants of these peoples were, at least in part, the Village Indians of historic times. In Wedel's (1959) words, "in Kansas, as in Nebraska, concentration of the historic tribes—the Kansa, Pawnee, and others—in one or two large villages or towns for each tribe, completed a long sequence of changing settlement patterns."

The over-all result was the formation of a cordon of mixed cultures on the borders of the Mississippian development. These had certain common features, some of which were not specifically Mississippian but rather a result of this interaction.

During the rise of the Mississippian Tradition it seems almost as if the old Hopewellian and Gulf predilections for lavishing wealth on the dead might have been overcome, with ceremonial revolving around the temple rather than the burial mound as heretofore. Yet the height of the Mississippian development coincides with the spread during A.D. 1100–1400 of what is called the *Southern Cult*—the lavish disposal of costume and ornaments with certain selected dead. Artifact styles and decoration were more specifically Mesoamerican than anything that had been present before. Yet these are thoroughly reinterpreted with other indigenous features, including some evidently present long before in Adena (Webb, Baby 1957:102–8). We may also suspect that embodied here is the old eastern idea of lavish mortuary expenditure. The mortuary program required craft specialists and extensive trade in raw materials, copper, mica, flint, and shells as before, but little obsidian. This development may or may not have begun in the Gulf area, but it spread through the Mississippian settlements to the regions beyond. It was once thought that the spread of the Southern Cult may have been as rapid as the much later Ghost Dance on the Plains (Waring, Holder 1945). Precise similarities in complex designs on shell and copper ornaments and regalia indicate, not only craft specialists whose products were spread over a great region, but the strict contemporaneity of many of the sites where they occur. Nevertheless, some elements may have been used before others. There are derivative designs in immediately succeeding times, but by the historic period only the slightest traces of Cult motifs remained in either material culture or mythology.

The earlier Hopewellian and Gulf climaxes had widespread effects, but the impact of the Mississippian seems to have been the greatest. On all sides of the Mississippian Tradition arose cultural balances showing varying kinds and degrees of Mississippian influences on the respective regional traditions. I wish to impress you with the symmetry of the historical structure here proposed.

1. There was a central region, later consolidated in what archeologists have referred to as "Middle Mississippi Culture," while at the same time the most distant Early Mississippi penetrations (e.g., Aztalan, Wisconsin; Macon Plateau, Georgia; Fort Walton [?], Florida) were being absorbed into the development of the new hybrid cultures surrounding Mississippian.
2. The surrounding hybrid cultures, representing the fusion of Mississippian with the various regional traditions, show significant similarities. Individual towns seldom reached the proportions of the great Mississippian centers, but fairly large sites are numerous, and some of these hybrid cultures—Owasco (in New York, Penn-

sylvania, and Michigan), Monongahela (Pennsylvania), Lamar (Georgia), and the Upper Republican and Nebraska cultures on the Plains—have been characterized as having the largest populations in their areas up to that time. In other cases, the sites of the Fort Ancient and Oneota aspects north of the Middle Mississippi region, Fort Walton in northwest Florida, and Bossier in Oklahoma are characterized by numerous sites with populations not greatly, if at all, inferior to the other regions. Except in those instances in which indigenous societies in Georgia and Florida adopted the Southern Cult for a time, we find little evidence of excessive ceremonialism.

3. Eventually there was a resurgence of regional styles even in some of the more centrally located areas of the Mississippian Tradition. The Dallas Focus of eastern Tennessee shows the increasing favor of the old cord-marked style of pottery decoration. The increased prevalence of the pottery-type Cahokia Cord-marked in the Upper Mississippi Valley may be a similar phenomenon.

4. By historic times the sites of the Mississippian Tradition from eastern Arkansas to central Illinois had experienced a population decline, and we are having great difficulty in relating the Mississippians to particular historic tribes. In a number of instances, however, it has been possible to connect historic tribes with the mixed regional cultures surrounding Mississippian.

With the closer look that historic ethnology brings, we may here note something that was probably slighted in the archeological evidence of the earlier periods—variability in the economic condition of the eastern tribes. In historic times there was, here and there, a decline of cultivation in favor of hunting. Reduced rainfall may have been a contributing factor on the Plains (Wedel 1959), and of course the reintroduction of the horse led some tribes away from cultivation to a new Plains bison-hunting specialization. In the first Great Lakes region and northward the fur trade had the effect of diminishing native food production. Trade in deer skins exported from Charleston, South Carolina, to Europe may have had a similar, if lesser, effect in central Georgia, where Fairbanks (1956:60) noted a decline in cultivation at Ocmulgee Fields.

There is a significant contrast between these various situations and the picture Quimby (1960:114) reports of the Huron relying heavily on agriculture, and we have other accounts of vast corn-fields observed by travelers. In the Cherokee towns thousands of bushels of corn were destroyed by British troops. We shall, then, have to close our story by asking a question that may eventually be answered by a combination of archeological and ethnological evidence. Is it possible that in some sections of the cordon of mixed Mississippian-indigenous cultures surrounding the old Mississippian heartland a new level of agricultural activity was arising? We remember that these areas had been characterized as having achieved their heaviest populations in late prehistoric times, and we should also mention that there is a hint of a new settlement pattern, at least among the Creeks and the Cherokee. Town clusters, which include miles of farmsteads strung along the rivers and streams (Caldwell n.d.), might be a more effective accommodation to agricultural necessities than the hypothetical major town and tributary villages pattern that some students believe to have been the usual settlement arrangement during Mississippian times.

SPECULATIONS

Perhaps I should have let matters stand at this, claiming that eastern prehistoric development was distinctive—or at least unlike that of the nuclear areas—and hence the forms of food production and settlement might well be different too. But I do not wish to imply that those might have been different simply because they were a result of a particular history. I should rather see them as different as a result of processes we are beginning to understand.

As a primary focus, the conceptions "food production" and "urbanism" allow one to ask interesting questions. Moreover, if we agree that these are bound to take different forms in different cultural developments, there is no reason why one cannot proceed to more analytic terms, more readily transposable from one developmental pathway to another. Steward (1955) has attempted this by one means, represented by the idea of "cross-cultural type," and it must be clear to the reader that the idea of separate developmental pathways is just another way of expressing Steward's pioneering conception of multilinear evolution. Here I shall experiment with rather different analytic terms in order to examine the questions of the emergence of food production and settled life in this region. Since we will be dealing with change, these terms will be concerned with "conditions of innovation" and adaptive situations. The result will be to exhibit forest efficiency, food production, and settlement as interrelated in particular ways. To whatever degree these proposed interrelations can be accepted as valid, they can qualify as additional historical "facts." But innovation is undoubtdly limited in determinate ways, and therefore there ought to be some chance, eventually, of using such conditions and interrelations for additional generalizations about historical development.

It is supposed that the major event characterizing eastern North America during late glacial and early postglacial times was a shift from economies based mostly on hunting—represented by fluted-point assemblages—to economies in which hunting and gathering were more nearly balanced—represented by the assemblages we call Archaic. The economic innovations involved in what we called "primary forest efficiency" can be taken together as primarily adaptive, that is, the discovery of new ways to obtain resources in the land, forests, streams, and shore. To call such innovations adaptive, moreover, could help us select situations elsewhere that might involve sequences of similar innovations to see what we could learn from this. We could select geographically—other temperate forest regions—or "processually"—steps leading to plains, desert, or maritime "efficiencies." Either approach should lead to some conclusions as to what kinds of innovations were possible, and what were not, in particular steps in the various sequences and thus help focus on relations among the innovations that actually occurred.

For example, if it turns out, as I think it must, that the regional assemblages that Willey, Phillips (1958:104–43) classified into a New World Archaic stage represent adaptive situations, it may then become possible to say that the various (and sometimes debatable) proposed hearths of early plant cultivation in the New World appear at the end of such sequences. Tamaulipas, Peruvian Coast, Amazonian lowlands, and the northern Mississippi Valley begin, or may be supposed to begin, cultivation after the development of a hunting-gathering type of economy is well under way or nearly completed. Moreover, these can be claimed to be, on empirical as well as logical grounds, specifically regions where the use of wild plant foods had become important as part of their initial adaptation to the land.

Other presumed consequences of such adaptive situations can be offered as reasonable hypotheses about the conditions under which plant cultivation emerged. In eastern North America one consequence of the adaptive trend toward primary forest efficiency was the ability of some societies to become more settled. This would also probably be an effect to any adaptive trend that did not take nomadism as one of the ways it could be achieved. In short, as more copious supplies of natural foods are attained, it is expectable that people need travel less to obtain them. We can say further that some degree of settled life usually would be a precondition for the acceptance of innovations pertaining to cultivation. Another precondition would be an interest and considerable knowledge of wild plants, something else that must have increased in the change from hunting to economies relying more on plant foods. We may never know exactly how the first cultigens were adopted in eastern North America—whether according to Edgar Anderson's (1952:136–50) "Dump Heap Theory" or by some other means —but, given the preconditions suggested above and generations of women with an empirical interest in wild plants and their properties, we should be less surprised if we found a possibly independent development of food production in the Mississippi Valley than if we did not, for the opportunity to innovate along these lines must have occurred innumerable times.

It is possible that early plant cultivation in the East, whether actually indigenous or somehow stimulated by early cultigens from southward, facilitated the introduction of maize from Mesoamerica. It has already, however, become a matter of debate in North America whether the Adena and Hopewellian manifestations, which certainly practiced some planting, actually had an effective food production. My own view is that by and large they did not. Only in later times, especially during the Mississippian period, can we with any confidence state that food production probably had notable social consequences. Even so, food production seems never to have provided as complete a basis for subsistence as is presumed to have been achieved in Mesoamerica by 1500 B.C. or in western Asia some thousands of years earlier. Elsewhere (Caldwell 1958), I have used this focus on conditions of innovation to suggest that the very efficiency of forest adaptation was a factor inhibiting the acceptance of food production as a major economic basis.

I do not think we can ever assume that a society will automatically turn to food production for its subsistence basis, even where the techniques of planting and harvesting are already known. In the instances in which this has happened we ought to try to discover the means by which it occurred. We can, for example, use a contrast between eastern North America and the nuclear regions

to go a little way into problems connected with the change-over
to substantial food production in the areas where civilizations arose.
Eastern North America provided innumerable sources of wild foods,
and its population, for reasons at present debatable (Kroeber 1939:
148–49), was far from reaching the limits of its wild and cultivated
resources. But the nuclear civilizations of southwest Asia and
Mesoamerica are somehow associated with dryer lands of less natural abundance. Wild resources ought sooner to have reached their
limits in portions of these regions so that some societies, already
"experimenting" with cultivated plants, could turn gradually to food
production as the older hunting-gathering activities became less
and less fruitful. It does not matter for this argument that tropical
areas are also found within or adjacent to early food-producing
civilizations. The archeological evidence would be whether the areas
within the nuclear civilizations that provided the most substantial
natural foods were later in turning to food production as the main
basis for subsistence.

Turning back to eastern North America, the Mesoamerican plants
maize, beans, and squash were involved in the picture here of a
gradually increasing reliance on cultivation. Probably these were
more productive than the native domestications that had preceded
and/or been stimulated by them. Mesoamerican borrowings notwithstanding, cultivation had to be adapted to the social necessities
of the eastern forest economy. What this meant, in the first place,
was that the cultivators were to be women, for as food-gathers
they probably had a greater knowledge and interest in plants than
did the men. Moreover, ordinary domestic duties would keep them
daily closer to home and the cultivated crops.

Another consequence of the forest economy is one that has not
been clearly delineated in the regions of nuclear civilization. As
dependence on food production gradually increased, women maintained their ascendancy in this activity. Even by historic times
there was nothing here corresponding to the farmer or agricultural
specialist. The men were warrior-hunters or, rarely, "specialists" of
other kinds. Agriculture, if we may use this term, was a part-time
occupation of women, and its increasing importance was probably
reflected in historic times by the prevalence of matrilineal institutions
among the more agricultural tribes.

The idea of a "primary farming community," which is coming
to be of the greatest usefulness in understanding the emergence

of the nuclear civilizations, can hardly have the same meanings when applied to these eastern North American communities of hunters and feminine part-time cultivators. "Forest communities" would be a better term. Increasing cultivation and borrowings from Mesoamerica were, most of us would agree, changing these forest communities to something else. But I am not at all sure that our understanding of the processes of change will be furthered by the assumption that these were leading to the kind of village-farming communities we believe to have existed in contemporary Mesoamerica. Nor do we have any evidence that Mesoamerican communities were introduced bodily into eastern North America. It is entirely likely that Mesoamerican civilization would in time have practically submerged this North American development. But the time was not yet, and Willey's (1960a:84) recent statement that "Middle American town life with its temple-mound-and-plaza complex, entered the Mississippi Valley sometime between A.D. 500 and 1000": has an odd ring in terms of the context I have been trying to discover and portray.

Primary forest efficiency had already given these communities a good start toward sedentism, but one that could be carried only so far. Even by historic times, hunting and gathering was still of sufficient importance that the entire population of an average town might in season depart for some other place where the hunting was better. This ease of movement, which offends some of our notions of how a town ought to behave, not only was a reflection of forest economy but also was of no disadvantage under the general conditions of warfare that had come to prevail by historic times, at least, and particularly among those tribes that relied most heavily on planting. Kroeber's (1939:148–49) view that, because of war, populations were kept down in the East and agriculture kept in the role of only a contributer to subsistence is one that archeology has not quite the sophistication to handle or yet to neglect. This warfare "insane, unending, continuously attritional, from our point of view; and yet . . . so integrated into the whole fabric of eastern culture, so dominantly emphasized within it, that escape from it was well-nigh impossible" may not, as Kroeber suggests, have kept "population down to a point where more agriculture was not needed," but may have kept agriculture down by placing some additional premium on the mobility of forest communities.

In short, food production and settlements in the East took forms that were not, or possibly at least not for long, characteristic of the regions of nuclear civilization. Granted that there may be some similarities—some inherent necessities that could evoke similar institutions among peoples of any background who might choose to bind themselves to the land or live in large aggregations—this had not yet happened in the East. We may never know whether a fully effective agriculture or a massive urbanism would eventually have appeared, but we may learn that the pathway actually taken was different, and therefore interesting. I have emphasized these differences in the hope that they may eventually become illuminating.

18 IMPLICATIONS OF VEGETAL REMAINS FROM AN ILLINOIS HOPEWELL SITE

Stuart Struever

ABSTRACT

Chenopodium seeds from Illinois Hopewell and Eastern Woodland contexts are described and discussed in terms of a hypothesis of a separate center of plant domestication in the East. Evidence for the role of plant foods in northern Hopewell subsistence is reviewed. Use of more refined field procedures for recovery of plant remains is recommended.

EXCAVATIONS undertaken by the writer during 1960 at the Snyders site, 40 miles north of St. Louis in the Mississippi Valley, have yielded a further glimpse into northern Hopewell subsistence, while serving more broadly to focus attention on the important problem of plant foods and their role in eastern Woodlands prehistory.

Snyders (Griffin 1950; Fecht 1961; Struever 1961) is a two-component site. Stratigraphic analysis of changes in pottery types and their frequencies from deep midden deposits, together with variation in refuse pit contents, indicate that it was occupied during the early to middle ranges of Illinois Hopewell. It is debatable whether habitation continued, or whether following a period of abandonment the site was re-occupied. Whatever the case, there is an early Late Woodland manifestation with a single radiocarbon date of A.D. 650 ± 150 (M–714).

Charred seeds recovered from two charcoal lenses, each located in separate refuse pits containing pottery of the Havana and classic Hopewell series exclusively, were identified in February, 1961 by Hugh C. Cutler of the Missouri Botanical Garden as *Chenopodium* sp.

Cutler noted that these seeds might have come from weeds growing on the site that subsequently and accidentally found their

Reprinted by permission of *American Antiquity*, from Vol. 27, No. 4, April 1962, and by permission of the author.

way into fires. Three facts suggest that, on the contrary, they represent food remains associated with the Snyders Hopewellian occupation:

1. *Chenopodium* seeds were found in each of the only two features uncovered during the 1960 excavations that showed evidence of fires (that is, hearths).
2. Included with these seeds and wood charcoal were fragments of acorns, large hickory nuts, seeds identified tentatively as Black Haw (*Viburnum* sp.), and unidentified grass stem fragments and seeds. The association of acorns and nuts with the *Chenopodium* seeds suggests that the latter were included in the diet of the Snyders inhabitants.
3. The relatively large number of seeds recovered (about 950).

If our inference is correct, and if *Chenopodium* was in fact an element in Illinois Hopewellian diet, broader historical implications are suggested. Recently, Witthoft (1959), in attempting to understand the accelerated technological changes that mark a number of regional complexes falling temporally between the late Archaic and succeeding Woodland horizons in certain favorable ecological niches, suggests that sites of these "transitional" cultures represent likely contexts for the development of an early plant domestication. The implication is that innovations characterizing Poverty Point and various stone bowl-making complexes in the northeast may be tied to cultivation of *local plant forms*.

In this light, Fowler (1957c) has re-opened discussion of a hypothesis originally developed by Jones (1936) to the effect that a separate center of plant domestication may have existed in the central Mississippi Valley prior to the diffusion of the maize-bean-squash complex into the East. This Eastern Agricultural Complex was based, Jones held, on goosefoot or lamb's-quarter (*Chenopodium* sp.), pigweed (*Amaranthus* sp.), giant ragweed (*Ambrosia trifida* L.), sunflower (*Helianthus annus* L.), and marsh elder (*Iva* sp.). The plant remains on which this theory was developed came from levels in the Newt Kash Hollow Rockshelter of Kentucky attributed to an Early Woodland Adena origin. Earlier, Gilmore (1931) identified the same range of plants from remains associated with Ozark Bluff Dweller deposits in northwestern Arkansas (Harrington 1924, 1960). Both Gilmore and Jones theorized, partly on the basis of size, that seeds of the above species from their respective sites were cultivated forms. Quimby (1946) has cautioned that an Eastern Agricultural Complex preceding maize cannot be taken as established on the basis of size of seeds, since this characteristic might reflect selective gathering and not cultivation.

To briefly summarize Fowler's arguments in support of the Jones hypothesis, he notes that most plants domesticated by man are open-habitat plants, and that refuse dumps accumulated through sedentary and semi-sedentary occupations constitute excellent open habitats. Taking his lead from Anderson (1952), he infers that a "somewhat sedentary existence is almost a prerequisite for agricultural beginnings." In this regard, Caldwell (1958) holds that Late Archaic to Early Woodland subsistence patterns in eastern North America were based on collecting and characterized by a high degree of exploitative efficiency and residential stability. These adaptations are depicted as strongly oriented to the use of plant foods. This is particularly interesting in light of the fact that *Chenopodium, Amaranthus,* and the various other plants under discussion prefer to dwell near human habitations in ground disturbed by man. The heavier midden deposits that mark Late Archaic-Early Woodland sites would have served as ideal habitats for these plants. In short, Fowler believes that recent developments in botanical and archaeological theory strengthen the hypothesis that local plants may have been cultivated in the eastern Woodlands at an early date.

New archaeological data from Snyders and other sites are pertinent to the question re-opened by Fowler. At the Pomranky site, Midland County, Michigan, Lewis R. Binford found three carbonized seeds with a cremation; two were unidentified, the third was *Chenopodium* sp. Pomranky included a single burial feature with 516 "cache blades," 13 turkey-tail points, limonites, and one fragment of a notched point. The burial consisted of the uncremated remains of one individual and the cremated remains of at least three others. Binford's guess date for Pomranky is 800 B.C. At the Hodgers site, Saginaw County, Michigan, the same investigator describes 68 *Chenopodium* and three *Polygonum* seeds found with a cremation. This site was a single burial in a crematory basin; associations were two broad rectangular gorgets, a plano-convex adz fragment, cache blades, scrapers, limonites, two small copper awls, and two types of notched points (termed Hodgers and Hunt). Also included were two Davis points originally identified at the Eastport site, Antrim County, Michigan. Binford notes that the Hodgers burial is quite similar to those uncovered by Ritchie (1944) at Oberlander No. 2, and therefore is best seen as an Early Point Peninsula manifestation. Commenting on the recovery of these seeds, Binford states in a letter, May, 1961:

> At the Hodgers site, I think it is quite likely that the *Chenopods* were included as grave furniture along with other uncremated materials. The same may be true at the Pomranky site. The small number of seeds there probaby reflects sampling technique rather than general absence.

This apparently premeditated deposition of *Chenopodium* seeds with Early Woodland burials in the north is of some interest. The recovery of carbonized seeds of the same species at Snyders indicates the continued use of this plant, probably as a food resource, at least into Middle Woodland times in the lower Illinois and adjacent Mississippi valleys.

Two additional occurrences in early contexts strengthen the impression that *Chenopodium* may have been important in prehistoric diet. Goslin (1957:42) records fragments of pumpkin (*Cucurbita pepo*) rind in association with "masses of charred Goosefoot (*Chenopodium*) seeds" beneath the "bank of earth thrown out of the central sub-floor tomb" in the Cowan Creek Mound, Clinton County, Ohio. This is a late Adena component bearing a radiocarbon date of A.D. 440±250.

The *Chenopodium* seeds described by Gilmore from the Ozark Bluff Dweller deposits present a problem, since both the cultural and temporal position of this complex—if indeed it can be regarded as a single unit—are in considerable doubt. Methods used to collect the Bluff Dweller materials left much to be desired. This fact notwithstanding, Miner (1950:10–12) indicates that projectile points from Cave Hollow, an Arkansas Bluff Dweller site, share their closest affinities with the Highland and Boone foci of central Missouri. The latter fall within a Middle to Late Woodland range. Willey and Phillips (1958:124) and others before them have noted a broad demarcation between a preceramic and a pottery horizon in many Bluff Dweller sites. Dellinger and Dickinson (1942) ind that Marksville and Coles Creek ceramic types are predominant, stating that "most pot-sherds in our collections from the final stage of the Bluff Dweller culture are Marksville."

Though far from clear, apparently the caches of *Chenopodium* and other seeds described by Gilmore as cultigens were associated at least with the early, prepottery manifestation in the Bluff shelters. If they occurred in the ceramic horizon as well it would indicate their use continued into Middle and perhaps Late Woodland times in northwestern Arkansas.

The crucial problem with respect to the Gilmore-Jones-Fowler hypothesis of an Eastern Agricultural Complex—and bearing directly on the problem of Hopewell subsistence as well—is whether cultivated or wild forms are represented in the preceding cases. Cutler's report on the seeds from the Snyders site does not address itself to this question. In subsequent discussions he has indicated that *Chenopods* growing as weeds on an abandoned village site (an example of Anderson's "dump heap" situation) could well develop, due to the high nutrient values of the soil, seeds of the large size Jones and Gilmore regard as one important evidence that local plants were cultivated by the inhabitants of the Kentucky and Arkansas rock shelters. Cutler notes, in short, that size cannot be used as a decisive criterion in determining the domestic or wild state of weed seeds recovered in archaeological deposits.

Indirect evidence exists that *Chenopodium* and certain other species were domesticates. Gilmore describes woven bags of select, large seeds from a number of these plants stored away in Bluff Dweller shelters, together with packets of corn, beans, squash, pumpkin, and sunflower seeds, apparently as stock for the next spring's planting. Also suggestive is the repeated association of goosefoot with remains of known cultigens. In addition to the Arkansas example, it occurs with squash and gourds at the Newt Kash Shelter; *Chenopodium,* together with sunflower seeds, is the major vegetal remains in the human feces preserved from that site. Of the sunflower seeds Jones (1936:150) says: "The uniformity suggests a single variety, obviously a cultivated type." Finally, there is the Cowan Creek Mound where *Chenopods* occur with pumpkin rinds.

As an archaeologist, not a botanist, I ask whether a comparative study of the *Chenopodium* seeds from these Michigan, Ohio, Illinois, Kentucky, and Arkansas sites might not be useful. If size alone is insufficient evidence that cultivated varieties are involved, perhaps uniformity and size together might be indicative. In any case, more analytical work on the part of botanists is required if the plant materials recovered from these various Archaic and Woodland contexts are to have a significant bearing on the question of an Eastern center of plant domestication.

Recently, considerable controversy has revolved about the question of whether the elaborate Hopewellian burial complex was based on a primarily food-producing or hunting-collecting economy; Griffin (1960a:21–22) takes the former view, Caldwell (1958:30) the latter. Theoretical arguments over the role of plant foods in Hopewell subsistence are plentiful in the literature but plant remains adduced to support them remarkably scarce. This highlights the fact that very few Hopewell village sites have been excavated and described. In his recent comprehensive review of Ohio Hopewell literature and unreported museum collections, Prufer (1961) lists charred nuts or acorns from Harness, Mariott 1, Ginther, Flint Ridge, Campbell, and Porter mounds. Unidentified seeds occurred at Harness, while pips of the wild cherry were found at Campbell. Wedel (1943:26) describes seeds of the pawpaw (*Asimina triloba*), hickory nut shells, and a single acorn from refuse pits at the Hopewellian Renner site near Kansas City, Missouri.

From the midden at the Irving site, a late Hopewell to early Late Woodland village in the Illinois Valley, McGregor (1958) recovered a variety of carbonized nut shells. Nut shells and acorns were included in the refuse at the Snyders site, while at nearby Kamp there were hazelnut shells. The latter is a Hopewell burial and habitation site in the lower Illinois Valley which I excavated in 1958 and 1959.

Aside from the frequent occurrences of nut and acorn remains, evidence of plant foods from Hopewellian sites is slim. It is likely this reflects archaeological collecting techniques and differential preservation more than their importance relative to other plant foods in Hopewell subsistence. Griffin (1960a) summarizes the three, and possibly four, reports of maize in a Hopewell context; two are from Ohio (Turner and Harness) and one from the Kansas City area (Renner). McGregor's attribution of maize kernels from the Ansell site (Illinois) to the Hopewellian component there is dubious.

Finally, the discovery of *Chenopodium* seeds in two early to middle Hopewell refuse pits at the Synders site is the first reported evidence that a plant of Jones' proposed Eastern Agricultural Complex was utilized in their diet. Whether or not it was a cultigen remains to be demonstrated.

CONCLUSIONS

Evidence discussed here indicates the use of seeds from a number of eastern plants beginning in the late Archaic and continuing, at least in the case of goosefoot, into Middle Woodland times in the midwest. Remaining to be shown is whether or not the prevalence of *Chenopodium* in archaeological sites is an indicator of its relative importance in early subsistence, and whether it and other weed species discussed here were used solely in their wild forms or brought under man's control.

The preceding discussion has certain methodological implications. First, contrary to general belief, under certain conditions plant remains are preserved and can be recovered from Hopewell and earlier occupation sites. Secondly, it seems clear that quantities of botanical materials are lost under current field methods; particular effort to recover these using more refined procedures is needed. Certainly vegetal remains will provide an important line of evidence in future investigations of both the Gilmore-Jones-Fowler hypothesis and the question of Hopewell subsistence.

Conditions of preservation in the East being what they are, it is doubtful whether seeds from Archaic or Woodland horizons will have survived outside of situations where they have been carbonized. Accordingly, particular attention should be paid to the contents of features in which ashes and charcoal are present. For example, at the Snyders site during removal of the two charcoal concentrations from which the *Chenopodium* seeds were later recovered, the latter went unobserved. Only when the entire hearth contents was subjected to a flotation process were the carbonized seeds noted. Since this was written, work at the Stillwell site in the lower Illinois Valley has involved excavation of a number of refuse pits. Small portions of the fill in four of these were subjected to the flotation process. In each case quantities of carbonized seeds, otherwise unobserved, were recovered. Stillwell is regarded as an immediately post-Hopewellian, Late Woodland occupation comparable to the second of the two Snyders site components.

Fowler (1957c) calls our attention to the fact that important clues to plant cultivation can be obtained from the ecology of the area in which the site is located. Techniques are available for extracting pollen from almost any deposit (Kurtz and Turner 1957). The

presence of *Chenopodium,* for example, in any given level might
not be indicative of plant domestication, though a sudden influx
or increase of this pollen might be. This would have greater significance if correlated with archaeological data indicating increased
plant utilization.

In summary, both the collection of pollen samples and meticulous
care in excavating features in which carbonized seeds might be
expected to occur are necessary, if the role of plant foods in eastern
Woodlands subsistence is to be ascertained.

19 AGRICULTURE AND VILLAGE SETTLE-MENT IN THE NORTH AMERICAN EAST: THE CENTRAL MISSISSIPPI VALLEY AREA, A CASE HISTORY

Melvin L. Fowler

INTRODUCTION

THE REGION of eastern North America is varied both in physiographic provinces and cultural history. Each area has a significant cultural history of its own and each can offer us some data on the problem at hand, viz. what are the effects of food producing on the adaptation of peoples to their environment and what effect does this have on the level of cultural complexity? Needless to say the answers to these problems are going to be different for the various areas.

In this paper I would like to concentrate on one large case history to cast light on our subject of discussion. The area I have chosen is that delineated by the drainages of the lower Ohio River Valley and the Central Mississippi River Valley. Roughly this covers the states of Illinois, Indiana, and Ohio and the border regions of the surrounding states. Physiographically this area is divided into two major sections: the southern deciduous forest and the prairie peninsula on the north and west. The major defining factors of this area are the large river drainages of the Ohio River and Mississippi River valleys. In southern Illinois the confluence of these rivers formed a hub of natural highways that served as avenues of communications of cultural impulses from this area for thousands of years.

Reprinted by permission of the Seminary of American Anthropology, University of Seville, from *XXXVI Congreso Internacional de Americanistas,* Vol. 1, pp. 229–40, and by permission of the author.

I

The background for the questions under discussion is in the development of the Archaic cultures in the region. These formed the platform upon which all later cultural developments took place.

Archaic cultures are known for the Mississippi River Valley area from as early as 8000 B.C. Their development covers a period of at least 5000 years. In the earliest data we have there is every indication that the economic base of the Archaic cultures was foraging, that is the collection and utilization of every food resource available in the area. There is evidence that seed collecting was early an important factor. In fact, to me it is this *generalized* usage of *local* food resources in depth that defines the term Archaic.

On this base there is evidence that there began to be a more selective usage of particular local food resources and an integration of a variety of these into a seasonal cycle of subsistence and territorial exploitation. By 3000 B.C. it is apparent that a seasonally shifting subsistence pattern was well established. Data on this is now available from several areas within the broader region under discussion such as northwestern Kentucky (Rolingson and Schwartz 1966), the Wabash Valley in Indiana and Illinois (Winters 1963) southern Illinois and the Central Mississippi Valley region (Fowler 1959b; Wittry 1959a; 1959b).

A possible seasonal round carried out by these people might have been as follows. Fall camps were established in the uplands in the vicinity of Oak hickory forests where the abundant nut supply was harvested. In the late fall and winter, camps were established in the lowlands to hunt deer and migratory waterfowl. In the spring fish were taken from the backwater sloughs and ponds. In the summer clams were collected from the low water stages of the rivers and streams and seeds of disturbed habitat growing plants such as sunflower, pigweed, etc., were collected.

In this cycle various stations or camps were established throughout the territory. One of these probably served as a base camp to which the people returned periodically. Some of the large shell middens of the Tennessee River appear to have the nature of a permanent camp. On the other hand the Ferry Site (Fowler 1957a) in southern Illinois may have been a fall station permitting a rather large but diverse group of people to gather during the harvest of acorns.

There is some evidence to suggest, if not to prove, that the cultivation of native plants was practiced in this late Archaic time thus providing a local prelude to the introduction of the exotic cultigens from the south. Such a plant as the sunflower was apparently domesticated in the middle west (Heiser 1949; 1951) and other plants such as the Marsh Elder may also have been. It is difficult from the finding of seeds to determine if a plant was an actual cultigen or not. However, there can be no doubt that these Late Archaic peoples were extensive users of such vegetal foods. It may be they actually cultivated the plants. In another paper (Fowler 1957c) I proposed some years ago, following the suggestions of Jones (1936 and personal communication) and Gilmore (1931) that plant cultivation actually was practiced by these late Archaic peoples. They were "naturally" led to it by their close association with seed plants and the fact that their extensive middens provided ideal open habitats for these nitrogen feeding plants. Following Edgar Anderson (1952; 1956) I called this the "Dump Heap" theory of agricultural beginnings.

At any rate, the subsistence pattern established by Late Archaic times (4000 to 2000 B.C. in the area we are discussing) was the basic pattern followed by many peoples for long centuries after that. Indeed with but a few modifications brought about by maize-based agriculture, this was the pattern followed by the historic tribes of much of central North America.

At the present time it is clear that the introduction of ceramics had little or nothing to do with the introduction or development of cultigens. Basically ceramics are added to this late Archaic complex and when this happens archaeologists start calling the period Early Woodland. Ceramics are probably present in the area as early as 1500 B.C. Little is known at present of the Early Woodland period settlement system. The few sites that have been excavated are filled with pits that perhaps served aboriginally as storage pits. Great quantities of charred nuts are found in these pits. So far no evidence of other vegetal food products have surely been associated with these pits.

II

A few centuries before the time of Christ there appeared in Ohio
River Valley area and in the Illinois River Valley a tomb-burial
complex. Manifestations of this complex spread out from these
areas to be found in various areas of the eastern United States
from New York to Kansas.

An early and localized variant of this was located in southern
Ohio and northern Kentucky and is called Adena (Webb and
Baby 1957). Adena probably began as early as 600 B.C. A few
centuries later the Burial Mound Cult was present in the Illinois
River Valley and by the time of Christ was in full swing in
the Ohio Valley in southern Ohio. It is probable that all three
of these expressions were manifestations of a widespread development that had its roots in Late Archaic burial practices as suggested by Ritchie (1955). They are all part of what my colleagues
in the Midwest are calling the Hopewellian Interaction Sphere
(Winters n.d.b).

The dominating theme of this interaction sphere is the tomb-
burial cult and its attendant grave paraphernalia. This has many
traits in common from one area of the interaction sphere to another.
Such things as platform pipes, fine incised, zoned, and polished
pottery, ear spools, mica, and conch shells are found in tombs
throughout the area.

This complex appears as an overlay, however, on local cultural
traditions which have their roots in the past before the appearance
of the tomb-burial cult. Traditions participating in this interaction
found in the Illinois River Valley are now known as the Havana
and Pike Traditions (Struever n.d.). Another besides the Adena,
found in the Central Ohio Valley area is known as the Scioto
Tradition. And, yet another found in the lower Ohio Valley
Region is known as the Crab Orchard Tradition. These five traditions represent differing degrees of the imposition of the burial
cult on the local cultures and participation in the interaction sphere.

It is in the Scioto Tradition where we find the most complex
expression of the tomb-burial complex. Here not only are tombs
present within large earthen mounds but the mounds themselves
are often enclosed in large earthworks surrounding many acres of

ground. Sometimes earthen banks will be on either side of what must have been an avenue leading from one earthwork enclosure to another. These earthwork enclosures are in the form of squares or circles. It is obvious that they represent a cooperative project of a large number of people and they surely represent a ceremonial center of major significance for the surrounding areas.

Little work has been done in the Ohio Region that would allow us to interpret these ceremonial centers in terms of the overall land use of the area by the peoples who built them. Prufer (n.d.) has likened them to the "vacant" ceremonial centers of the Maya area and proposes that the earthworks themselves were not occupied but that the people lived in hamlets and small communities in the surrounding area and congregated at these earthwork centers at appropriate times, such as the burial and attendant ritual following the death of an important personage.

Prufer's work of the past year or two seems to point up the fact that this may be the case, for he has excavated a village site in the region well away from the earthwork centers and in the alluvial plain. In this McGraw site he found, in indisputable association, charred fragments of Indian corn. This is the first corn found that can undeniably be associated with a Hopewellian context.

There are those who have argued that the finding of corn was not necessary to impute an agricultural base to the life of the people who built these stupendous earthworks. The level of socio-cultural integration necessary for them to have achieved such coordinated tasks implies a stable base such as only agriculture normally provides.

Prufer would include the Adena cultural manifestations as part of the Scioto Tradition. Because of the suggestion that it was partaking of the tomb-burial cult earlier than the other traditions, and the fact that it has unique characteristics and history, I prefer to keep it as a separate tradition. Little or nothing is known of the Adena settlements since the mound structures are about all that have been excavated. Whereas log-tomb mounds similar to those found in other traditions are known from the Adena area the tomb burials are often included in small mound inside of a singular circular house. The house was in turn burned over the small mound and a larger mound then built over this. At the time the Scioto Tradition was developing its large earthwork complex it has been suggested that there was a displacement of Adena to the east (Ritchie and Dragoo 1960).

Goslin (1957) made a rather detailed study of the food habits of the Adena people as evidenced by bone, seed, and fiber remains from various sites. In all of these there is no indication of maize being utilized. Cucurbits on the other hand were known possibly as early as 600 B.C. Cucurbits were among the earliest domesticated plants found in the sequences of northern and central Mexico (Cutler and Whitaker 1961; MacNeish 1961; 1962). Although it is obvious that some sort of plant cultivation was basic to the Adena culture growth, it apparently lacked maize.

The area of the Havana and Pike Traditions presents a different picture. Here the burial mounds are found in groups but without the elaborate attendant earthworks. Quite often the mound groups are in direct association with village sites. At other locales they are located on the bluffs edge or on top of ridges with the village sites nearby in the valley floor. Some of these may be "vacant" ceremonial centers while others are certainly associated with the actual habitation areas. Throughout the Illinois River Valley this type of situation persists.

Although extensive excavations have been carried out over the years in Havana Tradition villages, little can as yet be said about the settlement system in this area. Recent work attempting to define the subsistence base for the Pike Tradition has met with more success. Struever's (1962; n.d. and personal communication) work at the Apple Creek Site has produced large quantities of seeds of such plants as smart weed (*Polygonium* sp.) and various kinds of nuts.

Smart weed was not the only food resource being harvested in the vicinity of the Apple Creek Site as a large variety of fish bones were recovered from the pit residues by usage of the flotation process. The interesting thing about these fish bones was that they represented individuals of all different sizes. This indicates that fish were taken *en masse* rather than being speared or hooked. A possible way this could have been done would be through the use of poison which would stun the fish so that the entire population of a pond or slough could be harvested. The present picture then of the subsistence base of the Pike Tradition is that a simple horticulture was practiced based upon weed seed harvest and that intensive utilization of the animal food resources of the area was practiced.

The only site of the Havana Tradition that has corn associated with it is the Renner Site in Missouri (Wedel 1943:26). Radiocarbon dates and Griffin (1958) suggest that this site may date from the period of the first one or two centuries after the time of Christ. The corn at this site was associated with beans. The exact significance of this find must await further information. It is interesting to note that this is nearly the westernmost Hopewellian site and may represent the first introduction of basketmaker-type corn into the eastern North American area from the southwest.

Griffin (personal communication) has informed me that cucurbits remains have been found in the area of Grand Rapids, Michigan, on sites representing the northeastern extension of Havana Tradition.

The fifth tradition presents a different picture albeit even less well known. In the area of the Crab Orchard Tradition the Tomb Burial mounds are found only sporadically and then largely in the northern peripheries closest to the Illinois River Valley area and the central area closest to the Ohio River Valley, such as the lower Wabash. One of the most outstanding complexes of this type in the Crab Orchard Tradition area is that around Rising Sun, Illinois, near the mouth of the Wabash River (Neumann and Fowler 1952). Another is that of the Twenhafel Site in the Mississippi River Valley about 60 miles south of St. Louis. In other areas there are no burial mounds and little or no evidences that the tomb-burial cult reached or influenced the region (Maxwell 1951). The settlement system appears to have been largely small villages scattered throughout the area and the only indication found to date of the subsistence base are the bone fragments of the animals hunted and eaten and the charred remains of acorns.

In summary, the Middle Woodland period of the central United States was dominated by the Hopewellian Interaction. This was a cult concerned with the burial of the dead in Tomb Mounds. In some areas this was expressed more elaborately than in others. In all areas it overlays a local cultural tradition. In Ohio there is some suggestion that the building of the elaborate earthworks and the social integration implied was based upon some form of maize agriculture. The relationship of this maize agriculture to the rest of the subsistence base is not as yet known. The presence of corn cobs does not necessarily imply extensive reliance on corn as food. In Illinois the less elaborate tomb cult and the local village tradition seems to have been based upon a simple horticulture and intensive use of local animal food resources. In southern Illinois the village life of this period may have been supported by combined usages of acorns and animal food.

The Hopewellian Interaction was a spectacular spread of a religious idea. There is no doubt that there was widespread trade throughout areas of the eastern United States for goods to be utilized in the tomb burials (Winters n.d. b). This trade network probably extended back into the past and appears to have been a part of the late Archaic concepts and way of life as well (Winters n.d. a).

If the Ohio picture is that corn cultivation was taking place on a large scale, this could have provided the economic base upon which not only the elaboration of the already existing burial cult could have taken place but it may also have provided enough surplus so that the influences of this elaboration could have reached out over a large territory. Even though all of the participants of the Hopewellian Interaction Sphere may not have been full scale farmers, they participated in this interaction which *may have had its base* in such an effective plant cultivation.

Following the Hopewellian Interaction there seems to have been a cultural decline in the area. This decline took place in the sense that all areas were no longer tied together by the tomb-burial cult, its attendant ceremonialism, and the common fine goods associated with this practice. There seems to have been a return to regionalism in that the local ceramic traditions continued on. That this decline took place also in settlement size, population, and other facets of culture is sometimes implied but little data bearing on this is known. As a matter of fact, there may have been a population increase in this period over the Hopewellian Interaction. There is some evidence that corn can be associated with these post Hopewellian or Late Woodland settlements throughout the entire area. This seems to have been a period of distinct regional cultural expressions with little interaction. Until more is known of these regional cultures little more can be said about them in terms of our problem.

III

Centering around the central Mississippi Valley area a cultural development took place beginning about A.D. 800, that appears to have been the first surely agriculturally based culture in the region. This culture developed first in the St. Louis, Missouri area in a pocket of land known as the American Bottoms. From there its influences and migrations of people spread up and down the Mississippi Valley, up the Ohio and into the southeastern United States.

This culture known as the Mississippian is truly Mesoamerican in inspiration being characterized by temple mounds built around plazas, rather large fortified towns, and various art styles reminiscent of Mesoamerican motifs.

At the present time the status of our data does not allow us to say much about the origins of this culture. No one seriously proposes it as the result of migrations from Mesoamerica and, although there are similarities to Mesoamerica, there is as yet no known Mesoamerican cultural complex from which this could be specifically derived.

Caldwell (1958) sees Mississippian as the culmination of increasing cultural influences out of Mexico and the development of the Mississippian culture as a crystalization of these impulses with some local cultural ideas in the central Mississippi Valley area. Typologically the Mississippian communities are very much like the Formative communities of eastern Mexico.

The beginnings of Mississippian in the area of St. Louis seems to have been involved with the Late Woodland inhabitants of the area. Some people see this as a gradual outgrowth out of this Late Woodland manifestation. Personally it looks to me more as if the early Mississippian is an intrusion into the area where it lives side by side with the Late Woodland peoples already resident there. This leaves the question still open as to the point or time of origin of Mississippian.

This early Mississippian is characterized by distinctive ceramics unlike that found in the area previously. This complex is highly polished and decorated with curvilinear designs on the shoulder of the vessels. For the first time there is also a great variety of vessel forms that can be differentiated as to function. This complex is found in pits side-by-side with Woodland ceramics of the local types.

By about A.D. 1000 the area of the American Bottoms seems to have been a thriving metropolis with a large ceremonial center under construction. The ceremonial center was composed of large temple mounds, plazas, ceremonial enclosures or courtyards, and some large circles of poles which were probably calendrical observatories for the various solstices and equinoxes (Wittry 1964). Outlying communities were built at this period as well. One of these is the Mitchell site in the area where the Missouri and Illinois rivers flow into the Mississippi. It is a short period site that was constructed about A.D. 1000. It had temple mounds, plazas, a large ceremonial pole in the center of the plaza, and surrounding habitation areas (see Fowler *et al.* 1962; 1963).

During the early Mississippian period it is apparent that actual groups of people moved out from the Cahokia area into Wisconsin, Missouri, and Iowa where outposts were established that became the basis of development of the protohistoric communities in those areas. The influence of this community was felt to the south and southeast as well.

As yet we do not know the total nature of the Mississippian community. Everywhere archaeological manifestations of this are found they are in assocation with corn, beans, and squash indicating that it was agriculturally based. In two sites in Illinois low level aerial photographs taken of freshly plowed sites have shown areas of soil coloration that appear to have been aboriginal corn fields.

The idea we get of the settlement system is as follows: There is a site representing a ceremonial, political, and population center. This is a large town containing temple mounds, plazas, and other ceremonial and public structures. Out away from this are smaller towns containing fewer mounds, often a single plaza area, and residences. Then around the countryside are small hamlets completely without mounds and even small farmsteads of one or two families.

Major settlement areas of this type during Early Mississippian are the St. Louis or American Bottoms area, the central Illinois River Valley and southern Wisconsin.

In Late Mississippian times, possibly A.D. 1200 or after, there is a change in ceramics to more of a blending of the Late Woodland and Early Mississippian styles and a more diffuse spreading out of the Mississippian pattern. It is about this time that the Tennessee-Cumberland variant of Mississippian comes into being centered in lower Ohio Valley area and represented by such large sites as Kincaid (Cole 1951) in southeastern Illinois and Angel in southwestern Indiana (Black 1944). The settlement system seems to be about the same with perhaps more ceremonial and population centers than before.

In the American Bottoms section the intense occupation continues on. It is not certain as yet whether the strong ceremonial and political center is maintained. At the present time we do not even know the period when the largest of all the temple mounds reached its final proportions. This mound, Monks' Mound, covers 16 acres of ground and is over one hundred feet in height. In volume and size it is second only in North America to the Pyramid of the Sun at Teotihuacan and the large pyramid at Cholula.

In the north and west peripheries of the area under discussion, during late Mississippian times, there is a change in emphasis from a predominantly agricultural economy to a mixed bison hunting and farming economy. Griffin (1960b) sees this as a decline brought about by deteriorating climatic conditions. It is probable that during this period was established the spring and fall agricultural village alternating with the summer bison hunt and winter dispersal cycle that was characteristic of the village tribes of the Missouri River Valley and other areas of the midwestern United States in historic times. This was characteristic also of the central area as well, for by the time the French came into the Illinois and Mississippi valleys, the big centers were no longer utilized and the Illini Indians of the area were both farmers and bison hunters.

On the eastern and southern peripheries of the Mississippian development this change in economy was not apparent. Indeed, if anything, the trend was toward increasing dependence on agriculture. For example, the development of Iroquoian culture seems to have been *in situ* and more and more agricultural and sedentary through time (White 1963).

In the Tennessee-Cumberland area of Mississippian, the sites were apparently occupied up close to the time of white contact. Further to the south this type of settlement system was present right up to the time of white contact and towns of the type described above were seen by DeSoto and his men in their heroic march through the southeast.

It is tempting to suggest that some of these towns were vacant by the time Europeans reached the area due to the repercussions of white settlement of the eastern seaboard. The rapid and epidemic spread of European diseases far outran the Europeans themselves and may have brought about a de-population of some of these areas.

In proto-historic and early historic times there was a development in the eastern United States in political control of tribal and nearby groups; this can be termed the confederation of which the Iroquois is our best known example. While there is evidence that the specific form of the Iroquois confederacy may have been stimulated by European contact, still the widespread nature of this general type of alliance and the archaeological data suggest that this may have had its roots in the Mississippian development. If so, it may have come about as a result of population increase in the area due to the efficiency of agricultural food production and the concomitant need for population control.

IV

In general this synthesis of the Central Mississippi and Lower Ohio Valley area has pointed up the following ideas regarding the consequences of food production in the area.

1. There was a food gathering base that was part of the late Archaic subsistence pattern. This subsistence pattern was based upon a seasonal cycle settlement system.

A part of this system was the collection of seeds and a probable simple cultivation of seed plants such as sunflower, some forms of amaranth, marsh elder, and others.

2. Upon this base, and possibly with an increasing dependence on seed utilization, there developed a regional sedentariness and population increase over the area.

3. Based upon corn agriculture at its center but upon a continuation of the Late Archaic Subsistence pattern in other areas there developed an interaction emphasizing a tomb-burial cult of the dead we call Hopewellian. Whereas local traditions persisted, and, in this sense, each area had its own local cultural history, they were tied together by the detailed similarities of the tomb-burials and the goods utilized in this ceremonialism. The most complex area in Ohio was characterized by vacant ceremonial

centers of large earthworks surrounding the tomb mounds. The people supporting these apparently lived in hamlets and farmsteads in surrounding regions. In Illinois and other areas the ceremonial centers were often connected directly with villages and were not so complex.

4. About A.D. 800 a complex temple-town type of settlement came into the area which was based on full scale agricultural subsistence. The settlement system consisted of large towns with complex temple and ceremonial establishments which probably dominated an area of smaller towns and hamlets. This was first established in a center near present day St. Louis. Cultural influences and actual migrations from this center affected most of the eastern United States. After about A.D. 1200 there was a re-adaptation of the subsistence pattern of the settlements on the north and west to a mixed bison hunting and agricultural economy. In the east and south, however, this agriculturally based subsistence continued up to historic times. It is possible that the confederacy type of territorial control had its roots in the Mississippian times as a result of population increases brought about by full scale agricultural practices.

Part IV | THE NATURAL SCIENTIST VIEWS THE BEGINNINGS OF AGRICULTURE

20 PLANTERS OF THE OLD WORLD AND THEIR HOUSEHOLD ANIMALS

EXCERPT

Carl O. Sauer

ANTECEDENTS OF DOMESTICATION

IT TOOK MAN so very long to get around to the invention of agriculture that we may well doubt that the idea came easily or that it came from hunger, as is often supposed. Archeology has traced Neolithic farming back in the Near East for seven to eight thousand years, a late date in the history of the human race. These earliest Neolithic farmers were far removed in time and place, as I shall argue, from the origins of agriculture. Their crops, animals, and in part even their houses were not very different from those now existing in the same areas; one is inclined to say that they were nearer to the contemporary than to the original agriculture, the beginnings of which may well lie several times seven thousand years in the past.

It may be noted that the earliest Neolithic farmers lived at the time when the sea had risen to about its present level, that is, when a rough balance had been struck between ice formation and ice melt. I have previously made the inference that world weather was then not greatly different from the present. Before this time, that is, during the last deglaciation, the major part of the basic inventions of agriculture must have been made.

There is little dissent from the view that agricultural arts were first developed in the Old World and such origin is here accepted. The place and manner of their beginnings are the topic next under consideration, a central and classical question in anthropogeography. Geographers together with biologists in the past have contributed evidence on the nature and origins of agriculture. Com-

Extracted from *Agricultural Origins and Dispersals*. American Geographical Society, *Bowman Memorial Lectures,* Series Two, 1952, pp. 19–28, and reprinted by permission of the author and the American Geographical Society.

bined with the findings of archeology, a more adequate interpretation is now gradually taking form. The classical view, carried down from Roman authors, that mankind progresses on a general sequence of stages, beginning as collectors through hunting and pastoral nomadism to agriculture, is still current in serious writing. Humboldt made the first breach in this position by pointing out that the New World had advanced agricultures but no pastoral nomads. Ritter was impressed by the new favored foci in which progressive cultures arose and from which crops spread. Moriz Wagner originated a corollary to Darwin by the thesis that biologic variation arose through migration into a new environment. Ratzel formulated the principle of diffusion as dominant over parallel invention. Hahn based animal domestication on non-economic grounds. The anthropogeographers have been maligned as environmentalists; actually they have been least guilty of proposals that similar environments develop similar ways, and have been most critical of parallel inventions and of general succession of stages of culture.

My own observations on primitive agriculture have been gathered in various parts of the New World. I have used these as aids in thinking comparatively about what I have been able to read about the Old World. The evidence gathered from workers in various parts and different disciplines seems to me to indicate revised interpretation as to how agriculture arose. This presentation will serve its purpose if it is an incentive to further examination of the problem. First, certain basic premises:

1. Agriculture did not originate from a growing or chronic shortage of food. People living in the shadow of famine do not have the means or time to undertake the slow and leisurely experimental steps out of which a better and different food supply is to develop in a somewhat distant future. Famine foods, and there are a number that are so-called, seem to have little relation to the plants ennobled by cultivation. The improvement of plants by selection for better utility to man was accomplished only by a people who lived at a comfortable margin above the level of want. The saying that necessity is the mother of invention largely is not true. The needy and miserable societies are not inventive, for they lack the leisure for reflection, experimentation, and discussion.

2. The hearths of domestication are to be sought in areas of marked diversity of plants or animals, where there were varied and good raw materials to experiment with, or in other words,

where there was a large reservoir of genes to be sorted out and recombined. This implies well-diversified terrain and perhaps also variety of climate.

3. Primitive cultivators could not establish themselves in large river valleys subject to lengthy floods and requiring protective dams, drainage, or irrigation. I was bothered by the thesis of the potamic origin of agriculture in the great valleys of the Near East until I had assurance from Vavilov, in a visit of a quarter of a century ago, that all the investigations of his group pointed to origins in hill and mountain lands.

4. Agriculture began in wooded lands. Primitive cultivators could readily open spaces for planting by deadening trees; they could not dig in sod or eradicate vigorous stoloniferous grasses. Indian farming, except for the most advanced cultures, remained woodland farming. Years ago I objected to the then general European view that the loess lands were the lands of Neolithic agriculture because they were grassy. I proposed that they were colonized by early farmers because they were mesophytic woodlands, easily dug and productive (Sauer 1936:279). Lately, some European scholars have shifted to the view that farming began in woodlands (Clark 1946:57–71).

5. The inventors of agriculture had previously acquired special skills in other directions that predisposed them to agricultural experiments. Of all peoples those most given to hunting were least apt to incline toward domestication and breeding of plants, or, I think, of animals. There are suggestions in Paleolithic archeology that not the workers of flakes and shapers of blades, that is, the hunters, but the ax users, interpreted as woodland dwellers, were remote ancestors of the agriculturists.

6. Above all, the founders of agriculture were sedentary folk. I have already said that groups move as little as their needs of food, water, fuel, and shelter require. Mobility as a dominant character goes with specialized hunting economies or with life in meager environments. Growing crops require constant attention. I have never seen primitive plantings that are not closely watched over until the crop is secured. A planted clearing anywhere is a feast set for all manner of wild creatures that fly, walk, and crawl to come in and raid fruits, leaves, and roots. What is food for man is feast for beasts. And, therefore, by day and night

someone must drive off the unbidden wild guests. Planting a field and then leaving it until the harvest would mean loss of harvest (Sauer 1950:487–543).

THE PROGENITORS

After the Upper Paleolithic hunters of big game in Europe, the Aurignacian, Solutrean, and Magdalenian folk, and before the early Neolithic farmers of the Near East and Europe, an intervening culture is being recovered by archeology. This Mesolithic period differed largely from the preceding hunting ways, has been identified especially along the Mediterranean and in Atlantic Europe, and seems to have been immigrant into Europe from Asia and Africa. It used, and perhaps introduced the bow and arrow; it employed fishing gear, fishhooks and lines, nets and sinkers, boats and paddles, none of them known earlier; it had a new style of ax and adz, with chisel edge; toward the last there was crude pottery; especially, it brought the dog, unknown for the preceding hunters, but characteristic of Mesolithic settlements.

The main interests of this culture were not in hunting by land, but in living by sea, stream, and lake, depending on fishing and water-side hunting and collecting. These habits and the time of its coming are probably responsible for the meagerness of Mesolithic record. At that time, because the ice caps were melting away, sea levels were rising markedly, and hence rivers were filling their valley floors so that only chance locations not buried beneath sea or alluvium may be found. The known settlements may have derived from major cultural changes that took place far to the East as a western, marginal extension, a simplified frontier, frontiers being likely to carry a reduced and simplified form of the culture from which they spring. I lay weight especially on the appearance of the dog and the fishing arts. Europe, until late historic time, appears to have been always a far peninsula of the Old World, receiving belated and reduced ideas from east or south.

The progenitors of the earliest agriculturists I have sought in some well-situated, progressive fishing folk living in a mild climate along fresh waters. Fresh water is postulated rather than salt because seaside vegetation has contributed little and late to the making of crop plants. For sedentary living there must have been available a long season or year-round staple resource in fish and other aquatic life. Clustering of groups in permanent villages was made possible at sites continually advantageous for fishing, such as stream junctions, lake outlets, rapids. Waterways served as lines of communication with other villages and so for the exchange and growth of ideas. Waterfowl, riparian mammals, waterside plants gave diversity to food. Basts and fibers were used to make nets and lines and suitable woods were at hand for boats and paddles.

There seems to be a connection between fiber preparation and the taking of fish by use of plant extracts to stun or kill them. These stupefying substances, in Spanish *barbasco,* commonly are alkaloids, they often lather freely, and are likely to be taken from plants also used for cordage, making bark cloth, and as detergents. The latter uses may have come first, and through them, the discovery that fish were stunned when certain plants were macerated or retted in water, without affecting the food quality of the fish. In the Old World, this barbasco trait is most elaborated in Southeast Asia, whence it radiates outward through the Pacific Islands, westward through the Mediterranean to Atlantic Europe and southwestward through forest Africa. The procedure is sufficiently characteristic and complex that it may have a common origin. This curious way of fishing is apparently older than, and may be a forerunner of, agriculture (Sauer 1948:65–77).

THE CRADLE OF AGRICULTURE

As the cradle of earliest agriculture, I have proposed Southeastern Asia. It meets the requirements of high physical and organic diversity, of mild climate with reversed monsoons giving abundant rainy and dry periods, of many waters inviting to fishing, of location at the hub of the Old World for communication by water or by land. No other area is equally well situated or equally well furnished for the rise of a fishing-farming culture. I shall attempt to show that farming culture in origin is tied to fishing in this area, that the earliest and most literally domestic animals originated here, and that this is the world's major center of planting techniques and of amelioration of plants by vegetative production. I accept the familiar premise that man learned to plant before he grew crops by seeding.

PLANTING AND PLANT SELECTION

The creative curiosity of man in the monsoon lands has operated strongly with asexual plant reproduction. Multiplication and selection is from clones. A piece of a plant is set into the ground to make a new plant. This may be by an offset or sprout from the parent, by dividing a root stock, by a stem cutting, or by a piece of underground stem or tuber. An individual plant is divided and multiplied indefinitely. The thing grown is identical reconstitution of parent rather than variant progeny. Selection begins by choosing the individual plant to be divided in order to make a number of plants that are like the parent. Selection proceeds by observing and preserving desirable individual variation, as in propagating an attractive chance root or bud sport, or by noting an accidental self-sown hybrid that is then divided for planting. In the long course of time, this continuous attention to the individual plant, and inattention to its sexual seeds, has given rise to an extraordinary lot of forms that are completely dependent on man for their existence. Seeds being of no interest, many such cultivated plants have lost the capacity to bear viable seeds, some as sterile polyploids, some in other ways. This culture operates by a very specific and sustained idea of reproduction; break the continuity of this operation and the plant may be lost.

The list of such man-made plants, or cultigens, is large, with eastern India in first place as to origin. Botanically, it includes especially many and important monocotyledons: Southeast Asia is the original home of the bananas. Genetic studies lately have resolved the variations in the Asiatic bananas with the result that the old distinction between bananas and plantains must be abandoned. One cultigen line derives directly from *Musa balbisiana,* native from Behar up to the Himalayas, another from the Malayan *M. acuminata,* the third main line involves hybrids between the two (Cheesman 1948:293–96). The domesticated forms of the ginger family, such as turmeric, appear to be mainly Indian. Aroids, cultivated for root or stem, including especially the taro, which is probably Indian, form a major food source especially out through the island world. For the home of the greater yam (*Dioscorea alata*) Burkill favors the east side of the Bay of Bengal, for *D. esculenta,* Indochina (Burkill 1935;[1] 1951:443–98). A half-dozen species of cultivated yams, some of them carried to the farthest Pacific Islands, throw important light on cultural radiation from the Southeast Asiatic mainland. Certain palms, especially the sago palm, pandans, bamboos, and sugar cane, have been widely carried out of India and Indochina and greatly altered by man. Dicotyledons have yielded shrubs, vines, and trees, greatly changed by immeasurably long vegetative selection, such as the leguminous derris cultivated for fish poison and insecticide, the several breadfruits, the citrus fruits, and persimmons (ebony family). The majority of the plants that have been thus made over by man are at home in well-drained alluvial lands, a few are river swamp plants, and some are aquatic.

The basic cultivated food plants of moonsoon Asia do not constitute a balanced diet. They are sources of carbohydrates, mainly of starch, but also of sugar. Plant fats and oils are very minor, and vegetable proteins mostly lacking. The people who made the asexual crop plants had no need to develop a balanced vegetarian diet, for they got their fats and proteins from animal food, originally fish and shell fish. The great preponderance and diversity of carbohydrate cultigens sustains the thesis that this was a fishing culture before it became a planting one. Other strong traits of this culture are the attention to the growing of spices—Southeast Asia included the spice lands of early commerce—and the emphasis on the coloring of food, person, and clothing, especially yellow or red (as by turmeric), with ceremonial significance attached thereto as life-giving, from birth through marriage to funerary offering.

These food plants may serve other purposes, especially as sources of fiber. Perhaps we have here another suggestion as to why fishermen began the cultivation and alteration of plants. Fiber, food, and ceremonial color may come from the same plant. *Cordyline fruticosa,* or *terminalis,* in such joint use among Malayans and Polynesians, is apparently of ancient introduction. Some of the pandans or screw pines have been widely carried by man and greatly selected by cutting propagation for matting, cordage, fruit, and scent. Breadfruits also have been a major source of barkcloth and of yellow dyes. It may well be that among the earliest do-

---

[1] The main cultural conclusions of his taxonomic studies of the yam genus are incorporated.

mesticates were multi-purpose plants set out around fishing villages to provide starch food, substances for toughening nets and lines and making them water resistant, drugs, and poisons. Food production was one and perhaps not the most important reason for bringing plants under cultivation.

Plants that are grown from seed may be germinated before they are set out. Rice and coconut are familiar examples. Neither is considered to belong to the oldest planting culture. Rice probably originated in India; the place of origin of the coconut is still debated. Rice is the only cereal I know which is still a perennial, though in cultivation it is treated as an annual. The custom of starting it in a seed bed and later setting the individual plants out cannot be explained entirely by the necessities of paddy cultivation and it is not so restricted. It has been suggested that rice was originally a weed in taro fields (Haudricourt, Hédin 1943:153); in weeding it was replanted elsewhere and a grain crop was produced, with partial retention of the vegetative planting habits. There is no necessity of starting coconuts in a seed bed and transplanting them later. Both customs suggest partial retention of the older idea of plant reproduction.

Plants of different kinds, growth habits, and uses were assembled in the same cultivated patches, not fields but simple gardens. The ground was dug with a planting stick, that later became spade or fork; the loosened ground often being mounded and the plants given added aeration and food by the heaping up of top soil.

21 REVIEW OF "AGRICULTURAL ORIGINS AND DISPERSALS," BY CARL O. SAUER

Paul C. Mangelsdorf

THIS LITTLE TREATISE represents, in published form, the second series of lectures sponsored by the Isaiah Bowman Memorial Fund. The author, a geographer, defines his task as interpreting the meeting of natural history and cultural history. He begins with the premise that in the history of mankind the diffusion of ideas from a few hearths has been the rule, and independent parallel invention the exception. He concedes that agriculture was probably invented first in the Old World and accepts the dating of the earliest archaeological evidence of agriculture in the Near East at 7000 to 8000 years. But he contends that these earliest Neolithic farmers were far removed in time and place from the origins of agriculture, which may well have begun "several times seven thousand" years ago among people living in wooded lands in a tropical climate. The founders of agriculture were sedentary, well-situated fishing folk living along fresh waters. Fishing provided a staple and year-around food supply as well as leisure, and it was leisure, not necessity, which mothered the invention of agriculture. The waterways provided lines of communication for dispersing the art of agriculture, once invented, to other parts of the world.

As the cradle of earliest agriculture Sauer postulates Southeastern Asia. No other area is so well furnished, he believes, for the rise of a fishing-farming culture and none is so well located at the hub of the Old World for communication by land or water.

It is assumed that agriculture began with the planting of veg-

---

American Geographical Society. New York, 1952. Reprinted by permission of *American Antiquity,* from Vol. XIX, No. 1, pp. 87–90, and by permission of the author.

etatively-reproduced species, and that the growing of plants from seed is a more recent development. Among the cultigens thought to be indigenous to the cradle of agriculture are bananas and and plantains, ginger, yams, sago palm, varieties of pandanus, bamboos, sugar cane, breadfruit, citrus fruits, persimmons and derris, the last a leguminous plant cultivated as a fish poison. It is suggested that the use of fish poisons preceded agriculture and was perhaps a forerunner of it. It is suggested, further, that the use of fish poisons was discovered as a consequence of extracting fibers or bark cloth from plants by maceration. Rice and coconuts, which are grown from seed, are assumed to have been more recent additions to the list of cultigens in this region.

In addition to the cultivated plants there were also brought under domestication, primarily as household pets, the dog, pig, fowl, duck and goose. Domestication of both plants and animals was the work of woman. The idea that the dog, a hunting animal, became domesticated by joining man in his hunts is regarded as romantic; the use of dogs for hunting is said to be a late specialization among people of advanced cultures.

This ancient complex of cultivated plants and household animals was dispersed far and wide in all directions except northward where cold blocked the way. The dogs of Australia and the wild pigs of Timor and New Guinea are feral remnants of this dispersal. Rice, bamboos, bananas, taros, persimmons and yams were carried into China after first being remade by man in East Asia. The dog, fowl, bananas and taros were carried into Africa, not by way of the Fertile Crescent, but directly through the Abyssinian Highland and its foothills.

The Near East and Mediterranean regions are no more than recent peripheral developments of the dispersal from the original hearth in Southeast Asia. The plants of the Old Planter culture failed to reach the northern periphery; only the dog and the pig succeeded in doing this. The culture of olives is, however, thought to resemble the disciplined planting art of India and accounts for the fact that in one corner of the Mediterranean—that facing the ancient East—we find the origin of cultigens shaped according to the eastern model.

The art of seeding is assumed to be relatively recent in the Old World and marginal to the art of planting. Three centers of seed domestication, North China, Ethiopia and the Near East, all marginal to Old Planter lands, are postulated, although the third turns out, on close examination, to be a salient rather than a center and to comprise three areas extending from Central India to the Mediterranean. In each of these "centers" the climate rendered vegetative production difficult and facilitated seeding. Consequently each center developed cultivated cereal grasses, legumes as sources of proteins and fats, and usually an oil or fiber plant. The Chinese and Ethiopian centers are regarded as older than the central salient, and in the latter the Near East is regarded as later than the two sides of the Indus.

The history of agriculture in the New World parallels closely that of the Old. Here a hearth of tropical planters occurred in northwestern South America. Here people who resembled the Indonesians in a number of ethnic traits, including cannibalism, dog-eating, body-painting, fish-netting, superb boatmanship, and the use of fish poisons, began agriculture with a group of vegetatively-propagated plants including manihot, sweet potato, arracacha, native yams and Xanthosoma, the last an American counterpart of the Old World taro. The starchy diet derived from these plants was supplemented, as it was in Southeast Asia, by proteins and fats from fish and a variety of aquatic and waterside animals. The only animal domesticated in this hearth was the Muscovy duck.

From this hearth the pattern of vegetative planting was carried as far south as Chiloe, and several starchy root crops including oca, ulluco, año and the potato were added to the complex. Northward, however, the complex spread no further than Central America; beyond this the art of planting gave way to that of seeding.

The planting culture of the New World was probably initially indigenous, although it resembled that of Southeast Asia in many traits and was undoubtedly enriched at times by contacts from across the Pacific. Crossings are assumed to have been made in both directions. From the west to the east came diploid cotton, the gourd, Canavalia beans, the coconut, plantains, the chicken, the corn-mother myth, the use of masticatories with lime, the blowgun, dog-eating, and chicha fermentation by chewing. From east to west traveled the cultivated cucurbits, tetraploid cotton and the grain amaranths. Where maize originated and in which direction it was dispersed in pre-Columbian times is still a matter of speculation, although there is no doubt that the corn-mother myth came from the Old World to the New.

In the foreword the author is quoted as stating that "He does not try to give a well-polished abstract of accepted learning, as much as a prospectus of that which is not securely within our grasp." Yet his conclusions are bold and sweeping and amount, essentially, to a broad new theory of the early history of mankind, a theory presented in a consistently readable and often eloquent style imparting to it an aura of substance and plausibility which it scarcely deserves. Again and again this reviewer found it difficult to believe that statements presented so clearly and so confidently should contain, when carefully examined, so little fact. The theory is based not upon evidence but upon a lack of it. The author has indeed made a careful "prospectus of that which is not securely within our grasp" and upon this insubstantial foundation has erected a far-reaching theory.

It is impossible in this review to analyze all of the remarkable conclusions contained in the book but comment on several typical examples may be useful. At least so far as plants are concerned there is no evience of early agricultural hearths in either Southeast Asia or northwestern South America. The former may well be the center of ancient cultigens but it is only one of eight centers recognized by Vavilov. It is by no means the richest center nor is there any evidence that its cultigens are extraordinarily ancient. Southeast Asia may well be, as Sauer (following Vavilov) postulates, the home of a number of carbohydrate-furnishing food plants, but this does not make it the cradle of Old World agriculture. The coconut probably also originated in this area, but there is no evidence that its culture, because it is sexually reproduced, came only after the art of planting was well established. Actually the culture of the coconut, because of its large seeds, is more akin to planting than to seeding and Douglas Oliver tells me that the similarity is recognized even today by many Oceanic peoples who plant coconuts, along with other vegetatively-propagated plants, but in other respects have little conception of the art of seeding. There is no evidence whatever that rice is more recent than other Asiatic cultigens; on the contrary, if the number of distinct varieties is a criterion, rice is one of the most ancient.

There is no evidence that the use of fish poisons is a forerunner of agriculture (although in some parts of the world it undoubtedly preceded it) or that it is a consequence of the still earlier art of macerating or retting plants in water for their fibers or bark cloths. The most potent fish poisons—those most likely to have been first discovered—are derived from species of leguminous plants which are of little use for fiber and which furnish no bark cloths. Furthermore, in these plants the fish-stunning substance, rotenone, occurs in the roots while the fibers, if any, are obtained from the stem.

The evidence of routes of dispersal from the hearths is almost wholly nonexistent and the delineation of the routes themselves involves assumptions for which there is little basis either in geography or history. There is no evidence, for example, that the Chinese and Abyssinian centers of seeding are older than the Near Eastern center. Indeed, there is no evidence that the art of seeding is marginal and was adopted because the limits of areas suitable for planting had been reached. It seems more reasonable to suppose that planting was practiced in regions, mainly tropical, where the cultigens were derived from native, herbaceous perennial plants suitable for vegetative reproduction, and that seeding was practiced in other regions, mainly temperate or subtropical, where the cultigens originated from indigenous annual plants easily propagated by seed.

In the New World two of the principal cultigens with which agriculture is assumed to have begun, manihot and the sweet potato, are almost certainly not indigenous to the hearth (as it is delineated on the map) and were introduced from elsewhere. Does this suggest the existence of still earlier "pre-hearths"?

The evidence for trans-Pacific carriage is thin and fragmentary and does not add up to the picture of repeated cultural interchanges which is implied. It is now generally conceded that the sweet potato reached Polynesia several centuries before the discovery of America and that there may have been a few colonies of coconuts on the Pacific shores of America when the Spaniards arrived. There is no doubt that the gourd occurred in both the Old World and the New in prehistoric times. But both the coconut and the gourd are "drift" fruits designed by nature to be dispersed by water, and there is no tangible evidence that they were carried across the Pacific by man. The evidence on cotton, plantains, the chicken, the cucurbits and amaranths is either completely lacking or consists of nothing more than untestable hypotheses based on speculation. The Canavalia beans of the Old World and the New are now recognized as different species; whatever evidence they once provided was based on faulty botanical nomenclature. The reader may draw his own conclusions about the significance of cannibalism, dog-eating, body-painting, fish-netting and superb boatmanship in the two areas.

So much for specific examples; Sauer's basic premise—that diffusion of ideas has been the rule and widespread parallel invention the exception—also lacks substantial foundation. The old argument between diffusion and independent invention is not likely to be resolved either by this book or by any review of it. Indeed the argument itself is essentially futile since there is no doubt that both diffusion and independent invention occur and that both have played a part in man's cultural history. To ask which has been most important is like asking which link is most important in a chain. Certainly to say that one has been the rule and the other the exception not only goes directly against the evidence but also against the principles of evolution. The biologist who recognizes evolution as "the product of a sequence of highly improbable events" expects to encounter in cultural evolution, as in organic evolution, frequent examples of parallel development, and he is not disappointed. Independent parallel invention is a well-recognized phenomenon in modern societies, and there is no evidence that ancient man was inherently less intelligent than his modern counterpart. Familiar to most readers are the invention in prehistoric times, in both the Old World and the New, of arithmetic, including the decimal system, astronomy and calendars. The art of writing, called by Huntington "man's supreme achievement" was invented separately in four parts of the world. Less familiar are examples of the independent development of various uses of plants. I should like to mention three: caffeine-containing plants, arrow poisons and fish poisons.

Caffeine is a weak alkaloid for which man has no physiological necessity, but which he has learned to consume for the sense of well-being which it imparts to him some time after its consumption. Caffeine, although slightly bitter, has no other characteristic flavor or odor by which it can be positively identified. Yet man in nearly all parts of the world except Southeast Asia has screened the plants in his region and has identified those which contain caffeine or the closely-related substance theobromine. In six plant families he has discovered nine distinct species in nine parts of the world which contain caffeine (or theobromine) in sufficient amounts to be useful. And, by prolonged trial and error, he has found that part of the plant which contains the most alkaloid in palatable form: the leaves of tea, khat, cassine and mate; the seeds of coffee, cola, cacao and guaraná; and the bark of yoco. Can this complex situation be explained in terms of diffusion of one idea—the use of caffeine—and if so, what hearth gave rise to it and what routes of dispersal could possibly have resulted in its pattern of distribution?

The story of arrow poisons is almost equally complex. There is, it it true, a rather striking similarity between the use of arrow poisons in parts of Asia and South America. But it is difficult to prove that this has any real significance since there are different kinds of similarities between other regions. Arrow poisons have been used in almost all parts of the world—Africa, Asia, North and South America—and in America alone have involved at least 21 different plant families. At least 52 species of plants have been involved in the preparation of the South American arrow poison, curare. The number of ways of preparing arrow poisons is large, but is by no means infinite. It is almost inevitable that some similarities in their use would evolve in different parts of the world, especially when it is recognized that substances from which arrow poisons are prepared are sometimes quite similar, although the plants from which they are derived may be very different.

The similarities in the use of fish poisons in different regions of the world are especially impressive. Innumerable species of plants have been used, some for their saponins, others for their alkaloids. The use of rotenone-containing plants of the family Leguminosae, particularly of the genera Derris, Lonchocarpus and Tephrosia, is especially striking. In each genus several different species have been used. In the case of Tephrosia four different species, *T. astragaloides, T. vogelii, T. toxicaria,* and *T. virginiana,* indigenous to Australia, Africa, South and North America, respectively, have been employed. Primitive man has done such a thorough job of discovering the rotenone-containing plants of the world that entomologists, searching for new sources of rotenone for insecticides, began their survey with plants known to have been used in various parts of the world as fish poisons. If this is a case of diffusion where did the practice originate, what are the routes of dispersal, and what manner of "tribal memory" kept the trait alive while man lived in areas where Tephrosia does not occur?

If, in considering the invention and dispersal of agriculture, one must begin with a single basic premise (a questionable procedure), it would seem to this reviewer to be safer and more in keeping with the evidence to assume that man in all parts of the world, possessed of the same or similar needs and desires as well as of an insatiable curiosity, has experimented endlessly with all of the plants which surround him. When the same family, genus or species of plants occurs in different parts of the world (and the dispersal of plants over the globe, which is measured in millions and tens of millions of years, is much more ancient than the dispersal of man), it is almost inevitable that man should have found similar uses for similar plants in response to similar needs. Cultural similarities in the uses of plants are often nothing more than the consequences of plant geography, a fact which the author, for a geographer, seems strangely reluctant to take into full consideration.

To recognize the remarkable ability of primitive man as an empirical chemist in discovering sources of caffeine, rotenone and other alkaloids in different species, genera and families of plants, or to credit him (as Sauer does) with remarkably effective techniques of plant improvement still unknown to modern geneticists, and at the same time to deny the widespread existence of inventiveness, seems to this reviewer to produce a distorted picture, decidedly lacking not only in historical perspective, but also in an appreciation of man's inherent intelligence, curiosity and ingenuity.

A theory almost completely lacking in factual basis may still be stimulating and provocative and may be especially useful if it can be subjected to critical tests which would prove it wrong. I can think of no such tests to apply to Sauer's theory. His two principal hearths occur in regions where few archaeological remains have so far been found and where the climate almost precludes the long-time preservation of herbaceous cultigens. Practically all of his conclusions, although unsupported by evidence, are still virtually impossible to disprove. Indeed if one sought, as an exercise in imagination, to design a completely untestable theory of agricultural origins and dispersals, it would be difficult to improve upon this one. In creating such a theory, the author has at least demonstrated that there are still huge gaps in our knowledge of man's history.

22 ANIMAL DOMESTICATION
IN THE PREHISTORIC NEAR EAST

Charles A. Reed

FOREWORD

THE ARTICLE here reproduced was finished toward the end of 1958 and not published until a year later. Now, after more than ten years, many of the details are out of date due to new discoveries, which I hope were stimulated in part by the drastic pruning I applied to the thicket of misinformation and guesswork which had, before 1958, sprouted so luxuriantly on the subject of animal domestication in the prehistoric Near East.

As I expected a decade ago, the recognized beginnings of domestication have been pushed back several thousands of years for all of the five basic domestic animals (dogs, sheep, goats, pigs, cattle) here considered; the animals' bones have been uncovered by careful archeological excavation, the facts were determined by detailed laboratory study, and the whole pattern has been put into chronological order by carefully determined radiocarbon (C^{14}) 'dates.'

The earliest-known dogs are now dated at 9500 B.P. (Before Present radiocarbon years before 1950 A.D.) in northern England, at 9000 B.P. in south-central Anatolia, and at 10,400 B.P. in Idaho, U.S.A. The wolf, *Canis lupis,* is now generally thought to have been the dog's only ancestor (Scott 1968). Domestic sheep were probably present as early as 10,800 B.P. in northern Iraq, and remains of domestic goats date back to 9000 B.P. and perhaps to 10,000 B.P. in western Iran. Domestic pigs are known as early as 9000 B.P. in southern Anatolia, and the earliest known domes-

Reprinted by permission of *Science,* from Vol. 130, No. 3389, 1959, pp. 1629–39, and by permission of the author. Copyright 1959 by the American Association for the Advancement of Science.

tic cattle date possibly from 8500 B.P. in neighboring Greece. What had seemed to be the problem of the late introduction of Asiatic domesticants into Africa has been resolved by the discovery that domestic sheep and/or goats were present in Cyrenaica (northeastern Libya) by 6800 B.P., and had perhaps been there for 1500 years.

The above conclusions, and the evidence upon which they are based, have recently been summarized (Reed 1969), and the industrious student can find there the numerous pertinent references that will lead him deeper into the subject.

Many problems remain unsolved in our study of this period of early domestication, such as the determination of the sites of origin of domestication for different animals and the rate and path of the spread of the practice from such sites. Why, for instance, does the town of Catal Hüyük in southern Anatolia have only domestic dogs and cattle as late as 7850 B.P. (Perkins 1969) when numerous other sites in Anatolia and adjacent Iraq already were rearing sheep, goats, and pigs a thousand years earlier?

In the larger view, however, the listing of the dates presently known for the earliest archeological evidence of these domestic animals is essentially a kind of "numbers game," the details of which may change with study of the materials recovered from new excavations. More important by far has been a continuous broadening of the scientific base upon which the conclusions of prehistorians are determined. The student of the faunal remains excavated from archeological sites in the ancient Near East now can—indeed he must—correlate his own studies with those of his cooperating colleagues, who are numerous: glacial geologists, palynologists, invertebrate zoologists, animal and plant ecologists, botanists who specialize in taxonomy and cytogenetics, pathologists, animal behaviorists, and physicists who determine prehistoric trade routes by tracing the sources from whence came the obsidian used for small tools over most of the ancient Near East. All are prehistorians, each in his own way, but all of these multiple studies must then be synthesized by the archeologist who is in charge, and who in so doing will then incorporate his own studies of settlement patterns, population size and density, and the details of the cultural changes as indicated by the study of thousands of artifacts (Braidwood, in press).

When all this is done, we think now we begin to see a pattern leading to the beginnings of animal domestication: The rate of cultural change was quickening during the several millennia of the late Pleistocene, when the earth was warming gradually and the continental ice sheets were melting; man in parts of southwestern Asia so intensified his local food quest that he could support self and kin without roaming as widely as before and so by approximately 11,000 B.P. began to settle into organized villages with permanent (although at first extremely simple) houses; the evidence for animal domestication and purposeful plant cultivation begins between 11,000 B.P. and 10,000 B.P., and accumulates thereafter. Admittedly, this brief outline is too simple a pattern to be complete, but provides a hypothesis to be tested by future research.

While at present we know by purposeful experiment much about the way in which animals can be tamed, we know nothing of the way our prehistoric ancestors domesticated them. The change from man the hunter to man the protector was a new adaptive shift in cultural evolution, and the pattern of human behavior whereby this event occurred remains unknown to us.

Last, and very recently, serious doubts have been expressed about the supposed diffusion of Neolithic culture from the Near East to the Far East; instead, on the basis of the most recent archeological evidence, an independent center for agricultural origins is now postulated in northern China, based on millets, pigs, and dogs (Chang 1968; Ho 1969).

For those who have the spark of interest which can be fanned to flame by the joy of achievement, there is work to be done!

Charles A. Reed
September 1969

The long path in time leads to ourselves from a hominoid group which abandoned forelimb brachiation for hindlimb bipedalism. Once on that path, we can say with the wisdom of hindsight, man was unique as no other animal group ever had been. Combining ever greater skill at abstraction and communication with ever-increasing utilization of energy sources, the main pattern of human culture has led through the successive major steps of tool invention, tool improvement, plant cultivation, animal domestication, urbanization, and political integration, and so finally to the industrial revolution. Looking forward, this path bids to lead us to other planets and other planetary systems.

Seen thus in the long perspective, the initiation of cultivation and domestication—the Neolithic or "food-producing revolution" (Childe 1958a)—was one of three of four great cultural innovations, and a fundamental and necessary prelude to civilization (Braidwood 1952a; 1958). (I claim no originality for the above ideas; they are discussed at length in many anthropological writings.) It is true, however, that in spite of our certainty that agriculture and stockbreeding must have had beginnings, changing man from a roving hunter and gatherer to a settled village-farmer, and in spite of our knowledge of the vast ultimate consequences of this technical revolution, we know as yet very little about the details of these origins. Archeology, the discipline upon which we have traditionally depended for our understanding of these beginnings, has been either uninterested—spending its vigor instead in more glamorous pursuits—or incapable of the fine analyses necessary (Braidwood 1957b). For we have here a difficult field of paleo-natural history, where the geomorphologist, climatologist, soil scientist, paleoethnobotanist, agronomist, ecologist, geneticist, taxonomist, and comparative anatomist must add their skills to those of the field archeologist. Not all of them have yet done so, and certainly the future will witness greater coordination all along the line.

The literature which shows the attempts of an earlier generation of Near Eastern archeologists to be their own natural-history experts, particularly in the field of zoological identification, is generally a sorry one and should be quietly dieregarded. Inevitably and unfortunately, however, the conclusions published in these primary sources are those which have become crystallized into subsequent review papers and textbooks. Too often, also, the intriguing discoveries of the cultural complexity uncovered in the daily digging (particularly in the mounds representing remains of prehistoric towns) argued so strongly for an agriculturally based economy with assured food production that flocks and cultivated fields were assumed. Since the actual proof of the presence of the plants and animals was not thus regarded as necessary, the carbonized grain and the broken animal bones, which should have been considered of primary importance whenever they were uncovered, were too often shoveled onto the dump heap (Reed 1960).

Often, simply, the archeologists of an earlier day—trained as they were in the arts, and in the literature of classical or Biblical history—simply did not know what to look for, and the institutions financing them were not interested in excavating for "natural" (nonartifactual) materials which yielded merely ideas. Instead, the archeologists sought what their home institutions expected of them: display objects, written records, sculptures, and monuments. The more subtle interpretations that are made possible by the cooperation of teams of archeologically oriented natural scientists, working at the excavation, have thus only recently become intellectually and financially possible, and even now the budgetary problems involved in including all of the desired personnel in a major archeological expedition are very great (Taylor 1957).

With the exception of a forthcoming book by F. E. Zeuner, none of the major works on the origins of animal domestication[1] are in English; this field of study has been preeminently a German one. Previous summaries were limited (as is always the case) to the knowledge available at the time; most such information was of the European Neolithic and the *historical* periods (as gleaned from writings and pictures) of the ancient Near East. Except for the peripheral Iranian site of Anau (Duerst 1908), little was known of the all-important late *prehistoric* cultures of southwestern Asia—the cultures actually representative of the period and the area of incipient domestication.

The more recent summaries on domestication by Herre (1955a; 1958a) are those of an experienced morphologist with full knowledge of modern taxonomic practice and evolutionary theory, yet these do not attempt to make an evaluation of the kind attempted here—a critical analysis of our present knowledge of particular phases of the origin of animal domestication by one who has collected and worked in southwestern Asia, who has excavated much of the pertinent material at several of the most important sites, and who is studying the collections from these and other important sites.

---

[1] *Domestication* to me means simply that the animals are under the control of man to such a degree that, if he wishes, their choice of mates is determined. Artificial selection is thus possible and usually, to some degree at least, inevitable. In a very important sense, then, domestic animals (as well as plants) are a type of human artifact, since they exist in a form changed by man.

DIFFICULTIES

In spite of a prolific literature, dating well back into the 19th century, the central problems concerned with the origins and early history of animal domestication remain unsolved. In large part, as mentioned, this unfortunate situation is due to archeology's not having asked itself the right questions, or, if it has done so, to its having assumed the answers without having saved the evidence. Thus, too many of the reports on prehistoric Egyptian and southwestern Asian cultures merely assert the presence of domestic animals without offering any anatomical proof.

Even if saved, the "evidence" may well run to tens of thousands of broken animal bones, which have to be cleaned, sorted, and individually studied in an effort to identify the bone and to determine the age, sex, and species of the animal (when this is possible). Where wild and domestic forms existed together in the same area, attempts must be made to segregate them.

Heretofore, a major deficiency in attempting in America to study the faunal remains from archeological sites in the ancient Near East has been the almost complete lack of comparative skeletal material with which to make correct identifications. Ideally, one should have complete skeletal series of all the species which existed in the area of the prehistoric culture, to allow one to study age, sexual and individual differences, and differences between wild and domestic forms of the same species. But far from having such series, we had, until recently, practically no study skeletons from the Near East in the Western Hemisphere; indeed, several of the species have become extinct within historical times, and others are perilously near that state. However, a beginning, at least, of such a collection has now been gathered and is available for study in Chicago.[2]

Piles of dirty broken bones have little appeal to most zoologists, busy with their own researches, nor is the upper Quaternary (particularly the sub-Recent, with its modern-type fauna) of interest

---

[2] A grant from the National Science Foundation to the department of anthropology of the University of Chicago allowed me to spend the year 1954–55 in southwestern Asia, collecting living animals in addition to doing archeological work with the Iraq-Jarmo Project. The zoological specimens collected were deposited in the Chicago Natural History Museum.

to most paleontologists. Such problems really, then, must be undertaken by zoologists who know the area concerned and who have collected in it, who have worked cheek-by-trowel with the archeologists, and who are not only ecologically sensitive to the environmental problems presented but are also anthropologically oriented to the nuances of evolving human cultures. Such zoologists are few (although the field, open and new, will be a promising one once it acquires the respectability of institutional support [Braidwood 1957b]).

Under these conditions, even when osteological collections from important sites have been made, the bones have sometimes lain around for years while the archeologist vainly tried to get someone to study them. Perhaps finally succeeding, he has in turn too often been handed a list of generic and specific names, meaningless to him, to be duly published as an appendix to the site report.

Without interpretation, both environmental and cultural, biological studies related to prehistoric sites have practically no meaning.

Another basic difficulty—aside from the fundamental one of the tremendous expense of putting properly staffed expeditions into the field halfway around the world—is the real paucity of fundamental evidence to date. We have less than a dozen sites in the time range immediately prior to incipient domestication (and not all of these have been studied in detail or published completely), and we have fewer yet for the suspected crucial period of actual domestication. Furthermore, due to political accidents of modern history, these sites cluster either in Palestine or in Iraq, with the intervening gap archeologically unexploited.

A last difficulty, and at the moment one of the most frustrating, is the failure of the radiocarbon (C^{14}) technique to yield dates of certain dependability. Although it was hailed as the answer to the prehistorian's prayer when it was first announced, there has been increasing disillusion with the method because of the chronological uncertainties (in some cases, absurdities) that would follow a strict adherence to published C^{14} dates. This is not to question the validity of the physical laws underlying the principle used, or the accuracy of the counters now in operation around the world; the unsolved problem, instead, seems to lie in the difficulty of securing samples completely free from either older or younger adherent carbon. At least to the present, no kind or degree of chemical

cleaning can guarantee one-age carbon, typical only of the time of
the site from which it was excavated. What bids to become a
classic example of "C14 irresponsibility" is the 6000-year spread
of 11 determinations for Jarmo (Braidwood 1958), a prehistoric village in northeastern Iraq, which, on the basis of all archeological
evidence, was not occupied for more than 500 consecutive years.

THE PROBLEM

What is needed—and what the various members of the Iraq-Jarmo
Project are trying to accomplish—is a thorough analysis of all
the evidence bearing on the origins of agriculture, animal domestication, and the village-farming way of life. The parts of the problem
have different degrees of dependence upon each other (for instance,
most of the geological and climatic events would have transpired
in the absence of man), but all are intertwined. One cannot think
of domestication, thus, as happening independently of the geographical factors (terrain, climate, flora) that always determine
animal distribution, or independently of the culture—including the
primitive agriculture—of the domesticators.

We must then, like good reporters, try to answer the five W's
and the lone H: When, Where, Who, What, Why and How?

WHEN

Although it has been suggested that reindeer were domesticated
during the upper Paleolithic in western Europe (Patte 1958), no
real evidence of animal domestication can be shown for any
Pleistocene period;[3] we are dealing entirely, so far as is known,
with terminal-Pleistocene and post-Pleistocene phenomena.

Stockbreeding, assuring a steady supply of animal fat and protein,
came somewhat later than incipient plant cultivation—so far as
we know. (The necessarily recurrent use of the phrase "so far as
we know" illustrates how badly needed are thorough investigations

---

[3] I follow the common practice of most European geologists and of the
U. S. Geological Survey (Morrison *et al.* 1957) in dividing the Quaternary into
Pleistocene and Recent, although at least one eminent authority rejects any
such differentiation (Flint 1957). The Recent is generally considered to have
begun between 10,000 and 11,000 years ago, the difference depending only
upon whether the several hundred years of the Younger Dryas is included in
the Pleistocene (Wright 1957) or in the Recent (Cooper 1958).

of sites falling within the time range of "incipient cultivation" (Braidwood 1958; Braidwood, Reed 1957), when animal domestication was also undoubtedly being initiated). There is no *proof* as yet that any of the "incipient-cultivation" sites known—Karim Shahir (Braidwood 1952a), Zawi Chemi (Solecki 1957b; 1959), Mallaha (Perrot 1957), and the various Natufian sites in central Palestine—had domestic food animals, and I personally am doubtful concerning the presence of the Natufian dog (discussed below).

Although we must be properly cautious in accepting as valid any lone C^{14} determination from an individual locality, the four available dates for sites of the period of incipient cultivation have a comforting closeness in time, being close not only to each other but also to what we had expected on the basis of accumulating evidence of the last few years. The date for the short-time occupation site of Zawi Chemi is $10,870 \pm 300$ years and that for a typologically contemporaneous level in nearby Shanidar Cave is $10,600 \pm 300$ years (Solecki, Rubin 1958). Two determinations for Early Natufian levels at Jericho are 9850 ± 240 years and 9800 ± 240 years (Kenyon 1959a). Since milling stones were present at Zawi Chemi and mortars and pestles, plus flint sickles, are known from early Natufian sites in Palestine, we can say, in easily remembered round numbers, that by approximately 10,000 B.P. (before the present), reaping and milling of wild cereals was most probably a reality, with purposeful planting a possibility.

Domestication of the primary food animals followed[4]—but by how long? We cannot be certain as yet. I am convinced, however, that in the somewhat later village-farming community of Jarmo we have found multiple specimens of domestic goats, as indicated by the shape of the male horn cores. The time is difficult to assess, in view of the 6000-year spread of C^{14} "dates," but probably Braidwood's (1958) estimate of about 8500 B.P. is as accurate as any that can be obtained now. The conclusion that the domestic goat was present in an early level at Jericho (Tell es-Sultan), although based at first on a single male horn core (Zeuner 1955), has since been verified by finding additional material (Zeuner, personal communication).

There is no *proof* as yet of domestication of any other food

---

[4] But see C. O. Sauer (1952) for the conflicting opinion that the pig was domesticated earlier, in southeastern Asia, and was then brought westward.

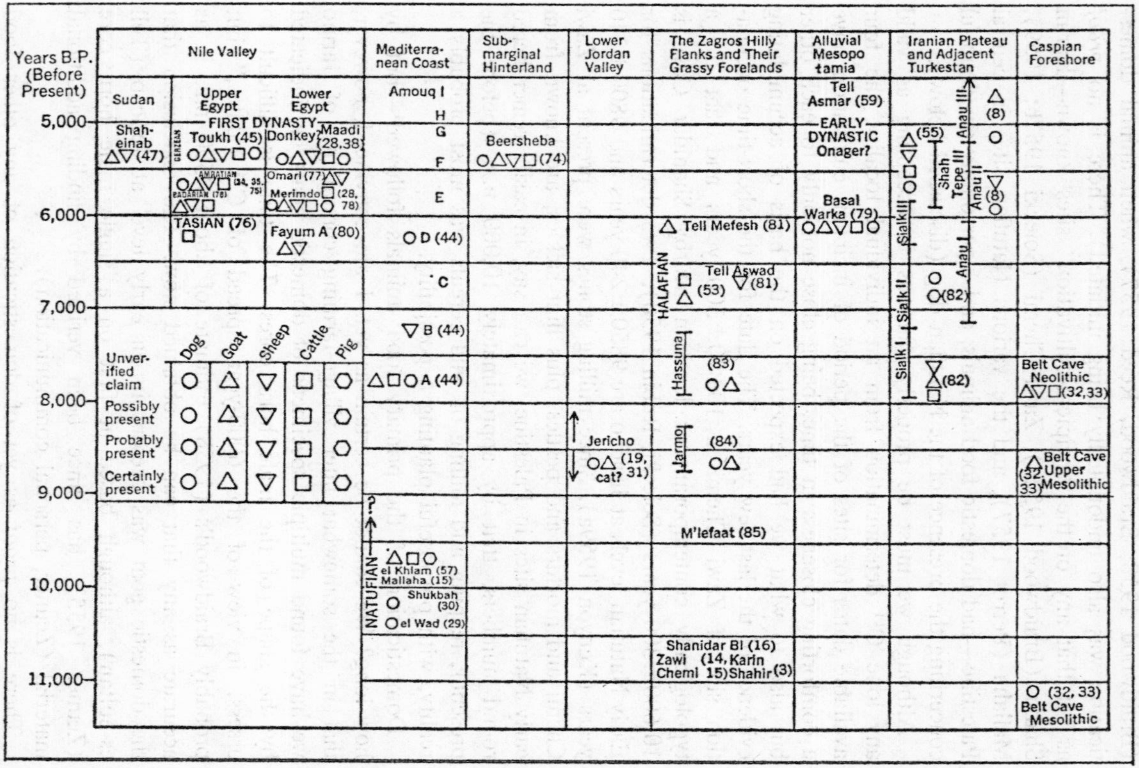

Chart: Animal Domestication in the Prehistoric Near East — distribution of dog, goat, sheep, cattle, and pig (symbols: O = dog, △ = goat, ▽ = sheep, □ = cattle, ⬡ = pig) by region against time in Years B.P. (Before Present).

Time scale (left axis): 5,000 — 6,000 — 7,000 — 8,000 — 9,000 — 10,000 — 11,000 Years B.P. (Before Present)

Column headings (left to right):

Nile Valley			Mediterranean Coast (Amouq)	Sub-marginal Hinterland	Lower Jordan Valley	The Zagros Hilly Flanks and Their Grassy Forelands	Alluvial Mesopotamia	Iranian Plateau and Adjacent Turkestan	Caspian Foreshore
Sudan	Upper Egypt	Lower Egypt							

Entries by column:

Nile Valley — Sudan:
- Shah-einab △▽(47)

Nile Valley — Upper Egypt:
- FIRST DYNASTY — Toukh (45) Donkey (28,38) O△▽□O
- GENERAL
- BADARIAN (34, 35, 78?) O△▽□
- TASIAN (76) □

Nile Valley — Lower Egypt:
- Maadi △▽□O
- Omari (77) O△▽□ (28, 78?)
- Merimde □ (28, 78?) O△▽
- Fayum A (80) △▽

Mediterranean Coast (Amouq): I, H, G, F, E, D, C, B, A
- O D (44)
- △□□ A (44)
- ▽ B (44)
- O C
- NATUFIAN
- el Khiam (57) △□□, Mallaha (13)
- Shukbah (30) O
- el Wad (29) O

Sub-marginal Hinterland:
- Beersheba O△▽□(74)

Lower Jordan Valley:
- Jericho O△(19, cat? 31) ▽

The Zagros Hilly Flanks and Their Grassy Forelands:
- △ Tell Shemshara Tell Mefesh (81)
- Tell Aswad (81) ▽ (53)
- HALAFIAN
- Hassuna (83) □△ O△
- Jarmo (84) O△
- M'lefaat (85)
- Shanidar BI (16), Zawi Chemi (14), Karim Shahir (15), Shahir (3)

Alluvial Mesopotamia:
- Tell Asmar (59)
- EARLY DYNASTIC Onager?
- Basal Warka (79) O△▽□O

Iranian Plateau and Adjacent Turkestan:
- Anau III △(8), O
- Anau II, Tepe III — Shah (55) ▽O(8)
- △▽□OO
- Sialk III, Sialk II, Sialk I
- O X(82)

Caspian Foreshore:
- Belt Cave Neolithic △▽□(32, 33)
- Belt Cave Upper Mesolithic △▽□(32, 33)
- Belt Cave Mesolithic O(32, 33)

Legend (symbol key):

	Pig	Cattle	Sheep	Goat	Dog
Unverified claim	⬡	□	▽	△	O
Possibly present	⬡	□	▽	△	O
Probably present	⬡	□	▽	△	O
Certainly present	⬡	□	▽	△	O

animal at Jericho or Jarmo (see the discussion below concerning the dog), or for some time thereafter.

Thus, at present we can only say that domestication of the goat probably falls within the millennium between 9000 and 8000 B.P., and that the domestication of the other three primary food animals (cattle, sheep, pigs) followed some time thereafter (see Fig. 1). We cannot say anything as yet, however, about the absolute time or the chronological order of domestication of these three.

WHERE

All archeological work to date in the Near East suggests that both agriculture and animal domestication (with the possible exception of that of the dog) had their origins in the hilly, grassy, and open-forested flanks of the Zagros, Lebanese, and Palestinian mountains. These data have been treated fully elsewhere (Braidwood 1952a; 1958; Braidwood, Braidwood 1953; Dyson 1953) and need not be repeated here. On the basis of the data assembled by Dyson (1953) and of recent archeological evidence from central Asia, the highly respected ethnologist von Fürer-Haimendorf (1955) has strongly discounted the old notion that animal domestication arose during an early stage of pastoralism. He stressed that, although the dog appeared with preagricultural hunters, the basic food animals always appeared in a context of early village-farmers. Further, he said, the domestication of the horse and reindeer, it must now be realized, came relatively late and had no influence on the earliest agricultural communities or their immediate historical derivatives.

FIGURE 1 A chronological chart, subdivided into geographical areas, of the known history of animal domestication in the prehistoric Near East. The estimated time is not to be regarded as absolute; the top of each column is fairly well fixed, temporally; but any part of any column may become elongated or shortened as a result of future discoveries.[5]

---

[5] The chronological chart was based primarily on Ehrich (1954). Radiocarbon dates, to mid-1958, are summarized by R. J. Braidwood (1959). Additionally, I had advice from staff members of the Oriental Institute, University of Chicago. Other sources consulted were E. Massoulard (1949); I. Rizkana (1952); and R. P. Charles (1957).

From the primary center in the open-forest hills of southwestern Asia, the village-farming way of life diffused in all directions, carrying with it its trademarks: the village, cereal agriculture (wheat and barley, primarily), and the basic domestic food animals. In Egypt, in Thessaly, in Baluchistan and the Indus valley, probably even in China (at least in northern China), the beginnings of village-farming life were later and seem to have received a cultural stimulus from southwestern Asia.

The case of Egypt is particularly instructive, as wheat, goats, and sheep do not occur wild in Egypt (nowhere in Africa do true sheep and goats occur wild[6]) and so, obviously, were introduced as cultivated and domesticated species. If the radiocarbon dates for the Egyptian Fayum are accurate (possibly they are not, as we do know of some later radiocarbon dates for Egypt which are obviously too recent), the earliest and simultaneous appearance of cereal agriculture and domestic goats (or goats *and* sheep?) in Egypt, at Fayum, was considerably later (about 6200 B.P.) than the probable time of their earliest associations in Asia (about 8500 B.P.).

WHO

The people who first turned the trick—who first grew grains and domesticated hoofed mammals—were, on the basis of skeletal evidence, modern-type men of the Mediterranean race. Doubtless they would pass unnoticed, if suddenly resurrected, among the people of today in the hill country where they lived.

Questions arise, to which we have no answers: Would the "agricultural revolution" have had its start where and when it did if another people, of different color or head shape, had lived there? Or would these important events have occurred if our same Mediterranean peoples had had, by a historical accident, some slightly different cultural pattern?

---

[6] D. M. A. Bate (1953) has accepted a description of native goats in Algeria (Pomel 1898:1), but the age of the materials from which Pomel described these goats is uncertain (Arambourg 1929), and there is a distinct possibility, thus, that Pomel's *"Capra promaza"* is based upon Neolithic domestic goats.

WHAT

It seems logically probable—although we have as yet no direct evidence—that the cultivation of wheat and barley (or, at first, possibly of wheat alone) induced (or should we be more cautious, and say "allowed"?) the formation of the permanent villages. Probably both agriculture and village development were a necessary prelude to domestication of the basic food animals, although there are contrary views (Zeuner 1954).[7] These food animals, which undoubtedly contributed so much to the evolution of late prehistoric cultures in the Near East, were goats (*Capra hircus*), sheep (*Ovis aries*), cattle (*Bos taurus*), and pigs (*Sus scrofa*).[8] The dog (*Canis familiaris*) was also undoubtedly present (although its presence is poorly documented) but probably did not enter importantly into the cultural picture of the increasingly more complex village-farming and town-farming communities.

In addition, the zebu (*Bos indicus*) was certainly present prehistorically in Baluchistan (Fairservis 1956), and subsequently in the Indus valley. This whole area, however, is peripheral to the central (or "nuclear") Near East with which we are mainly concerned, and the earliest suggested date for domestic cattle (about 5000 B.P.) is late by Near East standards. The donkey (*Equus asinus*), domesticated from the Nubian wild ass, is of a similar antiquity, having been reported from the site of Maadi in Lower Egypt (Menghin 1934). By this time, too, the Syrian onager (*Equus hemionus hemippus*) probably had been domesticated in Mesopotamia. The other domestic animals, both birds and mammals (ducks, geese, chickens, horses, camels, yaks, water buffaloes, reindeer, rab-

---

[7] This paper is an important one on the "why" and "how" of domestication and forms a foundation for much of what I am saying here, even though I do not agree with Zeuner in every detail.

[8] It is interesting to note that all of these animals belong to the same order, the Artiodactyla, and that except for the pig they are not only all ruminants but are all bovids. Other bovids (water buffalo, zebu, yak) were subsequently domesticated, and many species of gazelles and antelopes, particularly, seem to be potentially domesticable. No other family looms so importantly in the history of domestication. Factors involved in the late origin (Miocene) and rapid and successful evolution of the Bovidae may perhaps play some role in their versatile adaptations to domestication. Actually, there may be no bovid which could not be domesticated.

bits, and so on), which we rightly consider to be and to have been important in various human cultures, were not present as domesticants in the late prehistoric of the Near East and so are not here considered.

Dog (Canis familiaris). Since Bate (1937; 1942) announced that a domestic dog was present in the Natufian period, prehistorians have generally assumed that the dog was the Near East's first domestic animal, ubiquitously present for a period of nearly 10,000 years. However, examination of her published reports and figures has not convinced me that she excluded the possibility that the bones being considered were those of the large Egyptian or golden jackal, *Canis aureus lupaster,* possibly still present in Palestine. If the Natufians did not have a dog, then the earliest records would seem to be from the 7th millennium B.C., by which time dogs are known from the Maglemosian period in northwestern Europe and from Jericho in southwestern Asia. Domestic goats are also known at this time, however, from both Jericho and Jarmo, so we can no longer be so certain that the dog was "the first domestic animal," as has been so glibly stated for decades.

The earliest valid evidence of the dog in all the Near East is from a lower "plaster-floor level" at Jericho (Zeuner 1958); dogs nearly as small as fox terriers are reported, while others are almost the size of wolves. The status of an even earlier "dog" from Belt Cave in Iran, with a C^{14} age of $11,480\pm550$ years (Coon 1951; Ralph 1955) must await the result of a study by a specialist in canid osteology.

I have not been able to convince myself that there were dog bones among the midden remains from Jarmo, although wolf and fox have been identified. However, since the bones are all extremely fragmented, a large dog could easily be mistaken for a wolf. The best evidence for a Jarmo dog is cultural, not zoological; several clay statuettes of what certainly appear to be dogs (the tail is curled over the back) have been found among several thousand statuettes, many of them identifiable as mammals native to the area. Even when identifiable as goats or sheep, however, these figurines are too crudely modeled to yield any clues about domestication.

In Egypt the first valid evidence of the dog is also artifactual; four dogs, led on leashes by one man, are represented on a pottery bowl (Hilzheimer 1932; Massoulard 1949) of the Amratian period.

They already show characters of the greyhound or seluki type, which by this time is also known (although the build is somewhat sturdy) from the Ubaid period in Mesopotamia by skeletons and, from a somewhat later time, by carvings on cylinder seals (Tobler 1950, pl. 37b; Frankfort 1939, pl. iva). The presence of this specialized breed at this time at both ends of the Fertile Crescent indicates a long, although undocumented, period of artificial selection in the Near East. Not until the late Gerzean period do we find definite skeletal evidence of the dog in Egypt (Moustafa 1955).

The general lack of skeletal evidence of prehistoric dogs in southwestern Asia and in Egypt is probably in part a reflection of the lack of attention given to such skeletal materials when they were found by archeologists during the last century, but perhaps in part it reflects the fact that dog carcasses were more likely to be available to scavengers than were the bones of the food animals. Perhaps, too, dogs were relatively rare as compared with the hoofed domesticants.

The wolf (*Canis lupus*) has generally been regarded as the ancestor of the dog. This supposition has been based (i) on the great morphological similarities, particularly as to dental details, between the wolf and the earliest dogs of the Mesolithic of western Europe; (ii) on the complete interfertility of dogs and wolves (with fertile hybrids); and (iii) on the great similarity of behavior (Scott 1954).

In spite of such evidence, however, several authors have suggested the golden jackal, *Canis aureus,* as the dog's ancestor, usually admitting later admixture with wolves for the more boreal breeds (Lorenz 1955). Certainly Bate (1937) regarded the supposed "dog" from the Natufian of Palestine as jackal-ancestored (although, as mentioned above, the animal may well *be* jackal and not dog). However, dog and jackal are dissimilar with respect to certain definite dental characters, and they have a different chromosome number (dog, 78; jackal, 74) (Matthey 1954). While dogs and jackals do interbreed, the fertility of the resulting hybrids seems not to have been established with the certainty usually assumed. Although the problem cannot be said to have been settled and there may have been some interbreeding of dogs (once established) with jackals, the preponderance of evidence indicates the wolf as the primary ancestor of the first dogs. The third possibility, that a hypothetical "wild dog" (C. Sauer 1952) or the pariah dog (Vesey-Fitzgerald 1957) actually represent an ancient stock from which the domestic dog was derived, lacks any historical evidence and fails to find (in my opinion, at least) the necessary paleontological support.

Goat (Capra hircus) and sheep (Ovis aries). Most of the bones—although not the horn cores or metapodials—of these two species are so similar that the species are often included together as "sheep/goat" or "caprovid" in archeological reports. Even when they are supposedly distinguished, one must always be suspicious of the validity of the identification.

Much careful archeological and zoological work remains to be done before we can know certainly whether sheep or goats were domesticated first, but present evidence indicates it was the goat. With goats, as with other animals, the earliest domesticants would be identical with, or very similar to, the wild form. Only after many generations could mutations accumulate that would so mark the domestic population that their broken bones would be distinguishable from those of wild individuals brought into the village by hunters. (Even now, where it is available, wild game is typically brought into the villages in the Near East for food.) However, population-age analysis based on the bones may show a shift from a stratigraphically lower level with random age distribution to a higher, and thus later, level with a greater proportion of young and near-mature animals. Such a shift would certainly suggest a change from wild-killed animals to domesticated ones, most members of the herd being harvested at optimum times. It is on the basis of this type of evidence, although on a rather limited series, that Coon (1951) made a claim for the domestication of goats and sheep at Belt Cave in northern Iran (C^{14} date of about 8000 years ago). At or before this time, however, domestic goats—as identified morphologically—are known from Jericho and Jarmo.

These Jarmo goats are distinguished from the wild type (which are also numerous in Jarmo) primarily by differences in the shape of the male horn core and, furthermore (in some of the Jarmo specimens), by a slight twisting of the horn. In contrast, the horns of wild goats, while curved over the animal's back like a scimitar, are not twisted.

Most of the archeological work in the Near East has been so lacking in attention to animal remains (Reed 1960) that we cannot be certain of the presence of domestic sheep for some thousands of years after the probable beginning of that domestication.

It would seem likely that sheep would have been domesticated as early as, or not long after, goats. Whereas we do have definite evidence of many domestic goats at Jarmo and Jericho (about 8500 B.P.), the records for sheep are extremely meager [if all unverified claims are discounted (Reed 1960)] for the succeeding 2500 years. Amschler (n.d.)[9] has reported both domestic and wild sheep from the Amouq sequence, but the sheep bones are exceedingly rare in comparison with the other domestic artiodactyls. It is only *after* 6000 B.P. that we find convincing evidence of sheep, from the Gerzean period in upper Egypt (Gaillard 1934), Warka in Sumerian Mesopotamia (Frankfort 1939, pl. iii*a*), and the Anau II level (Duerst 1908) in what is now the Turkoman S.S.R.

Throughout much of this period, between about 8500 and 6000 B.P., our record for goats is little better than that for sheep, but by the latter part of the period these domestic animals were probably raised not only in upper Egypt but up the Danube as well (Childe 1957), and only a little later in Baluchistan (Fairservis 1956). The goat, curiously, was late in reaching north into the oases of west-central Asia: it is reported only from the upper levels of Anau, whereas domestic sheep are definitely known earlier there (Duerst 1908). Up the Nile, however, goats—albeit dwarfs—seemingly preceded sheep; goats are known from the Sudan about 5300 B.P., while the contemporaneous evidence for sheep is meager and uncertain (Bate 1953).

If we assume, as we must on the basis of present evidence, that the earliest domestication of the goat occurred in southwestern Asia, there is little problem concerning the identity of the wild ancestor, as there *is* only one population (*Capra hircus aegagrus*) of wild goat in southwestern Asia. The ibex, various species of which occur in Europe, Africa, and Asia, has presumably never been domesticated and so does not complicate the problem, and the only other goat, *C. falconeri,* lives further east. With sheep, however, the pattern is not clear at all, due to multiple and conflicting taxonomic and nomenclatural problems. Students of domestication

[9] This collection of bones from the excavations of the Oriental Institute's Syrian Expedition is now in Chicago and is to be restudied before final publication of the results.

have argued endlessly about which kinds of sheep were evolved from which species of wild sheep, without ever really knowing what a species of sheep is, how many valid species occurred (if there was more than one in central and western Eurasia), how much actual interbreeding (and thus gene-flow) occurred between the different populations variously described as species or subspecies, or what genetic factors underlie the characters of horn, head, tail, and fleece that have been so ardently discussed.

The genetics of most of these characters is still largely unknown, and a true classification of Old World *Ovis* is now extremely difficult, due to dwindling numbers of many of the populations (Harper 1945). However, if it were sufficiently comprehensive, a gene-frequency study (Evans 1956) of ovid blood factors (potassium and sodium concentrations, hemoglobin types, blood groups), of both wild and domestic sheep would undoubtedly help clarify the muddled taxonomic situation and would also aid in tracing the ancestries and interbreedings of the different races of domestic sheep. Additionally, detailed study of many bones from many archeological sites would give valuable collaborative evidence with historical depth. Until such data are forthcoming, I prefer the simplified taxonomic scheme of Tzalkin (1951), who believed that, aside from *Ovis canadensis* of far eastern Siberia, all the Old World sheep belong to several subspecies of but one species, *O. ammon*. Thus, the detailed anatomical differences which have been so thoroughly studied and discussed by many students of sheep domestication in tracing the phylogeny of different breeds would never have had more than subspecific value.

Cattle (Bos taurus). The large, long-horned, wild *Bos primigenius* illustrated with such magnificent artistry at Lascaux, hunted and portrayed by the Assyrians, described with wonder by the Romans, and extinct in 1627, was distributed throughout the forested regions of Europe, North Africa, and southwestern Asia into historic times. Whether or not a second, short-horned species (*B. longifrons*) occupied much of the same area has been endlessly disputed; perhaps these short-horned animals were merely females of *B. primigenius* (Koby 1954; Zeuner 1953).

In addition, the European bison (*Bison bonasus*) extended its range into southwestern Asia, and in Iraq, at least, a wild water buffalo (*Bubalus*) undoubtedly existed (Hatt 1959). In the marshes of the Nile of prehistoric Egypt, in addition to true wild cattle, probably at least one kind of African buffalo (possibly two) existed (Reed 1960).

The simultaneous presence of these several Bovini in the Near East, the nuclear area of animal domestication, is important—primarily because of the very fact that it has been generally disregarded. The result has been that any large bovines from prehistoric sites have usually, in the archeological literature, been labeled "domestic cattle" if, in any particular archeologist author's opinion, the time range fell within the limits of expected animal domestication. Generally the very real problem of the great difficulty of distinguishing between these various genera, particularly on the basis of a few teeth or broken bones, has simply not been recognized. Additionally, there is the much greater problem, even if the animal is *Bos,* of determining its status—wild or domestic.

The value of the scientific material relative to large bovines that has been thrown away unstudied is fantastic; in some cases the "identification" of the native workmen at the excavation has been accepted on the spot, and the skeletons or skulls have been discarded. The result is a woeful ignorance about the origins of cattle domestication; instead of evidence we have sweeping fictions by archeologists and culture-historians concerning the increasing complexity of human cultures throughout later prehistoric times, as based upon the presumed utilization of cattle and other livestock.

Bulls were important in the emotional life of the Halafian people, it is true, as shown by their art and deduced for their religion (Mallowan, Rose 1935); this emotional attachment of people to their cattle is a very real thing, with multiple manifestations, in all cattle-breeding peoples. Probably the Halafian and other Near Eastern peoples of the period *did* have domestic cattle, but the only evidence I can find has been hitherto overlooked (at least, so far as I can discover; certainly evidence has not been demanded in the archeological literature!). The particular item is a small but clear reproduction of a cow's head, from a basal Halafian level at Arpachiyah (Mallowan, Rose 1935), which has horns that are short and curve forward, quite like those of some cows today.

It is not until very late prehistoric times (about 6000 to 5000 B.P.) that we find actual proof, both zoological and cultural, of domestic cattle. The beautifully clear delineations on the cylinder seals of Warka and other early Sumerian towns testifies to the importance of cattle in these communities, as do the careful anatomical studies of Duerst (1908; Amschler 1939) on the cattle bones from the roughly contemporaneous Iranian sites of Anau II and Shah Tepé III, respectively.

In Egypt, throughout this same 4th millennium B.C., most prehistorians discuss with confidence the cattle-breeding cultures of the Badarian, Amratian, and Gerzean periods, without realizing that valid evidence of domestic cattle is lacking. As with the Halafian and some other Mesopotamian periods, the conclusions were too often assumed, while the need for evidence was ignored. Only at the Gerzean site of Toukh (Gaillard 1934) was a careful study made of the faunal remains; here Gaillard emphasized the resemblance of the excavated bones of the short-horned cattle to those found in adjacent but earlier Paleolithic sites, and also stressed their resemblances to bones of known domestic short-horned cattle, both prehistoric and modern. He never, however, spoke of the Toukh cattle as being domestic, particularly as wild cattle of that type were living in Egypt then and later. Even the relative youth of most of the cattle killed cannot be considered evidence of purposeful control of domestic herds, as the gazelle bones in the same middens were also mainly from subadult individuals. (Were, then, the gazelles perhaps domesticated?)

The prehistorians are probably correct in thinking that domestic cattle were present and important in the human cultural evolution of Egypt of the 4th millennium B.C., prior to dynastic times and the beginning of written history, but these same prehistorians must become aware of the lack of zoological or cultural evidence for their assumptions.

Pig (Sus scrofa). During the late prehistoric times here considered, many subspecies of wild pig were native to North Africa and much of Eurasia. In spite of this wide distribution, the ancestor of *all* domestic pigs has been singled out as one southeastern Asiatic subspecies, *S. s. vittatus* (Klatt 1927; Sauer 1952) if it is true that this subspecies is the common ancestor, domestic pigs must have been moved westward, presumably slowly, to reach the Near East and most of Europe in prehistoric times. As yet I have not investigated this problem, but the general pattern seems illogical. I suggest that we at least reinvestigate the possibility that domestication of pigs may have occurred several times, from different wild populations.

Pigs are not as difficult to tame as one might imagine; an adult wild boar or sow, it is true, is not an animal one approaches casually, but several people have easily reared the young of wild pigs to adulthood, the females having then produced litters to be reared in captivity (Reed 1960). Such pigs are surprisingly docile.

Although a domestic pig has been mentioned for the Natufian the evidence—a single phalanx—is unacceptable. The earliest record to merit serious consideration is that for Amouq A, in the northern Levant. Here, as in later levels of the Amouq sequence, Amschler (n.d.) listed both domestic and wild pigs, but without any explanation of his basis for differentiation.

Other than for the Amouq, there is little osteological evidence for the presence of domestic pigs in the prehistoric Near East except in the north across Iran, near the base of Anau II (Duerst 1908), where domestic pigs were suddenly introduced with no prior, and little subsequent, evidence of wild pigs having been hunted. By this time (about 3800 B.C.) or before, the pig was quite probably an important food animal in southern Mesopotamia, although this conclusion is based on what I consider to be slight cultural evidence (Van Buren 1939). Certainly, pigs are known to have been important in Sumer in early historic times. However, the only study (Hilzheimer 1941) on the osteological remains from a Sumerian city (Tell Asmar) is from a time so late as not to appear on my chronological chart.

Egypt, it would seem to me, might well have been an independent center of pig domestication, considering its semi-isolated position and late cultural development. It is difficult for me, for instance, to imagine pigs being driven across the desert of Sinai, but the *idea* of domestication could pass readily, perhaps by way of a Syrian visitor. There are numerous pig bones from the sites of Merimde and Maadi in northern Egypt, but there is no published study of them known to me to vindicate Menghin's (1934) oft-quoted claim that pig breeding represented an important cultural difference between the late prehistoric cultures of upper and lower Egypt. When Gaillard, an experienced morphologist, *did* carefully examine the numerous bones of pigs from the midden of Toukh in upper Egypt he was unable to determine whether the animals had been wild or domesticated (Gaillard 1934). Domestic pigs may well have been present and important in the economy of prehistoric Egypt, but until we have zoological or cultural evidence for such domestication we must assume that the numerous bones of pigs found in the remains of prehistoric villages represent wild pigs from the adjacent Nile marshes.

WHY

Why did men domesticate animals at all? A religious motif has often been suggested (C. Sauer 1952), but probably at first there was little realization of what was occurring; there was merely a gradual strengthening of an association between two species of social animals (man and dog, man and goat, and so on), preadapted by their respective evolutions to be of mutual benefit. Everything we know about preliterate cultures argues against a sudden realization of the potential values of animal domestication, followed by planned action; man could have had no concept of the future values of animals' milk, or of wool not yet of useful length on the hairy wild sheep. Later, in literate societies, there *were* purposeful efforts at domestication. Some, such as the Egyptian Old Kingdom domestication of the hyena, of certain antelopes, and of the Nilotic goose, were seemingly successful but were later abandoned. The era of planned domestication was not limited to peoples of ancient history, however, for we note the successful 19th-century domestication of the budgerigar parrot and of the laboratory rat. Today, planned domestication of two large mammals is in the experimental stage—that of the eland (*Taurotragus*) in Rhodesia and of the musk ox (*Ovibos*) in northern North America (Burton 1956; J. Desmond Clark, personal communication; Teal 1958). The latter experiment, at least, is showing promise of success.

HOW

Man probably entered into a state of beneficial mutualism with certain animal species because, to put it in very general terms, the animals were already socially and psychologically preadapted to being tamed without loss of reproductive abilities. A second factor was the necessary one that the human culture milieu had evolved to a state of organization such that the animals could be controlled, and maintained generation after generation in a condition of dependence. At least to some degree the animals must be protected from predators and provided with food—the latter perhaps only in times of scarcity. The detailed pattern of the process leading to domestication naturally varied with both the particular species and the human culture that were interacting; certainly the domestication of the wolf to the dog by the Maglemosian hunter-collectors of northwestern Europe was different in detail from the domestication of the hoofed food animals by the post-Natufian cultivators. Unfortunately, we know nothing of the details of either process, partly because of our inability to reconstruct the behavior and cultural environment of the people involved and partly because of our ignorance of the psychology of the various wild animals involved.

With the exception of one of the most recently domesticated mammals, the laboratory rat, we know little enough about the behavior patterns of our common domestic animals, but we know much less about the behavior of their wild progenitors. Furthermore, detailed comparative observations of wild and domestic *Rattus norvegicus* emphasize the tremendous behavioral changes undergone by a species during domestication (Richter 1952). Thus, psychological studies on domesticants probably cannot yield the total behavior pattern of the wild ancestors. It was, however, these wild ancestors that man first tamed and reared.

The social enzyme that activated the union of man and beast was undoubtedly the human proclivity, not only of children but of women also, to keep pets (Gilmore 1950; C. Sauer 1952; Zeuner 1954), although purposeful capture of young animals by men, to serve as hunting decoys, may well have been another avenue toward domestication.

The psychological factor of "imprinting," explored particularly by Lorenz in a notable series of animal experiments, was undoubtedly a major influence in the domestication of birds with precocial young (chickens, ducks, geese, turkeys, and so on). *Imprinting* refers to the tendency, most pronounced in such precocial birds, to recognize, and psychologically to attach themselves to, the most frequently seen and heard living thing during an early and short "critical period." Typically this would be the mother, and we have thus an instinctive mechanism for recognition of the parent by an active newborn.

For mammals, we probably cannot speak of "imprinting" in as complete a sense as we do for birds. There are, of course, definite sequences of actions whereby mother and young learn to recognize each other; for the young mammal this is certainly a "critical period." Such recognition of the mother is then enlarged to include other members of the species. A lamb reared in isolation, for instance, rather thoroughly ignores other sheep for the remainder of its life (Scott 1953), even though it will mate and produce young. We would seem to have here, in correlation with the above-mentioned tendency to keep pets, a mechanism for the switching of psychological recognition and social dependence from a real mother to a human foster mother.

The "critical period" for hoofed mammals—whose behavior is similar in some respects to that of precocial birds—is within a few hours of birth, but for helpless-born young it comes several days or weeks later [three weeks and later for the dog, for instance—a phenomenon associated with myelinization of cephalic neurons (Scott, Fredericson and Fuller 1951)]. In such mammals, the critical period is probably not so limited in time or so well defined as to pattern as in the hoofed animals. The essential point, however, is that in the domestic mammals that have been studied, and presumably in the others, there is such a patterned behavior system as is here discussed, a biological mechanism so basic that it remains essentially unchanged in the transition from wild to domestic status.

Since the "critical period" in mammals always comes prior to weaning, we must assume that there was a human wet nurse for whatever small helpless suckler might be brought into the village; there are women of primitive tribes who still act thus and provide the proper model (C. Sauer 1952). Once the domestication of sheep and goats had been accomplished and the practice of milking had been established, milk would have been available for orphaned calves and colts, and thus the way for domestication of larger species would have been opened.

It is not, however, only the young of many mammals that can be kept and reared; even the adults of some artiodactyls seem to seek domestication. Arkell (1957) tells of a female wart hog, with young, that made a nuisance of herself about one of his camps during a famine period, and I myself have had the experience of having my car stopped (*not* during a famine period!) on a major American highway by two large males of that supposedly wild species the big-horn sheep, who then stuck their heads in the open windows begging for tidbits. These animals may not have known it, but they were *asking* to be domesticated.

Once the nuclei of herds had been established, human selection against the aggressive and unmanageable individuals would have been automatic, resulting in the decrease in production, generation by generation, of the adrenocortical steroids (with multiple attendant physiological changes)—a process that has been studied in detail for the short history of the laboratory rat (Richter 1952). Eventually submissiveness becomes genetically ingrained in the population (although some species, such as the sheep, seem more susceptible to such manipulation than others). Furthermore, those animals naturally adapted to breed best in captivity would contribute their characters in larger numbers to the gene pool of each succeeding generation. Such unplanned selection of various sorts must have long preceded the methods of purposeful artificial selection which led eventually to the establishment of different breeds within a domestic species.

However it originated, once domestication had occurred, the idea could be transferred to species other than the original ones—a type of cultural shift which seems to account for the domestication of the reindeer. I find no reason, either, to believe that domestication of the same species could not occur in different places at different times, probably as the result of diffusion of the idea. Thus, pigs and cattle could have been domesticated in both southwestern Asia and in Egypt, the stimulus having been transferred from the former area to the latter in the mind of a human migrant.

A last factor that must be considered in a discussion of the origin of domestication of animals in the Near East is the "propinquity" or "riverine-oasis" theory of domestication (Childe 1928; Wheeler 1956; Braidwood 1957a). Briefly, the increasing desiccation of the Saharan and Arabian areas during the post-Pleistocene supposedly enforced the juxtaposition of man and the potentially domesticable animals around the disappearing water sources, leading to conditions of beneficial mutualism and thus to domestication.

Aside from the fact that a variety of ecological and distributional data argue against the validity of such a view (Reed 1960), accumulating evidence indicates that the known climatic sequence itself makes the idea untenable. I suspect that the adherents of the "riverine-oasis propinquity theory" have been overly impressed by the grand sweep of the very real desiccation of North Africa since the Allerod (about 11,000 years ago) without having given due regard to the fluctuating climatological conditions (Alimen 1957; Butzer 1957; 1958a) that existed. There were, beginning in the late Pleistocene, several fluctuations of temperature and rainfall which had profound ecological consequences for the biologically sensitive area of North Africa, where the evidence is best known. However, there is no evidence of domestication during the periods in question (about 15,000 to 7000 B.P.) in this or in any other desert area. There then began the "Neolithic wet phase" [Butzer's (1957; 1958a) Subpluvial II and Alimen's (1957) "Second wet phase"], lasting from about 7000 to 4500 B.P. During much of this time[10] domestic bovids (sheep, goats, and cattle) were present all across the Sahara, as shown by innumerable engravings and paintings (Alimen 1957), and the subsequent dramatic desiccation to present conditions thus occurred long after the full pattern of domestication had been established.

The "oasis theory," based as it originally was on an idea of continuous desiccation during the post-Pleistocene North African climatic sequence, loses all meaning when transferred to southwestern Asia, the actual site of original bovid domestication. Here data on Saharan rainfall and temperature fluctuations *may* apply to the central desert areas proper (the evidence is scant and inconclusive) but seemingly have much less meaning elsewhere.

Particularly throughout the hills of the Zagros-Palestinian chain there was relatively little climatic change within the transition period from the upper Pleistocene to the early Recent (Reed and Braidwood 1960; Picard 1943; Shalem 1953:153; Wright 1960); in fact, these terms have relevance in a climatic sense only as we can correlate them with regions of former continental glaciation.

My own unfinished studies on the bones collected from half a dozen sites in northern Iraq, which bridge some 90,000 years of the late Quaternary, show that an essentially modern fauna has occupied the area during this period. This does not mean that there has been no climatic change during this time in these hills and mountains, but it does mean that such variations as have occurred in temperature and precipitation have done little more than simultaneously depress and/or elevate the upper and lower tree lines. The fauna (including prehistoric man, undoubtedly) moved slowly with the flora to the extent necessary to maintain a fairly static ecologic situation.

---

[10] This North African "Neolithic wet period" is to be correlated approximately with the central part of the "Atlantic" period of some authors, the "Hypsithermal" of others. See Cooper (1958) for a summary of a confusing terminology.

We must then face the seeming enigma that cultural evolution occurred even though the Hilly Crescent of southwestern Asia passed through no such end-of-the-Pleistocene environmental crisis as was experienced by Europe, North Africa, and North America. For Europe particularly, with the correlated cultural change from Paleolithic to Mesolithic (a degree of change perhaps often over-emphasized), the idea that there was intensive post-Pleistocene human adaptation to changing environments is generally accepted, usually accompanied by the concept (even though unexpressed) of the development of greater cultural complexity ("progress") in answer to the changing conditions.

In southwestern Asia, however, we have at approximately this time the profound cultural change to incipient cultivation, if not to actual cultivation, within that millennium which includes the Karim Shahir and Zawi Chemi materials of Iraqi Kurdistan and the Natufian of Palestine. But here we cannot point to a dramatic climatic change, furnishing a stimulus for sudden cultural evolution.

Indeed, the available evidence is quite the contrary; true, the Natufian had a more complex set of tools than any of its upper Paleolithic predecessors in southwestern Asia, and the culture was marked particularly by large numbers of very small flake tools (microliths) and by the introduction of mortars and pestles for seed grinding, but the whole assemblage is in the blade-tool tradition of some 40,000 years of Levantine history and undoubtedly evolved *in situ,* with a minimum of external influence (Howell 1959).

Still eluding us are the factors that led these particular peoples to inaugurate cereal agriculture, however incipiently, and thus, by way of many changes to furnish the food base of today's technological society. But increasingly the archeologist is looking for a greater variety of data from his excavations and asking different questions of those data. Increasingly, too, natural scientists are helping him collect and interpret that evidence. It is certain that, under these circumstances, we shall be getting more and better answers to our questions concerning the many unsolved problems in the study of the relationships between climate, man, and the origins of agriculture and domestication.[11]

---

[11] This article is the third in a series appearing in *Science* on the prehistoric Near East, having been preceded by articles by R. J. Braidwood (1958) and by Hans Helbaek (1959).

CONCLUSIONS

Concerning the animal aspect of the "food-producing revolution," present evidence indicates that domestication of goats and sheep occurred in a central core area in southwestern Asia in prehistoric times, probably about the 7th millennium B.C., cattle being domesticated somewhat later, and pigs even later.

Domestication of the food-producing animals probably occurred in village-farming communities in the Hilly Flanks area of southwestern Asia; thus, cereal agriculture and the settled village are considered to antedate the domestication of all animals except the dog.

Present archeological data indicate (although many archeologists have tended to ignore or discard the evidences) that relatively intensive and successful agricultural and stock-breeding (mixed-farming) societies developed in the Zagros hills and their grassy forelands (as well as in the lower Jordan valley) prior to the appearance of the earliest societies of this type elsewhere; similar Iranian and Egyptian cultures seemingly developed later and peripherally. At least for Egypt this seeming lateness—a matter of two thousand years or more—is probably not just a reflection of accidental or incomplete sampling.

No dramatic end-of-Pleistocene environmental change has been detected for southwestern Asia; thus, the all-important "food-producing revolution" was seemingly not stimulated by the challenge of a post-Pleistocene climatic change (Reed, Braidwood 1960; Howell 1959; Picard 1943; Shalem 1953; Wright 1960).

23 ON THE DOMESTICATION OF CATTLE

Erich Isaac

THE PROBLEM of animal domestication has proved a challenging one to the disciplines concerned with the history of man's economic and social development, for animal domestication has had a revolutionary impact on man's ecumene. Culture historians, geographers, and ethnologists in particular, have been intrigued by the host of psychological and technological questions inherent in the problem of animal domestication. Necessarily, however, in view of the darkness which shrouds the original achievement, their analysis has depended upon the construction of hypotheses. To the extent that they support one another, these offer a coherent picture.[1]

The problem of animal domestication has also been of increasing concern to geneticists and zootechnologists. For not only does domestication show the enormous potential variability in a given animal, hardly to be demonstrated in the wild state, but it also poses a whole set of questions, the answers to which could provide fundamental insights into basic problems of general zoology, taxonomy, and other disciplines. Thus, for example, why are there no barriers to crossing in widely differing domestic species of animals and plants which intercross to yield fertile hybrids, whereas natural species often distinguished by only minute differences are intersterile (Müntzing 1959)? The province of zoology up to the present, in a field beset by problems of verification, has been to define and explain the changes domestication has produced in animals by comparing present-day domestic animals or wild animals raised

Reprinted from *Science*, July 20, 1962, Vol. 137, No. 3525, pp. 195–204, and by permission of the author. Copyright 1962 by the American Association for the Advancement of Science.

[1] This article grew out of research in the larger problem of the origin and distribution of the breed groups of domestic cattle. I am indebted to the Ford Foundation, which supported a year's study in Africa devoted in part to the study of African animal husbandry and breeds.

in captivity with their wild relatives, by studying the fossil record, and more recently by studying modes of inheritance.

Of all the problems of animal domestication, none has been so extensively discussed by culture historians and cultural geographers as that of the domestication of cattle. Moreover, despite great advances in the study of heredity and domestication, the major cultural theory of the domestication of cattle has not required any important revision as the result of zoological study. Zoology, indeed, has little to say about the social conditions of domestication, and for clarification of this problem we must rely on the hypotheses of the culture historians. In the absence of conclusive evidence, they have constructed their theory of the origin and process of domestication of cattle largely on the basis of deductive reasoning (Hahn 1896; 1909; Boettger 1958:35).[2]

The cultural thesis which has been most widely accepted is that which asserts that cattle, probably the first of the great herd animals to be domesticated, were originally domesticated in western Asia. The thesis further argues that the domesticators of cattle were sedentary farmers rather than nomadic hunters, that domestication was deliberately undertaken and not haphazard, and that the motive was religious.[3]

---

[2] The classical statement of the theory is that of E. Hahn (1896). The most recent statement is that of C. R. Boettger (1958).

[3] The old ethnological view, dating back to the Greek geographer Dicaearchus (about 310 B.C.), that cattle were domesticated by nomadic hunters has been shown to be untenable, notably by Georg Cancrin (1774–1845), Alexander von Humboldt (1769–1859), and Eduard Hahn (1856–1928). None of the steppes of the New World gave rise to herding complexes, although they were occupied by hunters and wild herd animals for an extensive period of historical time. The nomadic complexes of the Old World steppes were always contiguous to land areas of sedentary farmers who had the same domestic animals as the nomads. Conversely, in no steppes not adjacent to areas occupied by animal-using peasantry has pastoral nomadism developed from hunting nomadism (the steppes of Australia are an example). The South African Hottentots are only an apparent exception; they originated in the East African steppes occupied by other herding peoples. Moreover, present-day nomadic hunters do not domesticate animals; the use of animals in hunting (such as the cormorant, the hawk, the cheetah, and the mongoose) is an invention of peasant cultures, whether the animals are used as decoys, as trackers, or as agents of the kill. Primitive hunters do not even use dogs in the hunt. On the subject of the land areas occupied by peasants and nomads, see K. J. Narr (1953). On Hottentot origins, see T. F. Dreyer and H. J. D. Meiring (1937; 1952), P. V. Tobias (1955) and J. C. Trevor (1947).

ARGUMENTS FOR AGRICULTURAL ORIGIN

There are a variety of suggestive facts which, taken together, support an agricultural origin for domestication.

1. Harnessing methods used by a nomadic society are clearly modifications of harnessing methods of nearby farmers, devised for handling herd animals in the field (Hancar 1956:441).

2. All wild bovines that have been domesticated lived in the realm of the ancient peasantry of western Asia, whereas no wild bovines whose range was primarily in the realm of nomadic hunters have been domesticated, despite the fact that these animals (for example, the bison) are easily domesticated (Boettger 1958: 35).

3. Neither the European elk nor the African eland, both demonstrably easy to domesticate, has been domesticated by nomadic hunters. No deer or antelope species, with the exception of the reindeer, has been domesticated[4] and even reindeer do not belong to the oldest group of domestic animals (Herre 1955b:15–33; 1959).

4. Milking practices which have been considered peculiar to pastoral nomads, such as presenting the cow with a straw-stuffed calfskin to stimulate milk flow, blowing into the anal passage, and milking from behind, are now known to have been common in the realm of West Asian peasants and are presumably derived from that realm.[5]

5. The problem of feeding captured animals could have been solved only by an agricultural society producing a food surplus that might be used to supplement pasture.

6. The pastoral nomad's complete absorption in his herd animals, which has been cited by those who argue that domestication originated from nomadic hunting, has been shown to be irrelevant.

----

[4] Eland has recently been successfully domesticated in Southern Rhodesia by J. Posselt, near Gwanda and in the Union of South Africa. I owe my introduction to domesticated eland to Paul Donnelly, provincial agriculturist, Hulawayo, Southern Rhodesia.

[5] On African milking methods, see S. Lagercrantz (1950), T. M. Bettini (1944) and G. W. B. Huntingford (1953:21, 29). On ancient sources, see H. Plischke (1954) and J. L. Benson (1956:65, note 27).

American Indian hunters became horse-riding nomads shortly after the Spaniards introduced the horse into North America.[6]

ARGUMENTS FOR ASIAN LOCATION

The archeological evidence supports the view that cattle were first domesticated in western Asia (Hancar 1956; Dyson 1953).[7] Unfortunately, osteological study often leaves it unclear whether remains are those of domestic or those of wild animals. For this reason, an increasingly refined statistical approach has been used since the turn of the century. As Dyson (1953) observes,[8] the significance of this approach is that "an analysis of the fauna of a site over a period of time may indicate at some point a shift from reliance on small or 'wild' game to reliance on 'prodomestic' game, by which is meant potentially domesticable . . . i.e., those animals known as domestic in later periods. Subsequently a second shift, this time in the age at which prodomestic animals are killed, may be indicated. When accompanied by a constant increase of the percentage of the prodomestic group in the total these two shifts would seem to be reasonably good evidence for inferring cultural control over the animals in question."

Students using this method have found that a shift from a reliance on wild animals to a reliance on domestic animals had taken place in the Near East by the beginning of the 5th millennium B.C.[9]

----

[6] Homer Aschman (1960) has recently described the nearly complete absorption in pastoral husbandry of a society which was formerly a sedentary society of cultivation. See also K. J. Narr (1953:77–78) and J. Weisner (1959).

[7] C. A. Reed (1959). Proponents of the nomadic-hunter domestication theory have argued that the archeological record constitutes no proof, since the transient sites of early nomads are not likely to be identified. Certainly the archeological record is haphazard for vast areas, but as Narr pointed out, such evidence as there is does point to the agricultural origin of herd animal domestication.

[8] A statistical approach to determination of the presence of domestic animals has been used at least since the 1890's. See H. Krämer (1900) and J. U. Duerst (1904).

[9] Material currently being studied by Charles A. Reed at the Peabody Museum, Yale University, indicates that a shift from wild to domestic sheep occurred in northern Iraq as early as the 9th millennium B.C. Reed (1959) questioned recently the universal applicability of the statistical approach, for

In Europe, similar shifts in faunal deposits occur at least one millennium later, while in central, eastern, and southeastern Asia the shift occurs closer to two millennia after that in the Near East.

Support for the conclusions of the statistical approach lies in the discovery of evidence that it was in West Asia that cattle were first used as a source of animal power. It is here fhat sledge, wagon, yoke, and plow are first found (Hancar 1956:441, 449, 478; Bishop 1938; Childe 1954; Haudricourt 1948; Leser 1931). Wagons and representations of wagons are found at Tell Halaf, the ancient Gossan, in the extreme north of Mesopotamia and at Ur in the southeast (Childe 1951c; Watelin, Langdon 1934:30–34; Wooley 1934:64). In Mesopotamian sites the burial of wheeled vehicles is firmly associated with royal funerals by 3000 B.C. (Foltiny 1959). At Susa, in Elam, a wagon was unearthed and dated to 2500 B.C. (Childe 1951c). By the beginning of the 2nd millennium cattle and wagons are always associated on representations of the Indus culture. The sledge was apparently the earliest vehicle to be developed, and records of sledges are found in Mesopotamia in pre-Warka IV layers. By the Warka IV period (3000 to 2800 B.C.), an ideograph for "wagon" was in use; thus, the wagon must have been in use by the end of the 4th millennium. Indeed, that cattle were used in Mesopotamia for traction, at least from the late 5th millennium onward, is indicated by the symbolism of the zodiac, which can be traced that far back. The constellation Taurus was then already interpreted as a bovine harnessed to a sledge or wagon. The earliest representations of plows show a similar regional distribution. They are found in Warka IV and in Egypt from about 2700 B.C. on. Plow figurines dated 2300 to 1900 B.C. have been recovered from Vounous Bellapais on Cyprus. Sumerian seals of uncertain date also depict plows. Representations of plows are more recent than those of wagons or sledges, but to which of these vehicles animal traction was first applied is not certain (Hancar 1956:412, 436).

The oldest type of harness strongly suggests that cattle were the

---

we find similar concentrations of submature individuals in instances where the animals never became domestic. Such finds, on the other hand, may mean that an attempt at domestication was made which was ultimately found to be impractical (see Bodenheimer 1949:Vol. 1, 56–57).

first animals to be used for traction. This is the double neck yoke, with which it is possible to control and utilize the great muscular power concentrated in the cervicothoracic region in cattle. This yoke has been found in Mesopotamia, associated first with wagons and later also with plows. The earliest representations of plowing, also from Mesopotamia, show that cattle were attached either by ropes tied directly to the horns or by ropes attached to a beam lashed to the horns (Hancar 1956:412, 436). The neck yoke was not known in Egypt until about 1600 B.C., and only the more rudimentary methods of harnessing (methods also used in Mesopotamia) were employed up to that time. When, subsequently, the onager was used for traction, the cattle harness, although inappropriate, was used (Hancar 1956:431; Bishop 1938).

ONLY ONE ANCESTRAL STRAIN

Zoological study of remains has cast little light on the question of when or where cattle were first domesticated. Zoology asserts that present-day types of domestic cattle are all derived from one ancestral strain, *Bos primigenius* Bojanus, or the wild urus, an animal which survived in Europe until the late Middle Ages (the last known remaining specimen died in 1627). *Bos namadicus* Falconer et Cautley, whose relics are found in Asia, and *Bos opisthonomous* Pomel, found in North Africa, are assumed today to be the same animal. The urus formerly ranged from the Pacific through Asia and Europe and from the Eurasian tundra to the Indian Ocean and into North Africa. The vast range occupied by the urus from the Pleistocene to the 17th century A.D. could well account for minor differences in the animal, and hence the names denote little more than its geographic range (Epstein 1957:40; Herre 1949; 1958b).

Early cattle remains reveal considerable differences in size. Fossil remains indicate that the wild urus, whose presence in Europe is first proven in the Riss glacial, was a large, long-horned and powerful animal (Lehman 1949). Remains of individual urus have been found, for the whole period of early domestication, which indicate that the animal stood over 2 meters high at the withers. But alongside remains of these enormous animals, fossil remains of considerably smaller cattle have been found (Herre 1956). Similarly varied finds have been made throughout North Africa and western Asia. The diversity in size has been interpreted in more than one way. It has been asserted that the smaller animals represent a dwarf urus, that they represent a separate ancestral strain of contemporary longifrons or brachyceros types, or that the size difference is due to the great sex dimorphism of the urus, the small animals being females, as in the case of the Tibetan yak. Certainly, dwarf varieties of other wild animals are known, especially in isolated locales—for example, dwarf elephant, crocodile, hippopotamus (*Hippotamus liberiensis*), buffalo (*Syncerus caffer nanus*), and antelope (*Neotragus pygmaeus*). In all cases, however, the animals are found in relatively restricted habitats (Jeffreys 1951) and do not have the wide range that the small bovine evidently had. The view that the smaller animal is indicative of a non-urus bovine has found least favor among zoologists. It seems fairly clear that animals domesticated between, roughly, 2000 B.C. and the present, including animals domesticated in this century, are of monophyletic origin (for example, the cat, rabbit, silver fox, and nutria), and the argument goes that it is unlikely that cattle and other old domestic animals should be of polyphyletic origin (Müntzing 1959). Although this argument constitutes no proof, recent studies have confirmed the view that the small animal was probably the female of the urus, the size difference largely disappearing in domestication (La Baume 1950; von Leithner 1927).

As to the social or economic conditions under which domestication of cattle arose, zoology has not made any serious attempts to critically analyze the postulates of culture history. Some—Herre, for example —accept the conclusion of culture history (Herre 1959), while others, such as Zeuner, content themselves with a general statement concerning the inevitability of symbiotic relationships developing between animal and man, who is assumed to be "an integral part of his physico-biological environment" (Zeuner 1954:327).

In the last 50 years great strides have been made in the comparative study of domestic and wild individuals of a species, and many changes which are the result of domestication, including changes in the soft parts of the body reflected in skeletal remains, have been clearly established, so that theoretically it should be possible to distinguish between wild and domestic animals in early finds and representations.[10] But the usefulness of the criteria which have been established in the examination of skeletal remains from the dawn of domestication is severely limited in that cultural domestication must have antedated any impact upon the osteological components of the animal. The difficulty is aggravated by the fact that osteological elements to which such diagnostic criteria might be applied are unfortunately missing in most of the earliest archeological finds, and one cannot exclude the possibility that the changes occurred in wild mutants, for in fact almost all the changes that occur in domestication are known to occur (though rarely, to be sure) in wild individuals (Bohlken 1958; Röhrs 1957; Kelm 1938). Thus, for all the progress that has been made in determining characteristics which develop in domestication, these criteria are insufficient for determining whether domestication had in fact occurred in the earliest sites in which prodomestic animals are found. Indeed, as Epstein (1958) a leading student of African domestic animals, has pointed out, the study of anatomic characteristics has been inadequate even for determining the racial history of long-horn cattle.

ARGUMENTS FOR RELIGIOUS MOTIVATION

The geographer Eduard Hahn (1896), in a series of writings at the turn of the century, posed the basic questions involved in study of

---

[10] In cattle a foreshortened and widened skull, decrease in the dimension of eye and ear openings, shortness of backbone, decrease in size—in short, overall infantilism—distinguishes domestic from wild varieties. It is remarkable that many changes are common to animals of different species that have been domesticated: curly hair instead of straight; retention of baby hair; pied coats instead of monocolored; reduction in differences between male and female; variability in size between different breed groups, leading to a pronounced contrast between giants and dwarfs; extremely one-sided development of certain characteristics, such as milk production, and sometimes pathological alterations, such as the short-leggedness of Dexter cattle, in which the responsible gene is lethal when homozygous. Some changes in the soft parts are reflected in skeletal remains. Muscular development or atrophy and changes in brain volume due to environmental modifications, such as differences in food supplied by man, or due to the specialized physiological performance required of domestic animals, mark the skeleton and lead to the development of characteristic processes, crests, or ridges. The changes are comprehensively summarized by H. Nachtsheim (1949) and treated in M. Hilzheimer (1926a), C. Darwin (1868), B. Klatt (1927; 1948) and A. Müntzing (1959).

the domestication of cattle. These are the questions still raised today, and they are still answered by culture historians substantially in the way he answered them. Hahn pointed to the exceptional position of cattle among animals that have been domesticated. In the case of some animals, domestication may have come about spontaneously. For example, the ancestor of the dog as well as that of the domestic pig probably, as scavengers, sought out man, and gradually man assumed the leadership in the relationship. One may indeed ask, "Who then initially domesticated whom?" (Klatt 1948: 32). Domestication, again, may have been furthered by instincts which make us cherish our own infants and which are aroused by young mammals of somewhat similar bodily proportions. Piglets and dog pups are nursed by women in some primitive societies. But the domestication of wild cattle cannot be explained as an inadvertent process. Wild cattle presumably did not seek human company, and the initiative must have come from man (Boettger 1958:33). Furthermore, man must have had a strong motivation, since the wild urus was a powerful, intractable animal of whom it is said in Job (Job 3:9–10): "Will the urus be willing to serve thee, or abide by thy crib? Canst thou span him into a plowing harness or will he harrow the valleys after thee?"

Eduard Hahn has postulated that the motive for capturing and maintaining the urus in the captive state was to have available a supply, for sacrificial purposes, of the animal sacred to the lunar mother goddess worshipped over an immense area of the ancient world. The economic uses of the animal would then have been a by-product of a domestication religious in origin. Why the urus was selected as the animal sacred to the deity is uncertain, but this was probably because its gigantic curved horns resembled the lunar crescent. Studies in prehistoric and early historic religion have shown that the bovine was early regarded as an epiphany of the goddess or her consort and was slain in the ritual reenactment of the myth of her death. This myth involves the notion of the death and resurrection in new life of the deity. Of course, if cattle were domesticated because the horns of the urus resembled the moon's crescent, it is possible that other horned animals, such as sheep and goats, were also domesticated for their horns. Again, it is possible that an unsuccessful attempt to domesticate crescent-horned gazelles (Reed 1959; Bodenheimer 1949:Vol. 1, 56–57) was made for the same reason. On the other hand, the bison, domesticable but lacking crescent-shaped horns, was never domesticated.[11] The old 19th-century theory that animals were domesticated through being corralled for food was dismissed by Hahn as raising more problems than it answered.[12] It failed to explain the choice of certain animals and the rejection of others equally abundant, more easily captured, and more easily raised in captivity.[13] Hahn's theory, moreover, has the merit of fitting current attitudes toward cattle of many African and Asian peoples.

---

[11] It is interesting to note that B. Klatt (1948:34) suggests that the arni buffalo (*Bubalus bubalis*) was the first bovine to be domesticated in Mesopotamia, and that the reason for this was the near-perfect crescent shape of its horns, which made it a suitable epiphany of the lunar deity. The urus, according to Klatt, was probably domesticated as a substitute for the arni, which disappeared from Mesopotamia in early historic times. One might suggest that capture and subsequent sacrifice contributed to the disappearance of the arni, while the urus survived ritual domestication. It was J. U. Duerst (1899) who first pointed out that there was a relative abundance of representations of arni buffalo and a scarcity of representations of urus in early Mesopotamian art, and that subsequently representations of urus increased, whereas the arni vanished as a subject. The topic is also treated by M. Hilzheimer (1926b).

[12] J. F. Downs (1960:18–67) restated the enclosure-for-food concept. Hahn and subsequent authors were dubious about this view, at least in so far as it concerns cattle, partly because of the rejection of meat and animal products by many of great cattle-keeping cultures on religious grounds.

[13] The mummified cat interments of Egypt (at Bubastis near Zagazig and at the Alexandrinian Serapeum) are probably the best example of domestication for religious reasons. A complete record of mummified cats (the cat was the epiphany of the goddess Bast) exists, showing a sequence of development from the ancestral Libyan wild cat (*Felis catus* Libya) to the domestic cat. Domestic forms appear first in the course of the XIIth and XIIIth dynasties. Nowhere outside of Egypt were wild cats domesticated. It has been argued that the Libyan wild cat entered into some kind of symbiotic relationship with ancient grain-storing Egyptians [see K. Z. Lorenz, 1959:22–24]. The argument is not convincing, since even today there is a symbiotic relationship between the wild cat and man in southern Nubia, but despite the long history of this relationship no development toward domesticity has taken place. The rodent killer of ancient Egypt, as of the Mediterranean basin and most of Europe, was the housesnake, and the cat did not succeed in displacing it in many areas until the post-Christian era. The cat does not seem to appear in the Bible, but I think it is significant that the post-Biblical Hebrew term for cat is "the swaddled," undoubtedly referring to the tradition of mummification. Moreover, it is likely that our word *cat* ultimately derives from the old Semitic word for cotton, the material in which the mummy was swaddled. (On the cat in Egypt, see Bodenheimer 1949: Vol. 1, 1962. On the spread of the cat, see E. Werth, (1954:324). The cat is found in the Germanic culture area as sacred to Freya and has survived in folklore as the familiar of the witch.

CONJECTURES ON DOMESTICATION

Hahn's followers have conjectured that the process by which the urus was transformed into a domestic animal was as follows. The captured animals were kept in corrals, for sacrificial use. Types different from the original strains of captured urus developed, since the sacrificial stock, protected from predators and free to multiply, would have been either more inbred or more outbred than under natural conditions. As every zoo keeper knows, this factor alone would produce deviations from the wild parent stock. Obviously, animals with more infantile characteristics, such as fore-shortened heads, long legs, and relatively straight backs, as against the high withers and massive build of the wild cattle, could grow to maturity under the protective conditions of the sacred corral. Indeed, the selection of mature long-horned animals as epiphanies of the deity and thus the best animals for sacrificial purposes perhaps initially encouraged the survival of such individuals. Moreover, pied coats, which occur among many species as the result of domestication, developed in cattle as a result of breeding in confinement. Thus, the argument runs, *Bos taurus longifrons,* the first cattle to be economically exploited, emerged. On the other hand, the desirability for sacrificial purposes of the massive long-horned animal led to the perpetuation of a urus-like animal in the well-known sacred primigenius herds of the ancient Near East.

The development of infantile-appearing strains of sacred cattle more tractable than the parent stock widened the range of ritual uses to which the animal could be put. Representations indicate that the first known harnessing of cattle was to sleighs or wagons in religious processions. Mesopotamian frescoes show priests plowing and performing other tasks of husbandry. Priests are also shown performing rites involving cattle, either in the sacrifice of an animal or in processions in the temple precincts. The notion of using cattle for secular labor seems to have been derived from the use of cattle to pull sacred vehicles. Castration of the bull, which led to one of the most significant of agricultural developments, the ox, also had a religious origin. Neither the taming effect of castration nor its effect in improving the texture of meat could have been foreseen (Boettger 1958:37). Human ritual castration, a reenactment of the fate of the deity in certain cults of Near Eastern ritual mythology (Tammuz,

Attis, and so on) probably served as the model for the castration of bulls.

The earliest indication, apart from the osteological record, of the development of a domestic type distinct from the wild urus lies in representational art. From representations we find that the earliest strains of domestic cattle strongly resembled the urus. In many cases, of course, it is difficult to determine whether the animal portrayed was wild or domestic. On the famous standard of Ur, a bull is shown, and that it was probably domestic may be inferred from the ring through its nose. Certainly, some reliefs leave no doubt that the animal was domestic, as, for example, the copper relief of the temple of Mesannipadda (Boettger 1958:43), founder of the first dynasty of Ur (about 3100 B.C.), which shows priests milking. Other representations, such as the well-known victory tablet of King Narmer of Hierakonpolis (Kom el Ahmar, Egypt), undoubtedly depict wild bulls. However, much of the representational evidence, especially that which shows hunting scenes, is ambiguous. We may infer that the scenes depicting the hunt of cattle by Ashur-nasirpal (884–860 B.C.) show the hunting of wild cattle, from the existing lists of the game killed and captured. On a single hunt this king killed 50 urus bulls and captured eight live ones. From other Assyrian texts we learn that young cattle captured in the hunt were bred in captivity. In the existing lists, different symbols are used for wild and for domestic animals; the representations alone would not tell us conclusively that the animals were wild and not semi-domestic cattle kept on the open range. Even when a hunt is shown, or where the scene is that of an animal trapped in nets or trapped through the use of decoy cows, the capture that is shown may well be of animals from a semidomestic herd on the range. Boettger stresses that the capture of bulls depicted on two gold cups found in a tomb of Vaphio near Sparta and dating back to about 1500 to 1250 B.C. is very probably a capture not of wild bulls, as was previously supposed, but of bulls kept in a state of semi-domestication. Again, the long-horned massive cattle depicted in the bull-game scenes of Cretan frescoes probably are semidomestic animals, for they are pied. Indeed, on a picture of late Minoan times a cow of the same massive configuration is shown being milked in the old (and dangerous) Mesopotamian fashion—through her hind legs. This method is employed even today in Africa (Boettger 1958:35, 47, 49).

There is still another reason why one cannot rely completely on representational art as a source of information: styles in art may have persisted when they ceased to convey an accurate picture of the cattle of the period. The maintenance of conventions characterizes religious art in particular. In Austrian churches, until recent times, peasants offered little statuettes of long-horned cattle, although such cattle had been unknown in Austria for many centuries (Antonius 1922:184). Herre's comparative study of skeletal remains, and of pictures of domestic animals contemporary with the remains, from medieval Hamburg revealed that very different conclusions would be drawn from the study of either alone (Herre 1950b). That Egyptian representational art was characterized by the same maintenance of artistic conventions has been pointed out by Boessneck (Boessneck 1953).

Although there are thus difficulties in judging from early representational art what kind of cattle were in fact used, it is possible to distinguish domestic cattle in later representations, when the specifically domestic characteristics are stressed—in representations of cattle with pied coats or extremely large udders, or of shorthorned or polled cattle (*Bos taurus akeratos*) such as we find represented on the mural relief of King Ti and Queen Neferhotpes at Saqqara (25th century B.C.).

PRIMIGENIUS AND LONGIFRONS EMERGE

From the wild urus two races of domestic cattle emerged early. The heavy horns of the urus caused the development of wide and flat parietal bones, so that the top of the skull, when the animal is seen head on, appears almost horizontal. Domestic cattle which retained a urus conformation of skull and body are called "primigenius" cattle, descendants of *Bos taurus primigenius*, the earliest domestic cattle. When shorter-horned domestic cattle developed, the frontal and parietal bones, released from the excessive weight of horns, became domed; this is, of course, most evident in polled animals. This type of animal, because of its characteristic long and narrow face and upward convex parietals, is called *Bos taurus longifrons*.[14]

---

[14] Fundamental studies on horn and skull conformation were made by J. U. Duerst (1926). Duerst's later views, especially those on the parietal angle, are quoted by H. Epstein (1958).

Longifrons cattle, differing markedly from primigenius cattle, like the latter first appear in Mesopotamia. While it is difficult, in the early Mesopotamian representations, to distinguish between urus and primigenius cattle, in the case of longifrons it is clear that a domestic type is represented. Generally, moreover, longifrons cattle are depicted in association with agricultural performances or symbols. Probably the first representation of longifrons is on a bowl of the Jemdet Nasr period, and subsequently longifrons cattle are depicted more and more often, although never so frequently as primigenius types. Boettger has proposed that the distinction between longifrons and primigenius was one between an economically exploited breed and a strain maintained primarily for ritual purposes. The distribution of longifrons cattle outside the Near East is taken by Boettger to indicate that longifrons was spread intentionally and did not originate independently in a number of places. In spite of the fact that longifrons cattle appear much later than primigenius in Mesopotamia, their docility, their manageability, and their overall usefulness account, according to Boettger, for their having reached both the Atlantic and the Pacific peripheries of the Old World continents before primigenius cattle did (Boettger 1958:52).

With the spread of longifrons into the European periphery, a number of dwarf varieties appeared, constituting, in the view of the culture historian, a deterioration of the introduced strain. This deterioration may have been initially the result of inexperience in handling, and of inadequate feeding before a proper balance of feed crops was grown or before pasture systems were developed. Dwarf longifrons cattle, formerly called *Bos taurus brachyceros,* occur in the Swiss Neolithic, and in the Balkans and Caucasus in the 2nd millennium B.C. Certain present-day cattle (still kept under relatively poor conditions of husbandry) are counted among the modern representatives of this type—for example, the Polish Maydan and Hutsul cattle, Polesian and Polish Red, Spanish Mountain, Italian Piedmont, Brown Mountain (Austria), and Bulgarian Rhodope cattle. Eventually, animals larger than longifrons or its dwarf varieties developed. Crosses with wild cattle undoubtedly occurred, and the products of such crosses resembled in conformation the primigenius types of West Asia. These were favored in some areas and through selective breeding gave rise to *Bos taurus frontosus,* a broad-faced type which is represented today by some economically very important European breeds such as the Dutch

Friesian and the Meuse-Rhine-Yssel, the Swiss Fribourg and Simmentaler, the German Yellow Hill, and the Austrian Pinzgau. Elsewhere, cattle with a dwarfed primigenius conformation but a short skull developed—*Bos taurus brachycephalus* Wilkens, whose modern representatives include the French Tarentaise, the Swiss Hérèns, and the Austrian Tux-Zillertal.[15]

THESIS CONSISTENT WITH ZOOLOGY

There is no fundamental disagreement between zoology and culture history on the question of how domestic breeds of cattle developed, even though the notion of a religious motive is not germane to zoological analysis. Of course, to find out if there was even a possibility that the urus voluntarily joined human society, zoologists would have to recreate the animal by back-crossing. Apparently successful attempts to recreate the urus have been made. Both H. Heck, at the Hellabrunn Zoo of Munich, and his brother L. Heck, at the Berlin Zoo, were able from different breeding stock to create bovines which bore a remarkable resemblance to medieval representations of the urus. Unfortunately, however, we have no precise knowledge of the physiology and psychology of the urus, so that even if one produced an animal that looked exactly like the urus (and medieval representations are generally stylized), it would not be possible to know whether the animal behaved like the urus.[16]

The zoologist, like the culture historian, asserts that new strains would almost necessarily appear as a result of the accidental capture of foundation stock from different breeding groups and the establishment of larger breeding units. Even under wild conditions, where there are animals heterozygous for numerous genes, segregation of deviating individuals occurs constantly. But although as a rule deviant individuals are eliminated by natural selection, the protection against predators afforded by the simplest enclosure would suffice to allow deviating animals to develop and reproduce. Polled cattle, whose senses are poorly developed in comparison to those of wild individuals and who lack a primary defense, would survive.

---

[15] Schmid (1942: Vol. 1). Names of breeds and breed groups are given according to I. L. Mason (1951).

[16] H. Heck (1951); Heck's popular claims have been severely criticized by O. Koehler and by W. Herre.

Even in the case of nonsocial animals, such as cats, living in a human settlement, the increase in population density has the effect of increasing variability (Herre 1959).

The history of the domestic rabbit is known with some completeness and shows the same pattern of changes taking place under conditions of enclosure. In fact, the rabbit is taken by students of domestication to illustrate the process of change in a wild animal under the influence of domestication (Müntzing 1959). The domestic rabbit is derived from wild rabbits, imported from Spain during the period of the Roman Empire, which were enclosed in leporaries where they lived as in the wild but were accessible to hunting parties. From old engravings it is apparent that hunting rabbits in leporaries was held to be a suitable and safe pastime for ladies. Not until the 17th century had the rabbit changed by mutation from wildness to tameness and assumed the characteristics of the present-day rabbit. That the urus differentiated under conditions of domestication into primigenius and longifrons is thus not unlikely, even if the degree of control and selection was less than the thesis of religious motivation assumes.

WHAT WAS TRANSMITTED—ANIMAL OR IDEA?

Although the culture historian assumes that the small cattle which are the first to appear in Old World strata outside West Asia were longifrons which West Asian migrants brought with them, all that zoology can state with certainty is that a pronounced diminution in size differentiates this animal from the urus; such diminution could, of course, come though local domestication. In fact, in Europe a steady diminution in size continued until the Middle Ages. While the urus had stood at more than 2 meters at the withers, the average height at the withers in the Iron Age is given by Herre as 1.10 meters, and the average in the Middle Ages, as 1 meter or less. Herre asserts that domestication must have been local, since the earliest domestic cattle in Europe, occurring long after domestic characteristics were well developed in Near Eastern cattle, were transitional forms with respect to the local representatives of the urus (Herre 1956). Herre does not deny that domestication first occurred in the Near East but asserts that the technique and idea of domestication were transmitted rather than actual domestic animals. He supports his view with reference to "substitute" domestications (*"Erastzhaustieren"*)—animals domesticated outside the range of the wild form of an already domesticated animal, such as the ass (*Asinus africanus* Fitzinger 1857) in place of the horse (*Equus cab. przewalski* Poliakov 1881), the yak (*Bos Poëphagus grunniens* Przewalski 1883) in place of the urus, and so on (Herre 1959).

There are additional weighty arguments put forth in support of the thesis of local domestication of the urus in disparate areas. The general average decline in size of the early European cattle was accompanied, as the osteological record shows, by a great over-all variability in size and conformation. Such remarkable multiplication in conformational types and increase in the growth range of adult animals follows, even today, upon the domestication of wild animals, as practical work with domestic fur-producing animals has shown. Thus, the silver and blue fox, themselves mutants of the red fox, have in a short time given rise to a series of other types: platinum, white-faced, golden platinum, pearl, perlatina, glacier blue, Washington platina, radium, and pastel fox (Müntzing 1959). Similar results have been achieved with mink and nutria. The great variability observed in early European domestic cattle remains a strong argument against the thesis of the introduction of a developed domestic strain.

Should, then, the thesis of the introduction of longifrons into Europe be thrown out? Were it not for the appearance simultaneously with domestic cattle of tools, pottery, and art stylistically related to and often demonstrably imported from the prehistoric and early historic Near East, the thesis of actual introduction of the earliest domestic cattle would undoubtedly receive even less attention than it does in current treatment of the racial history of European cattle. And, of course, even where contact, trade, and migrations have occurred, actual movement of cattle cannot be proven. Nonetheless, there remains much to support the introduction thesis. Ersatz domestication, while it has occurred in many instances, has taken place in areas where the domestic animal cannot be introduced because of conditions of excessive physiological strain and stress, local bacterial faunas, dangers of worm infestation, and so on. Such conditions make it economically unfeasible to introduce many of the classical domestic animals into tropical or high-altitude areas even today, but there was never any bar to the introduction of cattle into Europe. Moreover, although local wild strains undoubtedly contributed to the formation of the earliest European domestic cattle, accounting for the "dwarf urus" which appears rather abruptly in stratigraphic layers (Herre 1949), unless domestic cattle were brought into Europe and crossed with the local urus, the difficulty of domestication would have been scarcely less in Europe than it had been millennia previously in West Asia. It is conceivable, in fact, that the European wild urus played a smaller part in the formation of frontosus and primigenius types than was formerly assumed. Certainly in historic times efforts have always been made to prevent cross breeding between the urus and domestic cattle so as not to increase the wildness of the domestic races (Boettger 1958:48). Perhaps the locally occurring European primigenius and frontosus races are, after all, products of selection from the early introduced longifrons, and from the subsequently introduced West Asian or Mediterranean primigenius cattle.

Of interest in this connection is the fact, pointed out by Nobis, that in regions dominated by the Roman camps of the European *limes,* primigenius or "pseudoprimigenius" cattle are found (Nobis 1955). These may be introductions from the Mediterranean world, or products of the application to local stock of the more expert Roman husbandry, or the result of both. There was no lasting improvement in the near-dwarfed local cattle of the surrounding areas, and after Roman times pseudoprimigenius all but vanishes from the osteological record of these areas. It is tempting to draw an analogy with the more recent history of cattle in southern and central Africa. After the disastrous rinderpest epidemic of 1896, there were massive introductions of European stock (Nobbs 1927), but in spite of large-scale cross-breeding, the contribution of the European stock to the conformational characteristics and productive capacity of native cattle was all but negligible. Under the rigorous conditions of the African veld, natural selection operated in favor of animals of overall ruggedness rather than of animals of indifferent stamina though of higher potential as a source of meat and milk.[17]

---

[17] I am greatly indebted to D. A. Robinson, director of the Department of Native Agriculture, Southern Rhodesia, and to the scientific personnel of that department's animal husbandry research centers. I also wish to express my gratitude to the many individuals who were associated with Institut National pour l'Etude Agronomique du Congo Belge (INEAC) and Institut pour la Recherche Scientifique en Afrique Centrale (IRSAC) centers at Luiro, Bukavu, and Nioka in the Belgian Congo, and with breeding centers at Entebbe in Uganda; at Sangalo, Maseno, Kibigori, Kissii, and Kabinga in Kenya; and at West Kilimanjaro and Arusha in Tanganyika. I wish to express my special thanks to the department of agriculture, University College of Rhodesia and Nyasaland, for its hospitality, especially to its chairman, Prof. C. Davis, and to Dr. John Oliver, senior lecturer in animal husbandry.

EXPLANATION OF VARIABILITY

Great variability in size and even in conformation of a herd may be taken to imply a low level of animal-husbandry skill and does not necessarily mean that domestication has been recent. African domestic cattle today are almost entirely derived from repeated introduction of West Asian domestic races (Nobbs 1927; Curson, Thornton 1936; J. H. R. Bisschop 1937; Curson, Epstein 1934; H. Epstein 1933; 1934; 1955; Faulkner, Epstein 1957). Yet among Sanga cattle, the most important breed type in central and southern Africa and represented as far west as Nigeria and as far north as the Sudan, the variation in conformation, in animal size, and in horn size is enormous. Often gigantic-horned, long-horned, short-horned, and polled animals occur in a single herd (Epstein 1957; 1958). Some Sanga, such as the Shona or Karanga cattle of Southern Rhodesia, have truly dwarfed and short-horned representatives,[18] whereas another Sanga, Bechuana cattle, includes gigantic specimens[19] whose enormous horns approach and even exceed in length those of Indian Pliocene ancestors of the urus.[20] The fact is that where, for whatever reason, the herder selected for small size, a small Sanga appeared. Similarly, megaloceratic horns in African Sanga herds persist only because of continued careful selection for gigantic horns. Where there is no selection for special points, the Sanga herds are made up of generally small, although widely divergent, individuals. This state of affairs obviously does not prove that the Sanga was locally domesticated. Thus, perhaps the dwarfing and variability of European neolithic cattle indicates that an introduced race—longifrons—deteriorated under conditions where a desire for a large number of animals outweighed considera-

---

[18] Dwarfed Sanga, *Tumembe mapako*, are by now probably extinct in Southern Rhodesia. In 1946 E. A. B. McLeod, a Rhodesian rancher, tried to obtain government assistance in collecting a remnant of the dwarfed animals, but failed.

[19] Bechuana cattle from the Lake Ngami area stood nearly 6 feet high at the withers. The Africana Museum, Johannesburg, possesses a skull whose horns measure 8 feet 8 inches from tip to tip. The total length along the contour of the horns and across the forehead is 13 feet 7 inches.

[20] These ancestors were *Bos planifrons* Rütim. and B. *acutifrons* Lydekker. Descriptions of them appear in Rütimeyer (1877).

tions of carrying capacity and productive potential of the individual animal—as it so often does in African husbandry.

It is noteworthy that recent and more sophisticated methods of investigation have tended to support the thesis that cattle were introduced into Europe from western Asia. Electrophoretic studies of the distribution and mode of inheritance of different types of hemoglobin in cattle (Bangham 1957) support the thesis that Jersey (Boston 1954:19–42) (a brachycephalus type) as well as Guernsey and South Devon cattle (the former brachyceros, the latter brachycephalus) had an African, and ultimately a Mesopotamian, origin. The superior performance of Devon and Jersey cattle at high temperatures, demonstrated in studies at agricultural research centers in Africa, as well as the exceptionally high butter-fat content of milk from these breeds, characteristic also of milk from cattle native to tropical regions, tends to reinforce the argument that these types had a western Asian origin.

CONCLUSION

The thesis of Eduard Hahn and of those who have followed his lead has stood up well in the light of progress made in zootechnology, animal psychology, the comparative anatomy of domestic and wild species, and the study of non-European native cattle. On the other hand, Hahn's hypothesis can in no way be said to have stimulated work in the zoology of domestic species, although such work has gone far to confirm its plausibility. But if Hahn's thesis has had no particular bearing on the zoological study of domestication, in what can its value be said to lie? Like all cultural theses, it provides an insight into historical processes. Specifically, Hahn's thesis also constituted a protest against the materialistic assumptions underlying 19th-century German social and economic theories. Hahn affirmed the importance of irrational forces in major technological advances of mankind. His thesis, moreover, has stood up better than most of the broad and more spectacular cultural theses of our day, where close examination by experts in any specific and relevant area has led to steady erosion of the overarching argument. In the study of domestication the scientist and the cultural historian join forces, each playing a role which the other discipline, by its very nature, cannot fill.

24 DOMESTICATION OF CORN

Paul C. Mangelsdorf, Richard S. MacNeish, Walton C. Galinat

THE PROBLEM of the origin of corn has intrigued botanists and other students of plants for more than four centuries. The plant was unknown in any part of the Old World before 1492, while in the New World it was the basic food plant of all pre-Columbian advanced cultures and civilizations, including the Inca of South America and the Maya and Aztec of Middle America (Mangelsdorf, Reeves 1939). Although these facts point strongly to its American origin, some writers have continued to argue eloquently for an Old World origin. A living wild form of corn has never been discovered, despite the extensive searches for it which have been carried on in various parts of the hemisphere. The absence of a wild form has been conducive to speculation—sometimes reaching the point of acrimonious debate—about its probable nature. There has, however, been general agreement that modern corn is unique among the major cereals in its grain-bearing inflorescence (the ear), which is completely enclosed in modified leaf sheaths (the husks), the plant being thus rendered incapable of dispersing its seeds. How, then, did wild corn, which to survive in nature must have had a means of dispersal, differ from modern cultivated corn? Where did it grow? How did it evolve under domestication? These are some of the questions that comprise the corn problem.

Close collaboration in recent years between archeologists and botanists has furnished at least partial answers to all of these questions, and has also contributed to solving the problem of the beginning of agriculture in America and the rise of prehistoric cultures and civilizations.

The first substantial contribution of archeology to the solution

Reprinted from *Science*, February 7, 1964, Vol. 143, No. 3606, pp. 538–45, and by permission of the authors. Copyright 1964 by the American Association for the Advancement of Science.

of the corn problem was the finding of prehistoric vegetal material in Bat Cave in New Mexico, excavated by Herbert Dick, then a graduate student in the Peabody Museum of Harvard University, in two expeditions, in 1948 and 1950. Accumulated trash, garbage, and excrement in this cave contained cobs and other parts of corn at all levels, and these cobs and parts showed a distinct evolutionary sequence from the lower to the upper levels (Mangelsdorf, Smith 1949). At the bottom of the refuse, which was some 2 meters deep, Dick found tiny cobs, 2 to 3 centimeters long, which were dated by radiocarbon determinations of associated charcoal at about 3600 B.C. Anatomical studies of these cobs led to the conclusion that the early Bat Cave corn was both a popcorn (a type with small, hard kernels capable of exploding when exposed to heat) and a pod form (a type with kernels partly enclosed by floral bracts which botanists call glumes and the layman knows a chaff) (Mangelsdorf 1958c).

Because the Bat Cave corn was both a popcorn and a pod corn, Mangelsdorf undertook to produce a genetic reconstruction of the ancestral form of corn by crossing pod corn and popcorn and backcrossing the hybrid repeatedly to popcorn. The final product of this breeding was a pod-popcorn bearing small kernels enclosed in glumes on ears arising from the upper joints of the stalks (Mangelsdorf 1958c). This reconstructed ancestral form had two means of dispersal: seeds borne on the fragile branches of the tassel and seeds on ears at high positions on the stalk which at maturity were not completely enclosed by husks. The reconstructed ancestral form served another useful purpose in showing the archeologist approximately what to look for in seeking prehistoric wild corn.

PREHISTORIC CORN IN NORTHERN MEXICO

A second important collection of prehistoric maize came from La Perra Cave in Tamaulipas in northeastern Mexico, excavated in 1949 by MacNeish, who was then associated with the National Museum of Canada. The specimens from this cave, like those from Bat Cave, showed a distinct evolutionary sequence from the lower to the higher levels of the accumulated refuse (Mangelsdorf, MacNeish, Galinat 1956). The earliest corn, dated 2500 B.C. by radiocarbon determination of associated wood and leaves, was identified as an early form of a still-existing race, Nal-Tel, which Wellhausen *et al.* (1952), who have classified the present-day maize of Mexico, described as one of the four Ancient Indigenous races of Mexico. These earliest cobs were somewhat larger than the earliest cobs from Bat Cave and so gave some support to the assumption that the two radiocarbon dates involved, 3600 and 2500 B.C., might be relatively if not absolutely correct.

While excavating La Perra Cave, which is located in eastern Tamaulipas, MacNeish also made some preliminary soundings in several caves in southwestern Tamaulipas which persuaded him that still earlier corn, perhaps even prehistoric wild corn, might be found in the lower levels of the refuse of these caves. Accordingly in 1954, with the assistance of David Kelley, then a graduate student in anthropology at Harvard, he excavated two caves, Romero's Cave and Valenzuela's Cave, in Inferniello Canyon. The earliest corn from these caves proved, disappointingly, to be not earlier than the La Perra corn but slightly later, about 2200 B.C. (MacNeish 1958). It was, however, of a race different from the La Perra corn and showed some resemblance to the Bat Cave corn.

Of even greater interest was the discovery in Romero's Cave of a few specimens of teosinte, the closest relative of corn. Well-preserved specimens of the fruits of this plant occurred in a level dated 1400 to 400 B.C. Fragments identified as teosinte occurred in feces in a level dated 1800 to 1400 B.C. Since teosinte has not been found growing in Tamaulipas in modern times, it may be assumed either that its range is more restricted today than it was several thousand years ago or that teosinte was planted with corn as a method of improving it, a practice reported by Lumholtz (1902) to be characteristic of certain Indians of the western part of Mexico.

While the excavations in Tamaulipas were in progress, another series of excavations was being made in caves in the states of Chihuahua and Sonora in northwestern Mexico by Robert H. Lister of the University of Colorado. In one of these caves, Swallow Cave, Lister uncovered at the lowest levels several tiny cobs similar in shape and size to the Bat Cave cobs, though slightly larger. Since it seemed inadvisable to sacrifice these to obtain radiocarbon determinations, they have not been dated. However, the fact that they occurred at a considerable depth (about 2 meters below the surface) and in a preceramic context suggests a substantial age. These earliest Swallow Cave cobs were identified as prototypes of Chapalote (Mangelsdorf, Lister 1956), another of the Ancient

Indigenous and still-existing races of corn of Mexico described by Wellhausen *et al.* (1952).

During this same period another important discovery was made when Barghoorn *et al.* (1954) identified as pollen grains of maize some fossil pollen isolated from a drill core taken at a depth of more than 70 meters below the present site of Mexico City. This pollen was assigned to the last interglacial period now estimated by geologists to have occurred about 80,000 years ago. Since this period antedates the arrival of man on this continent, the pollen was thought to be that of a wild maize which once grew in the Valley of Mexico and has since become extinct. Other pollen, considered to be that of cultivated corn, occurred abundantly in the upper levels—above 6 meters. The earliest of these upper-level pollen grains are assigned to the later part of the post-glacial optimum and are therefore no earlier than the earliest corn from Tamaulipas or New Mexico. Although the criteria used in identifying the fossil pollen grains have been questioned (Kurtz *et al.* 1960), more recent studies made by Barghoorn and his associates (1954) using phase microscopy, have revealed features in which the pollen grains of corn and its relatives differ conspicuously and have confirmed the earlier identifications. There now seems to be no doubt that at least some of the fossil pollen grains were those of corn. Thus, this fossil pollen settles two important questions: it shows that corn is an American plant and that the ancestor of cultivated corn is corn and not one of corn's relatives, teosinte or *Tripsacum*.

On the basis of his excavations in Tamaulipas and the discovery of fossil corn pollen in the Valley of Mexico, MacNeish (1958) concluded that the evidence for the earliest domestication of maize and the beginnings of agriculture in America must be sought further south. A reconnaissance made in Honduras and Guatemala in 1958 yielded no results of promise. Excavations in 1959 of Santa Maria Cave in Chiapas in southern Mexico uncovered corn and other vegetal material, including pollen, but none older than that which had already been found further north. Turning northward again, MacNeish made a reconnaissance of sites in Oaxaca and Puebla which led to the conclusion that the Tehuacán Valley of southern Puebla and northern Oaxaca might, because of its dry climate and ever-flowing springs, offer the most promising site so far discovered for seeking prehistoric wild corn and the beginning of agriculture. A preliminary sounding in 1960, in one of the numerous caves in the cliffs surrounding the Valley, uncovered cobs which were thought to be those of wild corn. Full-scale excavations conducted the following season confirmed this.

The physical features of the Valley of Tehuacán are described by MacNeish (1964a) which also describes the culture phases that have been recognized. At first glance this Valley, with its semiarid climate and its predominantly xerophytic, drought-resisting vegetation, may not seem to be a suitable habitat for wild corn, and in earlier speculation about where wild corn might have grown we did not associate it with such plants as cacti and thorny leguminous shrubs (Mangelsdorf, Reeves 1939). Closer examination, however, suggests that the habitat furnished by this arid valley may, in fact, have been almost ideal for wild corn. The average annual rainfall at the center of the valley is low (approximately 500 millimeters a year) and becomes somewhat higher both south and north of the center. About 90 percent of the annual rain usually falls during the growing season, from April through October.

The other months are quite dry—in midwinter the Valley is virtually a desert—and comprise a period during which the seeds of wild maize and other annual plants could have lain dormant, ready to sprout with the beginning of the summer rains and never in danger of germinating prematurely and then succumbing to the vicissitudes of winter. Thus, although the perennial vegetation of this Valley, which year after year must survive the dry winter months, is necessarily xerophytic, the annual vegetation (and wild maize would have been an annual) need not be especially drought-resistant. Modern maize is not notable for its drought-resistance and probably its wild prototype was not either.

The corn uncovered by MacNeish (1958) and his associates in their excavations of the caves in Tehuacán Valley is, from several standpoints, the most interesting and significant prehistoric maize so far discovered.[1] (i) It includes the oldest well-preserved cobs yet available for botanical analysis. (ii) The oldest cobs are probably those of wild maize. (iii) This maize appears to be the progenitor of two of the previously recognized Ancient Indigenous races of Mexico, Nal-Tel and Chapalote, of which prehistoric prototypes

[1] The archeological excavations were supported by a grant from the National Science Foundation; the botanical studies, by a grant from the Rockefeller Foundation. Both grants are acknowledged with appreciation and thanks.

had already been found in La Perra and Swallow caves, respectively. (iv) The collections portray a well-defined evolutionary sequence.

PREHISTORIC CORN FROM FIVE CAVES

Before considering the corn itself, we should say a word about the caves in which the remains of maize were uncovered. Five major caves which were excavated—Coxcatlan, Purron, San Marcos, Tecorral, and El Riego—yielded maize in archeological levels. The caves were situated in three or four different environments, which might have had considerable bearing upon the possibility of wild corn's growing nearby and which might have affected the practice of agriculture.

Coxcatlan Cave, first found in 1960, was one of the richest in vegetal remains. Excavations revealed 28 superimposed floors or occupational levels covering two long unbroken periods—from 10,000 to 2300 B.C. and from 900 B.C. to A.D. 1500. Fourteen of the upper floors, those from 5200 to 2300 B.C. and from 900 B.C. to A.D. 1500, contained well-preserved corn cobs. The cave, a long narrow rock shelter, is situated in the southeastern part of the Valley in one of the canyons flanking the Sierra Madre mountain range. The shelter faces north and looks out on a broad alluvial plain covered with grasses, mesquite, other leguminous shrubs, and cacti. Supplementing the meager annual rainfall is some water drainage from the nearby mountain slopes and this would have made it possible for wild or cultivated corn to grow during the wet season. In other seasons of the year irrigation would have been necessary for corn culture.

A few miles south of Coxcatlan, in the same set of canyons, is Purron Cave. This is a somewhat smaller rock shelter but it contains a long continuous occupation (25 floors) from about 7000 B.C. to A.D. 500. It is archeologically much poorer than Coxcatlan and only the top 12 floors (from 2300 B.C. to A.D. 500) contained preserved remains of food plants.

El Riego Cave, situated in the north end of the Valley only a mile north of the modern town of Tehuacán, is a deep recess which contained an abundance of preserved specimens. Its five archeological zones, however, do not extend far back in time and were deposited between 200 B.C. and A.D. 1500. The cave is in the travertine face of a cliff and faces south. Under these cliffs and flowing out from them are the famous Tehuacán mineral springs, and the soils in front of the cave are fertile and well watered. Because of the fertile soils and the abundant water there is an oasis-like vegetation around the cave. This is an excellent area for agriculture and it may even have originally supported a vegetation too lush for wild corn to compete with.

The last two caves, San Marcos and Tecorral, occur in a steep canyon in the west side of the Valley. They are small shelters situated side by side, facing east. Tecorral contained three floors and only the top floor (about A.D. 1300) had a few corn cobs. San Marcos, however, was very different; although small, it yielded five superimposed floors with an abundance of preserved maize and other remains. The top four floors have been dated, by the carbon-14 method, at about 4400 B.C., 3300 B.C., 1100 B.C., and A.D. 300, respectively, while the earliest one is estimated to have been laid down about 5200 B.C. The shelters look out over broad alluvial terraces covered by grass and small thorny trees. Plants collected from this canyon bottom reveal a number of endemics—species not found elsewhere in the Valley. The surrounding travertine-covered canyon walls and hilltops, however, have a vegetation like that of the Sonoran Desert. The area receives water in the rainy season and much of it floods the lower terraces. All occupations found in the caves were from the rainy seasons. Agriculture would have been possible in the rainy season with or without irrigation. The alluvial terraces would have furnished an almost ideal habitat for wild corn.

In all, 23,607 specimens of maize were found in the five caves; 12,857 of these, or more than half, are whole or almost intact cobs. There are, in addition to the intact cobs, 3273 identified cob fragments and 3880 unidentified cob fragments. Among the remaining specimens are all parts of the corn plant: 28 roots, 513 pieces of stalks, 462 leaf sheaths, 293 leaves, 962 husks, 12 prophylls, 127 shanks, 384 tassel fragments, 47 husk systems, 6 midribs, and 600 kernels. There are also numerous quids, representing 64 chewed stalks and 99 chewed husks.

The prehistoric cobs from the five caves can be assigned to six major and five minor categories. The frequency polygons of Fig. 1 show graphically the time of first appearance of a type of corn, the corresponding cultural periods, and the relative prominence (in terms of percentages) of the number of identified cobs for each of

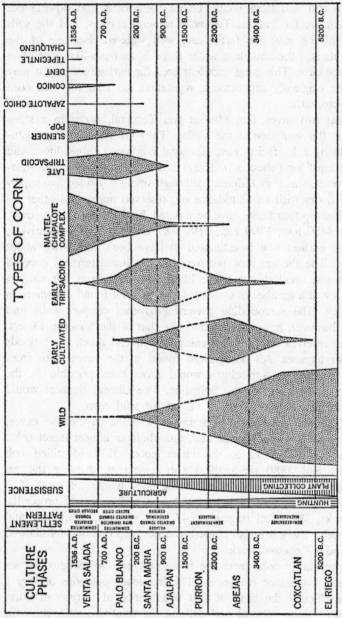

FIGURE 1 Frequency polygons, in terms of percentages of number of cobs identified, showing changes in the types of corn in the Valley of Tehuacán from 5200 B.C. to A.D. 1536. Specimens of prehistoric corn were almost totally lacking for the Purron culture phase, which is recognized by other types of artifacts.

these categories. The polygons show patterns similar to those exhibited by artifacts, and for good reason—man's cultivars are artifacts as surely as are his weapon points or pottery. A brief description of the types of maize represented by these categories follows.

PREHISTORIC WILD MAIZE

The earliest cobs from the El Riego and Coxcatlan cultural phase, dated 5200–3400 B.C., are regarded as being those of wild corn for six reasons. (i) They are remarkably uniform in size and other characteristics and in this respect resemble most wild species. (ii) The cobs have fragile rachises as do many wild grasses; these provide a means of dispersal which modern corn lacks. (iii) The glumes are relatively long in relation to other structures and must have partially enclosed the kernels as they do in other wild grasses. (iv) There are sites in the Valley, such as the alluvial terraces below San Marcos Cave, which are well adapted to the growth of annual grasses, including corn, and which the competing cacti and leguminous shrubs appear to shun. (v) There is no evidence from other plant species that agriculture had yet become well established in this valley, at least in the El Riego phase or the earlier part of the Coxcatlan phase. (vi) The predominating maize from the following phase, Abejas, in which agriculture definitely was well established, is larger and more variable than the earliest corn.

This combination of circumstances leads to the conclusion—an almost inescapable one—that the earliest prehistoric corn from the Tehuacán caves is wild corn. We shall assume here that it is.

The intact cobs of the wild corn vary in length from 19 to 25 millimeters. The number of kernel rows is usually eight but a few cobs with four rows were found. None of the earliest cobs have kernels, but the number of kernels which they once bore can be determined by counting the number of functional spikelets. These vary from 36 to 72 per cob. The average number of kernels borne by the earliest intact cobs of wild corn from San Marcos Cave was 55.

The glumes of the spikelets are relatively long in relation to other structures and are soft, fleshy, and glabrous (lacking in hairs). On some cobs the glumes are rumpled, probably as a result of the forcible removal of the kernels. The cobs have the general aspect of a weak form of pod corn.

The spikelets are uniformly paired and are attached to a slender, soft, and somewhat fragile stem (technically known as a rachis) in which the cupules, or depressions in the rachis, are shallow and almost glabrous, bearing only sparse, short hairs.

Most of the wild-type cobs were apparently once bisexual, bearing pistillate (female) spikelets in the lower regions and staminate (male) spikelets above. Of 15 apparently intact cobs from San Marcos Cave, ten had stumps at the tip where a staminate spike had presumably been broken off. In this respect the Tehuacán wild maize resembles corn's wild relative, *Tripsacum,* which regularly bears pistillate spikelets below and staminate spikelets above on the same inflorescences.

The uniformly paired spikelets and relatively soft tissues of the rachis and glumes provide further proof, in addition to that furnished by the fossil pollen of the Valley of Mexico, that the wild ancestor of cultivated corn was corn and not one of its relatives, teosinte or *Tripsacum.*

The wild maize declined somewhat in prominence in the Abejas phase, where it comprises 47 percent of the cobs. It persisted, however, as a minor element of the corn complex until the middle of the Palo Blanco phase, dated at about A.D. 250.

What caused the wild corn finally to become extinct? We have for some years assumed that two principal factors may have been involved in the extinction of corn's ancestor. (i) The sites where wild corn grew in nature might well be among those chosen by man for his earliest cultivation. (ii) Wild corn growing in sites not appropriate for cultivation by hybridizing with cultivated corn, after the latter had lost some of its essential wild characteristics, would become less able to survive in the wild. Of these two causes of extinction the second may have been the more important. Corn is a wind-pollinated plant and its pollen can be carried many miles by the wind. It is virtually inevitable that any maize growing wild in the Valley would have hybridized at times with the cultivated maize in nearby fields, which was producing pollen in profusion. Repeated contamination of the wild corn by cultivated corn could eventually have genetically "swamped" the former out of existence.

There is now good archeological evidence in Tehuacán to suggest that both of these assumed causes of extinction were indeed operative. The alluvial terraces below San Marcos Cave, where wild corn may once have grown, now reveal the remains of a fairly elaborate system of irrigation, indicating that the natural habitat of wild corn was replaced by cultivated fields. Abundant evidence of hybridization between wild and cultivated corn is found in the prehistoric cobs. We have classified 252 cobs as possible first-generation hybrids of wild corn with various cultivated types and 464 cobs as backcrosses of first-generation hybrids to the wild corn.

Is there a possibility that wild corn may still be found in some remote and inaccessible locality in Mexico or elsewhere? We suspect not. Whatever wild corn may have persisted until the 16th century was almost certainly rapidly extinguished after the arrival of the European colonists with their numerous types of grazing animals: horses, burros, cows, sheep, and—worst of all—the omnivorous and voracious goats. To all of these animals young corn plants are a palatable fodder, one that is to be preferred to almost any other grass.

WILD CORN RECONSTRUCTED

A well-preserved early cob, an intact husk system consisting of an inner and outer husk from the Abejas phase in the San Marcos Cave, and a piece of staminate spike from the Ajalpan phase of the same cave provide the materials for a reconstruction of the Tehuacán wild corn. An ear with only two husks was probably borne high on the stalk and its husks opened at maturity, permitting dispersal of the seeds. Other early specimens show that the plants lacked secondary stalks, technically known as tillers; the leaf sheaths were completely lacking in surface hairs; the kernels were somewhat rounded and were either brown or orange.

In its lack of tillers, its glabrous leaf sheaths, its rounded kernels, and the color of its pericarp, the Tehuacán wild corn differs quite distinctly from a third Ancient Indigenous race of Mexico, Palomero Toluqueño, described by Wellhausen *et al.* (1952). This finding suggests that the latter may have stemmed from a different race of wild corn growing in another place. Fossil corn pollen from the Valley of Mexico suggests still a third locality where wild corn once occurred. It is becoming increasingly apparent that cultivated corn may have had multiple sites of origin, of which southern Mexico is only one, but the earliest one so far discovered.

The corn which we have called "early cultivated" is similar to the wild corn except in size. It has the same long soft glumes and the same soft, somewhat fragile rachises. It is probably a direct descendant of the wild corn, slightly modified through growing in a better environment. Initially the better environment may have been nothing more than that produced by the removal, by man, of other vegetation competing with wild corn growing in its natural habitat. Later the corn was actually planted in fields chosen for the purpose. Still later it was irrigated.

Exactly when the maize was first cultivated in Tehuacán Valley is difficult to determine. Two cobs classified as early cultivated appeared in the Coxcatlan culture, dated 5200 to 3400 B.C., but we cannot tell whether the cobs represent the upper or lower part of this phase. Since remains of the bottle gourd and two species of squashes (*Cucurbita moschata* and *C. mixta*), as well as tepary beans, chili peppers, amaranths, avocados, and zapotes, occurred at this phase, there may have been at least an incipient agriculture and it is not unreasonable to suppose that maize, too, was being cultivated. However, two cobs scarcely furnish conclusive evidence on this point.

What we can be certain of is that during the Abejas phase, dated 3400 to 2300 B.C., this corn was definitely a part of an agricultural complex which included, in addition to maize, the following cultivars: the bottle gourd, *Lagenaria siceraria;* two species of squashes, *Cucurbita moschata* and *C. mixta; Amaranthus* spp.; the tepary bean, *Phaseolus acutifolius,* and possibly also the common bean, *P. vulgaris;* Jack beans, *Canavalia enciformis;* chili peppers, *Capsicum frutescens;* avocados, *Persea americana;* and three varieties of zapotes. Among the 99 cobs representing this phase, 45 (almost half) were classified as early cultivated. Thereafter this type gradually decreased in relative frequency, becoming extinct before the beginning of the Venta Salada phase at A.D. 700.

OTHER PREHISTORIC TYPES

Making its first appearance in the Abejas phase but represented there by a single cob, and becoming well established in the Ajalpan phase, is a type which we have called "early tripsacoid." The term *tripsacoid* is one proposed by Anderson and Erickson (1941) to describe any combination of characteristics which might have been introduced into corn by hybridizing with its relatives, teosinte or *Tripsacum*. In both of these species the tissues of the rachis and the lower glumes are highly indurated and the lower glumes are thickened and curved. Archeological cobs showing these characteristics are suspected of being the product of the hybridization of maize with one of its two relatives.

Since neither teosinte nor *Tripsacum* is known in Tehuacán Valley today and since neither is represented in the archeological vegetal remains, we suspect that the tripsacoid maize was introduced from some other region, possibly from the Balsas River basin in the adjoining state of Guerrero where both teosinte and *Tripsacum* are common today.

The introduced tripsacoid is a corn somewhat similar to the race (Nal-Tel) described by Wellhausen *et al.* (1952) but smaller. This introduced corn evidently hybridized with both the wild and the early domesticated corn in the Tehuacán Valley to produce hybrids with characteristics intermediate between those of the parents. First-generation hybrids, in turn, backcrossed to both parents to produce great variability in both cultivated and wild populations.

The introduced tripsacoid maize, together with its various hybrids, was the most common maize during the Ajalpan and Santa Maria phases from 1000 to 200 B.C. Thereafter it declined in frequency until it became almost extinct in the Venta Salada phase. But this complex apparently gave rise to two still-existing races of Mexico, Nal-Tel and Chapalote, and to a prehistoric type which we have called "late tripsacoid."

The earliest cobs from the Tehuacán caves were, because of their shape and glabrous cupules, thought to be prototypes of Chapalote, one of the Ancient Indigenous races described by Wellhausen *et al.* This race is today found only in northwestern Mexico in the states of Sinaloa and Sonora. Archeologically it is the predominating early corn in all sites excavated in northwestern Mexico and the southwestern United States.

Some of the later cobs from the caves, because their cupules were beset with hairs, a characteristic of the early Nal-Tel of La Perra Cave, seem to resemble this race more than they resemble Chapalote. Also, since Nal-Tel is found today in southern Mexico, it would not be surprising to find its origin there.

Actually Nal-Tel and Chapalote are quite similar in their characteristics, the principal conspicuous difference between them being in the color of the kernel, which in the former is orange and in the latter chocolate brown. Our hope that the first kernels to appear among the remains would enable us to distinguish between the two races was not realized. Of the kernels occurring in the Santa Maria phase, about half were brown and the other half orange, and both brown and orange kernels were also found in the later levels. Being unable, by any single criterion or combination of characters, to distinguish the cobs of the two races, we have designated this category the Nal-Tel-Chapalote complex.

It was this corn, more than any other, which initiated the rapid expansion of agriculture that was accompanied by the development of, first, large villages and, later, secular cities, the practice of irrigation, and the establishment of a complex religion. If it is too much to say that this corn was responsible for these revolutionary developments, it can at least be said that they probably could not have occurred without it. Perhaps it is not surprising that present-day Mexican Indians have a certain reverence for these ancient races of corn, Nal-Tel and Chapalote, and continue to grow them although they now have more productive races at their command.

A type which we have designated "late tripsacoid" corn differs from the early tripsacoid primarily in size. It comprises principally the more tripsacoid cobs of the Nal-Tel-Chapalote type and were it not that it includes some tripsacoid cobs of a slender popcorn, it could be considered part of the Nal-Tel-Chapalote complex to which it is closely related and with which it is contemporaneous. If the tripsacoid cobs resembling Nal-Tel or Chapalote are considered along with these late tripsacoid cobs, this complex seems even more likely to have been the basic maize of the Tehuacán cultures from 900 B.C. to A.D. 1536, representing about 65 percent of all the corn at the end of the Venta Salada phase.

A type called "slender pop" has very slender cylindrical cobs, many rows of grain, and small rounded kernels, yellow or orange. This may be the prototype of a Mexican popcorn, Arrocillo Amarillo, one of the four Ancient Indigenous races described by Well-hausen *et al.* (1952). This race, which is now mixed with many others, occurs in its most nearly pure form in the Mesa Central of Puebla at elevations of 1600 to 2000 meters, not far from the Tehuacán Valley and at similar altitudes.

Appearing first in the Santa Maria phase between 900 and

200 B.C., the slender pop increased rapidly and steadily in frequency, comprising 20 percent of the cobs in the final phase.

Judged by its cobs alone, the slender pop might be expected to be less productive than Nal-Tel or Chapalote, and its increased prominence deserves an explanation. A plausible one is that, although the ears are small, the stalks may have been prolific, normally bearing more than one ear. The present-day race to which it bears some resemblance and to which it may be related is prolific, usually producing two or three ears per stalk.

Minor categories include cobs and kernels which appear in later levels and which are recognized as belonging to several of the modern races of Mexico described by Wellhausen *et al.* (1952). They occur much too infrequently to be of significance in the total picture of food production but they are important in showing that these modern Mexican races were already in existence in prehistoric times. The only previous evidence of this was the fact that casts of ears appear on Zapotec funerary urns.

OTHER PARTS OF THE CORN PLANT

In all, 3597 specimens of parts of the corn plant, other than cobs, were found in the five caves. These specimens confirm the conclusions reached from the study of the cobs. There has been no change in the basic botanical characteristics of the corn plant during domestication. Then, as now, corn was a monoecious annual bearing its male and female spikelets separately, the former predominating in the terminal inflorescences and the latter in the lateral inflorescences, which, as in modern corn, were enclosed in husks. Then, as now, the spikelets were borne in pairs; in the staminate spikelets one member of the pair was sessile, the other pediceled. The only real changes in more than 5000 years of evolution under domestication have been changes in the size of the parts and in productiveness.

The importance of these changes to the rise of the American cultures and civilizations would be difficult to overestimate. There is more foodstuff in a single grain of some modern varieties of corn than there was in an entire ear of the Tehuacán wild corn. A wild grass with tiny ears—a species scarcely more promising as a food plant than some of the weedy grasses of our gardens and lawns—has, through a combination of circumstances, many of them perhaps fortuitous, evolved into the most productive of the cereals, becoming the basic food plant not only of the pre-Columbian cultures and civilizations of this hemisphere but also of the majority of modern ones, including our own.

SUMMARY

Remains of prehistoric corn, including all parts of the plant, have been uncovered from fire caves in the Valley of Tehuacán in southern Mexico. The earliest remains, dated 5200 to 3400 B.C., are almost certainly those of wild corn. Later remains include cultivated corn and reveal a distinct evolutionary sequence which gave rise ultimately to several still-existing Mexican races. Despite a spectacular increase in size and productiveness under domestication, which helped make corn the basic food plant of the pre-Columbian cultures and civilizations of America, there has been no substantial change in 7000 years in the fundamental botanical characteristics of the corn plant.

25 ORIGINS OF AGRICULTURE
IN MIDDLE AMERICA

Paul C. Mangelsdorf, Richard S. MacNeish, Gordon R. Willey

THE STORY of agriculture in Middle America begins with an era
of "incipient cultivation." By this term it is meant that domesticated food plants played only a minor role in the subsistence
of societies dependent for the most part on the collecting of wild
plants and the hunting of small game. Gradually, the cultivated
plants assumed greater economic importance. More plants were
brought under domestication, and others were improved over the
centuries by selection. Eventually, with agriculture becoming the
primary and established subsistence mode, the era of incipient
cultivation came to an end. We present here a summary of this
early history of plant cultivation in Middle America. We will consider, in order, native wild plants of the area, circumstances favorable for their cultivation, a review of the archaeological evidence for
plant domestication, plant genetics, plant distributions, and the place
of Mesoamerican cultivation in the larger setting of the New World.

Let us first note, briefly, the position and context of the "era
of incipient cultivation" which is to be our main concern (Willey
1960a; 1960b). The fully agricultural basis of life for pre-Columbian Mesoamerica is known from 16th-century records and
from ethnographic observations of modern times. For the centuries
immediately preceding the Spanish conquest, agriculture is known
or inferred from a variety of archaeological evidences. Going back
somewhat further in time, to the Preclassic period of the first and
second millennia B.C., it is generally assumed that the earliest
cultures of this period were supported by the cultivation of food

Reprinted from "Natural Environment and Early Cultures" (Robert C. West,
Vol. ed.), *Handbook of Middle American Indians* (Robert Wauchope, Gen.
ed.), Vol. 1, 1964, pp. 427–44, by permission of the University of Texas
Press and by permission of the authors.

crops (Willey, Ekholm, Millon 1964). The "era of incipient cultivation" precedes the Preclassic period. Actually it is an era or period of food collecting together with "incipient cultivation." The societies of that time were small bands, living under seminomadic conditions and gaining a livelihood by collecting wild plants, killing and snaring small game, and, to a minor extent, planting and reaping. The span of time involved for such an era is estimated, on the basis of radiocarbon dates, to have been about 6000 B.C.±1000 years to 1500 B.C.±500 years (MacNeish 1964b). It is believed that prior to 7000 B.C. man's food quest in ancient Middle America was oriented more toward the pursuit and killing of large animals, under Pleistocene environmental conditions (Aveleyra 1964) than toward plants and small game. With the onset of a warmer, drier climate, following the Pleistocene, the small game-hunting and plant-collecting subsistence came into being; and, at least in certain Mesoamerican regions, plant domestication developed in this context.

PLANT CULTIVATION IN MIDDLE AMERICA

Circumstances favorable for development of agriculture

There can be little doubt that the agriculture of the New World is an indigenous development. The Asiatic peoples who crossed Bering Strait on the wide land bridge, which almost certainly existed at a time when the sea level was 150–180 feet lower than at present (Hopkins 1959), were undoubtedly strangers to the art of cultivation. Agriculture had not yet been invented in the Old World and, if it had, it would not have been extensively practiced in northeastern Asia, where these migrants to the New World originated, or successfully carried across the barren tundras of the strait into a not much more favorable area of what is now Alaska. Even after these peoples reached the region now the United States and southern Canada, which has subsequently proved to be well suited to agricultural enterprises, there were few plants which could have been successfully domesticated. Only one cultivated plant of any importance, the annual sunflower, has originated in the region now the United States; its domestication may have come relatively late (Heiser 1955) and may have been inspired by the experience of successful domestication farther south.

Not until these nomadic hunting and food-gathering peoples reached the region now Mexico and northern Central America did they encounter a combination of conditions which were conducive to the development of plant domestication and the practice of agriculture.

One of the factors involved in creating centers of domestication, according to Vavilov (1951a), is a great diversity in the natural vegetation. As an example he cites the two small republics of Central America, Costa Rica and Salvador, which have areas about one hundredth that of the United States but which possess a number of species as great as is found in all of North America including the United States, Canada, and Alaska. Although taxonomists may question this particular statement, it is undoubtedly true that the floras of the countries of Middle America are rich and exhibit a great diversity of species and varieties. This diversity in vegetation is the product, in substantial part, of a corresponding diversity in habitats, which is provided by a wide range in altitude, temperature, and rainfall, and which promotes geographic differentiation in the genera and species inhabiting the area.

In addition to a rich flora, which is more likely to include plants amenable to domestication than a sparse one, there must be other factors and conditions which contribute to the invention and development of agriculture. On this point there is a variety of opinions.

Payne (1892) has suggested that agriculture probably originates first with root-crop culture, since the disturbance of the soil in the search for roots has in itself the character of tillage. Also the act of planting a root scarcely differs from that of digging one up; the implement used being the same for both, a simple fire-hardened stake, the universal implement of primitive agriculture. To Payne's arguments it should be added that no complex processing operations are required in preparing the majority of roots for consumption. Many can be eaten raw or cooked by simple means: roasted over hot coals or steamed in shallow pits over heated stones. No implements or utensils are needed for threshing, milling, or baking. The growing and processing of roots is undoubtedly more simple than comparable operations involving the cereals.

Sauer (1959), like Payne, has New World agriculture originating with root culture but for somewhat different reasons. He postulates that hunting and fishing people living a comfortable life began to cultivate the native, vegetatively propagated root crops not from necessity but because with leisure on their hands they had time to take steps to improve their lot by providing themselves with, among other things, a source of carbohydrates to supplement an otherwise highly proteinaceous diet. Sauer suggests that New World agriculture began in northern South America, perhaps in Colombia, with manioc, the native yam, arracacha, *Xanthosoma* (the American counterpart of the Old World taro), and other root crops. As this type of agriculture spread into the Andes other root or tuberous crops especially adapted to high altitudes, including oca, ulluco, año, and the potato, were added to the complex. The peanut was domesticated because a plant which buries its fruit resembles, superficially at least, the root crops which store their food reserves underground. This root-crop type of agriculture was also extended northward to its limits but was not adopted in Mexico in early times because no suitable root crops were available. Instead the requirements for a balanced diet were met by domesticating plants reproduced by seed, especially maize, beans, and squashes.

Sauer's hypothesis, though in many respects plausible, has little evidence to support it. True, there is some indication from the finding of griddles, presumably used in the preparation of manioc bread, that the cultivation of this plant began at a relatively early date, perhaps as early as 1000 B.C. (Cruxent and Rouse 1958), but it is doubtful that it preceded the cultivation of maize, beans, and squashes in Mexico.

Recent archaeological evidence tends to support not Sauer but Spinden who (1917) expressed the opinion that agriculture would be more likely to originate under conditions that were hard rather than under those which were easy. An environment producing a healthy but hungry population, particularly a semiarid environment, would offer special inducements to the first agriculturists. Here they would encounter no heavy work in preparing the soil, and irrigation would make them the masters of nature.

Even before irrigation had been invented, however, there would have been obvious advantages in a semiarid climate where weeds, insect pests, and fungus diseases are less of a problem than in tropical lowlands and where living conditions in general are more healthful. Also the plants on which the earliest agriculture of Mexico was based—primitive maize, beans, and squashes—are plants better adapted to intermediate and fairly high altitudes, to a *clima medio,* than to the tropical lowlands. The beginnings of agriculture should be sought, we think, at intermediate altitudes in tropical regions which have distinct rainy and dry seasons and natural vegetations of great diversity. These conditions are met especially well in parts of Middle America and it is here where the earliest archaeological remains of several important American cultivated plants are found.

Review of the Archaeological Evidence for Early Plant Cultivation
The earliest occurrences of cultivated plants in Middle America and the most complete record of their development through time come from archaeological sites in the Mexican states of Tamaulipas and Puebla. The former region lies at the northeastern margin of Middle America; the latter is near the geographical center of the area. There are also evidences of early, probably cultivated, maize in pollen taken from soil borings made in the Valley of Mexico, and from cave deposits in Chiapas in southern Mexico.

The archaeological sites in Tamaulipas are dry caves in which the plants themselves, and plant particles in human feces, are found in deeply stratified layers of dusty refuse. The cultural contexts of these plant finds are described elsewhere (MacNeish 1964b). In discussing the plants it will be necessary to refer to phase names, and dates, of two archaeological sequences, one for the Sierra de Tamaulipas and the other for the Sierra Madre Oriental of the southwestern part of the State of Tamaulipas. These sequences are closely related, and they are cross-referenced and dated in Table 1.

The earliest of the Tamaulipas culture phases with plant remains is the Infiernillo. It is dated at 7000–5000 B.C., and a number of plants are attributed to it. Some of these are definitely wild, such as the agave, the opuntia, and the runner bean (*Phaseolus coccineus*) (Kaplan, MacNeish 1960; MacNeish 1959b). Possibly wild or possibly domesticates are the gourd (*Lagenaria*) and the chili pepper (*Capsicum annuum* or *C. frutescens*) (Whitaker, Cutler, MacNeish 1957; Callen, MacNeish n.d.). The best case for a cultivated plant at this early time is the summer squash or pumpkin (*Cucurbita pepo*). The plant, apparently, was first utilized for its seeds. Several of these seeds have been found in an Infiernillo deposit, and some authorities believe domesticates to be

TABLE 1. Correlation of Two Regional Sequences of Tamaulipas, with Phase Datings Based Largely Upon Radiocarbon Readings For more detailed presentation, discussion, and radiocarbon dates see MacNeish) (1958: Table 30, pp. 193–99).

	Sierra Madre	Sierra de Tamaulipas
A.D. 1750		
	San Antonio	
1300		Los Angeles
	San Lorenzo	? (hiatus)
900		
	? (hiatus) (Late)	
		La Salta
500	Palmillas	
	(Early) ? (hiatus)	Eslabones
0		
	La Florida	Laguna
500		
	Mesa de Guaje	
		? (hiatus)
1400		
	Guerra	
1800		
		Almagre
	Flacco	
2200		
		La Perra
	(Late)	
3000	Ocampo	
4000	(Early)	Nogales
5000	? (hiatus)	
		? (hiatus following Paleo-Indian Phases)
B.C. 7000	Infiernillo	

represented among them (Whitaker, Cutler, MacNeish 1957; MacNeish 1959b).[1]

Indisputable domesticates, yellow and red large beans (*Phaseolus vulgaris*), come into the Tamaulipas sequence in the phase succeeding the Infiernillo, the Ocampo, dated at 5000–3000 B.C. (MacNeish 1958:167–68; 1959b; Kaplan, MacNeish 1960). Also, Ocampo pumpkins are a larger seeded variety than those of the preceding Infiernillo, and there is now no doubt that they are cultivated (Whitaker, Cutler, MacNeish 1957). A new wild plant, eaten in Ocampo times, is *Panicum sonorum,* a type of millet (Callen, MacNeish n.d.).

The great American Indian domesticated plant, maize (*Zea mays*), dates first from La Perra times, somewhere between 3000 and 2200 B.C. in the Tamaulipas sequence (MacNeish, 1958:155).[2] It is a primitive corn, represented by two varieties (A and B) of the early *Nal-Tel* race (Mangelsdorf, MacNeish, Galinat 1956; Callen, MacNeish n.d.).

After 2200 B.C. the Tamaulipas cave sequences show a rapid build-up of cultigens. The Bat Cave, or *Chapalote,* race of maize appears in the Flacco phase (2200–1800 B.C.), and in the Mesa de Guaje phase (1400–500 B.C.) both Bat Cave and new hybridized varieties of corn are present along with the maize-tripsacum cross, teosinte. In the Laguna phase (500 B.C.–0) there are three new important races of hybridized corn, *Breve de Padilla, Dzit-Bacal,* and *Nal-Tel* (Mangelsdorf, Reeves 1959a; 1959b; Mangelsdorf, MacNeish, Galinat 1956). Shortly after this, in early Palmillas phase times (0–A.D. 500), black beans, small red beans and the lima bean (*Phaseolus lunatus*) come into the sequence (Kaplan, MacNeish 1960) and a great increase in the varieties of pumpkins (*Cucurbita pepo*) occurs (Whitaker, Cutler, MacNeish 1957). In addition, the cushaw squash (*Cucurbita moschata*) is known from the Guerra phase (1800–1400 B.C.) and the Walnut squash (*Cucurbita mixta*) from the Palmillas (A.D. 300–800) (*ibid.*). *Amaranthus,* a well-known Mexican food plant, is as old as 2200 B.C., although its status as a wild or a cultivated one is uncertain (Callen,

---

[1] Of the six pumpkin seeds (*Cucurbita pepo*) in Infiernillo refuse, three are quite small and probably wild; but in the opinion of Whitaker and Cutler the other three seeds, all larger, appear to be domesticates.

[2] The evidence for maize in La Perra is from corncobs.

MacNeish n.d.). Cotton (*Gossypium*) is first noted in the cave debris in the Guerra phase (1800–1400 B.C.), and the first tobacco (*Nicotiana rustica*) is placed in Palmillas (A.D. 300–800) (MacNeish 1959b). *Manihot dulcis,* or sweet manioc, a possible domesticated food plant, is known from the Laguna phase (500 B.C.–0). This Tamaulipas manioc, although closely related to the *Manihot esculenta* of the South American lowlands, had a separate and local history of cultivation.

To sum up the Tamaulipas cave sequences and to relate the development of plant domestication in these sequences to other aspects of culture and society, we note the following trends. During the Infiernillo, Ocampo, and La Perra phases, or from about 7000 to 2200 B.C., domesticated food plants make up no more than 10 to 15 per cent of the total diet. The pumpkin and the bean were the earliest domesticates; maize, of a primitive sort, was added later. Communities were small and life probably seminomadic with only seasonal return to the cave sites. From 2200 to 500 B.C., in the Flacco, Almagre, Guerra, and Mesa de Guaje phases, cultigens increase to as much as 40 per cent of total diet by the terminal date. Sites are larger and some of them might be described as the village locations of semisedentary populations. New races of maize appear and are hybridized. Still later (500 B.C.–A.D. 500), more food plants are added to the complex, diet becomes essentially agricultural, and stable villages and towns appear (MacNeish 1958:199–203; 1959b).

It will be noted that this transition from early incipient to full village agriculture in Tamaulipas is chronologically somewhat behind the dating estimates given in the introduction to this article. By 1500 B.C., or even 1000 B.C., the cave dwellers and semisedentary villagers of the Tamaulipas mountains had not achieved a fully established agricultural economy. In fact, this does not seem to have been attained here until sometime between 500 B.C. and A.D. 500, well into Preclassic or even Classic times if measured against developments farther south in Middle America. The implications of this are that plant cultivation, in both its incipient and fully established stages, are probably earlier near the "heart" of the Mesoamerican area than they are on the Tamaulipas peripheries. What archaeological plant evidence is there to support this hypothesis?

To date, the most significant discoveries pertaining to this problem have come from a dry cave at Aeyerado, near Coxcatlan, in southern Puebla. Although only test excavations have been carried out so far, six maize cobs were recovered from deep refuse levels. Three of these cobs are probably domesticates; but the other three from the very deepest levels are quite primitive in appearance and it is possible that these latter three represent the wild ancestor of cultivated maize. In the upper preceramic levels of Aeyerado Cave, maize cobs are definitely domesticates, and some show teosinte introgression. The Aeyerado sequence terminates with the appearance of Preclassic and Classic pottery and well-developed maize.[3] Although only a preliminary examination of the earliest Aeyerado artifacts has been made, the chipped stone tool types appear to correlate most closely with those of the upper preceramic levels (5000–3500 B.C.) of the Santa Marta Cave in Chiapas as well as with the Ocampo phase of the Tamaulipas sequence. If this correlation is supported by an early radiocarbon date for the lower Aeyerado levels, it would strongly suggest an early Mesoamerican hearth of maize domestication well to the south of Tamaulipas.[4]

The Puebla maize discoveries have some corroboration in studies of fossil pollen made in the Valley of Mexico, a short distance to the north but still well south of Tamaulipas. Here, pollen of what is probably domesticated maize has an early post-Pleistocene geological estimated date (*ca.* 5000 B.C.). In this connection, it is interesting to note that there is still older maize pollen, presumably wild, from the Valley of Mexico (Barghoorn, Wolf, Clisby 1954).[5]

The most significant generalization which emerges from all of the archaeological facts on plant cultivation in Middle America is that there were regional specializations at a very early time. In Tamaulipas, squash and then common beans were cultivated long

---

[3] Excavation of the Aeyerado Cave was carried out by MacNeish in early 1960. Mangelsdorf examined the maize cobs from Aeyerado in March of the same year. Aeyerado Cave was later called Coxcatlan Cave. See also Addendum.

[4] Samples have been sent to the University of Michigan Laboratory for radiocarbon analysis.

[5] See also Deevey (1944) for a record of maize pollen in soil borings, taken from vicinity of Lake Patzcuaro, Michoacan. Maize pollen in this sequence cannot be dated definitely although there is the reasonable likelihood that it may be as ancient as the early post-Pleistocene.

before maize; in Puebla, maize has the earlier history.† By about 2000 B.C., however, there had been sufficient diffusion of cultivated plants within the Middle American area to produce a complex of agricultural foods—essentially maize, beans, squashes, and chili peppers—that revolutionized the whole nature of plant growing from a level of incipient cultivation to one of village agriculture. By the time of the advent of the Spanish the Middle American agricultural complex—augmented by new cultigens developed locally and imported from other American areas—was the richest assemblage of food plants in the western hemisphere.

Cultivated Plants of Middle America

The most intensive studies which have been made of the cultivated plants of the world are those of the Russian botanist, Vavilov, and his collaborators. These have involved numerous expeditions on a world-wide scale conducted between the two world wars and the most extensive collections of cultivated plants ever assembled. As a result Vavilov (1951a) recognized eight world centers of origin of cultivated plants, one of which includes southern Mexico, Central America, and the Antilles and is considered to be the center of origin of more than 50 cultivated species.

Vavilov's list is not complete, however, and is undoubtedly in error in assigning the origin of the sweet potato to this center and in omitting one of the most widely grown squashes, *Cucurbita pepo*. More recently Dressler (1953) made an exhaustive study of the literature, including early historical sources as well as Vavilov's and other Russian works, which are concerned with the cultivated plants of Mexico. Dressler lists 88 different species, of which 71 are regarded as being of Mexican-Central American origin and 17 were introduced from elsewhere or are of uncertain origin. Although Dressler's work is concerned principally with Mexico, most of the species which he lists are grown also in Central America.

In Table 2 we have combined the data of these two authors, following the procedure of Vavilov in listing the plants in categories, based upon their use, but employing somewhat different categories, and following Dressler with respect to the Latin names, since he has made a special effort to determine for each species the cor-

---

†See Addendum.

rect Latin name which meets the requirements of the rules of botanical nomenclature. To make the table as complete as possible we have added the names of the families to which the species belong and we have indicated with asterisks those species which we consider not to be indigenous to Mesoamerica but to have been introduced from elsewhere. A few species are included in more than one category.

The list of plants set forth in Table 2 is impressive, not only in the large number of species which it includes but also, in calling attention to the fact that a number of genera, notably, *Phaseolus, Cucurbita, Annona, Opuntia, Theobroma, Agave,* and *Dahlia,* are each represented by several species. This provides tangible evidence of the fact, mentioned earlier, that the Mesoamerican floras, because of their richness and diversity, undoubtedly contained many species amenable to domestication and it suggests that the Mesoamerican people, once they had learned the art of domestication practiced it whenever they encountered such species. The list of cultivated plants also shows that the domestication of plants in Mesoamerica reached an advanced, indeed in some respects a highly sophisticated, state—a number of species being cultivated as ornamentals and several as host plants for "domestic" insects. However, the majority of the species listed in Table 2 are of minor agricultural importance and of limited usefulness in tracing the beginnings of agriculture in Mesoamerica. Consequently we shall confine further discussion to these species which are of major importance agriculturally and which may be critical in tracing the beginnings of agriculture and its subsequent spread to other parts of the hemisphere. These include maize, beans, squashes, the bottle gourd, cotton, and tobacco.[6]

SQUASHES. Both wild and cultivated squashes are represented in the vegetal remains of the Ocampo caves. Rinds and shells of the wild species, *Cucurbita foetidissima,* were found at all levels in the caves (Whitaker, Cutler, MacNeish 1957:356). Since the flesh of the fruits of this species is quite unpalatable, as its Latin name may suggest, it is probable that this squash was used for its seeds which are nutritious. Carter (1945:30) has suggested that

---

[6] For detailed information on other cultivated species not treated further here, the reader is referred to Dressler's paper and to its extensive bibliography of 220 titles.

the cucurbits in general first attracted attention for their seeds which are easily gathered, are palatable, and have a high oil content.

Three cultivated species of squashes—*C. pepo, C. moschata,* and *C. mixta*—were identified among the archaeological remains of the caves. A fourth species, *C. maxima,* cultivated in Peru, has never been found archaeologically in Mesoamerica, a fact which furnishes one of a number of examples of independent domestication in the two regions.

1. Pumpkin and Summer Squash, *Cucurbita pepo* L. This species in modern horticulture includes many varieties: the golden fall pumpkin; a diversity of summer squashes including yellow crookneck squashes, acorn squashes, scallop or pattypans, zucchinis, vegetable marrows; and the small inedible gourds grown for ornamental purposes. This species makes its first appearance in Mexico in the Infiernillo phase, 7000–5000 B.C. However, of these earliest seeds, those illustrated by Whitaker *et al.* (1957) in their figure 4, are very small and may well represent wild squashes. Somewhat larger seeds which may be those of cultivated squashes were also found at this level (see note 1), as well as in the Mesa de Guaje culture dated at 1400–500 B.C. The absence of *C. pepo* in Peru, like the absence of *C. maxima* in Middle America, is evidence that the domestication of the squashes was, to some extent at least, independent in the two regions.

2. Cushaw Squash, *Cucurbita moschata* Duchesne. This squash, represented in contemporary horticulture in the United States by the cushaw of the southern states and butternut squash of the northern states, definitely makes its appearance in the Ocampo Caves at 1400–500 B.C., and there is one peduncle, probably of this species, dated at 1800–1400 B.C. (Whitaker *et al.* 1957:357). It is impossible to determine from these early specimens—all peduncles—whether they are wild or cultivated. This species is also represented in the early levels of Huaca Prieta site in Peru dated at about 2000 B.C. (Whitaker, Bird 1949). The fact that *C. moschata* has its center of diversity in Central America and northern South America indicates that this may be the primary center of domestication. The criterion of diversity, however, is far from infallible and can result in serious errors such as that which Vavilov (1951a) made when he placed the origin of *C. pepo* in the Near East because the greatest diversity of its varieties

TABLE 2. The Cultivated Plants of Middle America
(After Vavilov, 1951a; Dressler, 1953)

COMMON NAME	LATIN NAME	PLANT FAMILY
	CULTIVATED FOR THEIR EDIBLE SEEDS	
Amaranth	*Amaranthus cruentus* L.	Amaranthaceae
Amaranth	*Amaranthus leucocarpus* S. Wats.	Amaranthaceae
Apazote	*Chenopodium Nuttalliae* Safford	Chenopodiaceae
Bean, common	*Phaseolus vulgaris* L.	Leguminosae
Bean, lima	*Phaseolus lunatus* L.	Leguminosae
Bean, runner	*Phaseolus coccineus* L.	Leguminosae
Bean, tepary	*Phaseolus acutifolius* A. Gray	Leguminosae
Bean, jack	*Canavalia ensiformis* (L.) DC.	Leguminosae
Chia	*Salvia hispanica* L.	Labiatae
Chia grande	*Hyptis suaveolens* Poit.	Labiatae
Maize	*Zea Mays* L.	Gramineae
Panic grass	*Panicum sonorum* Beal	Gramineae
Peanut*	*Arachis hypogaea* L.	Leguminosae
Sunflower*	*Helianthus annuus* L.	Compositae
	CULTIVATED FOR THEIR EDIBLE ROOTS OR TUBERS	
Coyolxóchitl	*Bomarea edulis* (Tuss.) Herb.	Amaryllidaceae
Manioc	*Manihot dulcis* (J. F. Gmel.) Pax	Euphorbiaceae
Manioc*	*Manihot esculenta* Crantz	Euphorbiaceae
Potato*	*Solanum tuberosum* L.	Solanaceae
Sweet potato*	*Ipomoea Batatas* (L.) Poir.	Convolvulaceae
Yam bean	*Pachyrrhizus erosus* (L.) Urban	Leguminosae
	CULTIVATED FOR THEIR EDIBLE GOURDLIKE FRUITS	
Chayote	*Sechium edule* Sw.	Cucurbitaceae
Squash, cushaw	*Cucurbita moschata* Duch.	Cucurbitaceae
Squash, summer	*Cucurbita pepo* L.	Cucurbitaceae
Squash, walnut	*Cucurbita mixta* Pang.	Cucurbitaceae
Squash	*Cucurbita ficifolia* Bouché	Cucurbitaceae
	OTHER EDIBLE FRUITS	
Anona	*Annona purpurea* Moc. & Sessé	Annonaceae
Anona	*Annona glabra* L.	Annonaceae
Bullock's-heart	*Annona reticulata* L.	Annonaceae
Cherimoya*	*Annona Cherimolia* Mill.	Annonaceae
Ilama	*Annona diversifolia* Safford	Annonaceae
Soursop	*Annona muricata* L.	Annonaceae
Sweetsop	*Annona squamosa* L.	Annonaceae
Avocado	*Persea americana* Mill.	Lauraceae
Avocado	*Persea Schiedeana* Nees	Lauraceae
Caujilote	*Parmentiera edulis* DC.	Bignoniaceae
Capulin cherry	*Prunus serotina* Ehrh.	Rosaceae

COMMON NAME	LATIN NAME	PLANT FAMILY
Tejocote	*Crataegus pubescens* (HBK.) Steud.	Rosaceae
Cashew*	*Anacardium occidentale* L.	Anacardiaceae
Hog plum	*Spondias Mombin* L.	Anacardiaceae
Jocote	*Spondias purpurea* L.	Anacardiaceae
Coconut*	*Cocos nucifera* L.	Palmaceae
Elderberry	*Sambucus mexicana* Presl.	Caprifoliaceae
Guava	*Psidium Guajava* L.	Myrtaceae
Guayabilla	*Psidium Sartorianum* (Berg.) Niedenzu	Myrtaceae
Mamey colorado	*Calocarpum mammosum* (L.) Pierre	Sapotaceae
Sapote, green	*Calocarpum viride* Pitt.	Sapotaceae
Sapote, yellow	*Pouteria campechiana* (HBK.) Baehni	Sapotaceae
Sapodilla	*Manilkara Zapotilla* (Jacq.) Gilly	Sapotaceae
Matasano	*Casimiroa Sapota* Oerst.	Rutaceae
Sapote, white	*Casimiroa edulis* La Llave & Lex.	Rutaceae
Nance	*Byrsonima crassifolia* (L.) DC.	Malpighiaceae
Papaya	*Carica Papaya* L.	Caricaceae
Pineapple*	*Ananas comosus* (L.) Merrill	Bromeliaceae
Pitahaya	*Hylocereus undatus* (Haw.) Brit. & Rose	Cactaceae
Prickly pear	*Opuntia streptacantha* Lemaire	Cactaceae
Prickly pear	*Opuntia megacantha* Salm-Dyck	Cactaceae
Prickly pear	*Opuntia ficus-indica* (L.) Miller	Cactaceae
Ramón	*Brosimum Alicastrum* Swartz	Moraceae
Sapote, black	*Diospyros Ebenaster* Retz.	Ebenaceae

POTS HERBS AND OTHER VEGETABLES

Chaya	*Cnidosculus Chayamansa* McVaugh	Euphorbiaceae
Chipilín	*Crotalaria Longirostrata* Hook. & Arn.	Leguminosae
Pacaya	*Chamaedorea Wendlandiana* Hemsl.	Palmaceae
Tepejilote	*Chamaedorea Tepejilote* Liebm.	Palmaceae
Tomato	*Lycopersicon esculentum* Mill.	Solanaceae
Tomato, husk	*Physalis ixocarpa* Brot.	Solanaceae
Yucca	*Yucca elephantipes* Regel	Liliaceae

CONDIMENTS AND OTHER FLAVORING

Chili pepper	*Capsicum annuum* L.	Solanaceae
Chili pepper	*Capsicum frutescens* L.	Solanaceae
Vanilla	*Vanilla planifolia* Andr.	Orchidaceae

COMMON NAME	LATIN NAME	PLANT FAMILY

STIMULANTS AND NARCOTICS

Cacao	*Theobroma Cacao* L.	Sterculiaceae
Cacao	*Theobroma angustifolium* DC.	Sterculiaceae
Cacao	*Theobroma bicolor* Humb. & Bonpl.	Sterculiaceae
Maguey	*Agave atrovirens* Karw.	Amaryllidaceae
Maguey	*Agave latissima* Jacobi	Amaryllidaceae
Maguey	*Agave mapisaga* Trel.	Amaryllidaceae
Tobacco	*Nicotiana rustica* L.	Solanaceae
Tobacco*	*Nicotiana Tabacum* L.	Solanaceae

FIBER PLANTS

Cotton	*Gossypium hirsutum* L.	Malvaceae
Henequen	*Agave fourcroydes* Lem.	Amaryllidaceae
Maguey	*Agave atrovirens* Karw.	Amaryllidaceae
Maguey	*Agave tequilana* Weber	Amaryllidaceae
Sisal	*Agave sisalana* Perrine	Amaryllidaceae

DYE PLANTS

*Achiote**	*Bixa Orellana* L.	Bixaceae
Indigo	*Indigofera suffruticosa* Mill.	Leguminosae

CULTIVATED FOR ITS RESIN, USED AS INCENSE

Copal	*Protium Copal* (Schlecht. & Cham.)	Burseraceae

CULTIVATED AS HOSTS FOR WAX AND COCHINEAL INSECTS

Piñoncillo	*Jatropha Curcas* L.	Euphorbiaceae
Cochineal cactus	*Nopalea cochenillifera* (L.) Salm-Dyck	Cactaceae

FRUITS USED AS UTENSILS

Bottle gourd	*Lagenaria siceraria* (Mol.) Standl.	Cucurbitaceae
Calabash	*Crescentia Cujete* L.	Bignoniaceae

PLANTS USED FOR LIVING FENCES		PLANT FAMILY
Dahlia	*Dahlia Lehmannii* Hieron	Compositae
Pitayo	*Pachycereus emarginatus* (DC.) Brit. & Rose	Cactaceae
Yucca	*Yucca elephantipes* Regel	Liliaceae
Piñoncillo	*Jatropha Curcas* L.	Euphorbiaceae

ORNAMENTAL PLANTS

Cypress	*Taxodium mucronatum* Ten.	Pinaceae
Dahlia	*Dahlia coccinea* Cav.	Compositae
Dahlia	*Dahlia excelsa* Benth.	Compositae

COMMON NAME	LATIN NAME	PLANT FAMILY
Dahlia	*Dahlia Lehmannii* Hieron.	Compositae
Dahlia	*Dahlia pinnata* Cav.	Compositae
Marigold	*Tagetes erecta* L.	Compositae
Marigold	*Tagetes patula* L.	Compositae
Tiger flower	*Tigridia pavonia* (L.f.) Kerr.	Liliaceae
Tuberose	*Polianthes tuberosa* L.	Amaryllidaceae

*Probably not native to Mesoamerica.

occurs in Asia Minor. Centers of diversity may be centers of convergence as well as centers of origin.

Although *C. moschata* occurs in both Middle America and Peru and although it makes its first appearance in the two regions at about the same date, it is represented by distinct types, a brown-seeded one in South America and a white-seeded one in Mexico. These are sufficiently different to be regarded by some authorities as distinct subspecies (Bukasov 1930).

It cannot be said, at least with any degree of confidence, that *C. moschata* was first domesticated in Peru and later introduced into Mexico or vice versa. If any conclusion is to be drawn at this point it would be that domestication of *C. moschata* probably occurred independently in the two regions from somewhat different wild geographic races or subspecies.

3. Walnut Squash, *C. mixta* Pang. This species, coming quite late (A.D. 150–850) in the cultural sequence and never reaching South America, has little bearing either on the beginnings of agriculture or on its subsequent spread.

BEANS. Four species of beans—the tepary beans, the runner bean, the lima bean, and the common bean—are known today in Middle America and with the exception of the first all have now been found archaeologically, as noted above, in this region. The relatively early dates at which they occurred suggest that they may be native to the region and there is support for this supposition in the occurrence of wild forms of several of these species.

1. Tepary Bean, *Phaseolus acutifolius*. A. Gray. Wild forms of the tepary bean occur in northern Mexico and in the southern part of the southwestern United States (Carter 1945) and since this species is unknown in South America either archaeologically

or as commonly grown cultigen in modern times, there can be little doubt that it originated either in Mesoamerica or near its northern periphery. It has not yet been found archaeologically in early Mexican sites and may represent a comparatively recent addition to the Middle American agricultural complex.

2. Runner Bean, *Phaseolus coccineus* L. This bean, like the tepary, is clearly not of South American origin since it is unknown there archaeologically and is little used in contemporary agriculture. Wild plants of this species have been collected in Guatemala and in the states of Puebla, Zacatecas, Coahuila, Mexico, Jalisco, and Chiapas in Mexico (Kaplan, MacNeish 1960). These authors also conclude that the runner beans found archaeologically in the Infiernillo phase of Romero's Cave, dated at 7000–5000 B.C., may have been those of wild plants although this species is not known in the wild in Tamaulipas today. They suggest that a second thermal period may have been the cause of the extinction of *P. coccineus* from this part of its native range.

3. Lima Bean, *Phaseolus lunatus* L. Since the lima bean does not occur archaeologically in Middle America until A.D. 0–500 and has been identified from preceramic levels dated at 2000 B.C. in the Huaca Prieta site in Peru (Towle),[7] it might be supposed that this species represents an introduction into Middle America from South America. However, the lima beans in the two areas are quite different, the Peruvian form being a large-seeded type and the Mexican a small-seeded type known to horticulturists as the "sieva" lima. Mackie (1943) has placed the origin of the lima bean in the Guatemala-Chiapas area, where wild forms of a small-seeded type have been collected. Recently a lima bean has been collected in Peru growing on the terraces of Ollantaitambo in the Urabamba Valley by Ing. Alexander Grobman of the National School of Agriculture. Because of its hard, thickened shell, which differs from that of any cultivated lima, this bean has been identified as a wild form by Dr. R. W. Allard, University of California. The same form is reported by Ing. Alfonso Cerrate to be common in the Department of Ancash in Peru.[8] This wild lima has seeds much larger than those of the wild lima of Guatemala. It seems probable, therefore, that the lima beans of Mesoamerica

---

[7] Personal communication, M. A. Towle, 1960.
[8] Personal communication, A. Grobman, 1960.

and of South America represent separate domestications of two distinct wild races or subspecies.

4. Common Bean, *Phaseolus vulgaris* L. The situation with respect to the common or kidney bean is in some respects a counterpart of that involving the lima bean. Wild beans of this species, or one closely related to it, have been found in both Middle America and South America (Kaplan, MacNeish 1960:53), which suggests at once the possibility of an independent domestication of beans in the two regions. Furthermore the modern bean varieties of Mexico and South America, although regarded as belonging to the same species, are quite different in many of their horticultural characteristics, including various physiological responses to environmental conditions, disease resistance, and productiveness. Nevertheless, the fact that this species appears quite early in Mexico, 5000–3000 B.C., and relatively late, 400 B.C., in South America is consistent with the hypothesis of a Middle American origin and a later spread to South America. More data on the genetic and cytological relationships of the cultivated varieties to the various wild forms are needed before final conclusions on this problem can be reached.

MAIZE. Of all the cultivated plants of Middle America, maize was by all odds the most important. There was no well-developed, prehistoric agriculture in any part of this region in which maize was not the principal crop. Even today there are millions of "indígenas" in Guatemala and Mexico to whom maize is quite literally the staff of life and whose agriculture is based upon the growing of this plant.

Whether maize originated in this region, and only here, are questions to which complete answers have not yet been found. The evidence is conflicting and authorities do not agree. Earlier students of maize were virtually unanimous in postulating a South American origin: St. Hilaire assigning it to Paraguay, DeCandolle to New Granada, and Darwin to Peru (cf. Mangelsdorf, Reeves 1939). Later when the close relationship of maize and teosinte was discovered the scene shifted from South America to Mexico. Except for Sturtevant, who still held to a South American origin, opinions were almost unanimous that maize had its beginnings in Mexico and argument was confined, as Collins once stated, "to the rival claims of particular Mexican localities." Harshberger, Collins, Kempton, Kempton and Popenoe, Vavilov, Kuleshov, Weatherwax, and later Randolph, all postulated a Mexican or Central American-Mexican origin primarily because teosinte, the closest relative of maize, is confined to this general region and is unknown in South America except where it is rarely cultivated (Mangelsdorf, Reeves 1939).

Mangelsdorf and Reeves (1939), on the basis of their cytogenetic studies of maize and its relatives, concluded that teosinte is a hybrid of maize and Tripsacum rather than the progenitor of maize, and postulated that maize as a wild plant originated in the lowlands of South America and that the Andean region became the primary center of diversification. Later, however, when fossil maize pollen was discovered in the Valley of Mexico (Barghoorn *et al.* 1954), Mangelsdorf (1954) concluded that "maize undoubtedly had at least one center of origin in Middle America."

In spite of conflicts of opinion certain facts are reasonably clear. There is little doubt that maize is an American plant. There have been periodic attempts to place its origin in Asia but there is no tangible evidence of any kind—archaeological, ethnographic, linguistic, ideographic, pictorial, or historical—of the existence of maize in Asia before 1492 (Mangelsdorf, Oliver 1951). On the other hand, there is overwhelming evidence of its American origin, among the most convincing of which is the recent discovery of fossil maize pollen, mentioned above, in the Valley of Mexico. This fossil pollen not only proves that there was once a wild maize native to this hemisphere but also suggests strongly that cultivated maize may have had one center of origin in Mexico.

There is archaeological evidence to support this suggestion. As noted, the most primitive prehistoric maize so far found in Meso-america are the tiny cobs from Aeyerado Cave which may be wild maize. This maize has definite affinities with a cultivated race, *Chapalote,* still found in Mexico. Archaeological specimens of this same race have been found in the lowest levels of Swallow Cave in Chihuahua (Mangelsdorf, Lister 1956) and it is possible that the earliest corn of Bat Cave is also of this race (cf. Mangelsdorf, Lister 1956).

The earliest maize of La Perra Cave in Tamaulipas, dated at 4450 years, is related to another living Mexican race, *Nal-Tel* (Mangelsdorf, MacNeish, Galinat 1956) and shows that even at this early date there were already distinct races of maize in Mexico. This indicates either that domestication had already proceeded to the point of producing considerable diversification in cultivated maize or that distinct geographical races of wild maize occurred in various parts of Mexico and were domesticated wherever they were found.

It is now possible to identify with respect to race these archaeological specimens of maize in Mexico because of the comprehensive studies of living maize of Mexico made by Wellhausen *et al.* (1952). These authors recognized in Mexico four primitive races: *Palomero Toluqueño, Arrocillo Amarillo, Chapalote,* and *Nal-Tel,* which they designated as "Ancient Indigenous" because there is no evidence of their having been introduced from elsewhere. Four additional races, *Cacahuacintle, Harinoso de Ocho, Olotón,* and *Maíz Dulce,* were designated as "Pre-Columbian Exotic Races" because they clearly have affinities with the maize of South America and because several of them became the parents of hybrid races which are known, from replicas on funerary urns, impressions in lava, and actual prehistoric specimens (including those of *Breve de Padilla* and *Dzit-Bacal* mentioned earlier), to have originated in pre-Columbian times. The South American affinities of these exotic races are well established by the subsequent studies of Roberts *et al.* (1957) on the races of maize of Colombia and of Wellhausen *et al.* (1957) on Guatemalan maize. The latter shows that several other races in addition to the four Mexican races mentioned above were introduced into Middle America from South America. It may be worth noting in passing that all these introductions of South American maize occurred in western parts of Guatemala. This is also true of three of the Mexican exotic races.

These introduced races from South America were more productive than the indigenous races. Why, if maize originated in Middle America, it should have evolved more rapidly in South America than in its native region, is a question not yet completely answered, although there is evidence that there has been hybridization in South America, not only between distinct races, but also with corn's hardly wild relative *Tripsacum* (Mangelsdorf, Reeves 1959a:400–04; 1959b:421–22). The important fact for the present discussion is that the introduction of these productive South American races and their subsequent hybridization with indigenous races and with teosinte to produce still better races, the "Prehistoric Mestizos" of Wellhausen *et al.*, undoubtedly had a revolutionary effect on the agriculture of Mesoamerica. Indeed it is quite possible that the flowering of civilization in Mesoamerica is related to the arrival in that region of the agriculturally superior South American races.

The old idea, that agriculture in this hemisphere came into full development when maize was domesticated, is no longer tenable. The wild maize with which domestication began was certainly not a particularly promising food plant—both beans and squashes were probably more productive in the early stages of agriculture. That maize eventually became the basic food plant of the pre-Columbian cultures and civilizations of the New World is due to its remarkable ability to evolve rapidly in a man-made environment.

COTTON. The New World cultivated cotton, *Gossypium hirsutum* L. of Mexico and G. *barbadense* L. of Peru are 26-chromosome allopolyploid hybrids between two 13-chromosome cottons, one of which must have resembled the wild cotton, G. *Raimondii* of Peru, and the other, one of the Old World cottons, G. *arboreum* or G. *herbaceum*. There is general agreement among students of cotton on this basic fact. Opinions differ, however, on the question of when this hybridization occurred. Hutchinson, Silow, and Stephens (1947) postulated that the hybridization took place in relatively recent times after man, crossing the Pacific by raft or canoe, introduced the Old World cultivated cotton, G. *arboreum*, into Peru where it came within the range of the native wild cotton, G. *Raimondii*, with which it hybridized. The cultivated Peruvian species, G. *barbadense*, and the Mexican species, G. *hirsutum*, as well as the wild 26-chromosome Hawaiian species, G. *tomentosum*, are assumed to have evolved from this original hybrid.

There are numerous objections to this theory, one of the most formidable being that it does not allow time enough for the differentiation of the New World 26-chromosome cotton into three distinct species and a number of well-differentiated varieties, *punctatum* and *marie-galante* of G. *hirsutum* and *brasiliense* of G. *barbadense*. Especially difficult to reconcile with the theory is the wild G. *tomentosum*, a typical Hawaiian endemic, a lintless cotton far removed in many of its characteristics from its mainland relatives. Other students of cotton, although recognizing the hybrid nature of the 26-chromosome species, have assumed that this hybridization occurred before the New World and Old World species had become completely separated in their ranges at a time in the remote geological past when the floras of parts of America and parts of the Old World, South America and Africa, for example, were more or less continuous. This assumption has received support from recent cytological studies which indicate that *G. barbadense,* the cultivated cotton of Peru, is probably more closely related to *G. herbaceum,* the cultivated cotton of Africa, the Near East, and India, than it is to *G. arboreum,* the cultivated cotton of western India, China, and other parts of Asia.

Whatever their origin, the two American cultivated cottons are quite distinct and probably represent separate domestications. *G. hirsutum* appears to have its center of diversity in southern Mexico and Guatemala with one of its two varieties, *punctatum,* extending into the Greater Antilles and the other, *marie-galante,* into the Antilles and northern South America. *G. barbadense* is the cotton of Peru and western South America with one of its varieties, *brasiliense,* spreading into northeastern South America and through the Antilles. Hutchinson *et al.* (1947) assumed that this spread from the original centers is recent but we are convinced that it is ancient, much, if not most, of it having occurred before man arrived on the scene.

The earliest archaeological remains of *G. hirsutum* in Mexico and of *G. barbadense* in Peru occur at about the same time, 1700 years B.C. for the former and 200 years B.C. for the latter. The similarity in dates is probably a coincidence. Both remains probably represent wild cotton and the domestication of the two species was probably quite independent.

TOBACCO. Tobacco, like cotton, is represented by two cultivated species, *Nicotiana Tabacum* L. and *Nicotiana rustica* L. The former is South American in origin but it is possible that its use spread to parts of Central America and southern Mexico in pre-Columbian times. In most of Mexico, however, as well as throughout the southwestern and eastern United States and eastern Canada the cultivated tobacco was *N. rustica,* which has a nicotine content three to four times as high as that of *N. Tabacum,* a fact which may account for the circumstance that many tribes used the toxic weed only ceremonially and not for pleasure.

The tobaccos, like the cottons, are allopolyploid hybrids. *N. Tabacum* has never been found in the wild but its putative parents, *N. sylvestris* and a species of the section *Tomentosae, N. otophera,* are in contact today in northwestern Argentina and adjacent Bolivia which suggests that this may be the original area of its natural distribution (Goodspeed 1954:373).

The other cultivated species *N. rustica,* apparently has for its progenitors *N. paniculata,* which has a range comprising nearly the entire length of western Peru, and *N. undulata,* which ranges from northern Peru to northwestern Argentina. The hybrid species, *N. rustica,* is highly polymorphic with a long history as a cultigen. It is unknown in the wild with the exception of the variety, *pavoni,* which ranges from the southwestern Ecuadorian inter-Andine highlands through the western flanks of the Andes of southern Peru and adjacent northern Bolivia (Goodspeed 1954:355). This wild variety is quite different from the cultivated forms which probably had their origins in Mesoamerica.

It is probable that the domestication of *N. rustica* in Middle America was independent of that of *N. Tabacum* in South America.

BOTTLE GOURD. Belonging to the same family as the edible squashes is the inedible bottle gourd, *Lagenaria siceraria* (Mol.) Standl. Remains of this gourd represented by fragments of rinds were found in all levels of the Ocampo Caves beginning at 7000–5000 B.C.; however, seeds, which furnish a more positive identification, did not appear until the Mesa de Guaje phase at 1400–500 B.C.

If we accept the identification of the early specimens based on rinds alone, we are presented with a puzzling problem. *Lagenaria* has never been found in the wild in America and it is known to be an Old World cultigen probably of considerable antiquity. How did it reach Tamaulipas in Mexico at so early a date? Towle (1952:182) has suggested that the fruits of this species may have been carried to America from Africa by ocean currents and the experiments of Whitaker and Carter (1954) on floating fruits in sea water have shown this to be a possibility. It might be supposed, however, that such ocean currents would have introduced the plant into the eastern part of South America, and it may be as Sauer (1950:506) has stated that, "The theory of its accidental dissemination involves, in addition to the undamaged transit of an ocean, a waiting agriculturalist who carried it in from the sea shore to a suitable spot of cultivation."

If this assumption has validity, then agriculture in America must have had its beginnings not in Mexico or Peru but in eastern

South America, not with a native seed plant but with a root-culture tradition, probably based on manioc, serving as the ready recipient for the ocean-borne *Lagenaria,* an exotic species whose fruits were useful primarily as utensils. The culture of *Lagenaria,* minus the manioc, must then have spread at very early dates to both Mexico and Peru. Such an hypothesis demands an improbable number of fortuitous circumstances.

Perhaps the time has come to take a broad new look at the genus *Lagenaria.* Perhaps it, like the genus *Gossypium* and many other genera both living and fossil, was common to both America and Africa and its great diversity, even in the earliest times, is the product, not of centuries of domestication but of millions of years of evolution in nature. The bottle gourd, perhaps more than any other species involved in tracing the origins of American agriculture, needs the attention of taxonomists, geneticists, and cytologists.

MIDDLE AMERICAN PLANT CULTIVATION
IN THE NEW WORLD SETTING

In pre-Columbian times Mesoamerica enjoyed a cultural dominance on the New World scene. Along with Peru it was one of the geographic centers from which the influences of civilization radiated outwards to areas of lesser cultural intensity. To what extent was this role of dominance a function of priority in the development of agriculture? Although centers of cultural elaboration are not necessarily centers of origin as well, archaeological evidence strongly suggests that Middle America was an important primary hearth, as well as a zone of climax, for plant cultivation. It is highly likely that maize, beans, and squashes—those three staples of native American diet—were all first cultivated within or very near to Mesoamerica.

The earliest archaeological occurrence of domesticated squash or pumpkin (*Cucurbita pepo*) comes from northern Middle America in Tamaulipas. These Infiernillo and Ocampo appearances of pumpkin seeds antedate the New Mexican Bat Cave findings of pumpkin by more than a thousand years (C. E. Smith 1950) and the Adena pumpkin remains of the Ohio Valley by several thousand years (Goslin 1957). South of Tamaulipas, in Mesoamerica, the pumpkin is not abundantly documented from archaeological levels.[9] Still farther south, in Peru, this pumpkin does not occur. These data, few though they are, virtually establish a point of domestication in or near Middle America. Another squash, the *C. moschata,* is placed at about 2000 B.C. in both Tamaulipas and in distant Peru (Whitaker, Bird 1949). These findings, together with the discovery of *moschata* in preceramic Aeyerado Cave in Puebla as well as the greatest modern diversity for *moschata* being established in southern Middle America, hint at a southern Middle American primary domestication well before 2000 B.C. with a subsequent spread northward and southward at least to northwestern South America. *C. mixta,* the walnut squash, seems to be the latest of the three as a domesticate. It has been found in both Tamaulipas and in Ventana Cave, Arizona, at about A.D. 300 (Whitaker, Cutler, MacNeish 1957). Almost certainly, it is a north Mexican or Mesoamerican domesticate.

The cultivated common bean, *Phaseolus vulgaris,* is known first from the Ocampo phase in Tamaulipas, at 5000–3000 B.C. In the Southwestern United States *P. vulgaris* is found in Bat Cave at about 1000 B.C. (C. E. Smith 1950), and in the eastern United States it is no earlier than the Hopewellian horizon of the time of Christ or later (Wedel 1943:26). In Peru, *P. vulgaris* does not appear until approximately 400 B.C. (Bennett, Bird 1949: 142). These dates and distributions favor Middle America as the first seat of domestication of *P. vulgaris,* although it should be remembered that the Peruvian form of this bean may have had a separate and independent domestication. Within Middle America it is not likely that Tamaulipas was the original point of cultivation. The presence, today, of a wild variety of bean in southern Mexico and Guatemala argues for a southern Mesoamerican homeland (Dressler 1953). The lima bean, *P. lunatus,* is no earlier than the early Palmillas phase (A.D. 0–500) in the Tamaulipas sequence, but in Peru it is one of the oldest domesticates, dating back to 2000 B.C. Again, as mentioned earlier, this does not signify a south-to-north diffusion, as the Middle American and Peruvian varieties of *P. lunatus* are clearly different and it is likely that they represent separate and independent domestications of wild beans.

[9] MacNeish (1964b) refers to a *Cucurbita pepo* seed in late preceramic levels of Aeyerado Cave, southern Puebla.

For *Zea mays* or American Indian corn the archaeological evidence is predominantly on the side of a Middle American primary domestication. Most likely, this was a southern Mexican domestication beginning as early as 2000 B.C. or before. It would appear that the earliest diffusions of this primitive but cultivated maize were northward from this center, to Tamaulipas, Sonora (Mangelsdorf, Lister 1956), and the southwestern United States (Mangelsdorf, Smith 1949; Irwin, Irwin 1959). Even at this very early date (*ca.* 3000–2000 B.C.) there were two races of *Z. mays*. The Sonoran, Southwestern Tamaulipas, and Bat Cave New Mexican specimens belong to a pod-pop type which has affinities with the modern race, *Chapalote,* while that from the Sierra de Tamaulipas caves is an early *Nal-Tel* type (Mangelsdorf, MacNeish, Galinat, 1956). Apparently, the spread of primitive Middle American maize to Andean South America was somewhat later than this. On the north Peruvian coast it is dated between 1400 and 1200 B.C. (D. Collier 1959). Whether or not maize had also been domesticated independently in Peru before this, is an interesting question. If, as Mangelsdorf and Reeves (1959b:422) have suggested the great diversification of maize in Peru is the result of hybridization between the early and primitive Mesoamerican popcorn with the Peruvian popcorn, *Confite morocho,* then it might be argued that *Confite morocho* resulted from a separate Peruvian domestication of local wild maize. As yet, however, this problem is not resolved.

Several other important plants have an early history in Middle America although they did not necessarily originate there, nor is it certain they are all early domesticates. The chili pepper (*Capsicum annuum* and *C. frutescens*), the ubiquitous Middle American condiment, is one of these. It occurs in Tamaulipas in the Infiernillo phase (7000–5000 B.C.), and in Peru it is known from the earliest Huaca Prieta levels (*ca.* 2000 B.C.) (Bird 1948). As wild chili ranges, intermittently, over an area from the southwestern United States to Brazil, it is possible that domestication took place, independently, in several localities (Dressler 1953). Although it is difficult to tell wild from cultivated varieties, the absence or scarcity of the wild species of *Capsicum* in highland Tamaulipas today suggests that the archaeological specimens of the plant found in that region are domesticates (MacNeish 1959b).

New World cotton occurs as two species. *Gossypium hirsutum* is as early as 1700 B.C. in Tamaulipas and a closely related variety is in the southwestern United States by the first millennium B.C. (Martin *et al.* 1952). The other species, *G. barbadense,* is found in Peruvian preceramic contexts at 2000 B.C. (Bennett, Bird 1949). Apparently these were separate and independent domestications. The story of tobacco is probably similar. *Nicotiana tabacum* seems to have been first cultivated in the South American tropical lowlands, spreading from there to the West Indies and possibly to Central America and southern Mexico. *N. rustica,* the species known earliest from Middle America and eastern North America, probably originated as a domesticate in Middle America and gradually spread northward from there to the southwestern and eastern United States and eastern Canada. This was the tobacco known in the Mississippi Valley as early as the first millennium B.C. (Webb, Baby 1957). *Lagenaria,* the bottle gourd, which dates from the Infiernillo phase in Tamaulipas, is also early in Peru (Bennett, Bird 1949; Towle 1952), in Bat Cave, New Mexico (C. E. Smith 1950), and in the eastern United States (Funkhouser, Webb 1929). The ambiguities and problems surrounding the history of this particular plant have been discussed in detail above. In any case this plant is not the most critical for the rise of Mesoamerican agriculture as are some others.

A number of "root crops," belonging to a South American tropical lowland tradition of "vegetative planting," were introduced into Middle America as domesticates in relatively late prehistoric times (Sauer 1959). Among these the peanut (*Arachis hypogaea*), the sweet potato (*Ipomoea batatas*), and manioc (*Manihot esculenta*) were the most important. Manioc occurs at Huaca Prieta in Peru on a time level of 750–400 B.C. (D. Collier 1959); in Tamaulipas it is first found at 500 B.C.–0 when it probably was not a domesticate but the wild Mexican *M. dulcis* (Mac-Neish 1959b). It is almost certain that it was cultivated in northeastern South America much earlier than any of these dates (Willey 1960a).

To conclude, within the larger New World setting Middle America was a primary center for plant domestication. Native agriculture developed slowly here at first over a span of several millennia which we have designated as an "era of incipient cultivation." Then, as plants were improved through cultivation and selection they were also interchanged throughout the area so that by the beginning of the first millennium B.C., if not considerably before, Middle America became essentially dependent on an agricultural way of life. From the very earliest beginnings of incipient cultivation there appears to have been diffusion of plants and ideas concerned with their domestication out of the Middle American area. Then, with the establishment of full village agricultural subsistence, Middle America became even more of a heartland for the propagation of agriculture to lands beyond its borders. Conversely, it also assimilated cultivated plants originating in other areas; and it was the recipient of new improved secondary types of old Middle American cultigens which elsewhere had hybridized with other races and wild relatives, and thus had evolved more rapidly than the primary types in their original center. Such, very briefly, is the history behind the amazing agricultural richness and diversity of Middle America which Cortés viewed in the early 16th century.

ADDENDUM

Since this article was written in the early summer of 1960, there have been a number of significant developments related to the origins of agriculture in Middle America. Especially important are the results that have come from the excavations conducted by MacNeish and his associates in a number of once-inhabited caves in the Valley of Tehuacán, Mexico (MacNeish 1964b; Mangelsdorf, MacNeish, Galinat 1964; C. E. Smith, MacNeish 1964). These show a transition, over a period from 7200 B.C. to A.D. 1540, from a hunting and food-gathering subsistence to a full-fledged agriculture which included many species of plants and employed a well-developed system of irrigation.

The earliest remains of plants occurred in the El Riego phase, 7200–5200 B.C., and included a number of species later domesticated: a species of squash, *C. mixta,* chili peppers, avocados, and cotton. In the Coxcatlan phase, 5200–3400 B.C., gourds, amaranths, tepary beans, yellow and white sapotes, another squash, *C. moschata,* and, most important of all, maize had been added to the list. Some of these plants may have been cultivated; the maize was almost certainly wild and is the first prehistoric wild maize to be uncovered (Mangelsdorf, MacNeish, Galinat 1964).

The Abejas phase, 3400–2300 B.C., shows definite evidence of agriculture and the addition to the food plants of common beans, *P. vulgaris,* another squash, *C. pepo,* and cultivated maize.

The Purron phase, 2300–1500 B.C., is poor in plant remains, but in the succeeding phase, Ajalpan, 1500–900 B.C., the people were full-fledged agriculturalists, growing a hybridized corn, three species of squashes, beans, chili peppers, amaranths, and cotton.

Irrigation may have had its beginnings in the Santa Maria phase, 900–200 B.C. It was certainly employed systematically by full-time agriculturalists in the Palo Blanco phase, from 200 B.C. to A.D. 700.

The final phase, Venta Salada, A.D. 700–1540, was characterized by a highly developed and productive agriculture with irrigation capable of supporting a large population living in secular cities or towns—a population perhaps 5000 times as large as the original number of inhabitants of the valley, which is estimated to have consisted of not more than three microbands of four to eight people each.

Although providing earlier dates than were previously available for several of the plants discussed above, the new evidence tends, to a rather remarkable degree, to support the principal conclusions set forth in the earlier part of this article.

26 ARCHEOLOGY AND DOMESTICATION IN AMERICAN PHASEOLUS (BEANS)[1]

Lawrence Kaplan[2]

THE GENUS *Phaseolus* comprises about 160 species (Willis 1951). Because of extensive synonymy in the genus, particularly in the Old World species, it is likely that the number is considerably less. On the basis of Piper's (1926) monograph of the American representatives, about eighty species are native to the New World.

Many of the New World species are perennials. Flowers are white, or, more often, pigmented with red to purple anthocyanins. Yellow is uncommon. Pods of the cultivated species are medium to large, cylindrical or broad. Many of the Old World species have yellow flowers, and all have morphological features of the flowers that contrast with floral structure of the American beans. Six Asian-African species, including the grams, urds, mung, and rice beans, are widely cultivated in Asia. These are annuals, have small seeds and small cylindrical pods. Differential susceptibility to certain fungus diseases further distinguish the Old and New World species.

In the New World, four species have been most prominent as food crops:

P. vulgaris L., common bean, frijol (derived from a name for the Old World, *Vicia faba*); etl, yetl (Nahuatl); buul, chenek (Mayan); poroto (Quechua and Aymara). This polymorphic, poorly

Reprinted by permission of The New York Botanical Garden, from *Economic Botany*, Vol. 19, No. 4, October–December 1965, pp. 358–68, and by permission of the author.

[1] Presented at a meeting of The Society for Economic Botany as part of a symposium entitled *Integrated Research in Economic Botany VI: Ethnobotany of Some New World Cultures. Part II: Crops of major importance.* December 30, 1964. AAAS Meetings. Montreal, Canada.

[2] University of Massachusetts, Boston, Mass. Received for publication June 17, 1965.

understood species includes hundreds of cultivated varieties, such as, for example, Navy, Red Kidney, Pinto. *P. vulgaris,* and the three species discussed subsequently, include strongly to weakly vining forms as well as bush or erect forms. The distinctions between green, string, or snap beans, and dry or field beans, is based on use rather than on botanical characters.

This is the most widely grown of all food beans. In tropical indigenous American agriculture, common beans are grown on neutral to slightly alkaline soils from sea level to over 2000 meters.

P. acutifolius Gray var. *latifolius* Freeman, tepary, escomite. At the present time, this bean is not cultivated on a commercial scale, although some field stations have been investigating its potential as a dry land seed or forage crop. The seeds are smaller than those of other cultivated American beans, but they overlap in size the smaller-seeded common bean varieties. Collections made a few decades ago show the tepary to have been common in markets along the Pacific coast of northern Mexico. In 1954, it was infrequent in that region. The disjunct range of this bean, the Sonoran desert region south through Jalisco and then a gap until the Tapachula-Guatemalan border region, suggests that the present distribution is a relic one (Fig. 3).

P. lunatus L., sieva, small Lima, frijol de haba (this also applies to the introduced *Vicia faba,* the broad bean), comba (Guerrero), patashete (Chiapas), guaracara (Venezuela), cubace (Costa Rica). The curved pod and smaller, often flat seed distinguishes the sieva from the Lima, *P. lunatus* var. *microcarpus* Bentham (synonym *P. limensis* Macf.) (big Lima, pallar, in Peru). Any Lima bean encountered in Mexico, Central America or in indigenous areas of the southwestern United States is likely to be a sieva bean. Peruvian Limas, the big Limas, are grown commercially in humid coastal valleys of California.

The morphologically similar sievas and Limas are fully interfertile and produce viable, fertile offspring (Mackie 1943). This, in the genus *Phaseolus* where interspecific crosses do not readily occur (*P. coccineus* x *P. vulgaris* is a noteworthy exception), leaves little question but that the two groups should be regarded as conspecific. On the basis of the distribution of the wild species and the archeological evidence, it is now clear that these groups are independent domesticates deriving from geographically separate races or subspecies. Wild *P. lunatus* (R. W. Allard, personal communication) ranging from Mexico to northern South America, evidently had undergone the formation of South American and Central American subspecies that correspond to the differences separating the domesticated groups. Archeologically, the geographic separation of sievas and Limas attests to independent domestication. The Lima is present in pre-ceramic, pre-agricultural times (5200 years ago, collections from Chilca by Dr. Frederic Engel) and continues into later times on the North Coast of Peru. It is absent in the archeology of Middle America. The sieva, with the possible exception of a few pods of problematic identity in later agricultural (Cupisnique) times is absent from Peruvian sites.

P. coccineus L., runner beans, ayecote (Nahuatl derivation), botil in Chiapas, patol, in northern Mexico. The most common variety in the United States is the large-seeded Scarlet Runner, often listed in seed catalogues as an ornamental with edible seeds. Seeds of most varieties are larger than those of sieva beans and common beans and are usually purple or variegated purple, although there are white-seeded varieties. The flowers of the purple-seeded varieties are striking red, those of the white-seeded kinds are white.

Indigenous runner bean cultivation is most highly developed in the cool humid uplands of Chiapas and Guatemala in the oak-pine regions above 1800 m. In these areas the cultivars and their abundant wild relatives are perennials. Sprouts from the tuberous roots often take over maize fields for the first year or two of the fallowing period. The strongly vining runner beans are interplanted with maize in some fields and in plots adjacent to houses. In the house gardens, they are treated as perennials with a life span of from two to several years. [In Majorca (Lowe 1868) the roots persist for seven years and are regarded as poisonous.] Tubers of the branching root system may be taken up from time to time, boiled and eaten. The cooking water is said to be discarded.

Runner beans are cultivated to a more limited extent in the northern Mexican States of the Central Plateau, in Costa Rica, Panama, and Colombia, according to Bukasov (1930).

Several New World *Phaseolus* species have been cultivated locally or sporadically for food (*P. adenanthus* and *P. polystachios,* for example), as ornamentals (*P. caracalla*) or have been recommended as forage plants or ground cover.

The principal economic significance of *Phaseolus* beans has probably always been in their well known role as sources of vegetable protein in the form of dry seed. Several species, particularly *P. vulgaris,* supply edible immature pods and seeds, that is, snap beans, but because of their high water content (about 89%, Block and Weiss 1956) at this stage, they do not function as an important dietary protein, although, on a dry weight basis, the total protein content of snap beans, immature pods and beans is about 10% (Chatfield and Adams 1940) or about one-half that of dry mature seeds (about 22%, Block and Weiss 1956).

The close relationship between beans and corn in the indigenous diet of the populous cultures of Mesoamerica and the Andean region is, like other traditional dietary combinations, no accident. Quantitative chemical analyses (Jones, *et al.* 1938) of corn and beans of contemporary Yucatan Indians have shown complementation in the amino acids of zein, the principal corn protein, and *a* and *b* globulins of the black beans (*P. vulgaris*) that form the mainstay of the diet with the corn tested. Later studies cited by Block and Weiss (1956) and Albanese (1959) indicate that where zein is the protein in the diet of a monogastric animal, lysine is the limiting amino acid and, hence, must be made up from another source. Beans, with their relatively abundant lysine supply this amino acid deficient in the main foodcrop, maize, with the result that a protein of high biological value is achieved. It should be noted, however, that, while this protein appears to be adequate for the hardworking male, it is inadequate for the more protein sensitive members of the population, lactating mothers and young, recently weaned children (Altschul 1962).

Beans of different varieties and even of different *Phaseolus* species are high in lysine and tryptophane. Corn varies considerably in total protein, but it is always deficient in lysine and tryptophane (Block and Weiss 1956). It is now clear that maize and beans in some areas, Tamaulipas (Kaplan and MacNeish 1960) and Coastal Peru (Towle 1961) for example, were not domesticated simultaneously nor did they necessarily diffuse together.

Because amino acid complementation exists in any combination of many corn varieties and bean species and varieties, a kind of universal flexibility in adaptation of these dietary components resulted. Corn or beans could diffuse freely and independently into new areas. Wherever the two met, an immediate adaptive combination favored by human selection was formed. The effectiveness of the corn and bean combination may suggest ease of diffusion, but it also argues for parallel and independent origin.

The evolution of human diet is marked by synergistic combinations perhaps to a greater extent than by small increments in the food value of individual nutrient sources. Corn could presumably be selected for increments in total protein. However, because the nutritional insufficiency of plant-seed proteins is the result of limiting amino acids rather than total protein content, raising the total protein of corn would not solve the problem. The answer to the problem of lysine as a limiting amino acid in corn in indigenous America has been supplementation with beans rather than the development of new amino acid-sufficient strains of corn.

How did such a useful combination come about? Natives sampled the available flora. Probably the only answer to this question is that the seasonality, yield, compatability with other crops and ways of human life as well as nutrients were factors in adoption of a supplementary crop. Sampling over a period of many thousands of years prior to the establishment of corn and bean agriculture about 7000 years ago (MacNeish 1962) in Middle America was evidently sufficient to establish this combination. There is no reason to believe that, given sufficient time, a comparable flora and similar human practices, the same plants would not be domesticated.

In some regions with different floras, say, the Great Basin of western United States or humid eastern United States, indigenous plants do not appear to have been brought under cultivation to the extent that corn and beans were in Middle America. Why does domestication take place in some areas but not others? Archeological and botanical methods are now becoming available that should enable groups of specialists to weigh the roles of time depth and sequence of human culture, climates and floras of the past in approaching this question.

ETHNOHISTORY

Because of the paucity of beans in some pre-Columbian sites, it has been suggested that beans came into widespread use and have been an important part of the diet only in post-Hispanic times. There is, however, ethnohistoric documentation to show that beans with corn and some other crops were well established as items of tribute a century before the Spanish Conquest.

A major source of information on pre-Hispanic tributes is the Codex Mendocino or Codex Mendoza (Clark 1938), a manuscript based upon older sources prepared at the direction of the Viceroy Antonio de Mendoza, who served in New Spain from 1535 to 1550. The second part of the Codex is made up of tribute lists from towns and villages subject to Moctezuma Xocoyotzin II, the last Aztec Emperor. Some 371 towns were required to make annual, semiannual or every 80th day payments or all three. Maize and beans were contributed annually. In addition to large quantities of these staple foods, the tribute lists include: bales of cotton; spun thread; woven garments; shields; battle dress; precious feathers; jewels; gold dust; amber; cochineal; honey; cultivated food plants. The symbols for maize and beans were "troxes" or bins shown filled with corn kernels, beans, other small seeds or mixtures of these. J. C. Clark (1938) the editor and translator of the Codex, says of these ". . . the troxe was a large 10 foot high chest of woven oziers and plastered inside with mortar. The *etl* or bean can easily be recognized as the black variety, with the white eye commonly cultivated in Central America and Mexico."

The Summary of Moctezuma's annual tribute, collected from 371 towns, includes the following agricultural produce:

Maize, bins of	28
Beans, bins of	21
Purslane, bins (sic amaranth?)	18
Maize flour and Cacao mixed baskets of	160
Maize flour and sage (chia) mixed baskets of	160
Cacao red, loads of	160
Cotton, bales	4400
Chilis, bales	1600

Clark estimates that each bin represents 4–5000 *fanegas,* and that 5000 fanegas are equivalent to 8000 bushels.

Eric Wolf (1959) sums up the annual food tribute of the Mexican state as:

280,000 bushels of maize
230,000 bushels of beans
200,000 bushels of amaranth

Frederick A. Peterson (1962), using the Codex Matricula de Tributos and the Codex Mendocino, estimates that the Aztecs received annual tribute of about 7000 tons of corn and 5000 tons of beans, among other items.

Another ethnohistoric source, Historia Chichimeca, presents a detailed account of the operations of the *mayordomo* or chief steward of Texcoco in the reign of Nezahualcoyotl (before 1472). Clark (1938) states that ". . . Matlalaca, being in charge of all rents and taxes of that city, its suburbs and hamlets was obliged to maintain the Palace and court of Necaualcoyotl for 70 days, sending each day 25 *tlacopintlis* of maize, and 3 of *frijoles;* twenty loaves of *iztayaualli* or salt, 20 baskets of large chillis and 20 of small chillis, 10 baskets of tomatoes and 10 of *uauhtli.* This amount seems large but it must be remembered that all officials lived in the Palace and received their salaries in kind." Each *tlacopintli* equals 93 bushels.

CERTAIN STRUCTURAL CHANGES ASSOCIATED WITH DOMESTICATION

Although the domesticated beans differ in several ways from the wild species, the occurrence, with few exceptions, of only pods and seeds in archeological remains limits the record of change for certain anatomical features.

SEED SIZE. Seeds of the cultivated taxa vary greatly in size, but they are always larger than the seeds of the most closely allied wild species. The increase in size has maintained approximately the same ratio between size of the cotyledons and that of the meristematic embryo. This trait is the best direct indication of domestication in beans that is available in studies of the archeological materials. Increase in seed size can be determined directly from the seeds or indirectly from remains of pods.

The archeological materials available show no transitional phases in seed size increase. The early pod remains of *P. vulgaris* at Ocampo and Tehuacan contained seeds within the size range of moderately large commercial beans. The earliest tepary beans at Tehuacan and the earliest big Limas at Huaca Prieta are not smaller than later prehistoric or contemporary cultivars of the same species. Thus, from times of incipient agriculture, when remains of *P. vulgaris, P. acutifolius,* and Peruvian *P. lunatus* first appear, no significant size changes have occurred. The archeological evidence clearly points to transition in seed size in times earlier than have been excavated, that is, early incipient agriculture or perhaps even in non-agricultural times.

Any conclusions regarding the cultural context of seed size transition or the selective conditions under which this occurred must at best be speculative and tentative.

The association in time of early corn and beans at Tehuacan (Kaplan 1967) over 6000 years ago suggests that this transition may have come about among beans that were interplanted with corn. Possibly, large seeds, by providing an abundance of energy for the young bean vines enable them better to survive in competition for light with the young rapidly growing corn.

PERMEABILITY TO WATER. "Hard-seed," an agronomically important trait in beans, is an inability of the seeds to imbibe water. When this occurs in a substantial proportion of seeds designated for planting, the result is uneven germination, the soft or permeable seeds imbibing water promptly and germinating and the hard seeds exhibiting a delay in germination. There has been considerable discussion, much of it reviewed by Kyle and Randall (1963), regarding the site of water entry, and methods of testing for impermeability and the genetics of impermeability. Water may enter the seed at various places, but, in seeds having non-fractured seed coats, the micropyle, hilum and raphe or suture opposite the micropylar end of the hilum are most important. The unbroken seed coat, except for a few domesticated varieties (Navy and White Marrow, for example), is impermeable. Growing and storage conditions may increase or decrease initial permeability. In some collections of Mexican beans (for example, *P. coccineus* cultivars from Cholula), 50% of the seeds fail to have absorbed water after from 24 to 48 hours of immersion in water at room temperature. Some cultivars exhibit very low frequencies of hard seeds. Seeds derived from wild species, i.e., *P. heterophyllus; P. polystachios; P. polyanthus; P. vulgaris* f. *aborgineus; P. obvallatus,* are 100% impermeable and remain so for periods of more than one year when stored under a variety of conditions. Permeability appears to have increased under domestication.

The widespread practice in Mexico of boiling beans without preliminary soaking may reflect the high incidence of impermeability in the local bean cultivars. Imbibing of a seed lot of varying permeability followed by boiling produces an unevenly cooked pot of beans. Boiling of dry seed reduces the differences in cooking time between permeable and impermeable seeds. This method may produce a uniformly palatable pot of beans, but some protein value may be lost. Heating, at cooking temperatures, of relatively dry protein and carbohydrate mixtures causes indigestible protein-carbohydrate complexes to form (Ellis 1959). A high proportion of impermeable seeds probably reduces the protein food value of beans. Roasting of dry seeds prior to grinding, as in the preparation of pinole and *shicayu,* a bean pinole of the Oaxaca coast (Kaplan 1956) is probably even more detrimental nutritionally.

SEED DISSEMINATION. Economic annuals grown for their seeds or achenes, chiefly legumes and grains, have usually undergone a reduction or loss in the ability to release the seeds. Wild legumes having pods dehiscent along both sutures forcibly expel their seeds by a twisting of the pod valves that results from dessication of the inner parchment layer. This process of expulsion takes place violently among wild species but less so or not at all among cultivars, owing to reduction of the parchment layer among domesticates.

The oldest *P. vulgaris* materials, pods from Ocampo and Tehuacan, have reduced parchment layers and are considered, for this reason as well as for their size, to be derived from domesticates. The oldest *P. coccineus* pods from Tamaulipas (Kaplan, MacNeish 1960) are tightly curling wild types.

LIFE CYCLES. Perennialism is more prevalent in *Phaseolus* than is annualism and is based on drought resistance of the tuberous root or root-hypocotyl system. Studies of species descriptions, notes on herbarium sheets, and field studies suggest that perennial growth occurs probably quite regularly under field conditions in about 90% of the American species. *P. vulgaris* and *P. acutifolius* are known only as annuals with fibrous root systems. Some cultivars of *P. lunatus* and *P. coccineus* are perennial tuber forms particularly under short day conditions. Although annualism is a feature common to the cultivated species and contrasts with the perennial habit that prevails among wild species, there is insufficient knowledge of the early phases of domestication in *Phaseolus* to know whether annualism occurred under domestication or long prior to the advent of human selection.

Behavior of the perennial tuberous root in *P. obvallatus,* a wild species allied to *P. coccineus,* indicates the existence of a dormancy mechanism that may be comparable to seed dormancy. Dried tubers of *P. obvallatus* collected at the end of the rainy season in Mexico failed to sprout when watered at that time. However, after several months of dry storage, they sprouted spontaneously. This may indicate a moisture stress requirement for resumption of shoot growth.

Impermeability of seeds, as discussed earlier, functions ecologically as a dry-season dormancy mechanism. Apparently, the tuberous root and the wild-type seed are ecological equivalents. Because seed impermeability and tuber formation of the roots are reduced among bean cultivars, an ecological distinction may be added to the morphological ones between the wild and domesticated species. This is a reduction or loss of dormancy mechanisms geared to the wet-season dry-season cycle resulting in a crop plant that is flexible in adapting to new climatic regimes, house garden cultivation, or to irrigation.

ANTIQUITY OF CULTIVATION

Figures 1–3, give the geographic distribution and some early dates in years before the present time for the occurrence of beans in archeological sites. References to reports on these sites are as follows: Basketmaker II (Kaplan 1956); Chilca (correspondence of F. Engel); Durango (Carlson 1963); Dzibilchaltun (G. Willys Andrews); Ft. Ancient (Yarnell 1964); Huaca Prieta (Towle 1961); Nazca (Towle 1961); Ocampo (Kaplan and MacNeish 1960); Oneota, and Owasco (Yarnell 1964); Rio Zape (Brooks *et al.* 1962); Snaketown, Tehuacan, Tularosa Cave, Verde Valley (Kaplan 1956).

P. vulgaris (Fig. 1). In the American Southwest (Tularosa Cave) and in Middle America (Ocampo, and Tehuacan) *P. vulgaris* is pre-ceramic. In the Southwest, maize and *Cucurbita pepo* (pumpkin) are earlier than common beans (Martin *et al.* 1952), but in Ocampo (Cutler and Whitaker 1961; Kaplan and MacNeish 1960) domesticated *Cucurbita pepo* was used 9000 years ago, antedating the presence of cultivated *P. vulgaris* by at least 3000 years. *P. vulgaris* in Peru, appears in north coast sites in Cupisnique about 2200 years ago, coinciding with the introduction of maize and long after *Cucurbita moschata* squashes were present at Huaca Prieta 3000 to 5000 years ago (Towle 1961). Lima

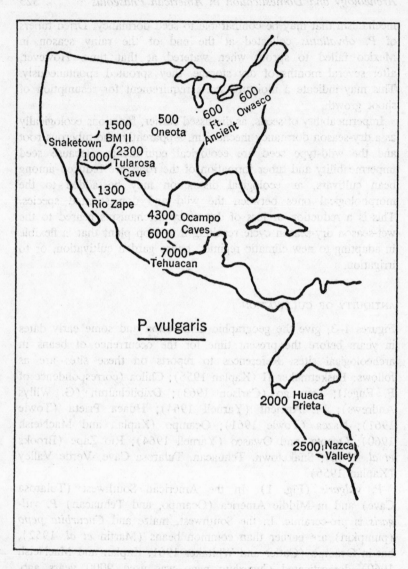

FIGURE 1 *P. vulgaris.* Archeological distribution and some early dates in years before present time.

beans (Fig. 2) are present in the earliest levels of Huaca Prieta, antedating common beans by at least 2000 years. The late appearance in a period of culture change of *P. vulgaris* in coastal Peru where vegetal materials are well preserved and have a long record strongly suggests that the common bean is an introduction to coastal Peru. Further studies of Peruvian *P. vulgaris* beans may indicate affinities to Middle American bean types.

The earliest remains of beans that are clearly domesticated occur in the Coxcatlan phase of Coxcatlan Cave of the Tehuacan valley (Kaplan 1967). One well preserved, uncharred pot valve is present in a context having a carbon[14] date of 4975 B.C.±200. The breadth of the pod and absence of a well developed parchment layer indicates that this is a domesticate. In Ocampo, Tamaulipas the earliest *P. vulgaris* remains are pods that similarly exhibit a reduced parchment layer and are morphologically identifiable with a *P. vulgaris* variety that occurs in later levels of the Ocampo caves as a pod-seed variety. That these pods are domesticated beans is further substantiated by the fact that the pods occur in the cave habitations. These pod remains are mature, which means that dry pods were brought into the caves from where they grew. This practice is economically feasible only when the pods are non-twisting and retain their seeds after ripening.

In both the Tamaulipas and Tehuacan sites, the bean remains relate to major subsistence patterns in the same way. Common bean remains are present during periods when plant collecting is the chief food source but do not become abundant until agriculture has been established as the main subsistence base for some time. This was in the period of 1100 to 1800 years ago in the Ocampo caves of Tamaulipas and about 1000 years ago in Tehuacan. A similar sequence, but with later absolute dates and shorter time intervals, can be discerned in the Southwest (Kaplan 1956). At Tularosa cave, in western New Mexico and in the San Juan River and northern Arizona canyon regions, common beans were present 2000 years ago but did not become abundant until 800 years ago. Bean remains in the Southwest seem to be abundant in cultures in which pottery was utilized and agriculture was the main food source.

If one contrasts the archeological record for beans and corn, perhaps the most striking difference is the clear documentation of

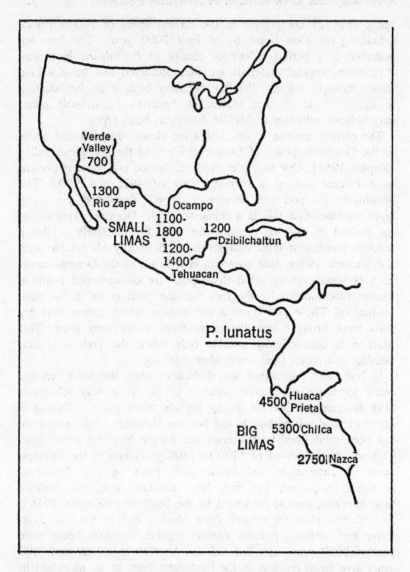

FIGURE 2 *P. lunatus.* Archeological distribution and some early dates in years before present time.

evolutionary change in corn and the absence of such evidence in beans.

The evidence from Tehuacan demonstrates the stability of bean varieties with respect to seed size and color patterns. One variety, first appearing 1000 years ago, is today obtainable in the Ajalpan market near Tehuacan. In Tularosa Cave, cultivars present in pre-ceramic levels 2000 years ago are represented unchanged 1000 years later in upper levels in the cave. Of course, there is much that one cannot tell from seeds or pods. While seed and pod characters have remained constant, other changes may well have taken place. Thus, transition from a vine to the erect habit may take place with no discernible effect on seeds; or alterations in ripening dates and other changes of great agronomic importance may be accompanied by no detectable changes in seeds.

Possibly, the transition from the vine to the bush habit in *P. vulgaris* and *P. acutifolius* had taken place in Tehuacan as early as their first appearance as domesticated seeds or pods there. The bush types in indigenous agriculture are invariably crops of dry land planting; the vining types are planted with corn or apart from corn with poles for support in humid lands. The aridity of the Tehuacan agricultural sites strongly suggests the growing of bush beans. The vegetative portions of the plants are seldom found among the remains available for study, but one specimen 800 years old from Tamaulipas (Kaplan, MacNeish 1960) includes the entire axis of one plant from root system to intact pods and is the bush type.

Within Middle America, the varietal composition of archeological *P. vulgaris* strongly suggests independent domestication centers. Bukasov (1930) estimated the number of cultivars of *P. vulgaris* to be about 500 in Middle America; other estimates are generally lower. Using seed characteristics as a means of distinguishing cultivars and allowing for some distinctions that may be based on trivial variations, about 35 *P. vulgaris* varieties have so far been recovered from sites in the Southwest and Middle America. Most of these have regional distribution, but some are restricted to a single site. This appearance of cultivar endemism may be illusory because of insufficient evidence or poor archeological methods of seed recovery. However, the degree to which endemism does exist suggests multiple domestication within Middle America from an ancestral species that was widespread and polymorphic.

P. coccineus. The very early remains at Ocampo (Kaplan, Mac-Neish 1960) are probably not domesticates for reasons indicated earlier. The oldest domesticated runner beans are those of Coxcatlan Cave, Tehuacan Valley. These beans and others found in El Riego Cave of the Tehuacan Valley in later times are comparable in size and external features with contemporary varieties grown in Chiapas. It is very doubtful that runner beans could have been grown in the immediate vicinity of these Tehuacan Caves because of high temperature and low water. Cultivation of runner beans was not noted in a brief reconnaisance of the mountains above Coxcatlan in 1962, but, judging from the vegetation, good crops of these beans could be obtained there. Presumably, the runner beans present in the Tehuacan Caves were traded in from the humid uplands. In Chiapas, runner beans are a product of the Indian highlands regularly brought down into the central depression of that state.

Because runner beans and their wild relatives grow in humid uplands, where the preservation of vegetal remains in archeological sites is not favorable, an archeological search for early runner beans might be conducted in arid land sites adjacent to cool uplands in Chiapas and Guatemala.

The limited distribution of archeological runner beans may only reflect limited excavation in likely areas. However, although this species is cultivated by indigenous peoples from Hopi country in Arizona down to Colombia, it is restricted to higher elevations and seldom approaches the *P. vulgaris* beans in importance. Perhaps the major niches for vining bean cultivation were already occupied by the highly variable *P. vulgaris* cultivars by the time that runner beans were available.

P. lunatus (Fig. 2). As indicated previously, big Limas and sievas are best considered as conspecific subspecies for genetic and morphological reasons. The archeological distribution supports this conclusion. Sieva beans were absent from Peru and the big Limas were not present in Middle America. Despite the great age of big Limas in Peru, no forms transitional from the wild have been found. Because of the general character of the coastal vegetation, wild beans would not be expected in this area. Domestication of the big Lima may have taken place east of the Andean highlands in warm, humid lands. The archeological record of sieva beans similarly suggests that domestication took place in areas other

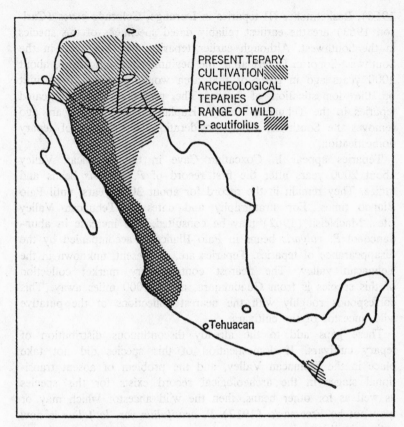

PRESENT TEPARY
CULTIVATION
ARCHEOLOGICAL
TEPARIES
RANGE OF WILD
P. acutifolius

Tehuacan

FIGURE 3 *P. acutifolius.*

than where they have been recovered. The close agreement in dates of appearance of sieva beans in Ocampo caves in Tamaulipas (Kaplan, MacNeish 1960), at Tehuacan (Kaplan 1967) and at Dzibilchaltun near Merida, Yucatan (specimens and correspondence from Dr. G. Willys Andrews) suggests their general introduction into eastern Mexico at about this time. Collections made by me of wild Limas that may be related to sievas in the Pacific coastal foothills of Oaxaca and Guerrero suggest this region as a likely one in which to search for early sieva bean domestication.

P. acutifolius (Fig. 3). Some authors have suggested the Sonoran Desert area as the center of tepary domestication (Kaplan

1956). Basketmaker III teparies in Durango, Colorado caves (Carlson 1963) are the earliest reliably dated specimens of this species in the Southwest. Although earlier teparies may be found in the Southwest-Sonoran Desert area, the beginnings of agriculture, about 2000 years ago in parts of that area would place a lower limit on the domestication of beans. The presence of domesticated teparies in the Tehuacan Valley (Kaplan 1967) 5000 years ago removes the Southwest from consideration as a center of tepary domestication.

Teparies appear in Coxcatlan Cave in the Tehuacan Valley about 2000 years after the first record of *P. vulgaris* beans and maize. They remain in the record for about 3000 years, until Palo Blanco times. For stratigraphy and dates of Tehuacan Valley sites, MacNeish (1962) may be consulted. The increase in abundance of *P. vulgaris* beans in Palo Blanco is accompanied by the disappearance of teparies. Teparies are, at present, unknown in the Tehuacan valley. The nearest contemporary market collection of this species is from Guadalajara, about 1000 miles away. This corresponds roughly with the nearest collections of the putative wild ancestor of the cultivars.

These gaps add to the already discontinuous distribution of tepary cultivars. If domestication of this species did not take place in the Tehuacan Valley, and the problem of absent transitional stages in the archeological record exists for this species as well as for other beans, then the wild ancestor which may or may not be Freeman's (1912) *P. acutifolius* var. *latifolius* is now extinct in this region.

SUMMARY

The systematic and economic botany of American beans is discussed. Four species have been important food plants the main dietary role of which has been as a complementary amino acid source in combination with corn. Beans were prominent among agricultural products cited in tribute lists in pre-Hispanic times.

Some important morphological features distinguishing the domesticates from the wild species are: increase in seed size; decrease in impermeability of seeds to water intake; reduction in fleshiness of the root system and loss of perennialism; reduction in shattering of the pods and violent seed dissemination. For the most part, the archeological materials now available do not document these changes. Excavations in the Pacific highlands and coastal areas of Mexico may be expected to yield transitional bean materials.

Archeological bean distributions do show that, unlike maize, varietal characteristics of beans have remained remarkably stable from their earliest records to their most recent. *P. vulgaris,* the common bean, was domesticated in Mexico by 7000 years ago; *P. coccineus,* the runner bean, by 2200 years ago. *P. acutifolius* var. *latifolius,* the tepary, by 5000 years ago; *P. lunatus,* the sievas, or small Limas by 1400–1800 years ago, the big Limas by 5300 years ago in Peru. The present distribution of the tepary is a much contracted relic one. The tepary has been largely replaced by common beans. This process of replacement continues at the present time. Mexican sievas and Peruvian big Limas are separated throughout their archeological records, a fact that adds weight to the view that these are independently domesticated conspecific geographic races.

In the Tehuacan Valley, some kinds of beans and corn may have been domesticated in association with one another. Elsewhere, early records of corn and beans do not coincide. Although beans are pre-ceramic in the Southwest, Tamaulipas, Tehuacan and Coastal Peru, they did not become abundant in the Southwest and Middle America until agriculture was well established for some time.

ACKNOWLEDGMENTS

Field studies of perennialism were aided by a grant from the American Academy of Arts and Sciences and carried out in part under a Roosevelt University Faculty Research Fellowship. Investigation of archeological material was supported by a grant from Sigma Xi-RESA. My wife, Lucille N. Kaplan, wrote the section on ethnohistory.

27 THE EVOLUTION OF CORN
AND CULTURE IN NORTH AMERICA[1,2]

Walton C. Galinat[3]

CORN (*Zea mays* L.) has been recognized as the basic food plant of all the more advanced New World cultures, such as those of the Inca, Aztec, Maya and Pueblo Indians, as well as of our own. The development of these cultures was permitted not only by corn's great productivity and its adaptability to a wide range of growing conditions but also from an adaptation in structure which facilitates its utilization by man. Although the grain-bearing axis of the other cereals is like that of corn in having acquired the essential non-shattering characteristic, only corn has evolved the additional advantages of the familiar cob with its over-all enclosure of husks. The cob is a structure convenient for harvesting, storage and shelling by hand, as well as for chewing-off the sweet immature grain from roasting ears.

Although the structure of the modern corn plant is well known, the extinction of wild corn has created a mystery as to how its form became a function of serving man (Mangelsdorf, MacNeish, Galinat 1964). Early in domestication, the tassel, an inflorescence which terminates the main stalk, became entirely male, and its structure became that of a lax plume whose waving branches shed

Reprinted by permission of The New York Botanical Garden, from *Economic Botany*, Vol. 19, 1965, pp. 350–57, and by permission of the author.

[1] Presented at a meeting of The Society for Economic Botany as part of a symposium entitled *Integrated Research in Economic Botany VI: Ethnobotany of Some New World Cultures, Part II: Crops of major importance,* December 30, 1964. AAAS Meetings. Montreal, Canada.

[2] Contribution of the Massachusetts Agricultural Experiment Station.

[3] Associate Professor, Waltham Field Station, University of Massachusetts, Waltham, Massachusetts, *and* Research Associate at the Bussey Institution of Harvard University.

Received for publication March 1, 1965.

their pollen into the wind. The ear, which terminates the lateral branches, became entirely female, and its structure became highly specialized to the benefaction of man. Thereby, hundreds of large naked kernels were concentrated in many rows upon an enormous cob (rachis), and the entire structure became enclosed by many overlapping husks borne from below along a telescoped branch, and the silks (styles) had to extend out beyond these husks to where they could become exposed to pollen.

By the time white man arrived in the New World, most of the present races of corn had already evolved. The race of Northern Flint corn was prevalent in New England and westward for at least 400 years prior to this century and its importance to the survival of the colonists at Plymouth is apparent in the statement of Governor Bradford, "And sure it was God's good providence that we found this Corne, for else we know not how we should have done" (Ralph and Adelin Linton 1949).

While the husk leaves made the ear convenient for harvesting by hand, they also prevented the natural dispersal of seed, and, thereby, they prevented the survival of corn as a wild plant. Since wild corn became extinct, perhaps thousands of years ago, our knowledge of its early evolution must come from fossil and archaeological evidence. The oldest remains are in the form of fossil pollen grains, about 80,000 years old. They came from the lower part of a drill core taken from a depth of 200 feet below Mexico City. The large size of this pollen indicated that it was probably from corn rather than corn's relatives (Barghoorn *et al.* 1954); later, by using a new technique, Irwin and Barghoorn (1965) revealed features which showed conclusively that the pollen was from corn. As Mangelsdorf, MacNeish, and Galinat (1964) have pointed out, the great age of this fossil corn pollen shows two important things: 1) that corn is a native American plant; and 2) that the ancestor of modern corn is wild corn and not one of corn's relatives, teosinte or Tripsacum.

Our knowledge of wild corn comes chiefly from the dry refuse accumulations of ancient cave men who lived in the arid valley of Tehuacán, Mexico some 7000 years ago (Mangelsdorf, Mac-Neish, Galinat 1964). The tiny wild-type cobs were usually bisexual, being male above and female below. They bore usually eight rows of tiny kernels. Each kernel was partially enclosed in glumes and each ear as a whole was partially enclosed in a few husks.

In contrast, the modern corn cob has increased about tenfold in size over its wild counterpart, and its evolution includes the following structural modifications. Now the ear is usually entirely female, and the glumes are usually reduced to the base of the kernel. The husk system has become highly developed as a device to enclose and protect the ear. The number of kernel rows is usually increased over eight. In addition, the diversity of corn has increased to a fantastic extent, as represented by over 200 distinct races, described in a series of monographs published by the National Academy of Science, National Research Council; and these races have become adapted to particular locations in the area from the St. Lawrence valley southward to central Chile.

FIGURE 1 A longitudinal section through a young ear of modern corn and its associated silks, husks, shank, subtending leaf, and stalk at about the time of pollination. Note that the husks (h) have not only formed a tight lateral enclosure about the ear, but they also form a vertical extension above the ear. This necessitates the development of very long silks (s) which can extend up beyond the husks in order to become exposed to the pollen.

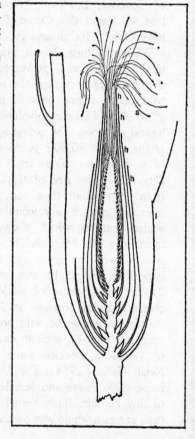

The question is then, "How could the many races of modern corn with their huge ears have evolved from this tiny wild corn of Tehuacán, even in 7000 years?" To find the answer, we have been trying to retrace some of the steps involved in corn's evolution under domestication.

In attempting to reconstruct wild corn by recombining primitive characteristics from various present races, Mangelsdorf (1958a) has made good use of the relic race called Argentine popcorn. Because this race bears a small ear at almost every node along its stalk, it provides a series of cob and husk types which are useful in showing some of the changes involved in the evolution of the modern ear. Progressing down the stalk, the shanks which bear the ears become longer from an increase in the number of nodes. As a result, the lower and larger ears get increased protection from a greater number of husks which are borne individually at these nodes. The ears borne near the top of the main stalk resemble those of wild corn in having a reduced husk system and a terminal male region.

The evolution of the husk system required more than just a lowering of the ear and an increase in the number of husks. It also involved an evolution in both silk length and pollen grain size. Fig. 1 shows how the tight lateral enclosure of husks about the modern ear required the development of long silks to extend up beyond the husks in order to become exposed for pollination. Note in the illustration that the silks from the base of the ear had to become longer than those from the tip of the ear in order to emerge. Now the pollen, too, had to evolve an ability to send its tubes all the way down these longer silks in order to cause double fertilization in the ovule at its base. Since modern corn is peculiar in the very large size of its pollen and the extreme length of its silks, it seemed that the large size of modern corn pollen might have evolved because a greater store of energy was needed to send pollen tubes down the longer silks which are borne on longer ears. This hypothesis was tested with data on pollen grain size and ear length already available on the Mexican races of corn. The results, as reported previously (Galinat 1963), showed an almost perfect correlation. That is, the primitive races had short ears and small pollen, while the evolved races had long ears and large pollen.

Corn-feeding birds, such as the common grackles, had a role

in the evolution of the modern ear. As the kernels from near the tip of the ear were frequently removed by the feeding of birds, the kernels from lower down on the ear, which could be fertilized only by the larger sized pollen, had a reproductive advantage. Furthermore, ears which could retain most of their grain within the protective confines of the husks, either because the ears were thickened (fasciated) at the butt or because the husks were longer or more numerous or both, would also have a selective advantage. Thus, with the help of man to disseminate the grain and the activity of birds in removing the "tip kernels," the evolution of the modern ear may have been an automatic process if the necessary variation was forthcoming.

The question of how these changes occurred in such a short period of time in an evolutionary sense may be answered in terms of the role played by corn's relatives. The dynamic nature of corn's evolution stems probably from a genetic flexibility acquired through an "introgression" or an introduction of genes (germplasm) from its wild relatives, teosinte and Tripsacum. Introgression from these relatives produces not only variation directly in corn; it also produces variation indirectly by means of a "mutagenic" effect (Mangelsdorf 1958b). In contrast, species resulting from various forms of polyploidy, in which there is little or no transfer of genes from one species to the chromosomes of another species, are known to be less flexible in their evolutionary adaptability (Stebbins 1950).

Although teosinte may be the immediate source of this introgression in corn, especially in Mexico and Central America, the apparent origin of teosinte from corn-Tripsacum hybridization places the origin of the introduced germplasm with Tripsacum (Mangelsdorf, Reeves 1939). Tripsacum, in turn, appears to be a polyploid form of hybrid between the now extinct wild corn and still another grass, Manisuris (Galinat *et al.* 1964). Therefore, the introgression in corn is ultimately from Manisuris. Cytogenetic studies now in progress indicate that the stage for this introgression was set in Tripsacum by rare exchanges (probably gross translocations) between the chromosomes of Manisuris and the chromosomes of corn both of which are within Tripsacum.

Following an introgression of this germplasm from Manisuris into corn, it seems that selection on a basis of whether a plant could scatter its own seed or whether the seed was gathered and then sown by man, has yielded two distinct products. Teosinte, $Z(XZ)$, is the product of natural dissemination and modern corn, Z(ZXZ) is the product of dissemination by man.

One of the most important archaeological records which shows the role of introgression in corn's evolution comes from the Tehuacán cobs previously mentioned. The series starts with wild corn at a radio carbon date of *ca* 5000 B.C. By *ca* 4000 B.C., the cobs were similar but slightly larger, as man had apparently learned the art of agriculture. Then, by *ca* 1000 B.C., the available gene pool was suddenly increased by the introduction of a new tripsacoid race presumed to be a product of hybridization with teosinte or Tripsacum. The evolution which followed gave rise to a more productive complex of corn types represented by the present day races of Nal Tel and Chapalote. The settled life of farming and the greater security gained from the storage of this higher yielding corn gave sufficient leisure to develop an advanced culture by *ca* A.D. 500.

The original corn in the Southwest, at Bat Cave, New Mexico (Mangelsdorf 1954), was also a tiny-eared type of Chapalote or pre-Chapalote similar to the wild corn of Tehuacán. The development of a more productive corn with an attendant advancement in culture was once again dependent upon the introduction of teosinte contamination in the corn, perhaps about 500 B.C. (Mangelsdorf, Smith 1949). As the yield of corn increased, the same pattern of settling down in permanent villages with stored up grain was followed and the Basketmaker and Pueblo cultures developed. There was probably an attendant rise in the population and this, in turn, would eventually result in increased demands for farmland and an expansion outward. In this case, the greater drought resistance of the tripsacoid Chapalote allowed an extension of corn culture into new and more arid regions. By the beginning of the Christian era, the settled way of life provided by this more drought resistant corn had extended the Basketmaker culture north into southern Utah and southwestern Colorado, as is revealed at numerous archaeological sites (Galinat, Gunnerson 1963).

The contribution of teosinte germplasm to increase productivity is a factor partly of hybrid vigor. In a large collection of archaeological cobs from Cebollita Cave in New Mexico studied by Galinat and Ruppé (1961), the longest as well as the shortest cobs were found to be the most tripsacoid. This type of relationship was interpreted as evidence of prehistoric hybrid corn. That is, the long cobs could have derived their greater length as a result of hybrid vigor from heterozygous teosinte germplasm, while the short tripsacoid cobs could represent detrimental effects from homozygous teosinte germplasm. In fact, very similar effects have been demonstrated experimentally in modern corn (Sehgal 1963).

Later, about A.D. 700, a third component, the race of eight-rowed corn, Harinoso de Ocho, entered into the evolutionary pathway and conferred even greater benefits in the form of higher productivity, easier milling, and adaptability to more northerly latitudes. The literature concerning the origin of this race, as reviewed by Grobman *et al.* (1961), shows that it may involve indirect introgression from a South American species of Tripsacum, *T. australe.* The blending of these diverse germplasms from corn, teosinte and Tripsacum would, as Grobman *et al.* have pointed out, produce many complicated forms of heterotic interactions which have great evolutionary potential.

The evolutionary potential of the interaction of a "teosinte-contaminated" race of corn (Chapalote) with a "South American Tripsacum-contaminated" race of corn (Harinoso de Ocho) was first realized in northwestern Mexico in the races Máiz Blando de Sonora and Cristalino de Chichuahua as found at Swallow Cave (Mangelsdorf, Lister 1956) and in their southwestern counterparts, the Pima-Papago and Pueblo races of corn (Anderson, Cutler 1942).

The data are still too few to establish the route by which Harinoso de Ocho traveled between its postulated homeland in the highlands of South America, as discussed by Galinat and Gunnerson (1963) and the American Southwest. But since its reputed ancestor, Cabuya of Colombia (Roberts *et al.* 1957) is adapted to high elevations, it is not surprising that little evidence of it can be seen along the west coast of Central America and Mexico. Even in northern Mexico, it is highly contaminated with the locally adapted corn. But in the high elevations of the Southwest, an essentially pure form of the eight-rowed corn, named Máiz de Ocho by Galinat and Gunnerson, is evident.

Since adaptability to high altitudes is essentially equivalent to adaptability to more northern latitudes, it is also not surprising to find Máiz de Ocho spreading out of the Southwest in a north-easterly direction to New England along an acceptable climatic pathway formed by the transition and upper austral life zones

(Galinat, Gunnerson 1963). The historic and prehistoric data on distribution of this race, as summarized by these authors, shows that this spread took about 700 years or from A.D. 700 in the Southwest to A.D. 1400 in New England.

The increase in food production associated with the introduction of Máiz de Ocho into the Southwest apparently triggered a sort of prehistoric population explosion and an expansion out onto new land where the corn would grow. Its presence coincides with the Pueblo II cultural expansion to an additional 250 miles farther north than had previously been possible. The movement of corn and people is especially apparent in that of the Fremont and Sevier groups spreading into northern Utah (Gunnerson 1960; 1962). People also moved into the Central Plains which had not been suited to the growing of the Chapalote maize previously available. As the area of corn cultivation expanded north and northeast, the corn encountered cooler and damper spring soils, as well as a shorter growing season. Thus, during its spread to the Northeast, natural selection filtered out certain features in the Máiz de Ocho germplasm with the eventual evolution of the race Northern Flint, which had become the sole Indian corn from the Dakotas across northern United States to the Atlantic Ocean by the early colonial period. The easier grinding, floury type kernels predominated from the Southwest to Nebraska and to some extent in the Dakotas, but the hard flinty kernels predominated eastward to New England where they were favored by natural selection during germination in cooler, wet soils.

But the most important contribution of this eight-rowed corn waited until only about 100 years ago. Then the white farmers migrated from two directions out into the area that we now call the Corn Belt. From the Southeast, in the area of Virginia, they brought a late-flowering dent corn called gourd seed. From the Northeast, they brought this early-flowering flint corn called the New England eight-rowed flint. According to Wallace and Brown (1956), when the higher yielding gourd seed gave poor stands, as it frequently did in the cooler, wet soils of the west, the farmers replanted the missing hills to the early New England flints. The hybridizations resulting from this interplanting eventually produced the world's most productive corn, the United States Corn Belt dent.

The geneology of the Corn Belt dent, as worked out by the various corn research teams sponsored by the Rockefeller Foundation in Latin America (Grobman *et al.* 1961) indicates that the high yields of this corn result from two major sources of hybrid vigor. First from teosinte germplasm in the gourd seed parent, and secondly from apparent South American Tripsacum germplasm in the New England flint parent. The gourd seed parent stems from Tuxpeño of the Gulf Coast of Mexico and it contains teosinte germplasm acquired by way of both parents, Olotillo and Tepecintle. On the other side, the New England flint corn traces back to the tripsacoid Cabuya of highland South America, as previously discussed. Thus, once again the explosive evolutionary effects of blendng these diverse germplasms, realized first in the Southwest, came to change the course of man's history.

The control of this hybrid vigor manifested in the Corn Belt dent represents the first significant achievement of modern man in increasing the yield of grain over that which he received from the Indians. H. K. Hayes (1963), in his book *A Professor's Story of Hybrid Corn* has shown that, because of the use of hybrid corn and better farming techniques, the acre yields of corn in the United States have doubled in the 30-year period between 1929 and 1959. Hayes attributes most of this increase to the use of hybrid vigor in corn breeding because of the much lower—29%—increase in the yield of oats over the same period. Since oats are a self-pollinated grass, it has not been possible as yet to use hybrid vigor in their improvement.

The advent of hybrid corn was well timed for the development of modern America. The extreme droughts of the early 1930's had made the usually conservative farmers desperate for changes. The new hybrid corn was anxiously tried on a wide scale. The yields from the use of hybrid corn immediately went up and since then both yields and percent acreage planted to hybrid corn have continued to increase until now more than 95% of the Corn Belt corn is hybrid. Although the three main creators of hybrid corn, Edward Murray East, George Harrison Shull, and Donald Forsha Jones, have all passed on now, their gift continues to nourish the rapid growth of our great civilization.

As modern corn and modern civilization have evolved together during the last 8000 years, they became equally productive, equally complex and mutually symbiotic. The modern Corn Belt dent, with its tall stalk bearing large, widely spaced leaves, is well designed for photosynthesis in depth and one or two large ears are centrally located to store the energy. Thus the modern corn plant, like modern civilization, is highly efficient in being organized and specialized. In the northern flint-type of ancestor before it, the energy is divided into several smaller stalks bearing several smaller ears. This division and reduction is even greater in the popcorn ancestors before it, a feature which represents a sort of breakdown in specialization in both the plant and the civilization which it nourished. Preceding this, in a primitive unprepared environment, there is a mere suggestion of the great things that have come to pass, in corn and civilization.

28 REVIEW OF "THE GRAIN AMARANTHS: A SURVEY OF THEIR HISTORY AND CLASSIFICATION," BY JONATHAN DEININGER SAUER

Volney H. Jones

A T THE time of the discovery of the Americas, the Indians had in cultivation somewhere near a hundred kinds of domesticated plants. Some of these, such as maize, white potato, sweet potato, tomato, peanut, and various beans and pumpkins, have been adopted into commerce and are well known. Many others have remained in folk agriculture and still are virtually unknown to Western civilization. The grain amaranth group treated by Sauer is an excellent example of this latter category. In spite of its apparent former importance and seeming respectable antiquity, this group has received little attention from either botanists or anthropologists.

The genus *Amaranthus* (family Amaranthaceae) is an exceedingly widespread one of many species occurring in the tropics and temperate regions of both the Eastern and Western hemispheres. The herbaceous plants of this genus are usually low-growing but may be lush plants higher than the head of a man. They are often aggressive weeds which take over disturbed areas and therefore follow man. Various species, either wild, semi-cultivated, or cultivated, have been of economic significance chiefly among primitive peoples as potherbs, food coloring agents, as grains for their starch, in magic and ceremony, and as ornamentals. Forms perhaps familiar to North Americans are the Love-Lies-Bleeding and Prince's Feather of our flower gardens.

Sauer's investigations of this important but relatively obscure

Annals of the Missouri Botanical Garden, Vol. 37, 1950, pp. 561–632, plates 10–14.

Reprinted by permission of *American Antiquity,* from Vol. XIX, No. 1, pp. 90–92, and by permission of the author.

group were carried out as a part of a doctoral problem at Washington University under the direction of Edgar Anderson. In the paper under review he confines himself to a discussion of the species cultivated for their seeds. An earlier short paper dealt with the dye amaranths of the Pueblo area of the Southwest (J. D. Sauer 1950a:412–15). Publication of data on uncultivated economic species is anticipated for the future. The paper is not presented as a conventional botanical "monograph" of the genus, but rather as a survey of geographical distribution, cultural association, the forms cultivated, and their economic and historical importance.

The data were drawn primarily from ethnography, travel accounts, and botanical sources. Archaeology as such was not included, as it had almost nothing to offer, but the paper has important implications for culture history. Sauer utilized a large amount of often obscure documentary materials (about 150 bibliographical items), and examined some 500 botanical specimens from various herbariums. This large task resulted in the reduction of a jumble of aboriginal names and scientific terms to some order, and the resolving of considerable taxonomic confusion. From a welter of previously named forms he emerges with only four species of cultivated grain amaranths. The materials are handled objectively and the report is clearly and concisely written.

Sauer's findings in essence are that in the Americas there were four essentially distinct centers of cultivation, each with its own separate species: 1) Mexico into the southwestern United States (*A. leucocarpus*), 2) Guatemala (*A. cruentus*), 3) Andean region (*A. caudatus*), 4) Argentina (*A. edulis*). Two of these species, those from Mexico and the Andean region, are also cultivated in Asia throughout a large area extending from Manchuria through interior China and the Himalayas to India, Afghanistan, and Iran. Records for Africa are feeble, but there is some indication that *A. caudatus* may have been present to a limited extent in the warmer regions.

Wherever the grain amaranths appear in cultivation today, they are secondary or marginal crops which apparently have been submerged by or pushed to the peripheries by larger seeded grain crops such as maize or rice. In Asia, they are largely in the hands of scattered hill peoples and there are no surviving records of their use by the more advanced peoples of the coasts. In America also, they are distinctly secondary and usually in isolated upland areas. From this pattern, Sauer infers that the amaranths were of ancient cultivation and of formerly greater economic importance, but now are a disappearing relic. Arguments to support this viewpoint are found in their wide but scattered distribution, persistence among retarded marginal peoples, and in their ceremonial association and veneration. Sauer discusses these points at some length particularly for the Mexican area, citing early historic tribute records and impressive ceremonial contexts.

If the grain amaranths have been displaced by larger seeded grains, then a chronological priority of the grain amaranths is implied. Sauer contends that a long association of the amaranths with man is indicated by the widespread use of the seeds by gathering peoples. A point not stressed by him is that the amaranths are almost ideal plants for seed gathering, particularly with gathering basket and seed beater. They produce a prodigious number of seeds concentrated in compact terminal position and at convenient height. The seeds fall readily at maturity. There is hardly a plant which would yield a greater amount of food in a short time. For temperate North America, at least, there is certainly abundant documentation of the gathering of seeds of wild amaranths. If there is any validity in the theory that the popping qualities of starchy seeds led to their early use and domestication, then again the amaranths can qualify.

From my own experience with North American materials, I can vouch that amaranth seeds are one of the more common kinds found in archaeological sites. They probably have occurred much more often than they have been saved, as the seeds are small and inconspicuous (about 1 mm. in diameter). They will pass through screens normally used and likely would not be noticed unless in caches or containers. All of the archaeological amaranth seeds which I have handled fall within the normal size range for seeds of wild plants and none by their size have obtruded themselves as necessarily cultivated. Some are from non-agricultural sites and levels.

Sauer points out, however, that cultivation has affected the quantity of seeds produced per plant, but has had little effect on the size of the seeds. He presents rather convincing evidence that the yield of grain amaranths per unit of land may be greater than that of corn. But the seeds are tiny and more difficult to handle and process. It might well have been that the amaranths could compete with earlier undeveloped forms of maize and rice, but eventually lost out as these crops were improved.

Sauer considers that all evidence points to an American origin for all four of the cultivated species of grain amaranths. This opinion is based largely on the greater botanical diversity of the amaranths in the Americas, the closer relationships of cultivated forms to wild forms here, and the more developed use of wild plants for grain purposes here. As two of the species (those typical of the Mexican and Andean centers) also appear in cultivation in Asia, transfer from America is indicated. Not only are the plants apparently identical, but also a complex of traits involving methods of cultivation, preparation, and use. The most common method of utilization was popping of the seeds and adding syrup as a binder to form cakes. This specific process occurs in such widely separated areas as China, Mexico, Nepal, and Argentina.

One cannot dodge the issue here by suggesting the floating of seeds, as this seems biologically impossible, and further, complexes do not float unattended by man. Sauer suggests that a movement of the grain amaranths from America to Asia in pre-Columbian times is indicated. He is exceedingly restrained and objective in his statements and does not push this interpretation. He does not construct land bridges or invoke Alexander's fleet, but modestly states his arguments and lets them stand on their own merits. He admits freely the possibility of post-Columbian transfer.

Sauer in stating his case for early transfer translates such factors as marginality, ingrained nature of the pattern, and ceremonial associations into chronological depth. I do not venture to refute him, but I do wish to submit that using a similar approach it can be argued that wheat was introduced into the Pueblo area of the Southwest in pre-Columbian times. These retarded "hill" peoples of the Southwest have archaic relic forms of wheat which are not found among more advanced lowland peoples of the coasts. They have a complex of very primitive methods of cultivation and processing, including threshing by trampling with horses, which are found only in marginal parts of the Old World or in earlier periods there. Wheat is considered by some of the Pueblos to be an ancient crop and there is no recollection of its introduction. Wheat among some of the Pueblos has ceremonial associations and is mentioned in origin myths as one of the original crops received from the gods at the beginning of the world. Yet in spite of these indications of great antiquity, we have clear evidence of the introduction of wheat by the Spaniards approximately 350 years ago.

Until recent years it was axiomatic in American anthropology that the cultural developments of the Old World and New World were independent and that any influences between the hemispheres were only by deculturizing northern routes. Almost the heart of the argument for this view was the essentially distinct inventory of crop plants and field methods in agriculture. It was recognized that the gourd and cotton did not quite conform, but there was a feeling that if we did not notice these problems they might go away. They are still with us, and recruits have been added in such crops as the sweet potato, corn, coconut, and we can now add the grain amaranths. These recalcitrant domesticates and perhaps others, refuse to remain neatly compartmentalized in one hemisphere or the other.

Loaded dice were used in the arguments for the distinctiveness of the American agricultural pattern from that of the Old World. Comparisons were always made to the Mediterranean pattern of seed cultivation with the plow and draft animals. Comparisons of American agriculture were not made to that of southeast Asia, where slash and burn clearing, root crop cultivation, and hand tools and methods were characteristic. The southeast Asian pattern and the American one appear to have more in common than earlier has with the Mediterranean complex. The fact that claims of transoceanic transfer almost always point to southeast Asia begins to gain significance.

The plant data continue to pile up suggestions of extensive contact across the Pacific in both directions. If these influences were in pre-Columbian times as seems increasingly indicated, a quandary exists in that anthropology cannot yet furnish appropriate human agencies to have affected the transfer. Cultural similarities are appearing, but these are chiefly in parallel items and not in broad patterns which can be pinned down precisely in time and to specific places. Certainly the information from archaeology, ethnography, and linguistics as presently construed is unable to support the burden imposed by the more exuberant interpretations of transfer of plants by human agency in remote times.

It is apparent that there is simply a lack of sufficient clearcut data to give answers to the questions which have arisen. In lieu of adequate data, one can take his stand either "for" or "against" trans-Pacific contact and defend his position by citing selected "authoritative" sources. But the problems involved are of considerable import to anthropology and to botany and deserve the best scholarly efforts which can be expended. In the meantime, little can be gained and much can be lost by acrimonious argument and character defamation. Bloody rearguard action and last ditch defense of fixed positions will avail nothing except perhaps the temporary salvaging of personal reputations. What is needed instead is a campaign of fluid maneuver with the perfection of present weapons and the development of new ones.

29 EARLY WOODLAND PLANT REMAINS AND THE QUESTION OF CULTIVATION

Richard A. Yarnell

ABSTRACT

Marsh elder (*Iva*) is considered on the basis of its distribution in Eastern Kentucky outside of its present range and the large size of the achenes from early sites. It is concluded that large seed size is not a function of large plants or of selection in harvesting. Thus *Iva* was probably intentionally cultivated in considerable quantity. The center of distribution seems to have been the central Mississippi Valley.

I T IS an anthropological tradition that subsistence of pre-Columbian farmers north of Mexico was based on an integrated crop complex consisting of corn, beans and squash. This may well be a valid concept for the proto-historic period of the Eastern Woodland. However, when one looks beyond the Late Woodland period, it is difficult to find supporting evidence for the presence of this crop triad. With the dubious exception of a report for the Middle Woodland Renner Site near Kansas City (Wedel 1943), there is no evidence for beans; and corn appears to be absent from Early Woodland sites, again with possible but unconfirmed exceptions. Squash is left as an uncontroverted Early Woodland cultigen, along with gourd and, presumably, sunflower; though several other plants (e.g., chenopod and marsh elder) have been suggested for this distinction (cf. especially Jones 1936; Fowler 1957c; Struever 1962).

Recently published evidence (Jackson 1960; Black 1963) indicates that an annual marsh elder (*Iva annua* var. *macrocarpa* Jackson) was an early cultivated food plant in the East. This conclusion is based primarily on a comparison of modern distribution

Reprinted by permission of the Florida Anthropological Society, from *The Florida Anthropologist*, Vol. XVIII, No. 2, June 1965, pp. 78–81, and by permission of the author.

and achene (seed) size of the species to the distribution and size of archaeological achenes (i.e. archaeological achenes are larger and occur in Kentucky well to the east of the present range of this species).

The distribution argument is, perhaps, contingent upon obtaining better phytogeographical data from Kentucky (however, during a cursory survey I was unable to locate *Iva* in the vicinity of Salts Cave, one of the locations in Kentucky where archaeological *Iva* has been found). The seed size argument has been disputed because of two possibilities. First, unusually large seed size may be the result of collection from large plants that grow in enriched soils, such as exist on sites of prolonged Indian habitation. Second, selection for unusually large seeds may have taken place in the harvesting process.

The latter possibility seems rather unlikely, because the archaeological occurrence of unusually large wild food seeds of other species are rarely reported. Seeds of Phalaris, Polygonum, and Amaranthus, for instance, usually are normal in size; though they may display some variation. (The sunflower could be taken as a major exception, but it is generally considered to be an Early Woodland cultigen.)

Another reason for doubting the significance of size selection in the case of *Iva* is the variation in size of achenes from different archaeological sites. Those from the Ozark Bluff Dwellings range up to 13 mm. in length. Very large achenes have been found at Newt Kash Hollow in Kentucky, whereas achenes from the Stilwell Site in Illinois and from Salts Cave are normal to large in size and those from the Apple Creek Site in Illinois and the Proether Bluff Site in Missouri are about the same size as achenes from the currently existing varieties of *Iva annua,* which range from 2.5 mm. to 4.5 mm. in length. (Incidently there is no *Iva* from contexts known to be later than Middle Woodland, so it may be diagnostic for certain pre-Late Woodland contexts.)

In order to test the hypothesis that larger plants produce larger seeds, I made two random collections of achenes from giant ragweed (*Ambrosia trifida* L.). A collection of 132 achenes came from a colony in an area where the plants ranged in height from 15 to 18 feet. A collection of 50 achenes was taken from the same colony in an area where the plants ranged from 4 to 6 feet in height. Achenes from the larger plants averaged 6.6 mm. long, while those from the smaller plants averaged 7.7 mm. long. However, during the examination, it became obvious that the sample from the larger plants included a higher percentage of immature achene than did the other sample. Therefore, all immature achenes and all those damaged or deformed were eliminated. The remaining 18 achenes from small plants and 11 from large plants were weighed and measured. In each case average weight was 33 mg. and average length was 8.4 mm. (It is interesting that 7 of the 18 achenes from small plants were longer than any from large plants.) However, since the samples were small, it would be well to repeat the investigation.

It is conceivable that similar results would not be forthcoming from measurements of *Iva* achenes from different sized plants, but suitable collections have not yet been made. Nevertheless, it seems unlikely that either plant size or selective gathering, or both together, could be responsible for the size of the Ozark achenes which are up to three times the length and many times the volume of the largest from the modern weed. However, selection of seeds for planting could have this effect on the marsh elder, just as it did on the sunflower, which is a member of the same tribe of the family Compositae and has somewhat similar achenes.

Thus I would consider unusually large seed size to be rather good evidence for domestication, a term which carries an implication of genetic distinctions in a plant which do not occur or occur only rarely or to a lesser extent in the ancestral form. On the other hand, I would consider the abundant archaeological occurrence of a plant well outside its present range to be good evidence for cultivation and perhaps also for propagation.

The questions of cultivation and domestication are somewhat more complex than generally stated, i.e. in terms of whether a given plant was or was not cultivated or domesticated. It would seem that more often the question is one of degree, i.e. to what extent or in what respects was (or is) a plant cultivated or domesticated? For all intents and purposes (excluding economic considerations) weeds are just as much cultivated or domesticated as are crop plants (or perhaps more so in some cases). In a lawn carpeted with Bermuda Grass, dandelions are considered noxious weeds; but Bermuda Grass plays the weed role in a cultivated field; while dandelions are utilized for food in some areas.

If weeds and cultigens are much the same biologically, being distinguished largely on the basis of cultural context, what do they have in common that distinguishes them from other plants? The answer to this question appears to fall into two categories. First, there is the great variability which is generally lacking in species growing in undisturbed habitats. This may be due to hybridization between closely related plant taxa or to the absence or suppression of certain factors which select against variation as they operate in natural plant communities. These two phenomena are not necessarily separate. In fact, the suppression of natural selection would tend to expedite the survival of hybrid offspring (cf. Anderson 1949; 1952).

A second distinguishing feature of weeds and cultigens is a close relationship to man. This is largely the result of man's activities in the suppression of the forces of natural selection that would tend to eliminate these plants, whereas man acts as an agent selecting against other plants and, in doing so, alters the balance of competition for survival in favor of weeds and cultigens. This generally amounts to cultivation, whether or not it is intentional or produces the desired results; though the term is not ordinarily used unless man's attitudes and activities in relation to a plant and its habitat are consciously oriented toward deriving some benefit from the plant. However, even then the term might not be used if man does not decide ahead of time when and where the plant will grow according to a traditional set of ideas and has himself carried out the objective.

Iva annua is a weedy species which favors wet prairie areas, river bottoms, and disturbed soil. Thus it grows in locations where selection through competition is at a low level. If we assume that it was not intentionally cultivated by Early Woodland peoples in eastern Kentucky, the most feasible explanation of its archaeological occurrence there would seem to be that it was introduced by man to that region where it took hold in habitats which he himself created perhaps as a result of intentionally cultivating other plants, and that he harvested marsh elder along with gourd, squash, and sunflower. This would mean that there was, in actuality, cultivation of marsh elder but without *intentional* propagation. Just such a phenomenon has been recorded for the Hopi by Whiting (1939). It is, perhaps, a simple step to add seed planting to this relationship when this is already part of man's relationship to other plants.

It may be significant that the human faeces from Newt Kash Hollow and from Salts Cave contain both sunflower and marsh elder achenes in considerable quantity and that squash seeds are present in

9 of 40 Salts Cave faeces examined. Even more significant, perhaps, is the occurrence of strawberry achenes with sunflower and marsh elder achenes in one specimen. This strongly indicates late spring or early summer as the season of deposition, which is three or four months earlier than the harvest season for sunflower and marsh elder. Thus it would appear that food from the latter two plants was available in quantities sufficient for storage and consumption throughout winter and spring. It seems rather unlikely that there was enough area in land adequately disturbed to allow for the perpetuation of *Iva* in such quantity unless the land was intentionally disturbed.

It seems likely that the large-seeded marsh elder originated in the central Mississippi Valley. This area is at the center of its known distribution, and *Iva annua.* Jackson (1960:813) states "Variety *caudata* is most distinct in Louisiana. In the northern part of its range it becomes somewhat diluted by hybridization with variety *annua.*" Thus the central Mississippi Valley is likely to be the region of greatest variation of the species. (Of course, it is not known when the ranges of these two varieties began to overlap, if they were ever separate; but the survival of hybrid offspring would likely increase as man increased his activities of habitat disturbance.) This same region is the center of archaeological sunflower distribution in the East, so I am inclined to agree with the suggestions of Jones and Fowler that this was the most critical area for early plant cultivation in the eastern United States and that its beginnings reach back to the Late Archaic period.

Part V | THE ROLE OF AGRICULTURE IN THE DEVELOPMENT OF CIVILIZATION

30 DEVELOPMENTAL ASPECTS OF HYDRAULIC SOCIETIES

Karl A. Wittfogel

1. THE GREAT CHALLENGE TO A UNILINEAL CONCEPT OF DEVELOPMENTS: HYDRAULIC ("ORIENTAL") SOCIETY[1]

AN AWARENESS of the developmental peculiarity of irrigation-based "Oriental" society kept the classical economists from advocating simple schemes of unilineal evolution such as were the order of the day during and after the Industrial Revolution. The present efforts of anthropologists to establish multilineal patterns of development are methodologically subtler, and their roots are complex. But it is probably no accident that these new efforts are greatly concerned with the developmental history of "irrigation civilizations" in the New and in the Old World.

Through my work on Chinese history I have long been impressed with the developmental lessons to be learned from a study of agrarian societies based on large-scale and government-directed waterworks. These societies covered more territory, lasted for more years, and shaped more lives than any other stratified agrarian society. In contrast to the stratified agrarian societies of Medieval Europe, they failed, of their own inner forces, to evolve beyond their general pattern. Both their historical significance and their institutional peculiarity make them a productive starting point for a new inquiry into the nature of societal development.

Reprinted from *Irrigation Civilizations: A Comparative Study*, published by the Organization of the American States (formerly Pan American Union), Washington, D.C. 20006, by permission of the publisher and by permission of the author.

[1] For a fuller presentation of the facts and problems discussed here, see my book, *Oriental Despotism; A Comparative Study of Total Power* (1957).

2. TWO BASIC PREREQUISITES AND A FEW TAXONOMIC COMMENTS

Such an inquiry requires, first, the postulation of recognizable patterns of societal *structure* ("culture types") and second, the postulation of recognizable patterns of societal *change* ("development"). Both prerequisites have been successfully met by Julian Steward (1949b:2 ff.; 1953:318 ff. and 321). Accepting the substance of his definitions, I shall, from the standpoint of the institutional historian, comment briefly on the morphology—and taxonomy—of societal types and changes.

a. Societal (culture) types

Societal types are operational units whose essential intellectual, technical, organizational, and social elements, although not necessarily specific in themselves, become specific through their dimension and the institutional setting in which they function. A substantially technological approach, as suggested by Leslie White (1949:365, 375 ff., 377, 390), can be very productive in a study of the Industrial Revolution. But it fails to explain the beginnings of industrial capitalism, which at first reorganized rather than re-equipped industrial production. And, on the level of pre-industrial life, it prevents a clear understanding of the institutional processes that separated, not temporarily and accidentally, but structurally and over time, the hydraulic from the non-hydraulic part of the agrarian world.

In a recently published paper, Gordon Childe states that his definition of the Neolithic "stage" rests on economic and not on geologic or technologic criteria (Childe 1953:193). Yet more than in the past, his discussion obscures the crucial socio-political differences behind similarities of material and technology; and also more than in the past, his use of the terms "neolithic revolution" and "urban revolution" obscures the peculiarities of the developmentally decisive hydraulic revolution.[2]

---

[2] In his earlier writings Childe stressed emphatically the ecological and organizational peculiarities in irrigation-based "Oriental" societies. He noted the pioneer position of these societies in the "second" neolithic revolution; and he took pains to distinguish the Oriental Bronze Age from the Bronze Age of temperate Europe (see Childe 1948:105, 109, 128 ff., 140 ff.; 1946:62 ff.,

The men who accomplished this revolution often employed the same work tools (hoe, shovel, basket) and the same work materials (soil, stone, wood) as did the rainfall farmers. But by specific organizational means (large-scale cooperation, rigid subordination and centralized leadership) they established societies that differed structurally from societies based on rainfall farming.

The comprehensive use of metal contributed to the further growth of hydraulic societies and non-hydraulic agrarian societies, but it did not bring them into being. And the urban revolution that followed the hydraulic revolution was radically different in its socio-political content from the urban revolution that occurred in the non-hydraulic agrarian world.

Above the level of simple tribal life, and in most cases evolving directly from it, there obviously existed a number of higher pre-industrial civilizations whose diversities can be ascribed only to a limited extent to technological factors: stratified pastoral societies, hydraulic societies, the non-hydraulic and non-feudal agrarian societies of ancient Greece (with *metics* or free peasants as cultivators) and of republican Rome (increasingly employing slave labor in agriculture), the feudal societies of Europe (based on rainfall farming) and of Japan (based on small-scale irrigation); and perhaps some others that are less distinct typologically and less important historically.

b. Developmental patterns

Our reference to the multiple origins of higher agrarian societies indicates that societal development, like societal type, may show substantial and definable diversities. A comparative study of development has to recognize the possibility of single as well as multiple origin, and the possibility of multiple modes of development following upon both types of origin. It has to recognize societal stagnation and change, circular change (resulting in restoration) and permanent change (development proper). It has to recognize that in terms of values, development may be progressive or retrogressive, or ambivalent, its positive and negative values being determined (if not

76, 161, 189, 198, 272). In his more recent writings these distinctions become less meaningful (see Childe 1951 a *passim* [based on lectures given in 1947/8]; and in his paper *Anthropology Today* (cf. Childe 1953:208) they all but disappear.

as easily as the 19th century evolutionists thought) by a judicious appraisal of technical, organizational, and social factors, and such basic human assets as freedom of opinion and opportunity for creative expression.

And then there is diversive change—societal transformation brought about, not developmentally, that is, not "spontaneously" and "from within" (cf. Kroeber 1948:241), but by extraneous forces which compel the target society to move in a direction that it would not have taken without external interferences either at the moment of change or in a foreseeable future.

These developmental patterns occur in many combinations. All are pertinent, and some are crucial, for an understanding of the typological and developmental position of hydraulic society.

3. HYDRAULIC SOCIETY: THE OVER-ALL CONFORMATION AND SOME MAJOR SUB-TYPES

a. Hydraulic ("oriental") society and "oriental despotism"

I suggest that the term "hydraulic agriculture" be applied to a system of farming which depends on large-scale and government-directed water control. I suggest that the term "hydraulic society" be applied to agrarian societies in which agro-hydraulic works and other large hydraulic and non-hydraulic constructions, that tend to develop with them, are managed by an inordinately strong government. I suggest that the term "state" be applied to a government that, on the basis of a sufficient surplus, is operated by a substantial number of full-time specialists: civil and military officials. I suggest that the term "hydraulic society" be used interchangeably with "Oriental society" in recognition of the geo-historical fact that the societal order under discussion appeared most significantly and lastingly to the east of those European countries, in which social scientists first tried to define these phenomena. To the best of my knowledge, John Stuart Mill was the first to use the formula "Oriental society" (Mill 1909:20).

Although little effort has been made to clarify the underlying institutional facts, the term "Oriental despotism" has been widely accepted. Following Milukov, we may apply the designation "Oriental despotism" to a state that is stronger than all other forces of society (Milukov 1898:111).

b. Basic institutional aspects of hydraulic society

The extraordinary power of the hydraulic state results from a number of institutional features that interlock and mutually support each other. Among them I consider outstanding the state's constructional, organizational, and acquisitive achievements; its success in keeping private property weak and in keeping the dominant religion attached to itself; and its specific type of ruling class—a monopoly bureaucracy.

The constructional achievements of Oriental despotism include the creation and maintenance of large waterworks for productive and protective purposes (irrigation and flood control) and, under certain conditions, the creation of navigation canals and extended aqueducts for conveying drinking water. Among the non-hydraulic installations that tend to grow with the growth of the various hydraulic installations we find monumental defense works (long walls and fortresses), far-flung roads, "big houses" (palaces, temples), and colossal tombs (pyramids, etc.).

The organizational achievements of Oriental despotism include certain operations inherent in large-scale and planned construction (counting, record-keeping, handling of large numbers of corviable persons), processes of using what has been constructed (management of hydraulic and non-hydraulic installations), and the application of the thus acquired organizational techniques to other operations: to quick communication and intelligence (the state post), and to the maintenance of coordinated and centrally directed armies. Tribal hydraulic communities are superior in food production to most of their non-agricultural neighbors; but the former are at a military disadvantage because of their fixed and, for the most part, small residences. They therefore excel in the defensive arts of war.[3] It is the larger and state-centered hydraulic societies that integrated and relatively numerous armies provide the means for aggressive warfare and for regional and, eventually, super-regional expansion.

The acquisitive achievements of the hydraulic state include a variety of measures aimed at controlling the population's labor and/or the fruits of its labor. Under simpler conditions, agricultural corvee labor on "public fields" and government-assigned office land prevails; under more complex conditions, the government relies, in

[3] For a discussion of the elaborate defense measures taken by the Pueblo Indians and the Chagga, see Wittfogel (1957: Chapter II).

part or essentially, on raising taxes in kind and/or in cash. The acquisitive claim tends to affect the whole population; and being imposed from above, it tends to be heavy.

The hydraulic regime's power over the population's property manifests itself not only in its fiscal strength but also in acts of ruthless confiscation and in laws of inheritance which compel the more or less equal division of a deceased person's property among several heirs (usually his sons, but at times also his daughters or other relatives).

Still more consequential is the fact that the one-sided concentration of societal leadership in the government prevents the owners of private property, both mobile and immobile, from organizing independent and politically effective bodies, "corporations" or "estates." This was the case even for the non-office-holding members of the ruling class, the bureaucratic gentry. Only the executive activists were organized, and they were organized politically through the permanent operational centers (office, bureaus) that formed the administrative nuclei of the despotic ("apparatus") state. Jealously defending their monopoly of political organization, on occasion even at the expense of their proprietary interests, these men of the apparatus constituted a monopoly bureaucracy. In contrast to the representatives of so-called "monopoly capitalism," they were eminently successful in maintaining a monopoly of societal leadership (Wittfogel 1953a:97, note 3).

Professional functionaries of the dominant religion often, and particularly under simpler conditions, acted also as government officials. But they never established independent churches that counterbalanced the power of the state, as did the *ecclesia militans* of the European Middle Ages. Throughout the Oriental world, and in a variety of ways, the dominant religion remained attached to the absolutist government which often appointed its priests and usually administered its property.

c. Major sub-types of hydraulic society

These are important aspects of the culture-type, hydraulic society. Their implication for the macro-morphology of development are apparent. They become still more apparent after we have examined the major sub-types of the over-all conformation.

The institutional tissue of hydraulic society differs structurally and definably with regard to hydraulic and managerial "density." It also differs with regard to proprietary "complexity": the quality and dimension of active (productive) private property and private-property-based enterprise.

In Inca society, ancient Egypt, and Mesopotamia the greater part of all arable land seems to have depended on irrigation water provided by government-controlled installations. Hydraulic agriculture prevailed absolutely; and the density of the bureaucratic-managerial apparatus was extreme. Under such conditions we are faced with a "compact" hydraulic society.

Where the hydraulic centers are spread out among large areas of small-scale irrigation and/or rainfall farming, we are faced with a "loose" hydraulic society. A number of territorial states of the Mexican highlands and of early China and India fall into this latter category.

Loose hydraulic societies include regions which lack agro-hydraulic works, but which are subject to the same organizational and acquisitive controls that the despotic state employs in its hydraulic core areas. When such regions, after gaining independence, still preserve Orientally despotic methods of statecraft, or when, under the influence of hydraulic societies, such methods emerge in adjacent countries that practice little or no hydraulic agriculture, then we are faced with a "marginal" hydraulic (Oriental) society.

In some instances, the government of a marginal hydraulic society undertook large non-hydraulic operations (Middle Byzantium, the Lowland Maya, the Liao empire). In other cases, such large non-hydraulic operations were practically lacking (Muscovite Russia). This divergence poses important questions of origin and structure. But it is imperative to realize that, in terms of political, social, and economic relations, all these civilizations definitely belonged to the hydraulic world, while other societies that preserved some elements of Oriental despotism, but represented different socio-cultural patterns, belonged to the "sub-marginal" part of the hydraulic world.

One of the most remarkable examples of a hydraulically sub-marginal civilization is Japan, which, on the basis of small-scale irrigation, evolved a system of social leadership and dependency that was as similar to that of feudal Europe as it was dissimilar to the great hydraulic society of the near-by mainland, China.

Varying density in the hydraulic and managerial spheres involves a varying administrative (bureaucratic) density among those who do the ruling. Varying complexity in the proprietary sphere involves a varying social differentiation among those who are ruled. In primitive (tribal) hydraulic societies, a higher degree of hydraulic density and/or a larger population seems to bring about stronger government control over both land and water. In hydraulic states, the bulk of all cultivable land is, for the most part, not privately owned but, on the village level, regulated by local officials or semi-officials.

As a rule, substantial private property-based social differences seem to have arisen first from differences in active mobile property— the material foundation of handicraft and trade. Simple hydraulic societies have few independent artisans and merchants. Pharaonic Egypt, until the New Kingdom, and Inca society are cases in point.

Semi-complex hydraulic societies have substantial groups of professional and independent artisans and merchants. Maya and Aztec society, and of course traditional India until the arrival of the British, exhibit this semi-complex pattern.

It seems certain that elements of private landownership were present in many simple and semi-complex hydraulic societies. But prior to the recent processes of disintegration, such ownership under Oriental despotism prevailed in relatively few civilizations (pre-eminent among them: imperial China). The developments of the 19th and 20th centuries, which in many parts of the Oriental world (India and the Near East) weakened the traditionally strong despotic state and favored the growth of absentee landlordism, must not obscure the fact that, in the long history of hydraulic society, complex conditions of property (that is, the prevalence of mobile *and* immobile private property) were more the exception than the rule.

4. DEVELOPMENTAL ASPECTS OF HYDRAULIC SOCIETY

Recently the development of hydraulic society has been analyzed particularly with regard to local origins, regional maturation, and empire-like expansion. And the terms "Formative," "Florescent" ("Classic") and "Empire" (or "Fusion") have been suggested for these phases. Formation, growth, and dimension are indeed vital phenomena. Their institutional meaning will become clearer, if they are examined in the light of our just-defined criteria: managerial density and proprietary complexity.

a. Origins (Formative I and II)

Irrigation societies, in the form of independent village communities, have existed for many centuries in the Pueblo area of North America. But students of the formative phase have neglected them for the study of Chavín-Cupisnique, Salinar, and other cultures which are assumed to have had an incipient ruling class and state. This approach ignores valuable socio-typological information; yet it implies a recognition of the fact that, in the major areas of hydraulic development, primitive hydraulic commonwealths expanded quickly beyond the single-village pattern that the Pueblos exemplify so strikingly.

The radiocarbon data on the ancient Near East seems to indicate that "once food production came into being, the rate of technological (and cultural) acceleration was much more rapid than had been anticipated" (Johnson 1951:53). Obviously this thesis is not valid for regions in which limitations of water and soil caused the perpetuation of the single-village community. However, it may well explain why in the Andean zone, in Egypt, and Mesopotamia, the establishment of hydraulic society apparently occurred in two phases (Formative I and Formative II, if you wish), the second either quickly succeeding the first or being almost indistinguishable from it, and with groups larger than a single "local" unit combining for the initial communally-conducted hydraulic effort. Thus the criterion of dimension permits us to recognize, for the formative period of hydraulic society, a single-settlement type (Local I) and a multi-settlement and incipient city-state type (Local II).

In semi-arid settings, such as North China, early rainfall farmers probably practiced irrigation agriculture first along smaller water courses and later in the larger river plains and deltas, while they continued to cultivate and at times increase the extent of their non-hydraulic hinterland. Such a development would make for loose hydraulic societies. The agro-hydraulic conquest of arid regions, which often led to the establishment of compact hydraulic formations, may have been accomplished by representatives of loose hydraulic societies which had received their initial hydraulic experience in a semi-arid setting, or it may have been accomplished by rainfall farmers. The latter form of transition may have occurred in the main in areas in which innundation agriculture was possible. But circumstances permitting, it seems reasonable to assume that there was interaction between early loose and compact hydraulic societies.

In terms of hydraulic density then, the formation of hydraulic societies probably occurred in several ways. And in all likelihood a variety of leaders (war chiefs, peace chiefs, priests) spearheaded, and benefited from, the hydraulic revolution.

On the eve of this revolution there may have existed various forms of property (clan, private, and communal). But the new development favored government control over specialized handicraft and exchange together with government control over the bulk of all cultivable land.

b. Regional and inter-regional (empire-like) developments

Viewing the hydraulic "region," as juxtaposed to the local "community," as a larger ecological unit that draws its water supply from a whole river system, or a self-contained part of such a system, we find the regional type of hydraulic development correlated with a maximum growth of compact hydraulic societies: witness the city or territorial states of coastal Peru, of ancient Mesopotamia, and pre-Thinite Egypt, and the "kingdom" of Dynastic Egypt. The territorial states of Chou China rarely outgrew their loose hydraulic orgins:[4] but they often increased their hydraulic density. The northwestern state of Ch'in, which in 221 B.C. unified "all-under-heaven," eventually comprised two extremely compact and productive hydraulic areas: the Red Basin of Szechuan and central Shensi with its fabulous Chêng-Kuo irrigation system.

The fusion of several hydraulic regions into empire-like conformations occasionally stimulated the creation of interlinking navigation canals, such as the Chinese Grand Canal. But in the sphere of hydraulic agriculture a different trend became dominant. Since

---

[4] Renewed examination of the issue has convinced me that early historical (pre-Chou and Chou) China constituted not a hydraulically tainted feudal society, but a hydraulic society proper. The climate and the lay of the land made comprehensive hydraulic enterprises a basic prerequisite for permanent settlement and agricultural prosperity in the cradle of Chinese civilization, the river basins and plains of North China. Significantly, during the Chou period the rulers of the territorial states assigned land not to vassals who rendered limited and conditional services, but to officials who were expected to serve without limitation and unconditionally. Thus these lands were not fiefs, but office lands, a type of land-holding that is not at all infrequent under Oriental despotism.

the old core areas usually reached the saturation point of their hydraulic growth in the period of regional development, the despotic state, while eager to develop hydraulic enterprises in new areas (where this was possible and rewarding), asserted its imperial power by acquiring, whenever recognized advantage suggested, a maximum of territories with a low hydraulic potential, small-scale irrigation and rainfall farming pure and simple. In consequence the great irrigation empires were usually loose hydraulic societies, and compared with the conditions of regional hydraulic development, the period of inter-regional fusion generally represented a lower coefficient of hydraulic density.

Proprietary complexity changed in a different way. With growing dimension and inter-regional communication, simple conditions of property tended to yield to semi-complex and eventually, but much more rarely, to complex conditions of property. For obvious reasons, managerially compact regions that disposed over a larger bureaucracy were more reluctant to allow professional handicraft and exchange to fall into the hands of private property and enterprise. In Inca society the hydraulic sponge was so effective that, even under conditions of empire, private-property-based enterprise in handicraft, and particularly in trade, was insignificant.

The Inca case, however, seems to be the exception rather than the rule. In most peacefully interrelated territorial states (cf. Buddhist India and later Chou China), and in the majority of all hydraulic empires, new and substantial industrial and commercial possibilities were opened up. And what may be called the *Law of Diminishing Administrative Returns* induced the rulers to permit a substantial increase in privately operating artisans and merchants. Thus in the period of fusion, semi-complex hydraulic societies replaced in many parts of the world the simple hydraulic societies of the period of regional development.

Semi-complex, not complex societies. The empires and quasi-empires of the Mexican highland, the Near East, and India, and also the marginally hydraulic world of Maya Yucatán favored non-governmental handicraft and commerce; but they did not convert the bulk of the land from regulated to private property. The establishment of private landownership in China (which greatly stimulated the intensity of agriculture) remained, until the recent time of transition, an exceptional case of complex proprietary development as, at the other end of the institutional scale, Inca society remained an exceptional case of simple proprietary development.

c. Institutional growth, stagnation, epigonal attitudes, and conspicuous retrogression

Thus progress from regional to inter-regional and empire-like conditions increased man's freedom from government control (some scholars would say exaggeratedly: from "state slavery"). But this development rarely freed the villages from the bonds of official or semi-official regulation; nor was it paralleled by an expansion of hydraulic agriculture.

Worse, there was a tendency for hydraulic stagnation to give way to retrogression. The agro-managerial coefficient shrank *relatively* when Oriental despotism extended its non-hydraulic territory, while its hydraulically cultivated territory remained unchanged. The agro-managerial coefficient shrank *absolutely*, when the amount of hydraulically cultivated land decreased. This happened for internal reasons, when indigenous rulers paid less attention to maintaining agro-managerial standards than to invoking new methods of fiscal exploitation. This happened for external reasons, when hydraulically unconcerned "barbarians" placed themselves as conquerors over a hydraulic society. In the first case, retrogession might be combatted at intervals. In the second case, retrogression might lower the hydraulic effectiveness for long periods. This happened on a gigantic scale in the Old World, when, in the middle of the first millennium A.D. and in consequence of a great revolution in cavalry warfare, a net of Orientally despotic conquest societies spread over the Near East, India, and China.

The relations between maturation, stagnation, and retrogression are not easily defined. But a few major trends may be tentatively suggested.[5] The growth in the magnitude of a socio-cultural unit does not necessarily involve a corresponding institutional and cultural growth. Loose interaction between numerous independent units proves more stimulating than island- or oasis-like isolation. It also proves more stimulating than imperial fusion, which tends to give the initiative for experiment and change to a single center. This

---

[5] From this point to the end of this sub-section, see Wittfogel (1957: Chapter X, B, 1a and b).

probably accounts for the fact that the foremost representatives of Oriental civilization generally achieved the peak of their creativeness when they were part of a cluster of loosely related territorial states.

Practically all great Chinese ideas on the "way" (*tao*), on society, government, human relations, warfare, and historiography crystallized during the classical period of the territorial states and at the beginning of the imperial period. The establishment of the examination system and the psychologically slanted reformulation of Confucianism followed the reunification of the empire, the transfer of the economic center of gravity to the Yangtze Valley, and the building of an artificial Nile, the Grand Canal. Other significant changes occurred during later periods of imperial China in the field of the drama and the popular novel; but they were largely due to a new influence, the complete subjugation of China by two "barbarian" conquest dynasties. And none of them shook the Confucian foundation of Chinese thought.

The climax of creative expression in India is similarly located. Hindu religion, statecraft, law, and family patterns originated and reached their "classical" maturity either when India was a network of independent states or during the early phase of imperial unification.

The Arab-dominated conquest societies of the Near East began on an empire-like level. But here again most of the great ideas concerned with law, statecraft, and man's fate were formulated, not at the close, but during the first and the early middle period of Islamic society.

Within a given framework, creative change does not continue indefinitely. When the possibilities for development and differentiation have in great part been realized, the creative process tends to slow down. Maturation becomes stagnation. And given time, stagnation results in sterotyped repetition (epigonism) or outright retrogression. Conquest and territorial expansion favor acculturation. But the ensuing changes do not seriously alter the existing pattern of society and culture. They will be of minor consequence; and eventually they also will yield to stagnation, epigonism, and retrogression.

The trend toward epigonism and retrogression may merge—and, in the Oriental conquest societies of the Old World it did merge—with a trend toward reduced hydraulic intensity and increased personal restriction. In terms of managerial action, personal freedom, and cultural creativeness, most hydraulic societies of the late "Empire" period probably operated on a level lower than that reached during the days of regional and early "Empire" florescense.

5. HYDRAULIC SOCIETIES THAT LOSE THEIR INSTITUTIONAL IDENTITY

Under the shadow of the hydraulic state there arose no independent force strong enough to transform the agrarian order into an industrial society. Certain hydraulic societies evolved into non-hydraulic agrarian societies; but generally they did so in consequence of external aggression and conquest. They experienced a diversive rather than a developmental change. And recently many hydraulic societies have begun to lose their institutional balance, because they were shaken fundamentally by the imperialist, and non-imperialist, impact of modern industrial society. In a specific sense, they are hydraulic societies in transition.

a. Diversive changes

In the Mediterranean area diversive changes have expanded and reduced the hydraulic world since the time of Crete and Mycenae. This process was at work, when Greek influence in Western Asia rose and fell, when the Hellenistically despotic state of Western Rome collapsed under the attacks of non-Oriental barbarians, when the feudal kings of Castille and Aragon destroyed the Oriental despotism of Moorish Spain, and when the crusading representatives of feudal Europe paralyzed Byzantium.

b. Hydraulic society in transition

No comparative study of development in the hydraulic world may overlook the facts and patterns of these (and similarly structured) diversive changes. Nor may it overlook the developmental processes that recently have placed hydraulic society in its entirety in a state of transition. Marx, who, with significant inconsistencies (Wittfogel 1953b:351 ff.) maintained the Asiatic concept of the classical economists, was intrigued by the effect of British rule on "Asiatic society." Marx held no brief for British imperialism; he called its behavior in India "swinish." But he found that, by laying in India the foundations of a private-poverty-based modern society, the British accomplished "the only *social* revolution ever heard of in Asia" (Marx 1853).

Students of the developmental peculiarities of hydraulic society are uniquely prepared to explain why Japan, which was never hydraulic, evolved with relative ease into a modern industrial society. They are uniquely prepared to study the changes that, under direct or indirect Western influence, occurred during the 19th and early 20th centuries in India, Turkey, and Russia. They are uniquely prepared also to answer the question raised, in 1906, in a fateful discussion between the two top-ranking Russian Marxists, Plekhanov and Lenin, as to whether a new Russian revolution, irresponsibly handled might not lead to an "Asiatic restoration"—that is, to the restoration of Oriental despotism. The relevance of this question for the evaluation of contemporary Russia and China is evident.

By conscientiously and objectively studying the structure and the development of Oriental society, we may once again prove with new answers and new questions the scholarly (and the human) value of the social sciences which we serve.

31 DEVELOPMENTAL STAGES
IN ANCIENT MESOPOTAMIA

Robert M. Adams

COMPLEX PROCESSES of growth are divided into eras or stages only at the risk of distortion in the patterns of sequential events of which they are composed. It must also be admitted at the outset that the bare institutional and technological changes to which the condition of the archeological record largely limits us were always related to wider cultural correlates through a continuum of cause and effect. Nevertheless, for purposes of understanding historical development we can only proceed by isolating what we believe to be basic patterns of political and socio-economic organization to some degree from their cultural and historical setting. Reliance on such a method clearly rests on the assumption that these basic patterns succeed each other in relatively invariant fashion, and are independent, in many significant respects, of the different cultural matrices in which they may be embedded. If justification for this assumption is needed, it would seem to be adequately supplied by the striking gross similarities in the growth of different civilizations that have been the subject of anthropological study and speculation since the time of L. H. Morgan.

Mesopotamia today offers the earliest and fullest body of data pertinent to a study of the generalized historical processes by which civilizations came into being. In the past few years this problem has been brought more sharply into focus, both as a result of advances in other areas and of a renewed theoretical interest; in particular, J. H. Steward (1949b) recently has offered a typology of developmental stages largely derived from studies in the New

Reprinted from *Irrigation Civilizations: A Comparative Study,* published by the Organization of the American States (formerly Pan American Union), Washington, D.C. 20006, by permission of the publisher and by permission of the author.

World. Steward rightly insists that "criticisms of this paper which concern facts alone and which fail to offer better formulations are of no interest," (Steward 1949b:25) and it is not our purpose here to criticize the applicability of his ambitious synthesis to a particular sequence (cf. Braidwood and Braidwood 1949). However, it is clear that existing differences in approach between specialists in different areas sharply limit the degree to which their data (particularly as abstracted in secondary sources) are directly comparable; thus there is not yet a really adequate basis for documenting developmental regularities cross-culturally. As an interim step, therefore, it seems desirable to re-examine the Mesopotamian material from a viewpoint which, it is hoped, will be more intelligible to the generalizing culture historian.[1]

Over the long period of development in the drainage basins of the Tigris and Euphrates rivers two eras have been distinguished during which features taken for present purposes as diagnostic were qualitatively transformed: that of "Incipient Agriculture" encompassed the acquisition of a simple dry-farming subsistence pattern, while a "Florescent" era saw the emergence of a stratified urban society commanding a wide range of specialized technologies and based on intensive irrigation agriculture under centralized controls of a theocratic nature. Following V. Gordon Childe (1942:23 ff.), it is useful to consider these as times of revolution, although even in restricted and relatively homogeneous areas the transformations were ongoing processes that cannot easily be delimited with chronological precision. Intercalated between these two was a "Formative" era, during which simple village communities multiplied and spread. On the basis of what scant evidence is available, the tempo of cultural change was slower at this time and its basic institutional

---

[1] In attempting to utilize textual materials in portions of this paper the author, lacking any competence in their decipherment, has relied freely and perhaps eclectically on the advice of a number of Assyriologists. In particular, assistance that has been offered in a variety of forms and over an extended period by Thorkild Jacobsen, A. Leo Oppenheim, and Hans Guterbock is gratefully acknowledged, although they may differ with many of the interpretations put forward here. The kindness of Pinhas Delougas, in making available unpublished manuscripts and plans of sites in the Diyala region, and of Robert H. Dyson, Jr., for a critical reading of the first draft of the manuscript, is also acknowledged with thanks. Finally, much of whatever merit there is in the approach here offered is the result of the advice and interest of Robert J. and Linda Braidwood.

patterns persisted in their relation to one another; in other words, the defining characteristics of this "Formative" era as a whole are also applicable to each of its component periods. Finally, the "Florescent" era was followed by the onset of the dynasties, with a growing emphasis on militarism and a city-state political organization that came increasingly under the centralized control of secular forces. Table 1 outlines a chronological framework for the periods into which these eras are divided.

The terminology here employed is more or less consistent with that currently in use by Americanists, but it will be observed that the substantive content behind several of the designations is somewhat different. In particular, the term "Formative" has been restricted to assemblages for which full-time craft specialization (as reflected in the body of specialized technical equipment and knowledge assumed to lie behind the handicraft products themselves) and substantial concentrations of wealth under either secular or religious auspices (as reflected primarily in tomb furniture and "monumentality" of architecture) are apparently never implied. This usage does not have the advantage of coinciding with an easily observed transition in ceramics, but it does make possible an emphasis on some of the major trends in the growth of civilized society per se by setting them off separately, under the rubric of the following "Florescent" era. The characterization of an era as "Florescent," accordingly, has been based less on its overall cultural intensity or blossoming—the quality that is apparently sought most frequently in New World applications of the term—than on the evident coherence of several periods of growth during which a distinctively civilized pattern of living emerged out of a folk-village substratum. We believe it is possible to show that these modified concepts are useful in ordering the Mesopotamian material, but their wider applicability, of course, remains to be tested.

INCIPIENT AGRICULTURE

The older belief that enforced association of man, plants, and animals around the shrinking margins of oases and alluvial streams during a period of desiccation led directly to the development of irrigation agriculture does not appear to be tenable any longer. Studies of charcoal, molluscs, and fauna from Jarmo and Karim Shahir in northern Iraq suggest that rainfall and, to an even greater degree, the floral cover at about the time of this transition were at least as heavy as they are now, while the Natufian fauna from Palestine, once thought to reflect quite arid conditions (Garrod, Bate 1937:154), has been reinterpreted in the light of more recent work at Abu Usba (Stekelis, Haas 1952) to support the same conclusion. Moreover Braidwood (1952a:Fig. 4) has shown that known remains of earliest villages cluster in upland areas with sufficient normal rainfall to ensure crops, rather than in the alluvium.

But if the "neolithic" revolution can no longer be regarded as a sort of historical accident resulting merely from the fortuitous presence of man in a particular environmental setting, its cultural precursors are still elusive. Both the Karim Shahir assemblage and the roughly homotaxial Natufian are characterized by a greater number and variety of non-utilitarian objects in clay, bone, and stone than previously known, suggesting that the continuous requirements of the food quest had become generally less pressing, but there were apparently regional differences in subsistence pattern. Karim Shahir seems to have been the encampment of a much larger population than the earlier caves, although the small proportion of the flint industry which could be classified as sickle blades shows that in this phase of incipient agriculture cereals still played a minor role in diet. The sequence in Belt Cave, on the shore of the Caspian, has been claimed to show that domestication of sheep and goats began well before there is evidence of cereal cultivation (Coon 1951:50) and this accords with the dominant position of sheep and goat among the Karim Shahir animal remains. On the other hand, the animal bones found in the Natufian refuse indicate for the most part a certainly wild fauna, while greater dependence on cereal cultivation may be implied by the large number of sickles.

FORMATIVE

As with its beginnings, the final stage of the transition to food production is still obscure. The few incipient agricultural sites are followed by fully formed and completely sedentary villages; only at Jericho in modern Transjordan is an apparent stratigraphic succession emerging of true farmers over incipient agriculturalists (Kenyon 1952:117), and there are hints that the former may occupy this site somewhat later than its Mesopotamian equivalents.

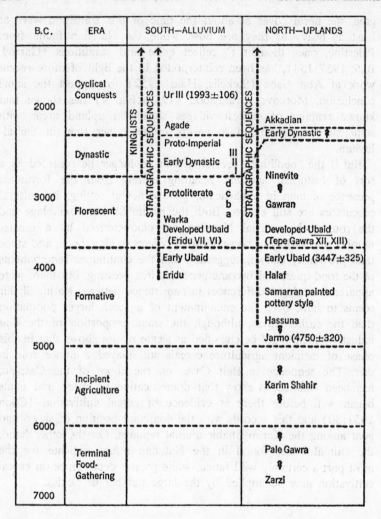

B.C.	ERA	SOUTH—ALLUVIUM	NORTH—UPLANDS
2000	Cyclical Conquests	Ur III (1993±106)	Akkadian
		Agade	Early Dynastic
	Dynastic	Proto-Imperial	
		Early Dynastic III / II / I	Ninevite
3000		Protoliterate d c b a	Gawran
	Florescent	Warka Developed Ubaid (Eridu VII, VI)	Developed Ubaid (Tepe Gawra XII, XIII)
4000		Early Ubaid	Early Ubaid (3447±325)
		Eridu	Halaf
	Formative		Samarran painted pottery style
			Hassuna
5000			Jarmo (4750±320)
	Incipient Agriculture		Karim Shahir
6000			
	Terminal Food-Gathering		Pale Gawra
			Zarzi
7000			

Table 1 Approximate Mesopotamian Chronology (C-14 dates in parentheses).

Except for pottery, the technical equipment of these early villagers was improved by few important additions until the succeeding epoch, and may even have deteriorated in aesthetic quality. Mortars, querns, celts, and finely polished vessels reflect the competent ground stonework from the very beginning, the toolkit of chipped blades included no types not known earlier, and numerous whorls indicate that twining or weaving was already well-established by the time of Jarmo. Mud-walled houses of two or more rectangular rooms, often with associated ovens and storage basins and sometimes placed around courtyards, were scattered haphazardly over one to six acres of habitation area; by the end of the era shaped mud bricks were being utilized for these constructions. Small shrines, still fairly fluid in plan, were also in use before the end of the era, and, as is customary in the religion of early cultivators, generalized "mother-goddesses" were present throughout. Simple burials with few Bei-gaben reflect a minimum of class differentiation, although the introduction of stamp seals in the Halaf period may be partly the result of an extension in conceptions of private ownership. Subsistence was based on the cultivation of wheat and barley and on herds of domesticated sheep and goats, while the importance of the buk-ranium motif in Halaf pottery, not long before the beginning of the Florescent era, should reflect the effective domestication of cattle by that time also. Several late sites of this time range are well outside the zone where farming is possible today without irrigation; those in the north lie close to river channels and may represent the southward infiltration of cultivators soon after the development of rudimentary irrigation techniques, but those like Eridu, in the extreme south, could hardly have been occupied until understanding of irrigation was further advanced.

Phases of early village life have been distinguished almost entirely on the basis of their pottery, and it is not yet possible to determine the degree to which the several wares have different geographical distributions that were overlapping in time. The contemporary existence of quite independent traditions in Syro-Cilicia and in Iraq near the beginning of the era argues, at least, for a rapid spread of pottery-making techniques without necessarily the concomitant spread of styles, and thus inferentially of populations. The fact that Ubaid-type pottery was introduced into Syro-Cilicia at a later time essentially without disturbance to the pre-existing tradition of flintwork also suggests that the role of migrations in the spread of pottery and the temporal distinctiveness of individual wares may have been overstressed. It has even been argued that the very distinctive Samarran painted pottery style, which is particularly difficult to place chronologically, is not the product of a "culture" at all but of roving groups of craftsmen (Braidwood *et al.* 1944), although it is difficult to find a place for this degree of specialization in the simple subsistence economy of the time. In a sense, the large areas occupied by homogeneous pottery traditions at this early time are surprising, since the village units were relatively self-sufficing and certainly politically autonomous. Perhaps they are to be explained as the result of prolonged, if attenuated, peaceful contact, for there was trade with the region of L. Van in Eastern Anatolia for obsidian and no hint of defensive fortifications.

FLORESCENT

The regimes of the Tigris and Euphrates placed formidable obstacles before the early irrigators. In order to avoid the searing heat of the Mesopotamian summer, crops are planted in September or October, but the meltwater runoff does not reach the alluvial plains before April or May. Since lifting devices were apparently uncommon before Assyrian times, canals that were deep enough to divert the streams at low-water levels had to be dug for long distances in order to irrigate during planting; hence, even without demographic pressures, there were strong inducements to intensive occupation and farming. Recently it has been shown that the Persian Gulf is a complex tectonic basin whose outlines have not been significantly affected by the huge annual increments of silt it has received (Lees, Falcon 1952), but silt that clogged the irrigation canals was not so easily disposed of. Without constant attention to its removal, canals quickly filled to the point where only high-water—carrying an even heavier burden of silt—could be admitted. Neglect of the canals for even a short period thus led to conditions that could only be corrected by a very heavy expenditure of labor under a strong central authority; this sequence of events seems to have recurred repeatedly in the later history of the area. Moreover, high- and low-water levels in the streams themselves were exceedingly variable; floods, famines, and destructive changes of channels were to be expected frequently.

As Ubaid farmers moved out onto the plains, not only were the tasks of land reclamation and irrigation imposed on them but also a new pattern of subsistence. Primary dependence upon cereal cultivation and herding was sufficient along the flanks of the Zagros mountains and in Assyria, but irrigation made possible a balance of these products with vegetable horticulture. Fish from the streams and canals added importantly to the diet, and their utilization as a food resource must have been partly responsible for the development of a sail for boats before the end of the Ubaid period (Lloyd, Safar 1948:118, pl. V). South of Samarra the date palm furnishes abundant preservable fruit when watered; since the ritual wedding of Dumuzi and Inana, symbolizing the reawakening of nature in the spring, accorded the central place to the date harvest this may even have been the most important staple. Unlike sheep and goats, which could be grazed during the dry summer months on stubble or patches of marsh-grass close to the settlements, cattle required considerable pasturage, and it is probable that holdings of cattle were centralized fairly early. At any rate, temple herds were depicted on cylinder seals toward the end of the Florescent era (Frankfort 1939: 20), and from later texts it seems clear that large herds were the exclusive property of palace or temple. Plowing, too, is seen to be a centralized operation in the Shuruppak texts of Early Dynastic times; plows are shown in the earliest pictographic writing (Falkenstein 1936:Zeichenliste No. 214), and their introduction may have followed closely the development of irrigation systems.

Technical advance in the Florescent era seems to have become more rapid as social stratification, advancing in step with the "urban" revolution as a whole, made effective new demands and sanctioned the devotion of increasing numbers of specialists to their fulfillment. Native copper had been worked on a small scale into pins and awls at Mersin in Cilicia and Sialk on the Iranian plateau already in the preceding era, and there is even evidence for casting in an Early Ubaid level of Tepe Gawra. But contemporary copper is absent in the southern sites, which presumably were further from outcroppings of ore; in fact, all through the Ubaid period in the south, sickles and socketed axes were made of fired clay since stone, too, is absent in the alluvial soil. Before the advent of a reducing kiln for pottery, smelting may not have been possible in this region and there is little reason to suggest a bifurcation in the craft of potter and smith, but with the introduction both of smelting and closed-mold casting in the Protoliterate—or even Warka—period the smith must have become an independent specialist. Thereafter, copper weapons and ornaments appeared in increasing quantities, precious metals were brought into use, and casting developed quickly to a high level of technique. The potter's wheel, like the reducing kiln, was introduced at the beginning of the Warka period, and presumably confirms the existence of specialized potters by that time. Carts are seen in the earliest pictographs (Falkenstein 1936: Zeichenliste 743, 744), and should also be roughly contemporary. Cartwheels, or at any rate the more nicely constructed chariot known from a fragmentary Protoliterate b cylinder seal (Frankfort 1939:22), would have required the services of specialized carpenters. Glyptic craftsmen must also have been highly specialized, for their products reached an extraordinary peak of technical and artistic perfection in the first half of the Protoliterate period, mastermasons and mosaic setters must have been required increasingly as the temples grew in size and complexity, stone vessels like the great alabaster vase from Warka (Heinrich 1936:Taf. 3) surely required the attention of specialized stonecutters, and the list of specialists undoubtedly would be extended materially if perishable articles of the time were better known.[2] To be sure, direct evidence does not yet exist that *any* of these functions was performed by craftsmen freed from the normal cycle of agricultural activities, but the rapid pace of technical progress, the heavy requirements of time for production with existing techniques, the uniformly high artistry, and the increasingly complex, exacting, and capitalized nature of the operations argues strongly that most of them were able to devote full-time to their specialized pursuits.

Undoubtedly population increased very substantially during the Florescent era, but only a few broad trends can be traced with data available at present. In the north, new techniques did not alter materially the prevailing mode of subsistence and the trend toward multiplication of village units, which Childe (1942:66) has pointed out is a concomitant of an essentially neolithic economy, must have continued through most of the Ubaid period. Our impression, based on a very limited amount of touring and surface collection, is that the *number* of upland settlements reached a maximum at about this time; even some of the more remote Kurdish mountain valleys are thickly dotted with Ubaid tells. As urbanization continued in the south under the stimulus of irrigation, however, population density in the north failed to keep pace. When most of the arable land was occupied competition for its use may have led to the amalgamation of groups of neighboring villages in townships fortified with

---

[2] Landsberger (1944) has presented a largely corroborative picture of the crafts at about this period, based on the presence of an archaic substratum in later Sumerian craft nomenclature.

walls or blockhouses—such as occur in Ubaid levels at Mersin and in immediately post-Ubaid times at Tepe Gawra—but several contemporary southern sites appear to have been appreciably larger and certainly were able to devote a greater surplus to the erection of temples. The greater potentialities of irrigable land seem, moreover, to have delayed militarization in the alluvium. Sporadic raiding is described in a number of early myths and may have gone on for some time, but the earliest archeological evidence for warfare there is a seal impression from Warka depicting captured prisoners and the "king on the battlefield" that can only be assigned to the Protoliterate b period (Frankfort 1939:23). Circumvallation of sites in the south did not occur, to our knowledge, before Jemdet Nasr, at the very end of the era.

The disparity in population density between north and south increased further after the end of the Ubaid period. Many of the Protoliterate centers in the alluvium were started on virgin soil, and the repeated enlargements of temple precincts that have been observed at Khafajah, Warka, Uqair, and Eridu must reflect something more than improved agricultural efficiency or techniques of coercion. Inferences about demography on the basis of architectural changes are always dangerous, but the magnitude of the effort involved in some of the edifices is impressive: Falkenstein (1939:24, fn. 2) has estimated that the A Ziggurat at Warka required five years to build with a full-time labor force of 1500 men. An estimate of the actual size of a late Protoliterate center can be made at present only for Jemdet Nasr, which is probably much smaller than average; using Frankfort's (1948:396, fn. 23) reasonable figure of 160 persons per acre the site would have been occupied by some 2800 people. Except for Brak—which shows so many close parallels with the south as to suggest something akin to colonization —few of the upland sites of the Gawran period were comparable with even this, although contemporary tombs were as richly furnished as any in the lowlands. Thus it is not unreasonable to suppose that urbanization in the north, in the sense not so much of population growth as class stratification and craft specialization, was largely an export from the alluvial plains in exchange for raw materials.

While the central importance of the temples in the socio-economic life of the lowland communities at the end of the Florescent era is apparent from the dominance of their position and the richness of their appointments, the manner of implementation of the temples' economic role is still doubtful. Temple officials are frequently shown engaged in cult activities, but the point at which the administration of the god's estate was placed in the hands of a *full-time* staff is not known. Beginning with the small and simple shrine at the base of Eridu and continuing through the Ubaid, Warka, and Protoliterate periods and on into historic times at every site where there is important material available there is evidence of no sharp break but instead of steadily increasing size and complexity combined with remarkable continuity in ritual and plan. The appearance of writing early in the Protoliterate period, at first in the form of tablets devoted to accounts but only slightly later to lists of gods as well (Falkenstein 1936), may serve to mark this step conveniently, for it must have been largely a by-product of the opportunities for reflection afforded to individuals who were detached from the normal agricultural life and charged with stewardship of the resources of community and god.

The confining of archeological attention in the past largely to monumental buildings has made it difficult to determine the extent to which the temple dominated the day-to-day economic life of its parishioners. Speiser's (1942:58) belief that a developed sense of private property is evident in the wide use of cylinder seals implies that a considerable amount of trade and other activities were directed toward the accumulation of private capital by the beginning of the Protoliterate period. Since the great majority of seals are found in temples while few if any have been recovered from graves of this period, however, a view of their function which focuses on the documentation of ownership for business transactions seems too narrow; sharing magically in their owners' personalities, seals may well have been intended to serve primarily as permanent representatives and spokesmen for their owners in the house of the god.[3] Evidence for the importance of a "private sector" in the economy thus is subject to serious challenge, although private economic activities such as barter undoubtedly were carried on.

At any rate, the temple precincts did serve as repositories for the communities' surpluses, and the term that later came to stand for the authoritative director of economic activities on the estate of a god has been recognized in late Protoliterate texts. If Jacobsen's (1943:167) suggestion that later myths retained a view of social

---

[3] I am indebted to Professor Delougas for this suggestion.

order consistent with an origin in the Protoliterate period is accepted, the active direction of the great irrigation projects and the like would fall to the temples by default, for no other source of authority is depicted but unwieldy *ad hoc* assemblies and short-term war leaders. We are frankly hesitant about assigning all of the elements present in the myths to a single stage in what must have been a longer development, but the known architectural remains bear out Jacobsen very strikingly. Except for the fragmentary remains of public buildings at Uqair, Uruk, and Jemdet Nasr, which differ from contemporary religious architecture and possibly served as "palaces," all monumental structures in the alluvium before the Dynastic era can be classed unreservedly as temples. A stage in which the economic controls of this highly sophisticated (if not quite urbanized) society were more important and more formalized than its political ones, and were primarily of a theocratic nature, can thus be isolated with considerable assurance.

DYNASTIC

Important technical advances or changes in modes of subsistence were not as intimately linked with the onset of the dynasties as they were with the beginnings of earlier eras. There is, in fact, no evidence for a change in the prevailing pattern of subsistence at all, and emphasis in the crafts was placed mainly on the elaboration of existing techniques to meet greatly expanded demands rather than on the implementation of new materials and processes. The introduction of bronze metallurgy by Early Dynastic II times is an important exception, but it should be stressed that the dominating position of southern Mesopotamia's metal industry at the end of the epoch was not the result of priority in this discovery; on the contrary, bronze seems to have been used earlier in north Syria than in Sumer or Akkad. Perhaps the Mesopotamian superiority may be explained instead by the greater quantity of metal that is seen in circulation there. The proliferation of tool, weapon, ornament, and vessel forms, for example, from the "Royal Tombs" of Ur, the export of tools and weapons that apparently can be established from typological study, and the reliance on a metal basis for exchange in the transactions among the palace texts of ancient Shuruppak (Deimel 1924; Jestin 1937) all point clearly to a rationalization of supply and production methods carried on under the aegis of palace or temple. The same sort of achievement in other fields is reflected in the organization of craftsmen into guilds at Shuruppak and the employment of nearly 200 slave girls in differentiated operations that were part of textile production at a single Lagash temple in the Protoimperial period (Deimel 1931: 97). On the other hand, not all the crafts were equally favored; as metal and stone vessels were increasingly employed for the service of kings and gods, pottery became largely restricted to the poorer households and declined in quality.

Characteristic of Early Dynastic archeology were a number of features which reflect the growing importance of royal authority and the obviously warlike proclivities of the period. Beside the ordinary burials there are a few vaulted tombs at Susa, Kish, and Ur, some employing the true arch, that were constructed from Early Dynastic I on; containing elaborate and costly furniture, the remains of vehicles that were probably chariots, and multiple sati burials, they commonly are taken as evidence of institutionalized kingship. As Childe (1952:151) says:

> Even the clumsy Sumerian war-chariot must have been extremely costly, and the "war-asses" that drew it must have been specially trained. Relative to the meager total resources of Early Dynastic societies, it was strictly comparable to the tank today, an arm that only civilized States and their personal embodiments could afford; against it no barbarian tribe nor rebellious peasantry could compete. The burial of such an engine in the tomb would therefore symbolize the incarnation, as a coercive force, of the State in a human dynast and justify the application of the epithet "royal" to such a tomb.

Undeniable palaces appeared slightly later at Kish and Eridu that rival or exceed in size the contemporary temples; one at Kish was protected by a thick outer wall, and additional security was provided by a very circuitous mode of ingress to the central chambers. Even the temples were sometimes provided with defensive walls, as Delougas' work at Khafajah and al' Ubaid has shown, and walled compounds of substantial private dwellings within the settlements are also known from Khafajah. Above all, the heavy ring walls around many cities were a dominant architectural feature of the time.

Childe (1952:156) speculates that population may have increased further during this period for a number of urban centers must have increased substantially in size. Scattered remains of Early Dynastic

Kish are known from an area of perhaps 700 acres; Khafajah occupied 100 acres, Adab perhaps 50, Shuruppak 300, while 1100 acres were enclosed behind the ramparts of Uruk. It is not likely that any of these sites was built up continuously, but Kish and Uruk, at least, may have had twenty to thirty thousand inhabitants. On the other hand, the abandonment of some centers at the beginning of the period and the fortification of most of those remaining suggests that the concentration in cities was motivated as much by a desire for protection as by a general population increase. This tendency toward concentration may also be reflected in the irrigation systems, upon which further population increases ultimately depended. Occasional extension of canals are described in early royal inscriptions, but the aspect of canals as arteries of communication, whereby the harvests could be quickly and easily concentrated in the central granaries, is also mentioned prominently.

Since virtually the whole of the era is marked by some evidence of warfare it may be suggested that population had expanded nearly to the limits that the land would afford by the end of the preceding era, and that what followed was a chronically precarious balance between population and food resources. Under these conditions, the rise of kingship may have been largely a self-generating process. In a widely known account, for example, Entemena described incidents that were only the most recent past of a long history of internecine rivalry between Lagash and Umma over border territories (Barton 1929:57 ff.; cf. Poebel 1926); under such a chronic state of emergency there was neither time nor disposition for the war-leader to relinquish his powers. Moreover, the enforcement of the onerous tasks associated with defense could no longer be left to the deliberations of an assembly but required the increasingly autocratic control of a single individual. Thus, on one interpretation at least, the citizens of Uruk had to carry their protest over the labor involved in building the walls of that city to the gods, for the Gilgamesh epic tells us that the king's source of authority was no longer a decision of his assembly but a heavenly appointment (Pritchard 1950:50). At the same time, it was the increasingly complex edifice of class and craft, erected by and in the shadow of palace and temple, which intensified the demands for corvees, raw materials, and food surpluses still further—demands which could only be met by mounting new raids on neighboring cities. By the end of Early Dynastic III, the Shuruppak documents tell of an army directed by palace officials and largely composed of craft guilds fighting in units under their foremen.

For most or all of the Early Dynastic period the raids and campaigns were not directed toward incorporating large areas under the hegemony of a single city-state, although there are hints that an occasional dynast exercised a shadowy suzerainty over a large part of Sumer (Gordon 1953:28). The subsequent establishment of an empire "from the upper to the lower sea" by Sargon marks the beginning of an era of cyclical conquests which terminate our interest in the present context. Several short-lived conquests under Sumerian predecessors in the Protoimperial period may have helped to prepare the way, but the accession of the Akkadian dynasty is still an event of dramatic suddenness, the background for which is not at all clearly understood.

It was customary for many years to interpret this unification of Sumer and Akkad as the outcome of a struggle between Sumerians and victorious Semitic tribes pushing into the settled alluvium from the desert. Jacobsen (1939) has convincingly demonstrated that both groups lived peacefully side by side; accordingly, the earlier view must be rejected. At the same time, it is possible that a Semitic dynasty was successful where others had failed because it was able to nurture and exploit barbarian kin loyalties that were not so deeply buried in a civilized past. As Frankfort (1951:74) has observed, Sargon appears to have:

> . . . allotted parts of lands of temple communities to his own followers, thus overriding the age-old local basis of land rights. No conquerer could rely on the loyalty of the defeated cities, and it seems as if Sargon had built up a personal following, perhaps exploiting kinship ties in the wide sense of tribal loyalty.

At the very least, a measure of Sargon's success may thus have been due to his creation of a new group of landed supporters in the centers of potential opposition.

There was a measure of centralization in the Akkadian achievement, however, which is not so simply explained. In part, it may have been the result of a finally successful transfer to secular political administration of bureaucratic techniques developed earlier in the temples. Perhaps it may be traced in part also to a new focus in warfare on the taking of prisoners. Earlier rulers had rarely mentioned captives, but beginning with the Dynasty of Agade prisoners in very large numbers were listed as trophies of the increasingly frequent and extensive campaigns. The figures given are undoubtedly exaggerated, but they still suggest an emphasis that is entirely new, and the increased availability of captives for public works and manufactories helps to make understandable the rapidly growing importance of the palace. Writing of the somewhat later Ur III period for which there is more adequate data, Siegel (1945: 390, fn. 67) has observed that slaves "permitted the palace to expand and consolidate its political hegemony by releasing field workers for army service. Slaves thus served at once to implement the enormous holdings of the royal domains and to maintain a considerable distance between the interpersonal relationships of town life, on the one hand, and of palace-temple activities, on the other."

It should be borne in mind, however, that debt-slaves in private hands probably were considerably more numerous than captives controlled by the state or given by the ruler to the temples of his city, and that all classes of slaves together were not comparable in numbers to the body of free citizenry.

Another element in the rise to power of the dynasties is also not well understood: the changing relation between palace and temple. Archives from the temple of the wife of the city god in Lagash have frequently been relied on to substantiate a picture of an almost undifferentiated "temple economy" which is exceedingly difficult to reconcile with the political events of the Protoimperial period (Deimel 1931:71 ff.). This important body of material apparently needs reworking from both a philological and interpretive point of view, but it seems incontrovertible that a considerable part, although by no means all, of the available land around a city belonged to temples that were relatively self-sustaining economic units within it. Part of a temple's land was cultivated directly for its use, while the rest was either held in fief by temple personnel or leased out on sharecrop to members of the community. In addition, the temples also served as sources of credit to private individuals, and engaged extensively in the production of textiles, as was indicated earlier, most of which were probably carried to ore-rich areas by private merchants and traded for copper or other raw materials.

Clearly, the director of the activities of such an enterprise was a powerful figure in the community, and during the Early Dynastic period he gradually took over the functions of a king in a number of cities. In general, however, the increasing prevalence of military crises seems to have projected a war-leader more frequently into kingship, and under these circumstances the director eventually became little more than an appointed official of the palace.

If the evidence for the dominant role of temples in the economy at the end of the era is fairly conclusive, a probable expansion in private economic activities can nonetheless be seen. From sale documents it is clear that houseplots, slaves, and occasionally fields were privately owned, although titles to land were not entirely clear but stood in some relation of reciprocal responsibility to a larger authority. Frankfort (1951:63) notes that many individuals known as recipients of wages appear also as holders of allotments of land and concludes that "every citizen whether priest, merchant, or craftsman, was a practical farmer who worked his allotment to support himself and his dependents." Since there is no apparent relation between field size and occupation this view would minimize both the extent of social stratification and of private commerce, but it seems more reasonable to suppose that the holdings of officials and craftsmen were frequently worked by peasants from neighboring fields on some sort of share-cropping basis.

The effects of increased stratification not connected directly with the central institutions of the society can be seen more clearly in the fairly extensive exposures of Early Dynastic private houses at Eshnunna. The large houses, of around 200 sq. m. floor area, flanked main roads that persisted for many levels. Crammed into the interstices between these well-appointed establishments and approached only by narrow, shifting alleys, were numbers of smaller residences, many of 50 sq. m. floor area or less, that must have housed the families of poor farmers or relatively unskilled workers in the crafts. Significantly, one of the largest houses was that of a merchant, for his showroom, complete with bins for his unknown stock, lay along the street in front of the residence proper.

This trend toward the accumulation of private wealth continued well into the second millennium, perhaps ultimately challenging the economic dominance of the temples. Transactions in land and slaves, rare in the earlier period on present evidence, became exceedingly numerous at the time of Isin-Larsa and First Dynasty of Babylon, and private ownership of large estates has been widely documented (e.g., Leemans 1950, p. 113). Under the successors of Hummurabi private capitalists even were able to insure the state against loss of revenue due to fluctuations in the harvest of various kinds of produce with which its taxes were met—an exceedingly lucrative undertaking, but one which must have required very substantial capital reserves not similarly tied to the vagaries of the harvest (Koschaker 1942:164–65). Like the Sargonic achievements, however, a fuller discussion of these developments would carry us far beyond our original concern with the interplay of forces responsible for the rise of urban civilization in Mesopotamia, and thus lies beyond the scope of the present paper.

We return, at last, to the north, where this long sequence of growth had its beginnings. Beyond its pottery, a range contemporary with the Dynastic era in the alluvium is difficult to define. The activities of resident smiths are unmistakable, and a few tombs that only slightly antedated Sargon's rise to power in Agade may have housed the remains of local dynasts. The dominant impression, however, is one of provincial towns, receiving occasional imports from the bustling cities of the lowlands but still imitating styles in glyptic that had ceased to be popular in the latter several hundred years earlier. The situation is exemplified at Brak, where scanty remains of the Ninevite period were superseded by the great palace of Naram Sin of Agade. Tardily and forcibly, the uplands finally were brought within a polity to whose earlier stages of growth they had been prime contributors.

The more general aspects of the foregoing analysis are summarized in Table 2.

TABLE 2 Developmental eras in Ancient Mesopotamia

Terminal Food-gathering. A hunting-gathering adaptation based on small, non-sedentary groups. Known mainly from caves in foothills, but may have occupied open sites as well.

Incipient Agriculture. Small semi-sedentary communities in hilly uplands acquired basic agricultural techniques for settled life.

Formative. Adoption and spread of typical upland village subsistence pattern, and perhaps also of its corresponding forms of social organization. Sedentary agriculture with digging-stick and hoe cultivation of wheat and barley, domestication of sheep, goats, and probably cattle, ceramics. Communities remained small and relatively uniform in size and composition but increased in number, spreading into the alluvium with the introduction of irrigation techniques. "Fertility cult," small shrines.

Florescent. Emphasis shifted to the lowlands with the development of plow-irrigation agriculture. Expansion of technology and appearance of full-time craft specialization; introduction of potter's wheel, cart and chariot, sail, copper metallurgy, early phases in the development of writing. Rapid growth in concentration of surpluses, largely in hands of priestly heirarchies, with consequent building of monumental religious structures in town-urban centers. Beginnings of warfare.

Dynastic. Separation and institutionalization of secular-political and religious-economic controls in true urban centers—the appearance of kingship and the city-state. Emphasis on fortifications and growing importance of warfare, culminating in Sargonic conquests. Slow growth of private capital in trading and manufacturing, but at the end of the era temples probably still dominated the economic life. Rationalization and expansion of handicraft production; bronze metallurgy, refinement of cuneiform script.

32 EARLY CIVILIZATIONS, SUBSISTENCE, AND ENVIRONMENT

Robert M. Adams

THIS SYMPOSIUM has accepted as its central problem the cumulative, if hardly constant, tendency of human society to grow in size and complexity. Its major substantive foci, of course, are the roots of our own Western tradition in the early civilizations of Egypt and western Asia. At the same time, it is clear that processes and institutions appearing first in the ancient Orient subsequently have recurred, with varying degrees of similarity, in widely separated regions and at different times. A better understanding of some of these recurrent features may help to clarify not only the picture of developing Egyptians and Sumero-Babylonian societies but also the cumulative development of society at large.

My task is to describe briefly some of the major ecological relationships which sustained the growth of civilizations in a number of "nuclear" areas. In addition to Mesopotamia and Egypt, the choice of pre-Spanish Mesoamerica and Peru seems most appropriate. It is supported not only by the volume and historical-archeological depth of relevant data that are available from the latter two areas but also by the likelihood that extreme geographic separation reduced their dependence on Old World precursors to a minimum. In spite of this separation there is a striking similarity, in scope and form, of nuclear American sociopolitical attainments to those of the Fertile Crescent area at a much earlier time.

J. H. Steward (1955:182) has argued convincingly that even the demonstrated fact of diffusion between two cultural traditions is insufficient to "explain" their likenesses. "One may fairly ask," he maintains, "whether each time a society accepts diffused culture, it is

Reprinted by permission of The Oriental Institute, the University of Chicago, from *City Invincible* (Carl H. Kraeling and Robert M. Adams, eds.), 1960, pp. 269–95, and by permission of the author.

not an independent recurrence of cause and effect." From this point of view, it is possible to regard all four areas as historically distinct examples regardless of the ultimate "origins" of particular traits. This is especially true for our purposes, since cultural-environmental relationships within an area are pre-eminently a matter of independent adjustment to local conditions and resources.

Moreover, the substantive evidence in these cases for the presence of diffusion from some outside source as a determinative factor is either lacking or at best equivocal. Each of the four areas stood out over its surroundings as a highly creative rather than a passively receptive center. While the complete absence of trans-Pacific stimuli for New World high cultural development cannot be assured, the conclusion of most Americanists today is that the latter "stands clearly apart and essentially independent from the comparable culture core of the Old World" (Willey 1955:571). There is certainly no suggestion of any New World–Old World contact as important as the relatively brief but catalytic influence of Mesopotamia on Egypt at about 3000 B.C., yet in the latter case Frankfort took pains to point out the selective, qualified, and generally transient character of the borrowing (Frankfort 1951:110). With respect to interrelations between Peru and Mesoamerica, it is sufficient to state that not a single object or record of influence or contact between these areas has been accepted as authentic from the long time span between the Formative (or Early Village) period and the coming of the Spaniards, although the over-all tempo of development in each is remarkably similar (Strong 1951:278–79). In short, it is both reasonable on a priori theoretical grounds and justified by present evidence to use Mesopotamia, Egypt, Mesoamerica, and Peru as essentially independent examples for a discussion of their internal ecological relationships.

Within the limits of this discussion it is neither possible nor necessary to explore fully the similarities in cultural development among these four areas. All clearly became civilizations, in the sense in which that term is defined here as a functionally interrelated set of social institutions: class stratification, marked by highly different degrees of ownership or control of the main productive resources; political and religious hierarchies complementing each other in the administration of territorially organized states; a complex division of labor, with full-time craftsmen, servants, soldiers, and officials alongside the great mass of primary peasant producers.

Each was a complex, deeply rooted cultural tradition displaying most or all of V. G. Childe's (1950) more inclusive civilizational criteria as well: monumental public works, the imposition of tribute or taxation, "urban" settlements, naturalistic art, the beginnings of exact and predictive sciences, a system of writing suitable at least for rudimentary records and accounts. The attainment of civilization, from a diachronic point of view, was expressed in each of the four areas by a series of parallel trends or processes: urbanization, militarization, stratification, bureaucratization, and the like (Adams 1956a). Of course, these processes were truncated in the New World by the Spanish Conquest—as a plausible approximation, after a level of development had been reached which was functionally equivalent to Old Kingdom Egypt or southern Mesopotamia under the Dynasty of Agade. However, this does not affect our comparisons here, which will be limited to earlier periods in the Near East for which New World equivalents are available.

It thus seems possible to group the four civilizations as representatives of a single type or class of social system. (Other members of the class would include the unknown Indus Valley polity of Harappa and Mohenjo Daro, Shang China, and perhaps certain West African city-states.) To be sure, this stress on structural and functional similarities needs supplementing by the traditional humanistic emphasis on the unique and relatively timeless qualities of each civilization for a properly balanced view. One example of the latter emphasis is the invocation of particular environmental features of different civilizations to account in part for their differing views of the natural world as reconstructed from works of ancient literature or art, for the distinctive structuring of their formal cosmologies, and perhaps even for dominant psychological attitudes (cf., e.g., Frankfort *et al.* 1946:31ff., 125ff.). A typological approach necessarily neglects, although certainly cannot deny, the unique total patterning of every culture irrespective of what proportion of its constituent elements may have close parallels elsewhere. Probably this patterning is expressed most systematically, concisely, and impersonally in stylistic or configurational terms. But in any case these widely ramifying, largely ideational, aspects of the interrelations between man and the natural world are beyond the scope of this paper. Here we are concerned only with the generalized social order common to a group of autochthonous civilizations with its relations to the environment.

Climate, physiography, resources, and population

Beyond the limitation of each of the nuclear areas to subtropical latitudes, the combined gross catalogue of environmental features is characterized mainly by its diversity. If Egyptian and Sumero-Babylonian civilization are restricted to great arid or semi-arid river valleys, no such uniform description holds for the zones occupied by either Mesoamerican or Peruvian civilization. Both of the latter range from sea level to high mountain slopes, with tropical, temperate, or even cold-temperate climates corresponding to their altitudes. If coastal Peru and much of highland Mesoamerica are sufficiently dry to be closely comparable with the Old World centers, this is progressively less true in the Peruvian sierra with increasing altitude and distance from the Pacific coast and not true at all in the Gulf Coastal lowlands of Middle America.

Both of the New World areas lack great inclusive river systems comparable to Egypt and the Nile or Mesopotamia and the Tigris-Euphrates. Instead, short, steeply descending watercourses that drain relatively small watersheds are common, and many of the largest of these are reduced in their pre-Hispanic importance by geographic factors. The main valley of the Rio Balsas and the inter-montane basins of the Bajío on the Rio Lerma in Mexico, for example, were lightly occupied before the Spanish introduction of draft animals and the iron-tipped plow made it possible for agriculturalists to deal with heavy soils and sod (Poole 1951:36). The Amazon headwaters in the eastern sierra and Montaña of Peru may be found to provide a more significant exception when they have been explored more adequately (Bennett 1946:67–68), but at least the lowland rain forest of the Amazon basin proper acted as a major ecological barrier to the expansion of Peruvian civilization. Since the potentialities of the Old World rivers for disastrous floods, for large-scale irrigation, and as arteries of commerce are often thought to have promoted political unification and the growth of trade in the ancient Orient (Childe 1941:106ff.), it is worth noting that the same cultural phenomena appeared independently in regions where these potentialities were absent or at last far less important.

With respect to natural resources, it is sufficient to recall the absence of even stone in the alluvial soil of southern Mesopotamia, as well as the extremely poor quality for building of the soft and quick-growing woods that alone were available locally. In contrast, parts at least of the New World nuclear regions were well favored, although with great altitudinal variation local self-sufficiency was often replaced by patterns of regional specialization and exchange. As with climate and terrain, then, we cannot identify a fixed constellation of raw materials which acted as a necessary precondition (much less as a "cause"!) for the emergence of civilization in every area.

While relatively continuous settlement in linear patterns coinciding with the positions of the watercourses was possible in southern Mesopotamia and Egypt, enclaves of dense occupation separated by stretches of relatively inhospitable terrain were more characteristic of Mesoamerica and Peru. The best known and largest of the Mesoamerican enclaves is the interior drainage basin called the Valley of Mexico, which has provided the bulk of population and subsistence resources successively for the great religious center of Teotihuacan, the Toltec realm with Tula as its capital, the widespread conquests and incipient empire formation of the Aztecs, and present-day Mexico City. Yet in spite of the unparalleled importance of this region its area does not exceed 8000 sq. km. In Peru the areas of intensive settlement and cultivation were all still smaller. Perhaps the largest of the mountain basins able to support a concentrated population is that of Huancayo, in the central highlands, with an area of only 1200 sq. km. The arable area of the Chicama Valley, the largest in the North Coastal lowlands, is approximately the same.

In all of nuclear America, only along the Gulf Coast and on the low-lying Yucatan Peninsula were the conditions suitable for relatively uniform and continuous settlement. There, too, the rivers most nearly resemble the Nile or the Euphrates in regularity of flow and ease of control. But the lateritic soils and heavy rain-forest vegetation impose a very long recovery period after brief use for slash-and-burn agriculture, which materially reduces population density (Sanders 1953; Palerm 1955) and perhaps helped to postpone for a considerable time the onset of urbanization processes which had been initiated in adjacent Mesoamerican highlands. A sharper contrast would be hard to imagine than that between Sumerians clustering in cities and Classic Mayans living in dispersed, essentially rural, hamlets while only a small elite permanently inhabited the elaborate religious centers (Willey 1956a:109 ff.). Yet both were civilized. In short, the distribution of population and settlements within the nuclear areas appears to have been as variable as the general environmental conditions within which they occurred, although average density in each case was surely much higher than in surrounding areas.

Variations in agricultural subsistence patterns

While the essential basis for subsistence in every civilization is obviously to be found in sedentary agriculture, this rubric covers impressive technical, botanical, and zoölogical differences when it is applied to the high cultures of both the New and the Old World. Largely following C. O. Sauer (1950), we may summarize these differences briefly.

New World agriculture, in the first place, essentially did not involve stockbreeding or the utilization of such animal products as dung fertilizer or milk. Domesticated Andean camelids such as the llama were used mainly for transport and were largely confined to the higher slopes; hence they cannot be regarded as important exceptions. Also missing in nuclear America, therefore, is the unique and powerful ambivalence of relations between herdsman and farmer, involving both symbiosis and hostility, which has shaped the social life, tinctured the history, and enriched the literature of the civilizations of the Fertile Crescent.

Second, nuclear American agriculture involves an entirely different range of cultivated plants, which nonetheless seem to have provided as balanced and adequate a diet as the cereal-date-vegetable livestock complexes of the ancient Orient.

Third, basically different methods of cultivation were employed in the New World. In the absence of draft animals, the major implements were the digging stick and the hoe instead of the plow. Instead of a definite brief harvest season, crop-gathering was prolonged by the use of the major food crops also as green vegetables during earlier stages of their growth and by the widespread practice of interspersing different crops within a single field.

Finally, corresponding to the greater variations in climate because of altitude, New World agriculture was far more variable. There is little difference in at least the potential yields of the Assyrian uplands and the Mesopotamian alluvial plain other than that due to the inability of the date palm to flourish beyond the northern limit of the alluvium and to the greater (but not exclusive) reliance on barley rather than wheat south of that limit. By contrast, coastal

Peruvian agriculture essentially revolved around a maize-bean-squash-cotton-fruits complex, while in the sierra subsistence depended on an entirely different complex composed of root crops like potatoes, oca, and quinoa. Similarly, maize, beans, and squash were the staple foods in both highland and lowland Mesoamerica, but they had been differentiated very early into altitudinally specialized varieties. Moreover, the cultivation of cotton, cacao, and many fruits was restricted to the lowlands.

Similarities in subsistence patterns

In spite of these profound differences, common features are not lacking. Perhaps something can be learned of the general place of subsistence in the growth of civilizations by outlining three common elements which seem to be of greatest importance.

One such significant common feature is that "farmers were persuaded or compelled to wring from the soil a surplus above their own domestic requirements and [that] this surplus was made available to support new economic classes not directly engaged in producing their own food" (Childe 1942:69). It must be understood that the notion of a surplus is related to fixed biological needs and the level of productive efficiency only in very general terms and that both the kinds and the quantities of available surpluses were determined to a considerable degree by the broad social contexts—"noneconomic" as well as "economic"—within which they occurred (cf. Pearson 1957; Harris 1959). Yet the institutional forms for the concentration and redistribution of surpluses show a high degree of uniformity among the early civilizations and serve to distinguish the latter sharply from societies in which no full-time activity other than primary food production finds sanction. Although it is impossible to quantify, it is only reasonable to assume that the proliferation of nonagricultural specialists common to all the early civilizations was correlated with a general increase in agricultural efficiency. It is, of course, quite another matter to assume that improved efficiency was independent of and prior to the whole ramifying network of concurrent social changes. Even purely technological advances, which in most instances these increased surpluses probably do not reflect, are usually linked with the social and cultural milieu, as Kroeber's (1917) study of independent and relatively simultaneous inventions was first to show.

A second common feature of some importance may be the complexity of the subsistence base on which each of the civilizations seems to have rested. We are dealing in no case with a single-crop economy or with one in which the bulk of the population normally could supply the entire range of agricultural produce for themselves. Perhaps the diversity of resources is partly to be understood as the protection against natural calamity necessary for long-term cultural growth. But also in part it must have been responsible for the development of trade, exchange, and redistributive institutions which in truth enhanced the growth of some form of centralized authority.

Mesopotamia is perhaps the best-documented example. The complementarity of dates and grain finds symbolic expression in the alabaster "Uruk vase" (Heinrich 1936:15–16, Pl. 3), of late Protoliterate date, where alternate palm and cereal shoots in the bottom register figuratively support the abundant ceremonial life illustrated above. Fishing was another essential subsistence pursuit; of the 1200 or so members of the Baba temple community in Girsu in the mid-third millennium B.C., more than 100 were fishermen (Deimel 1931: 98). The precise role of fishing in earlier times is difficult to ascertain, but quantities of fish offerings found in a late Ubaid temple at Eridu (Lloyd, Safar 1947:104) may indicate that it had already attained considerable importance by that remote period. Slightly less numerous than the Baba temple fishermen were its shepherds and herdsmen, but their numbers in that specific case do not adequately reflect the crucial position of sheep, donkeys, and oxen in the mixed economy of ancient Mesopotamias for plowing, transport, wool, and fertilizer as well as meat. Surely the prominence of the shepherd-and-byre motif in Protoliterate glyptic art reflects a high antiquity for husbandry as an essential part of the configuration of subsistence activities. In all of these cases it is interesting to note that the temple and state institutions played a vital part in the collection and redistribution of the agricultural produce.

To the far more limited degree to which there are pertinent data on diversification and specialization of subsistence in Old Kingdom Egypt, the picture is at least not inconsistent with what has been described for Mesopotamia. The idealized representations in the tombs of life on the estates of court officials record a great variety of craft activities and subsistence pursuits; since an organization of the work under foremen is sometimes illustrated, there must have been at least a partial specialization of function in the real world as well. While the great bulk of the peasant's caloric intake may always have been derived from grain, the cultivation of vegetables and fruits and fowling, fishing, and animal husbandry also play a substantial part in the tomb scenes of Old Kingdom officials (cf., e.g., Steindorff 1913; Duell *et al.* 1938). The importance of herding, in particular, may have been obscured by its limited modern role under very different conditions of land use. For obvious reasons the main center of husbandry was in the Nile Delta, and the close concern of the state for husbandry is clearly to be seen in the emphasis on livestock in lists of claimed tribute and loot, in periodic censuses of the herds, and in the appointment of numerous officials charged with responsibility of one kind or another for domestic animals (Kees 1933:18 ff.).

In the New World the differentiation of subsistence pursuits seems to have been mainly on a regional basis, perhaps as a consequence of the greater environmental diversity that has previously been alluded to. But the necessity for a wide interchange of agricultural products remained the same, and the organization of this interchange similarly must have helped to expand and consolidate the position of centralized social authority. In North Coastal Peru, for example, llamas from the sierra were already being ceremonially buried in a community shrine or public building in Late Formative times (*ca.* 800 B.C.; Willey 1953:56). In another case, the only llama bones from a contemporary site of the same period were found in association with the burial of an individual whose relatively elaborate *Beigaben* suggest a priestly status (Willey, Corbett 1954:19). By the succeeding Florescent era, the relative abundance of llama bones, wool, and droppings indicates that trading contacts with the highland centers of domestication for these animals had been regularized and enlarged (Strong, Evans 1952:213). Presumably cotton, maritime products, peppers, fruits, and coca were among the commodities moving in the reverse direction, as they were at the time of the Conquest. To some degree, regional specialization with regard to subsistence extended into craft production as well, as is implied by the importation of a colony of Chimu craftsmen to work for the Inca government in Cuzco (Rowe 1948:46). It is interesting to note that a high degree of specialization still characterizes the Quechua community (Mishkin 1946:434).

Similar patterns of differentiation in specialized production can be identified in Mesoamerica. Cotton from the lower-lying valleys of Puebla and Morelos was already being unterchanged with the Valley of Mexico in Early Formative times (*ca.* 1200 B.C.; Vaillant 1930b:31; Armillas 1951:21), and the securest archeological dating horizons of later periods are provided by distinctive pottery wares that were traded widely from their different centers of manufacture. For the Conquest period these traces of evidence can be greatly amplified with eyewitness accounts of, for example, the great and diversified market at Tlatelolco with its separate vendors for many varieties of fruit, meat, maize, vegetables, and fish (Maudslay 1908–16:II 70–73) and with a reputed daily attendance of 60,000 persons (MacNutt 1908:I 257–59). From a different point of view, the heterogeneity of native resources is also underlined by the *matricula de tributos* (Barlow 1949). Although it accounts for tribute levied by the Aztecs rather than for trade, the general concentration of assignments for particular kinds of produce (other than the ubiquitous mantles) to a very few provinces surely reflects earlier patterns for the interchange of normal regional surpluses. And by Aztec times, if not earlier, the integration of interregional trading with the needs and policies of the expanding state is well known (Acosta 1945:10–11).

A third significant feature common to the agricultural pursuits of the early civilizations was the development of some degree of intensive land use. Whether or not this was accompanied by a general increase in agricultural efficiency (output/labor input), certainly it must have increased at least the total agricultural output. However, the point of current interest is not so much the effect of intensive methods of cultivation on the volume of available surplus as their effect directly on social organization. The argument, following Ralph Linton's (1939) lucid portrayal of the introduction of wet rice cultivation in Madagascar, is that under conditions of intensive cultivation plots of land acquire different values based, for example, on cumulative improvements and the availability of water. Since water, or good bottom land, or some other similar resource was almost always relatively scarce, well-favored and improved plots came to be regarded as capital investments. While unimproved land was allotted equitably among all members of the village or extended kin group, under conditions of intensive cultivation the cohesiveness of the older social units broke down and tended to be replaced by a small number of individual families as the hereditary landholding units. The emergence of an authoritarian "king," of rudimentary social classes including nobles, commoners, and war-captive slaves, and increasing expenditures on warfare are some of the further consequences which Linton traces to the basic shift in cultivation practices. Under at least some circumstances, in other words, the social processes we have identified with the beginnings of civilization are closely interconnected with the beginning of intensive agriculture. No necessary distinction into "cause" and "effect" is implied, be it understood, between subsistence change and institutional change. The investment of labor in land improvement and the adoption of intensive cultivation techniques were as much influenced by contemporary social forms as they influenced the latter.

Intensive agriculture, in the case of the earlier civilizations, usually is taken to be roughly synonymous with irrigation. Indeed, without some kind of irrigation agriculture is and probably always was impossible in southern Mesopotamia, Egypt, and coastal Peru. But we shall attempt to show that in most cases irrigation was part of a broader range of intensive techniques and that some of the assumed implications of irrigation as a single, gross category are misleading when applied to the four nuclear areas where the civilizations with which this paper is concerned had their beginnings. Here, then, irrigation is subsumed under the general rubric of intensive cultivation rather than equated with it.

It is important to distinguish between the functional significance of different kinds of irrigation if we are to understand better the relations between ecology and cultural growth. Small-scale irrigation, including flood-water techniques and the construction of short lengths of canal serving small landholdings, does not seem essentially different in its social effects from those observed by Linton in Madagascar. It may make available for agricultural purposes only a fraction of the potentially irrigable land surface, since it will seldom extend very far from the streams and since short canals will not be sufficient everywhere to bring the water to fields at a high enough level. Alluvial situations, in which rivers tend to raise their beds above the level of the surrounding land, are particularly favorable for small-scale irrigation. For the same reason, they invite destruction of existing canals by silting and flooding, although this is not critical where canals do not represent a heavy investment in labor and can be quickly replaced. The construction and maintenance of this kind of irrigation, we submit, requires no elaborate social organization and does not depend on labor resources larger than those at the disposal of the individual community, kin group, or even family— or, at most, those easily available locally through patterns of reciprocity. To the extent that this kind of irrigation is important, its chief influence on social development would seem to arise from its encouragement of stratification based on differentiation of land-holdings. Perhaps also it encouraged the growth of militarism associated with increasing competition for developed canal networks and the most fertile and easily irrigated lands.

Large-scale irrigation, on the other hand, imposes technical and social demands of a different order. Masses of labor must be mobilized from many scattered communities, and their activities need close co-ordination. The problem of maintenance and super-vision is a continuous one and again demands a superordinate authority. Some kind of equitable distribution of the available ir-rigation water must be imposed on many competing communities, and disputes must be adjudicated. Since downstream users are inherently at the mercy of those higher up, large-scale irrigation networks are only durable where the entire area they serve is a politically integrated unit. As has often been observed, large-scale canal networks can only be associated with formal state super-structures in which the ultimate authority rests with an administrative elite.

The problem for us is an absolutely basic one, however sparse, refractory, and ambiguous most of the present evidence may be. To the extent that large-scale irrigation is found to have begun very early, its social requirements may be adduced as a convincing expla-nation for the origin of primitive states in the ancient civilizations. Processes of class stratification associated with intensive agriculture then might be a secondary and derivative phenomenon on this reconstruction; because of its monopoly over hydraulic facilities, the state bureaucracy is identified as the strongest social force. Largely following Karl Wittfogel (1957), Julian Steward (*et al.* 1955:63) took this position in a recent symposium with respect to Mesopotamia and Peru although not to Mesoamerica. Our view is firmly to the contrary. It is beyond the scope of a paper deal-ing with cultural ecology to argue that the primitive state is mainly linked instead with the emergence of a stratified society (cf. Adams 1956b), but at least it will be suggested here that the introduction of great irrigation networks was more a "consequence" than a "cause" of the appearance of dynastic state organizations—however much the requirements of large-scale irrigation subsequently may have influenced the development of bureaucratic elites charged with administering them. The admittedly still inadequate evidence for this proposition now needs to be briefly summarized.

Our present understanding of the antiquity of irrigation in Mesopotamia is derived mainly from surface reconnaissance in Akkad and the Diyala basin (Jacobsen, Adams 1958) and is obscured by the heavy and continuous alluviation with which the northern part of the alluvial plain has been particularly affected over the millenniums intervening since Sumerian times. At least in this region, however, there appears to have been little change in settlement pattern between the beginning of widespread agricultural occupation in the Ubaid period (*ca.* 4000 B.C.) and the end of the third millennium B.C. or even later. There is historical documentation for the construction of occasional large canals and irrigation works as early as the Protoimperial period, but on the whole the settlements followed closely the shifting, braided channels of the major rivers.

In other words, for a long time irrigation seems to have been conducted principally on an *ad hoc* and small-scale basis, which would have involved periodic cleaning and perhaps straightening of clogged natural channels, adjusting the location of fields and settlements in the closest possible conformity with the existing hydraulic regime, and for the most part constructing and maintaining only relatively small-scale field and feeder canals that were wholly artificial. Where the king explicitly claims credit for initiating dredging operations on either a canal or a natural watercourse (as in modern Iraq, the same word is used for both!), it is noteworthy that the aspect of canals as providers of irrigation water is entirely unmentioned (Adams 1956b:117). Moreover, whatever the rhetoric of the king's claimed responsibilities, the necessary labor forces for the maintenance work were apparently organized and directed by the individual temples (Falkenstein 1954:797). No Early Dynastic or Protoimperial record has survived of the mode of allocation of irrigation water, but at least in Ur III times this was separately handled in each temple constituency by a special official in charge of sluice gates (Schneider 1920:45 ff.). In short, there is nothing to suggest that the rise of dynastic authority in southern Mesopotamia was linked to the administrative requirements of a major canal system.

There are very few data yet available on the character or extent of

Egyptian irrigation during the period for which it might be compared with New World equivalents, that is, up to the beginning of the Middle Kingdom. Prior to the opening of the Fayyum depression to irrigation in the Twelfth Dynasty, there is nothing less ambiguous to demonstrate state responsibility for irrigation than the statement of a Sixth-Dynasty royal architect that he had dug two canals for the king (Dunham 1938:2-3). Unfortunately, the inscription fails to make clear whether the canals were intended for irrigation or only for the movement of royal supplies like building stone, as was the case with five contemporary canals dug to bypass the First Cataract of the Nile (Breasted 1906:146 ff.). Still another possible explanation of the significance of the passage is that it refers to land reclamation by swamp drainage, much as a very late (and therefore doubtful) tradition credits Menes with having drained the territory around Memphis (Kees 1933:31). Yet swamp drainage began long before any pharaoh appeared on the scene—if the obvious meaning is attached to the claim of a Third-Dynasty official that he "founded" twelve estates in nomes of Lower Egypt (Kees 1933:77)—and continued afterward without the necessity of royal initiative. In considering alternatives other than irrigation we are also confronted with a protodynastic scorpion macehead ostensibly showing the king breaking ground for a waterway of some kind (Quibell 1900:Pl. XXVI *C*). Again, an immunity charter of Pepi I protects the priesthood of the two pyramids of Snefru against any obligation for labor service on what may be a canal (Borchardt 1905:6, 9); here it is neither clear that the putative canal was for irrigation nor that the pharaoh was responsible for its construction. Interestingly enough, the same charter continues with an injunction against enumerating canals, lakes, wells, hides, and trees belonging to the priesthood for tax purposes and thus suggests that all of those categories were under purely local jurisdiction.

In short, considering the number of known records of royal building activity in the Old Kingdom, it seems only fair to regard their silence on the construction of irrigation works as strange if the demands of large-scale irrigation had indeed been responsible for the initial emergence of a pharaoh at the head of a unified state. On the assumption of a centrally administered irrigation system, the failure of officials with long and varied careers of public service to refer to administrative posts connected with canal maintenance or water distribution is equally puzzling. To the degree that an *argumentum ex silentio* ever carries conviction, the Egyptian case parallels that of Mesopotamia.[1]

Although there is serious danger of overgeneralizing from it, the data on Peruvian irrigation are reasonably consistent with what has been adduced from Mesopotamia and Egypt. Drawing principally from Gordon Willey's (1953) pioneer study of settlement patterns in a typical small valley transecting the arid North Coastal strip, we cannot presently trace large-scale irrigation earlier than the Florescent era (beginning probably at about the time of Christ). The distribution of Late Formative sites suggests, however, that small-scale experimentation with canal-building had begun in a few advantageous locales several centuries prior to this time, and some success with at least flood-water irrigation on the river flats is implied by the slow expansion inward from the valley mouth which began a millennium earlier. The Early Florescent (Gallinazo) canals, it is interesting to note, were built as integral parts of an elaborate and impressive complex of monumental construction which included fortifications and ceremonial pyramids as well; on present evidence, both of the latter types of monumental construction antedated the large canals. By mid-Florescent times at least, valley-wide systems of irrigation were in use on the North Coast (although our particular example comprises only 98 sq. km. of arable land!), and some individual canals are large by any standards: the canal of La Cumbre in the Chicama Valley, for example, is 113 km. long. A subsequent development, probably dating only from the Militaristic era (beginning after A.D. 700), was the still more extensive reshaping of natural drainage patterns through the introduction of intervalley irrigation systems in which urban zones occupied by a governing elite were set off from areas for agricultural exploitation (Schaedel 1951:240).

Irrigation apparently developed more slowly in highland Peru than on the North Coast, although the sharpness of the contrast may be a reflection in part of the lesser amount of archeological attention that the sierra has received. Terraces for soil conservation have been reported first for the Tiahuanaco horizon, at the outset of the Militaristic era (Bennett 1946:21). In the characteristically steep and narrow Andean valleys rapid runoff was perhaps a more serious

---

[1] I am indebted to Dr. Klaus Baer for supplying and checking many of the Egyptian references.

problem than paucity of rainfall, but in general the later terraces seem to have been associated with irrigation channels as well. The elaborate, well-cut, and extensive terrace-irrigation systems for which Peru is famous all were products of the labor-service obligation imposed by the Inca state as a tax in the final century or so of its successful expansion before the coming of the Spaniards. Even the Early Inca terraces, probably postdating the onset of the Tiahuanaco horizon by four or more centuries, have been described as "small and irregular, and probably the work of individual family groups" (Rowe 1946:210–11). As in North Coastal Peru, Egypt, and southern Mesopotamia, we seem to have evidence here of a very gradual evolution of irrigation practices beginning with local and small-scale terracing which emphatically did not require political organization embracing a large group of communities. Large-scale, integrated programs of canalization and terracing apparently were attempted only after the perfection of the Inca state as a political apparatus controlling the allocation of mass-labor resources. They are consequences, perhaps, of the attainment of a certain level of social development; we repeat that they cannot be invoked to explain the processes by which that level was attained.

For Mesoamerica the situation is more complex and not a little contradictory. The traditional view is that "there is little evidence that irrigation was of basic importance anywhere in Mexico, in pre-Spanish times, and that it is erroneous to speak of maize culture as having flourished most in arid or subarid regions of that country" (Kroeber 1939:218). Recently this conclusion has been controverted effectively by a number of investigators, although the full significance of their empirical findings is still open to dispute. On the whole though, the situation seems to be quite similar to that described for the other nuclear areas; in fact, it was primarily the recent findings in Mesoamerica which stimulated the reconsideration of irrigation that this paper represents.

The question of the role of irrigation in the formation of Mesoamerican civilization takes us back at least to the beginning of the Classic era (*ca.* A.D. 100?), if not earlier, and revolves particularly around the population and ceremonial center of Teotihuacan in the Valley of Mexico. The Pyramid of the Sun there, one of the largest pre-Hispanic structures in Mesoamerica, apparently antedates that era. It has been estimated that before its abandonment in Late Classic times (*ca.* A.D. 700) the site occupied 750 hectares or more of religious and civic buildings, residential "palaces," workshops, and clusters of ordinary rooms and patios housing "at least" 50,000 inhabitants (Sanders 1956:124–25). True, the observed limits of surface debris may reflect only the aggregate area of the center over a period of several centuries and not its maximum size at any one period. Moreover, the proportion of residential units within the built-up area of the site is still not at all clear. But even if the estimate is scaled down considerably, it certainly reflects an urban civilization in being. To what extent, if at all, did it depend on irrigation agriculture? No direct evidence for canal irrigation has yet been reported. Instead, we have the observations that irrigation is necessary today for cultivation of even a single yearly crop in the subregion of which Teotihuacan is a part, that according to paleoclimatic studies based on pollen analysis and fluctuating lake levels it was even more necessary during the time of emergence of Teotihaucan as a great center, and hence that the use of irrigation must be assumed (Millon 1954). The difficulty is that a center of the enormous size of Teotihuacan must have developed on a sustaining area far larger than its immediate subregion and that a major contribution from its immediate surroundings cannot be assumed to have been indispensable for the growth of the site. Monte Alban, Xochicalco, and other examples can be found which approach Teotihuacan in size but which lie at some distance from their main agricultural hinterland. A second argument is still less conclusive. It consists of the suggestion that irrigation is implied by representation of cacao and fruit trees along the banks of streams or canals in a mural from a Teotihuacan "palace" (Armillas 1949:91). Even if the indentification of cacao is accepted as correct, the location of the scene is unknown and the crucial question of whether the waterways are natural or artificial is unanswered. There remains only a distributional argument, based on the wide extent of Mesoamerican irrigation practices at the time of the Conquest. Like all distributional arguments, it is loaded with presuppositions and provides no real clue to the antiquity of the trait in question. And so for Formative and Classic times the existence of canal irrigation still remains to be demonstrated.

For the final, or Historic, era (beginning *ca.* A.D. 900 with the founding of Tula), on the other hand, the evidence for large-scale irrigation agriculture and other hydraulic works is incontrovertible. Perhaps such works are already implied by the legendary account of the formation of Tula in the Codex Ramirez which describes the damming-up of a river in order to form an artificial lake stocked with fish and waterfowl (Radin 1920:73). In any case, the Spanish conquerors were full of admiration for the scale and intricacy of the system of dikes and aqueducts that by 1519 was both supplying Tenochtitlan with potable water and controlling fluctuations in the salt- and fresh-water levels of the lakes surrounding the city (Mac-Nutt 1908:I 262 ff.). The sequence of construction of these works can be traced in some detail in historical sources, and the conclusion seems justified that they should be viewed "not so much as the result of many small-scale initiatives by small groups, but as the result of large-scale enterprise, well-planned, in which an enormous number of people took part, engaged in important and prolonged public works under centralized and authoritative leadership" (Palerm 1955:39). Elsewhere in the Valley of Mexico, an irrigation complex in the Old Acolhua domain has been described that was roughly contemporary with the Aztec construction and also seems to have been initiated by a dynastic authority and carried out as a planned large-scale enterprise (Palerm, Wolf 1954–55; Wolf, Palerm 1955). Finally, an impressive list of places, with a wide distribution throughout Mesoamerica outside the Maya area, can be assembled for which irrigation is definitely identified or can reasonably be inferred in Spanish contact sources (Armillas 1949; Palerm 1954). In short, the position that irrigation was not important anywhere or at any period in pre-Spanish Mexico no longer seems tenable.

It needs to be stressed again, however, that distribution is a highly unreliable index to antiquity and that even the examples from the Valley of Mexico appertain only to the final century before the Conquest. Moreover, with the exception of the above-mentioned Aztec system all the known Mesoamerican irrigation networks are quite small in comparison with those of the Old World and Peru. On present evidence, then, Wolf and Palerm (1955:275) rightly tend to regard planned large-scale canal irrigation not as a primary cause of Mesoamerican civilization but merely as its culminating activity in the economic sphere. They recognize, to be sure, that political controls in turn probably were centralized and intensified by the introduction of major irrigation works.

But if large-scale canalization is late in Mesoamerica, there are indications that other forms of irrigation and intensive cultivation—as in Peru and Mesopotamia also—can be traced to a more remote antiquity. Canal irrigation probably never became as important a technique in the Valley of Mexico as chinampa agriculture, that is, the cultivation of artificial islands made out of plant debris and mud scooped from the lake beds (West, Armillas 1950). Modern chinampas are largely devoted to truck gardening, but, since the tasks of construction and maintenance do not require extensive organization and capital, they may have been used aboriginally as highly productive subsistence plots for kin groups or even families. The only example of an apparent chinampa so far subjected to archeological scrutiny contained occupational refuse dating to about the beginning of the Classic period and suggests that the technique is sufficiently old to have been a factor in the subsistence of Teotihuacan. The means were at hand early enough, in other words, for differential returns from specialized farming to have provided the material basis for the growth of a stratified society.

Since chinampas were unknown elsewhere in Mesoamerica (or depended on conditions not repeated elsewhere), their high and perennial productivity may not have been a direct factor in the development of civilization throughout the whole area. At the same time, the Valley of Mexico was in many other respects the key area of development for the greater part of Mesoamerica, for a very long time the center of its most advanced political forms, its widest and most closely intercommunicating trade network, its densest population (Armillas 1951:20–21; Sanders 1953:74–78). To a degree, then, it may have set the course of development which elsewhere was merely followed with more or less local innovation. To that degree, chinampa agriculture may far exceed in importance its highly circumscribed geographical limits. Unfortunately, having largely set aside simple diffusion studies, anthropologists are only beginning to develop more functional approaches to the analysis of interregional relations, through which the supposed primacy of the Valley of Mexico might be understood and evaluated.

Another, and broader, aspect of intensive cultivation in Mesoamerica is perhaps to be seen in the maintenance of dooryard garden plots in close symbiosis with individual houses, which augment the production of foodstuffs through the use of leavings as fertilizer and encourage stability of residence (Palerm 1955:29). Although not subject to archeological confirmation at present, this practice was apparently well established at the time of the Conquest and is possibly very old (Palerm, personal communication). Again, crudely made terraces for erosion-control purposes have been observed at many places in highland Mesoamerica and in at least one instance in the lowland rain forest of the Yucatan Peninsula. Certainly in many cases of considerable pre-Spanish antiquity, they suggest agricultural regimes of greater intensity than the milpa system as it is practiced today. Although at present impossible to document for pre-Conquest times, a more intensive application of labor in the form of handweeding would have prolonged cultivation and increased output, particularly in the tropical lowlands. This might make less inexplicable or even "explain" the extraordinary cultural achievements of the Classic Maya in the lowlands (Steggerda 1941; Hester 1952–54).

By assisting in the establishment of residential stability and in the production of surpluses, all the above-mentioned practices would have provided at least a receptive hinterland within which the new and more complex social forms could expand and consolidate. The origin of innovations such as the primitive state might then be sought in a few small strategic regions such as the Valley of Mexico where the inducements to accumulate surpluses and institutionalize class differences were probably greatest. In a wider sense, it may be granted, the florescence of the state could only take place where conditions in the hinterland were also propitious, so that the pinpointing of precise points of origin is probably misleading.

Briefly to recapitulate, we have attempted to show that developments in modes of subsistence within Mesoamerica were substantially similar to those in Mesopotamia, Egypt, and Peru in that large-scale canal irrigation was a culminating, rather than an early and persistent, form of intensive cultivation. It is conceded that differences in the rate of development existed, probably in large part because of the fewer inducements and opportunities to depend on irrigation that Mesoamerica offered. But these, we suggest, are quantitative and not qualitative differences. In North Coastal Peru the culmination came in the mid-Florescent era—or even later, in the Militaristic era, if the introduction of intervalley irrigation systems is accepted as a significant later innovation. In Mesoamerica it came in late Historic or Militaristic times, as it also seems to have done in *highland* Peru. According to our Mesopotamian data, admittedly inadequate in detail and based on a possibly retarded Akkad instead of Sumer, the onset of large-scale artificial canalization did not occur until after the time of Hammurabi. Even in Sumer itself there is no justification for supposing that this process began any earlier than the late Early Dynastic or the Protoimperial period—a sound equivalent for the New World Historic or Militaristic era. In *no* area, then, at least on present evidence, was large-scale irrigation early enough to "explain" the emergence of the great theocratic centers of the Classic era or the dynastic states which closely followed them. The concern of Wolf and Palerm (1955:275), and latterly of Steward (Steward *et al.* 1955:62–63), over the distinction between "Theocratic Irrigation States" (Protoliterate Mesopotamia and Florescent Peru) and "Ceremonial Trade States" (Classic Mesoamerica) thus seems groundless.

Reciprocal effects of human culture on environment

This discussion so far has assumed that the natural physiography and resources of the four nuclear areas were relatively stable. The different cultural traditions have been regarded implicitly as evolving successive patterns of ecological adjustment and land use entirely according to some internal dynamic of their own. The effect of environment, in these terms, is merely that of providing a fixed framework of potentialities and limiting conditions which somehow is then exploited selectively by the creative cultural growth within it. Such a view is obviously an oversimplification of the processes of interaction between man and the natural world, even if decisive climatic shifts no longer are regarded as likely to have occurred during the span of time that led to the emergence of any civilization.

Unfortunately the reciprocal effects of changing patterns of human activity on the land and flora cannot be traced continuously for any area. Perhaps the clearest and best-documented example is provided by recent work in central Mexico, where it has been shown that intensive hill-slope cultivation during the last centuries of Aztec dominance had gone far to destroy the capacity of the soil to sustain agriculture even before the arrival of the Spaniards (Cook 1949a and 1949b). But the more remote history of occupance in even this relatively well-studied region is still insufficiently known for its environmental effects to be understood. The abandonment of the central Peten region by the lowland Classic Maya furnishes an even more dramatic case, with ecological processes such as sheet erosion, the silting-up of fresh-water sources, and the gradual replacement of forest vegetation by uncultivable savanna in the course of slash-and-burn agriculture all having been suggested as contributing factors.

But in spite of a generation of speculation and interest these factors still exist only as hypotheses, and in a recent general work on the Maya it is interesting to note that they are largely rejected in favor of an explanation of the collapse of at least the elaborate ceremonial life in purely historical terms (Thompson 1954:85 ff.).

In the alluvial valleys of the Old World civilizations, processes of erosion are less likely to have affected directly the course of cultural development. It is not impossible, however, that deforestation at the headwaters of the Tigris and Euphrates increased both the silt loads carried by those rivers and their flooding potential. In turn, this would have affected the continuity of occupation in the alluvium and the problems associated with constructing and maintaining irrigation systems. But, although deforestation undoubtedly went on, there are no empirical data at present on its rate nor on its consequences for the alluvial plain as a whole. Even the traditional assumption that the area of the plain has been continuously enlarged by the deposition of silt along the margin of the Persian Gulf has now been challenged by evidence that extensions of the land have been roughly counterbalanced by subsidence (Lees and Falcon 1952).

On the other hand, a group of different and important reciprocal effects is likely to have been initiated directly by the introduction of various techniques of intensive cultivation. Depletion of soil nutrients by inadequate crop rotation or fallowing cycle is one example. Salinization of poorly drained land as a result of continuous irrigation is another. Still a third may be the disturbance of natural patterns of drainage by the slow rise of canal beds and banks as a result of silting. To some degree all of these processes must have gone on, but their importance can only be gauged against the background of a far better understanding of ancient agriculture than we have at present for any area. To begin with, empirical studies are necessary of changes in the intensity of land use and of the exact nature of the full agricultural cycle over a long period in the past. At the time of this writing, a study along these lines has been undertaken for a small section of the Mesopotamian plain but not for any other nuclear area.

For the present, therefore, the distortions of a picture in which cultures are conceived as having evolved within a static environmental framework must remain uncorrected. If several possible types of correction have been mentioned, their effects cannot even be demonstrated satisfactorily with the evidence available from most areas, and in any case they are virtually impossible to quantify. One can only conclude that attempts to invoke changing ecological factors as "causes" of cultural development—however convenient they may appear as heuristic hypotheses—are still no more than a priori speculations.

In a broader sense, the lack of data on population density and land use underlines the purely speculative character of all those heuristic hypotheses which regard cultural change as an adaptive response to direct environmental forces. One account of the rise of militarism, for example, sees it as a consequence of the displacement of a population surplus (Childe 1942:66–67, 99, and *passim*), although there is absolutely no evidence of a concurrent reduction in the sustaining capacity of the environment or of a trend toward overpopulation in any of the nuclear areas. Another recent synthesis, going still farther, attributes not only the rise of large-scale warfare but also the cyclical character of the early empires in large part to population pressure (Steward 1955:204). How population "pressure" can be defined usefully except by reference to real patterns and intensities of land utilization and settlement pressing against clearly defined ecological limits—for which, we must emphasize again, the evidence is still almost entirely lacking—is not apparent.

There is always an attraction for explanations of historical and cultural phenomena that stem from "outside" the immediate field of study. They have the advantage of providing fixed points from which analysis may proceed in a straightforward chain of cause-and-effect processes. But on closer inspection many such fixed points will be found to dissolve into shifting relationships which are not as separate and distinct from cultural influences as they may appear. Premature dependence upon explanations in terms of the external environment only diverts the historian or anthropologist from unraveling the complex stresses within human institutions. In all but the simplest societies, it is forces within the social order rather than direct environmental factors which have provided the major stimulus and guide to further growth.

Conclusion

In retrospect, the significant common features of land use among the early civilizations of the Old and New World are so general that they are almost trite. If we have attempted to define the

terms more closely than is usual, there is certainly nothing unusual
about finding that all the great civilizational traditions rested on
surpluses made available through sedentary, diversified, intensive
agriculture. In addition, of course, it is implicit in this discussion
that the common social institutions and processes of development
identified in each of the four civilizations were bound up together
with this general constellation of subsistence practices in a functionally
interacting network which characterizes early civilization as a sort of
cultural type.

Against this simple and limited finding of regularity, the diversity
of other environmental subsistence features and the huge proliferation of cultural forms stand in sharp contrast. History is not a
mathematical exercise in the application of "laws," and the meaning
of human experience is not to be found by suppressing its rich
variety in the search for common, implicitly deterministic, de-
nominators. From this point of view, perhaps the lack of closer
specificity in the ecological relationships that are common to the
early civilizations is the single most important point to be made.
Much of sociocultural development seems to proceed very largely
on its own terms, including even some important aspects of ecological
adjustment. Societal growth is a continuously creative process, conditioned far more by past history than by directly felt environmental
forces. On the whole, then, one may reasonably conclude that for
an understanding of the meaning of the early civilizations—both in
their own terms and for the modern world—the natural environment
serves as no more than a backdrop.

33 SOME IMPLICATIONS
OF THE SYMPOSIUM
(FROM IRRIGATION CIVILIZATIONS:
A COMPARATIVE STUDY)

Julian H. Steward

AFTER the Symposium papers were presented at the American Anthropological Association meetings at Tucson in 1953, research bearing on the four areas disclosed new evidence. A continued discussion between the Symposium participants has appraised this evidence, discussed methodological problems generally, and suggested new approaches and points of view. It is not possible here to report fully or adequately the many matters discussed, but I shall endeavor to show some of the more important theoretical implications and research leads. The significance of these will perhaps be clearest if they are related to modifications of my general hypothesis or formulation of irrigation civilizations of 1949. I am prepared to go a little further than my associates in revising this hypothesis, perhaps, for I consider that new heuristic concepts as well as new evidence open up several important possibilities. It was not that the original hypothesis was wrong in either its factual basis or the nature of the formulation. Instead, it suffered mainly from a limited frame of reference.

Reconsideration of Mesoamerica in particular has suggested that several developmental processes or causative factors previously accorded little attention may have operated in these areas. While it is now an open question whether Classical Mesoamerica practiced irrigation, the possibility that it did not led to a search for explanations of the development of the Florescent theocratic society.

Reprinted from *Irrigation Civilizations: A Comparative Study*, published by the Organization of the American States (formerly Pan American Union), Washington, D.C. 20006, by permission of the publisher and by permission of the author.

This society was comparable to that of North Peru, China, and Southern Mesopotamia in having fairly large population clusters centering around an important ceremonial center, abundant evidence of specialized production of luxury goods that were largely ritual in nature, and differentiation of social classes. If irrigation were absent, the growth of such societies might have been caused by centralized control and monopoly of craft production, trade, and public construction, internal development of ceremonialism, need for regulation of farming rights, and possibly warfare. Although expanding, multicommunity irrigation projects in Peru, China, and Mesopotamia would have been impossible without some managerial authority, the factors that are perhaps recognizable in Mesoamerica no doubt operated also in the other centers. Consideration of these additional factors raises questions concerning the comparability of the principal eras in the different centers and the very adequacy of such concepts as ceremonialism, priesthood, political control, urbanism, surpluses, and many others. A reconsideration of the taxonomic position of Mesoamerica requires reevaluation of the very basis of taxonomy.

It is also evident now that my original hypothesis encountered unnecessary difficulties because I failed to pay sufficient attention to the very important typological and developmental differences between the key or core regions and the marginal regions within each of the four areas discussed. In Mesopotamia, as Adams shows, the South Alluvium area and the North Uplands developed quite differently. Collier considers that the formulation for Peru applies to the North Coast, the Highland and South Coast being distinctive. Lowland and Highland Mexico and Yucatán were dissimilar. North and South China also diverged in certain respects. The "typical" developments—those formulated in my previous hypothesis—were really limited to those fairly small key portions of the areas which lay largely within Coastal Peru, Southern Mesopotamia, and the Yang-tsze Valley in China. The other portions of these areas, although linked with the key regions through trade and ultimately incorporated in the expanding states or empires, had cultural ecological adaptations and a succession of cultural types peculiar to their marginal positions.

MODIFICATIONS OF THE HYPOTHESES

In this section I shall discuss some of the principal modifications of the earlier hypothesis, considering each developmental era in turn and referring especially to the data and comments of Collier, Adams and Palerm. In a subsequent section, I examine some of the broader methodological implications and make particular reference to the analysis of Wittfogel and the comments of Beals.

The following chart prepared by Collier shows when some diagnostic features first appear in each of the four centers. The Symposium members substantially agree on this. Differences in interpretation concern the functional importance of these features as factors in sociocultural integration and change. Thus, whether or not irrigation reached its maximum can be judged by some objective standard, but the role of irrigation along with other factors in welding the population of local communities into larger sociocultural systems may be interpreted in different ways.

Incipient Farming

The concept of Incipient Farming needs revision in several respects. As I now view the data, my original formulation incorrectly assumed that irrigation gave the earliest farm communities a distinctive character. It now appears that the first farmers in the Near East, Mesoamerica, and North China lived on what Braidwood has called the "hilly flanks" of the river basin, where rainfall was sufficient for farming. In Highland Peru, rainfall was also probably adequate, although the earliest farm settlements in this region are little known. Where Incipient Farming Villages were located on riverine flood plains, as in Egypt and Coastal Peru and possibly also in North China, ground moisture compensated for rainfall deficiency and there is no record of irrigation. These data show that these early villages apparently not only failed to use irrigation but that in many areas they were not located in the key regions.

This is expectable if the distinction between key and marginal is kept in mind. The key regions, where the large irrigation systems were constructed, were largely low valleys with such slight rainfall that crop cultivation in the dry soils would have been impossible without artificial watering. Owing, however, to the extensive occurrence of alluvium, the great fertility of the soil, and the presence of large rivers, the great productivity of irrigation agriculture afforded a basis for civilization not found in the marginal lands which were hillier and rainier and, lying at the headwaters of the large rivers, did not lend themselves to the construction of large hydraulic works.

These facts, it seems to me, justify the omission of Incipient Farming from the particular hypothesis explaining the development of irrigation civilizations. The Incipient Farming type of culture was widespread and unspecialized. It contained the potential for many divergent lines of development and lacked specific direction along lines determined by irrigation. Characterized by primary dependence upon rainfall farming, permanent habitations, and small communities which had little internal specialization and few if any intercommunity economic, social or religious ties, it represents a level and type of sociocultural integration that occurred in many places. It is substantially the type found among the Basket Makers and early Pueblo in the Southwest and probably among many of the first farm communities in the Eastern Woodland. No doubt comparative study would demonstrate that the general type was extremely common throughout the world. How frequently this type developed in marginal rather than key areas of different kinds can only be ascertained through archaeological surveys.

Wittfogel, although not primarily concerned with simple agricultural beginnings, had this in mind in stating "A comparative study of development has to recognize the possibility of single as well as multiple origin, and the possibility of multiple modes of development following upon both types of origin."

The Formative and Florescent Eras

It is best to consider these two periods jointly because we are more concerned with how the irrigation state developed than with drawing the line at that arbitrary point where its principal features had taken form but had not yet flowered. Moreover, Adams makes the cogent point that in the Near East, "florescent" does not necessarily have the attribute of "intensity" ascribed it by Americanists. Since in America, intensity really refers to degree of aesthetic development, skill in craftsmanship, and sheer size and elaborateness in construction, it is best not to obscure the fundamental question by making distinctions based on secondary features.

It must be understood that the terms "Formative" and "Florescent" or "Classical" have been used in two very different senses.

TABLE 1 STAGE OF FIRST APPEARANCE OF SOME ASPECTS OF CIVILIZATION

	COASTAL PERU	MESOAMERICA	MESOPOTAMIA	CHINA
Canal Irrigation	Late Formative	Militaristic; possibly Florescent	Formative	Formative
Irrigation Maximum	Florescent (Militaristic in Highland)	Late Militaristic	Militaristic	Late Florescent to Early Militaristic
Population Maximum	Florescent (Militaristic in Highland)	Late Militaristic	Militaristic	Militaristic?
Urbanization	Militaristic	Militaristic; began in Florescent?	Militaristic	Florescent
Fortifications	Late Formative	End of Florescent	Late Florescent or Early Militaristic	Florescent
Raiding	Late Formative	Florescent	Florescent	Florescent
Wars of Conquest	End of Florescent	Militaristic	Militaristic	End of Florescent
Private Enterprise (land, production, commerce)	Negligible	Militaristic merchants in Florescent?	Militaristic	Late Florescent to Early Militaristic
Bronze Tools	Militaristic	Militaristic	Militaristic	Florescent

First, from the point of view of cultural relativism, they have been used to designate periods when the culture distinctive of any area—the tradition or co-tradition—took form and then flowered. Daifuku (1952) applied the terms in this sense to the Southwestern Anasazi cultures, although this culture was typologically entirely unlike that of the irrigation areas, except in the case of Incipient Agriculture. Second, for the purpose of formulating cross-cultural regularities in a type of multilinear evolution, the terms designate a sequence of cultures with certain diagnostic features. In the irrigation areas, they refer to the formation of a supracommunity sociocultural system that is integrated principally through cooperation in irrigation works under the control of a theocratic class. Additional features of these two eras are the development of metallurgy, weaving, ceramics, craft specialization, architecture, writing, mathematics, and esthetics.

For some purposes, distinction between the Formative and Florescent Eras is useful. It appears, for example, that whereas the Formative Era styles were simple, unspecialized, and widespread, suggesting a peaceful, expanding, and possibly even a migrating population, the Florescent styles became more locally distinctive, while huge ceremonial centers were constructed, indicating that the sociocultural systems were more strongly integrated internally and more sharply divided from one another territorially. The Florescent Era represents a climax, a culmination of the Theocratic Irrigation State, caused by factors which gained intensity or momentum from the beginning of the Formative Era—increasing productiveness and surplus, larger irrigation works, growing population, greater specialization, enhanced power of the priesthood, and extension of territorial controls. In a qualitative sense, the Militaristic Era differs more from the Florescent Era than the latter does from the Formative Era.

The developmental processes and cultural classification of these Eras postulated earlier, however, must be modified in several ways. First, it is highly questionable, although not yet definitely proved, that irrigation was an integrating factor or that it was even known in Mesoamerica prior to the Militaristic Era. Palerm states: "The existence of irrigation in the Archaic (or Formative) Period in Mesoamerica is only a hypothesis, as I have indicated in my article. Actually, we have no definite proof of irrigation even in the Periods designated as Formative or Classical by Caso (corresponding approximately to the Classical or Florescent Periods of Armillas). Our evidence regarding irrigation corresponds to the Periods classified by Caso as Toltec and Historical (approximately the Historical or Militaristic Period of Armillas). I should add that the results of my most recent research in Mexico, together with Eric Wolf, during the summer of 1954 do not substantiate the hypothesis that important irrigation works existed prior to the Historical or Militaristic Period."

The contributors have not reached complete agreement on how to explain and classify the Mesoamerican Formative and Florescent or Classical cultures, but I seriously question whether these cultures should be included in the evolutionary type found in the irrigation area. The fundamental question is whether the Mesoamerican "cities" and "states" were the same as those of the other centers and can be explained in the same way.

Palerm states: "In my opinion, agriculture without irrigation could not sustain true urban centers of importance in Mesoamerica, especially in view of the low pre-Hispanic level of the technology of transportations. A special case may be that of the regions surrounding the lakes, where water transport could be used . . .

"Naturally we should keep in mind that just as the problem of the antiquity of irrigation has not yet been satisfactorily solved, neither has that of the character of the pre-Classical and Classical 'ceremonial centers.' It is obvious, nevertheless, that Classical Teotihuacán has some 'urban' characteristics (such as the planning of ceremonial structures and dwellings, a permanent non-agricultural population, social stratification and specialization of activities), and also some characteristics of the political integration of a number of separate geographical units." And Collier states: "Pending new evidence of earlier irrigation in Mesoamerica, the rise of civilization there will need to be treated as a special case of irrigation civilization in which factors other than irrigation made possible such elements of Classic culture as intensive craft specialization and the diversion of labor to the construction of monumental architecture." The principal facts of the Florescent (Classical) Era in Mesoamerica seem to be as follows: food production had increased apparently without use of irrigation; large population clusters had formed around such ceremonial centers as Teotihuacán, Monte Albán, Cholula, and Kaminaljuyú; there was specialized craft production by a non-farming population; there was a ruling priesthood, whose superior status is suggested not only by the magnitude of the mounds and temples but by special status burials, interments of particular individuals with abundant luxury goods. These features represent the culmination of a continuous process that began in the Formative Era. Palerm suggests that rainfall agriculture may have become more and more productive because the number of crops increased while varieties of each became better adapted to local conditions. Certain techniques which do not necessarily imply irrigation could also have considerably increased productivity. Among these Palerm mentions terracing and the use of fertilizer. Improved food production made possible an expanding population. With regard to population concentration, Adams suggests that "The extreme dispersal of areas suitable for civilized growth in Mesoamerica and Peru may have led to the rapid crystallization of semi-isolated state-like aggregates, while in southern Mesopotamia aggregates only became feasible when they stemmed from the forceful subjugation of a much larger region."

We are still faced, however, with the need to determine the nature of the integration evident in these Mesoamerican centers. Ceremonialism was a major function and an obvious integrating factor in Classical sites, but its origin needs explanation. To say that the centers grew because ritual acquired greater importance is circular reasoning that explains nothing. Even the function of ritual rain-making, which surely was present, does not explain why a massive concentration of people and appurtenances was necessary. In the Southwest, rain-making ceremonialism is held on a comparatively small, village scale.

Palerm and Eric Wolf have indicated lines along which the explanation may be sought. They note that since these centers also evidence unquestioned craft specialization and therefore presumably served as trade centers, a coordinating authority may have become necessary. In the absence of either military or strictly secular political authority, religious leaders perhaps assumed power over the distribution of goods. Wolf (1951) has shown that much the same relationship between trade and religion developed in Mecca. This kind of explanation is, of course, very general and entirely provisional, but it has the value of showing a possible function of ceremonialism that would cause these centers to develop and become cohesive in the absence of irrigation. With attention directed toward an hypothesis of this kind there is little doubt that pertinent archaeological evidence can be found. For example, a detailed settlement pattern study of such a site as Teotihuacán could pay special attention to differences between religious and secular quarters, to evidence of localized manufacturing and other kinds of specialization, and to internal disposal of craft products as shown by concentration of luxury goods in religious edifices, status burials, and the like, and by external distribution as disclosed by trade goods found in surrounding areas.

There are, however, other possible explanations of the Mesoamerican Classical State. Apart from external trade, certain internal trends may have led to monopolies by the priesthood. The evidence seems fairly decisive that luxury goods were destined principally for ceremonial purposes. If so, the priesthood evidently monopolized their production and controlled the craft specialists who made them. Another aspect of culture requiring strong centralization of authority may have been rights to use of arable land in a crowded farming area. Where land value depends upon water, the control of irrigation in effect determines rights of land use. In the case of rainfall farming, a society may also face the need for arbitration of disputes arising from competition for lands.

As to whether pre-militaristic Mesoamerica belongs with the Theocratic Irrigation State, some Symposium members, pointing out that since it resembled this type in all features except irrigation, remarked "Why throw out the baby with the irrigation water?" I believe, however, that it would obscure the fundamental causes of state development if, on the basis of present information, Mesoamerica were so classified. Irrigation and ceremonial trade are different causative factors, despite similarity in their effects. I suggest, therefore, that while the classification of Formative and Florescent Mesoamerica is now an open question, it might tentatively be called a Ceremonial Trade State or a Ceremonial Monopoly State. This type later became a Militaristic Irrigation State when a new set of developmental factors became effective. I make this suggestion in full awareness of Palerm's strong admonition that we are by no means certain that irrigation was not used during these eras. I have taken into account as well the observations by Armillas, Adams and Collier regarding the occurrence of irrigation in the Southwestern United States, probably beginning in A.D. 500–700. I also keep in mind Wittfogel's suggestion that "where the hydraulic centers are spread out among large areas of small-scale irrigation and/or rainfall farming," as in the Mexican Highlands and parts of early China and India, the proper category may be "loose hydraulic society." The concept of Ceremonial Trade State is so provisional that it will be as readily withdrawn as it is offered if future research invalidates it. It is suggested to stimulate research in a vast and highly varied climatological and topographical area that has been largely ignored from the point of view of irrigation and settlement patterns.

A second revision of my hypothesis concerns the Formative and Florescent Eras of Mesopotamia and possibly elsewhere. Adams' analysis of Mesopotamia points up the need of basing hypotheses upon much finer local territorial distinctions, which in this case, involve differences between the key or core area and the marginal area. My original formulation, which included periods from Incipient Agriculture through the Militaristic Era, used data from throughout all Mesopotamia. The typical development of the Irrigation State, however, occurred only in the South Alluvium area, which had no sites until the late Formative Era. As Adams states regarding this area, "the fact is simply that the practice of agriculture must have depended from the beginning on the harnessing of rivers quite beyond the scope of streams in Mesoamerica or Peru on which irrigation works were constructed at any period." Southern Mesopotamia suddenly entered the evolutionary sequence without previous local developmental background, its settlers bringing domesticated plants and farm techniques from elsewhere. That only Southern Mesopotamia developed the irrigation state patterns and that these appeared quite rapidly suggests the strength of the causative factors. This sudden emergence of the Theocratic Irrigation State with scarcely even a Formative antecedent is evidence also of the irrelevance of Incipient Agriculture to this kind of evolution. While the South Alluvium culture was originally derived from Incipient Farming, so was that of the North Uplands, which should probably be explained by a separate hypothesis, appropriate to its marginal position.

Finally, the Mesopotamian data suggest that excessive attention has been paid to criteria for separating the Formative from the Florescent Era. In my original article of 1949, I defined the Formative Era as the time when supracommunity sociocultural systems, which I then called "states," took form. Adams denies that there were states in Mesopotamia during the Formative Era. Since the first known settlements in the key area of the South Alluvium were independent communities of the Early Ubaid period, Adams is of course correct provided Early Ubaid is placed in the Formative Era. Communities began to amalgamate in irrigation states during the Developed Ubaid of the Florescent Era. One might argue, of course, that this disagreement could be resolved either by eliminating the concept of state formation from the definition of the Formative or by moving Developed Ubaid down from the Florescent into this Era. I think, however, that it is more important to identify developmental processes underlying the irrigation state than to draw dividing lines unless it is to separate qualitatively different eras. For reasons more fully explained below, it seems to me better to regard the Formative as a time when the causes of the irrigation state first were felt and to classify it as an ill-defined stage of change that culminated in Theocratic Irrigation States.

The Era of Militarism, Fusion or Conquest and Cyclical Empires

Interpretation of this Era has encountered relatively few factual and conceptual difficulties in the Symposium, although there are several important general problems to be discussed later. All participants agree that this Era was characterized by maximum irrigation and population in each center, by cities, by militaristic states, and by wars of conquest. The synchronization of these features is not perfect, however, since certain of them appeared earlier in some centers than in others.

Summary

The accompanying typological, developmental chart represents my own concept of how the original hypothesis should be revised. Three and possibly four qualitatively different cultural types are represented in the areas studied. The initial stage of agriculture, Incipient Farming, was present not only in the areas under discussion in these papers, especially in the marginal regions, but in many other parts of the world. Whether or not Incipient Farming includes many subtypes—and it probably does—so far as irrigation societies are concerned this type was too generalized to be a specific precursor of subsequent types in these areas. In Southern Mesopotamia, Coastal Peru, and North China, irrigation was the principal cause of multi-community or territorially-expanded, theocratically-controlled societies. In Mesoamerica, specialized production and trade may have been the cause of the emergence of a theocratically-controlled state, an evolutionary trend that diverged from the irrigation state. Finally, however, population pressures and competition for resources led all states to militarism and then to conquest. This may have begun with offensive border raids and developed into large-scale military operations. The militaristic state authority was able to concentrate population in large aggregates, which sometimes consisted of planned centers, and to enlarge irrigation works wherever it was feasible. Owing to shifts in the nature of warfare from defense and raiding to imperial conquest, and in power structure from theocratic to secular and military authority, the militaristic state should perhaps be regarded as a different type from the theocratic or irrigation trade state. In any event, at this stage of development, Mesoamerica converged to the same militaristic irrigation type of state as the other centers.

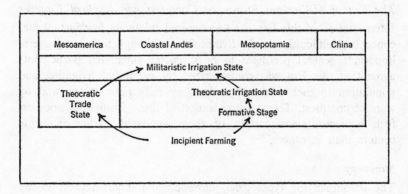

TABLE 2 Some Types of Cultural Development.

SOME GENERAL METHODOLOGICAL PROBLEMS

Fundamental to these studies is the problem of recognizing distinctive types, nodal points, or revolutionary phases in long sequences of fairly continuous development, of identifying the specific processes that produced the types, and of estimating when these processes became effective causes.

A type that has cross-cultural significance must meet two criteria. First, it must occur in each case in a developmental continuum characterized by similar processes or casual factors. Second, it must occupy a similar point in each continuum; that is, it must represent the same level of sociocultural integration. In the case of the irrigation societies, our inquiry centers around what has been called the Irrigation or Hydraulic State. There is need, however, to clarify what is meant in this context by "state" and by the closely associated phenomenon, "urbanization." Obviously, "state" cannot be ascribed particular characteristics of universal occurrence, for it would be impossible to distinguish between different types of states on the basis of equally particular characteristics. So far as universality is concerned, therefore, a "state" represents a supracommunity level of sociocultural integration but not a type. Within this level, types of states are distinguished by their diagnostic characteristics and determinants.

What may roughly be called a state level of integration is found widely throughout the world, and it includes innumerable types of states. Thus, Wittfogel includes among the "high pre-industrial civilizations . . . stratified pastoral societies, hydraulic societies, the non-hydraulic and non-feudal agrarian societies of ancient Greece (with *metics* or free peasants as cultivators) and of Republican Rome (increasingly employing slave labor in agriculture), the feudal societies of Europe (based on rainfall farming) and of Japan (based on small-scale irrigation); and perhaps some others that are less distinct typologically and less important historically." In the present analysis, we attempt broadly to determine which specific integrating or state-forming factors distinguished the hydraulic or irrigation society from other types. In effect, however, I believe that we have become primarily concerned with the Militaristic Irrigation or Oriental Absolute State rather than with its precursors, and that we have viewed developmental processes with reference to the final culmination of this type. I suggest that this is so partly because this kind of society more nearly conforms to the general conception that a state is a strong central, secular, political authority and partly because the Militaristic State was more recent and on the whole better known than its precursors. This is particularly true of China, where the Absolute State lasted much longer than elsewhere and, owing to written history, is far better documented.

Wittfogel characterizes the Oriental or Hydraulic State as a government that has inordinately strong power arising from large-scale, government-directed water-control and that "on the basis of a sufficient surplus, is operated by a substantial number of full-time specialists: civil and military officials." The state authority originated with hydraulic control and extended to construction of military and religious edifices, development of communications, regimentation of society, control of private property and enterprise, and subordination of religion as an independent locus of power. In regard to control of private property and enterprise, Adams suggests: "It may be useful to distinguish between two kinds of private property: small-scale ownership of houseplots and fields, providing for little more than the subsistence of the families who tilled them; and the concentration of many sources of productive wealth, including fields, craft manufactories, and the serfs and slaves who worked them, in the hands of a relatively small number of private individuals. While these two may have coexisted for long periods, there is considerable evidence in Mesopotamia for a general trend from the former to the latter, probably beginning more or less with the Early Dynastic period, and Kirchoff has recently argued for a similar trend in Mesoamerica (VI Mesa Redonda de la Sociedad Mexicana de Antropología, 1954). Thus it is possible that emerging state authority encouraged the growth of the second kind of enterprise while restricting the former." State authority, then, in its full-fledged form, not only tightened its internal structure, but engulfed and incorporated neighboring states within this structure.

As the culmination of a special kind of evolution, the typical Militaristic or Imperial State represents the end-result of processes that began much earlier. Regarding Florescent Mesopotamia, Adams states: "At this time warfare may first have begun to require the services of specialists, whose activities contributed in time to a new dimension of political leadership, and there is no lack of archaeological and documentary evidence that fighting began to leave its mark upon society. But for several hundred years at least of the succeeding Early Dynastic period we see not conquest, in the sense of centralized political authority and permanently-held subsidiary communities, or even in the sense of struggles for dominance between broad coalitions, but rather the persistent, small-scale squabbling of neighboring city states over land and loot and corvee labor." For this reason, he inserts a Dynastic Era on his developmental chart between the Florescent and Cyclical Conquests Eras.

If the point of reference is the full-blown Hydraulic or Irrigation State, which is territorially consolidated and controlled by priest-warriors or by somewhat secular authority, Dynastic Mesopotamia may be viewed as the earliest local manifestation of the kind of developmental processes that initiated a new cultural type in all irrigation societies. The transition from a comparatively peaceful, localized, Theocratic Irrigation State to a militaristic, expansionist state must have begun when "small-scale squabbling of neighboring city states over land and loot and corvee labor" began to supplant desultory raids. It developed perhaps through a phase of exacting tribute from subordinate or weaker states and culminated in the political incorporation and territorial amalgamation of conquered populations.

The Symposium seemed in general agreement that urbanization was essentially an aspect of the Militaristic State and appeared only doubtfully or to a limited extent in earlier periods. Collier summed up the general consensus as follows: "Urbanization did not occur until the period of military and political expansion in Mesopotamia and Peru but appeared already in the Florescent stage in China, according to Wittfogel. Urbanization is clearly associated with political expansion during the Militaristic stage in Mesoamerica but may have had its beginnings in the Florescent (the question rests in part on a decision as to whether Teotihuacán was an urban center as well as a great ceremonial center). At present it is not clear what economic and social factors (e.g., increased food production, economic specialization, increase in trade, political expansion) were invariably associated with urbanization. No doubt an examination of the kinds and intensities of urbanization in the four areas would clarify the problem."

Several problems concerning the development of the typical Militaristic Irrigation State involve special factors that will be considered subsequently—irrigation, militarism, trade, specialization, property, and urbanization. Other problems, discussed by Wittfogel, involve subtypes of irrigation states with special reference to hydraulic and managerial "density" and proprietary "complexity" as these features vary between the core or key areas and the marginal areas. They also involve problems of how the imperialist state is affected when its political, economic and hydraulic expansion incorporates what Wittfogel calls "territories with a low hydraulic potential, small-scale irrigation, and rainfall farming pure and simple." These problems are far too complex to discuss here. It may be suggested, however, that imperial organization of a territory extending far beyond the key or core area of great "hydraulic density" certainly must entail state functions not found in the earlier states that lay wholly within the key areas.

If militarism, territorial expansion, urbanization (defined as growth of secular, administrative centers), and strong central political authority as well as irrigation constitute a set of interrelated features characterizing the Militaristic Era, it perhaps follows that the Theocratic Irrigation State, lacking all but irrigation represents a quite different type. From this point of view, culture growth in the irrigation areas, culminated in two successive types, the Florescent or Theocratic State and the Militaristic or Fusion State, and was not a single development toward the final culmination. That there was continuity between the Theocratic and the Militaristic Irrigation States, the latter developing from the former, does not mean that all of the factors producing the latter were potentially contained in the former. This is especially true of militarism, which played a key role.

Although the term "revolution" has sometimes been used to signify fundamental culture change, there is value in distinguishing between revolution and evolution. Where one or more causative factors, such as irrigation, trade, and monopoly of special production initiated a developmental trend that culminated in a particular type of culture, such as the theocratic state, the process can be described as evolutionary. In some cases, however, new factors may have caused internal imbalance and conflict and entailed the destruction or subordination of older institutions by new ones. This process is revolutionary. Whether the emergence of the militaristic state entailed revolution or evolution is not clear. If internal pressures gave the priestly class an increasingly military character, it might best be considered evolutionary. If, however, a special class of warriors appeared—as would be the case if conquests originated from semi-civilized people on the outside of the theocratic states—there would have been a genuine power struggle between the warrior and priestly classes that had a more revolutionary character.

THE PROBLEM OF SPECIAL FACTORS

Analysis of the types of societies discussed herein, and in fact of any type of society, is directed to the question of the principal determinants of each special kind of evolution. The different lines or types of evolution are classified according to one or more seemingly predominant features, such as particular kinds of irrigation, economic patterns, militarism, and many others, operating in various combination. It is possible, however, that preoccupation with features that are ascribed their every-day meanings and are not precisely qualified may obscure the importance of other features; that incautious use of the methodology of unilinear evolution may vitiate the holistic approach which is one of anthropology's most valuable assets.

The analysis of factors causing culture change, however, is not only a matter of seeking every conceivable factor. It is even more importantly one of recognizing that each factor has innumerable functional potentials according to its specific characteristics and the total cultural context. In the following pages I attempt to point out some of the ways in which conventional cultural categories may be restated with reference to the problems at hand.

Militarism

We have, as Karl Wittfogel states, failed adequately to distinguish kinds of warfare and their functional importance in the development of irrigation societies. Previous discussion has suggested the need to ascertain the character of warfare in different periods. Used as a universal category of culture, "warfare" seems to connote some sort of group activity, although there is ample evidence that many "tribal level" societies had only individual raiding parties and entirely lacked group purpose and coordination. It is principally in late preliterate and historic periods that legendary and written records show unmistakably that conquest, tribute, slaving, empire-building, and defense against conquest were the purposes of militarism. Evidence of fighting in earlier periods is more difficult to interpret. In Peru, to judge by fortifications, paintings on ceramics, and other evidence, major intergroup hostilities appear to have been very pronounced during the Florescent Era if not earlier, and it might be concluded that militarism became a factor in state growth before the theocratic irrigation factors had run their course. In Mesoamerica, where the Classical periods are generally presumed to have been a time of peace, Robert Rands (1952) had shown indisputable evidence of hostilities and captive-taking, which, however, must have had a functional significance different than that of the Andes. Perhaps it was largely defensive, against the mountain people. Conquest seemingly was not introduced into Yucatán until the Toltec invasion of Chichén Itzá.

There is also need to distinguish the local nature of warfare within each area. As Adams shows, Mesopotamia cannot be treated as a whole. While, in the North Uplands, the population maximum was reaching its limits and fortifications were becoming numerous even though states were doubtfully present, in the South Alluvium area, irrigation works were expanding, constructive effort was devoted almost entirely to religious edifices, and theocratic states were developing.

An ultimate explanation of the rise of militaristic states will depend somewhat upon whether warfare arose from internal or external factors. One internal cause is population pressures brought about by shortage of resources—probably water limitations relative to irrigation techniques—which led to competition for border lands. Expansion ultimately entailed subjugation of neighboring states and in many cases inclusion of marginal areas far beyond. There are, however, several possible types of expansion. For example, the Inca Empire differed from the Circum-Caribbean states in that the former developed a rigid caste system, extreme authoritarian control, and a policy of political and economic incorporation of conquered people rather than of taking captives because its already densely settled country could not support more people. The Circum-Caribbean states had a social system based upon acquisition of status through military success and captive-taking, because "slaves" constituted economic wealth as well as evidence of status (Steward 1949a). I mention this to show that internal social structure, the special nature of slavery, and even property are features bearing upon the nature of warfare.

But there is also considerable evidence that in many cases dynasties originated, and perhaps in some cases warfare was first introduced, from the outside when semi-civilized border people raided the wealth of and conquered the Irrigation States. This is illustrated in the case of the Mongol dynasties in China, the Hyksos Dynasty in Egypt, the Chichimecs in the Valley of Mexico, and possibly the Semitic Dynasty in Mesopotamia. Even the Inca of Highland Peru were originally marginal to the North Coast.

Production and Trade

In social evolution beyond the level of simple, independent bands and villages there is a point where farm production suffices to release human energy for special kinds of craft, construction, and other activities. Products are exchanged between local groups and between special groups within communities. In certain lines of development, this trade leads to sociocultural systems dominated by economic enterprises, as in a mercantilist system. In the case of the theocratic and militaristic irrigation societies, the presupposition that craft production was largely controlled if not owned by the state authority has seemed to dispose of any problems arising from surpluses and specialization. Archaeological research, meanwhile, has been so preoccupied with using craft products to establish time horizons and developmental sequences that their implications for trade patterns have been largely ignored.

There is considerable evidence that production and trade may have been major factors in state integration, although their functional significance differed in the various development stages. To judge by simpler societies of recent times, individual economic freedom probably prevailed during the early periods of the irrigation centers. The volume of trade was small, the goods were fairly unspecialized and lacked the intrinsic value that certain objects had in later times, and there was neither need nor motivation for group control.

Under the Theocratic Irrigation State, production was largely controlled by the priestly class, although individual enterprise may have survived in some areas. In order to explain this new pattern it is necessary to recognize that during the Florescent Era enough labor power had been released to produce luxury goods of kinds not previously made. It is very likely that local exchange of household commodities and simple utility goods was still left principally to individual initiative, as in early times. Products in gold and other valuable metals, finely-woven textiles, carvings of precious stones, and such required days if not months of manufacture, implying clearly that craftsmen devoted full time to their work. To judge by the predominance of religious forms and symbols, the purpose of these goods was largely ceremonial and their destination was the temples—that is, they became part of the paraphernalia and in effect the property or monopoly of the priesthood which was synonymous with the "state."

The emergence of a distinct class of priests was gradual. In the irrigation areas, it is not difficult to see how this class developed from the managerial authority that controlled the expanding irrigation works. From control of the vital water supply, irrigated lands, and corvee labor, it would not be a long step to control of craft products, for no other group would be in a position to command the surplus food and other goods needed to support full-time craftsmen. In the absence of a system of large private land-holdings, the ordinary farmer could not possibly afford these goods. It is more difficult to understand how the production of luxury goods led to the rise of a priestly class in Mesoamerica if there were no irrigation. It seems justifiable to assume, however, that in Mesoamerica also, groups of full-time specialists created precious objects which were beyond the means of the farming class. These goods would presumably accrue to a religious authority—itself originally rooted in local shamanism and village priests—thereby at once enhancing this authority and providing the principal social integrating factor. It is hardly conceivable that in these early, prescientific, religiously oriented societies, purely private production and trade could have developed into secular monopolies. A concomitant of such development would necessarily have been the rise of large, landed estates. Both developments occurred much later, in different parts of the world under other circumstances.

It is entirely possible that a certain amount of private exchange accompanied theocratic control of craft production. Palerm mentions the *pochteca* or merchants and the private holding in land in Mexico at the time of the Spanish Conquest. He believes that these merchant groups, together with warrior groups who held independent properties, contributed to a reduction in the "oriental" character of the Mesoamerican state. Whether these predated the Militaristic Era is not known. Palerm believes, however, that the trade and traders may have had an important and direct relationship to the larger ceremonial centers during the Florescent Era.

While any interpretation of the role of production and trade in sociocultural integration during the Formative-Florescent Era is highly speculative, certain hypotheses can be tested to some extent by archaeology. It is probably too sweeping to speak of "trade," for it is very possible that theocratic control extended largely and perhaps only to manufacture of items that were very costly in terms of skills and hours of labor and to importation of commodities, such as salt, cacao beans, and others that did not occur locally. The physical distribution of archaeological objects should throw much light on this possibility. Presumably, the luxury items would tend to be drawn into the ceremonial centers, while the utility products distributed by free traders would be found in households and refuse dumps of the small farm settlements. Even though such distribution would not prove conclusively that utility objects also were not state-controlled, it would nonetheless show that there were distinct patterns of exchange.

In the Militaristic Era, state regulation of practically all trade in valuable goods and property was very great. It might be supposed that, even had all commerce been in private hands up to this time, political absolutism would draw it into the sphere of central authority. On the other hand, as Adams suggests, an absolute government may grant monopolies to private or bureaucratic groups. In Inca society, the state controlled all exchangeable surpluses and craft products, permitting individuals to barter only simple household goods on a local scale. Wittfogel notes that while Inca society represents an extreme of government ownership of both exchangeable commodities and real estate, the Mexican Highland, Near East, India and Yucatán "favored non-governmental handicraft and commerce" but retained control of most of the land.

While extreme state-controlled commerce may be the secondary consequence of absolutism, I suggest that the opposite view is better supported by the evidence. Militarism was not developed *ad hoc*, for its own sake, and political authority is a meaningless abstraction without reference to particular activities coming under state control. All inferences about the Militaristic Era strongly suggest that state conquest and the regimentation and coordination of society by a central authority ultimately arose from an acquisitive motivation that led to both predatory warfare and conquest and created the need for a bureaucracy to organize and control the people in order to extract tribute, taxes, and goods and labor in other forms. In the Inca empire it was evidently carried to the point of government regulation, standardization, and mass production on many basic household goods.

Irrigation

It is definitely implicit in our approach, even though we may have failed to make it explicit, that we seek causes. Irrigation is not only the principal independent variable from the point of view of correlations but, in terms of functional hypotheses, an explanation of the necessary and recurrent relationship between irrigation and the various "dependent variables" is in fact a statement of causality. Any such statement must show how use of irrigation brings about great population density and organization of the population in particular ways.

Beals comments that "large-scale irrigation is associated with fairly dense population . . . but which is the antecedent and which the consequent variable cannot possibly be answered at this point." As for sheer numbers of people—but not social patterns—I think the question is answerable if it is somewhat rephrased. There is obviously a relationship, although not a simple Malthusian one, between food supply and population. An increased food supply permits population growth, which in turn facilitates the expansion of food production through employing more workers and using more efficient methods. The early stages of irrigation were necessarily small-scale and produced far less food per man hour of labor than the later, larger systems. Through a gradual and continuing process, every improvement in farming permitted further population expansion which led to further improvement. The limitation on such growth apparently was availability of water to a society equipped with pre-industrial techniques. When the limits of water were reached, population probably continued to increase somewhat beyond the food supply, creating an imbalance and social pressures. Meanwhile, a considerable portion of the productive efforts had been released from farming for other cultural activities. This portion could not be returned to food production, however, because water rather than labor supply imposed the limits upon this production.

We have assumed that the construction of dams, canals, and ditches in intercommunity irrigation projects involved a kind and amount of manpower that required a central authority. Beals raises the cogent question of whether the managerial functions in irrigation may not be performed through patterns of community cooperation rather than a central authority, and he rightly observes that this question has been little explored. While more research is of course needed, I think the difficulty also arises from the failure to distinguish different kinds of developmental stages or irrigation societies and from the tendency to think of irrigation in terms of its maximum development in the late Florescent Era and the Militaristic Eras. I suggest the very general and provisional hypothesis that informal intercommunity cooperation is feasible in systems having only small dams and a few miles of canals, but that the expansion of these systems increases the need for a labor force and augments the "managerial density" until corvee labor supplants volunteer workers and a permanent, state-appointed bureaucracy supersedes temporary supervisors. Whether the managerial hierarchy rests upon religious, secular, military or political authority, or various combinations of these, however, depends upon the stage and kind of development.

The Northern Paiute of eastern California irrigated, but theirs was a system of diverting comparatively small mountain streams into ditches two or three miles long that watered only wild seeds. Some of the prehistoric Pueblo of Utah apparently irrigated cultivated plants by this same method, while recent Pueblo impounded rain run-off in dams, much like the modern "tanks" used to water live stock. Any intervillage cooperation needed in Paiute or Pueblo irrigation could readily be arranged on an informal basis. More ambitious systems, however, would require some over-all authority in order to plan canals, impress the necessary labor, and regulate water distribution. Among the Hohokam of southern Arizona, a single irrigation system might comprise several hundred miles of large canals serving many widely separated communities. The precise nature of Hohokam society is not known, since the culture reached its climax in prehistoric times and was not demonstrably perpetuated in any post-Columbian Indian society, but the irrigation surely required a managerial authority far stronger than that of the Paiute or Pueblo. This aspect of Hohokam culture merits far more study than it has yet received.

In the areas under consideration in these papers it might be postulated that, from the point of view of managerial controls, farming developed through the following stages. First, incipient farming was based on rainfall and each community or small local settlement was independent. It is conceivable that a supracommunity authority might have developed when population density became so great that competition for land led first to mutual or customary understandings regarding rights of cultivation and inheritance and later to state enforcement of laws governing these matters. Control of arable land was possibly a factor in the Mesoamerican development.

Second, irrigation began with small dams and ditches as a supplement to rainfall, probably on the upper tributaries of the main rivers, for small populations could hardly have coped with the main streams. During this initial stage, informal cooperation between neighboring villages probably met the managerial needs.

Third, the more arid, lower areas near the main streams, which ultimately became the key irrigation areas, could not be utilized extensively until it was possible to construct large dams and long canals and to reclaim swampy land. Population growth, however, was probably rapid, owing to natural increase and to the addition of settlers attracted by the greater productivity. When the extent of the irrigation systems required corvee labor and a full-time supervisory class, a centralized authority emerged which, in the absence of other authority patterns, was sanctioned by religion and led to the development of a priesthood. I suggest that a theocratic society developed because shamans had wielded great power over practical affairs in earlier societies lacking a priesthood because rain-making and seasonal changes in temperature, precipitation and the like were interpreted as supernatural phenomena, and because group agricultural ceremonialism is found among most early farmers.

Fourth, when the productive limits of irrigation were approached, the basis of power shifted from the priesthood to a more secular, political, and militaristic bureaucracy. While the state may have wrung slightly more produce from the land by exploiting irrigation to the maximum, it also became interested in canals as means of communications and transportation of goods for administrative purposes. These functions were very highly developed in Mesopotamia and China. In the Central Andes, where the rugged topography prevented this function from assuming importance, it appears that canals were nonetheless constructed for the administrative purpose of relocating populations rather than of increasing production. Thus, the partial amalgamation of the irrigation systems of the Chicama and Moche Valleys and the expansion of Chanchan at the mouth of the latter valley into a huge, planned city were perhaps done primarily to relocate and concentrate the population for state reasons. There is no evidence that greater productiveness or increased over-all population followed this change. In China and the Near East, the conversion of the larger settlements from religious centers to more secular, political, administrative and military centers was undoubtedly facilitated by these new uses of canals.

These suggestions, however, are broad and provisional. The Symposium has clearly brought out the need for much more detailed analysis. Local environmental differences, for example, posed dissimilar irrigation problems, the solution of which may well have affected the societies. In the Central Andes the engineering need was to divert streams originating high in the rugged and precipitous mountains and to utilize gravity to bring the flow to a maximum amount of farm land both in the valley bottoms and on the terraced hill sides. Since each river flowed a comparatively short distance from the Highland to the Pacific Ocean, each irrigation system and presumably the state controlling it embraced a single valley. The problem was very different in the case of such Old World rivers as the Hwang-ho, Yang-tsze, Tigris-Euphrates, Indus, and Nile. While these rivers cannot be lumped in a single category, they had in common the need to be diverted well upstream of the lands they watered, a need which may have affected the size if not the nature of the states. Moreover, there were many problems particular to the different areas. In Mesopotamia, as Adams points out, there was the difficulty that the run-off of melting snow in the mountains reached the lowlands during a time disadvantageous for growing crops. The difficulty might have been remedied by impounding water in reservoirs, but it is doubtful that early technology could achieve water storage on an important scale. Another difficulty of these huge systems of canals is that since many of them ran considerable distances with only a slight gradient they were subject to sedimentation.

Among the many technical problems involved in irrigation—and of great importance today in connection with efforts to conserve renewable natural resources—are alkalinization and leaching of farm lands to the point of ruining the soil, formation of such impermeable deposits as caliche, erosion and other topographical changes, alteration of the water table, and possibly changes in rainfall and climate, all produced in part by man's use of the land. It need hardly be added that archaeology, history, irrigation engineering, agronomy, geography, and other disciplines find a common ground in these subjects.

Finally, it is worth considering whether the crops in irrigation areas were as important in shaping the culture as the method of growing them. In many areas, one or more well adapted crops constitute the principal subsistence—e.g., the potato in the cool climates of Chile and the Andean Highlands, manioc in the Tropical Forests, yams in Oceania, etc. In the irrigation areas, the staples were largely cereal crops—wheat, millet, rice, barley and oats in the Old World and maize in the New World. To a certain extent, the method of cultivation—sowing, propagation by cutting, transplanting, and many others—is dictated by the nature of the plant. There are several compelling reasons, however, for believing that in the case of the key irrigation areas, the use of irrigation was far more important than the plant species.

In the first place, a dense population is a precondition but not a cause of a developed "civilization." The Central Valley of Chile had very productive farming and compared favorably demographically with the Central Andes, but its society consisted only of fairly small, localized lineages. It lacked irrigation or other integrating factors. In the second place, practically all the cereal crops of the irrigation areas were utilized also in a variety of rainfall areas. In the third place, while it is possible that special plant varieties had become adapted to irrigation conditions, the biological ecological adaptability of plants is so great as to be very deceiving. Dr. Inez Adams in a thesis at Columbia University showed that what had been considered for many years to be two quite unlike, genetically-determined kinds of rice (*Oryza*), (namely, "dry rice," which is grown without irrigation in fairly arid areas, and "wet rice," which is always irrigated) were apparently the same plant which flourished under a surprising variety of conditions.

While the extent to which techniques of cultivation are determined by the plant itself is of course an empirical question in each case, there seems little doubt that in the major irrigation areas technology was the distinctive determinant of increased productivity, of population growth and, according to the different kinds of irrigation, of types of social coordination and managerial authority.

Community Types and Urbanization

There is a very great need for an adequate means of characterizing and distinguishing settlements of different sizes and kinds, particularly since our terminology is so impoverished that "urban" is used to designate most of the larger and more important settlement types throughout the world. Such wholly unlike population aggregates as those of feudal Europe and native west Africa are called "cities." "Urbanization" has served as a synonym for the basic type of change that produced the irrigation state and as a characterization of one of the principal aspects of industrialization that affects contemporary farm as well as city populations. I hesitate to comment directly upon the use of this concept in the Symposium, because, in falling heir to current terminology, we have not had the opportunity to make a critical examination of its conceptual basis.

Beals puts his finger on part of the difficulty when he asks whether "a large, dense settlement with undifferentiated characteristics [could] be simply a large town, whereas a smaller settlement with highly differentiated functions perhaps [could] be an urban settlement." Since a quantitative approach is so basic a part of contemporary social science, one may easily minimize the importance of anthropology's fundamental qualitative methodology. To be useful in analyses of functional relationships and of causes of culture change, a taxonomy must be concerned with "what kind?" and not "how much?" The comparatively dense population in aboriginal California and the Central Valley of Chile would have supported sociocultural systems organized on a higher level than the tribelets, small villages, lineages, and other groups found in these areas. The qualitative nature of such groups, however, would have been the results of particular kinds of processes of change. While the larger settlements commonly found in societies with a supracommunity level of integration may be measurable in terms of numbers of persons and of groups of specialists, kinship units, bureaucracies, religious organizations, and other kinds of components, qualitative identification and characterization of such components must obviously precede quantification. Similarly, in class-structured societies, the nature of each class and of inter-class relations is a qualitative question to be answered in substantive terms in the case of each society. Mere numbers of persons—for example, whether there is one upper-class member to ten or one thousand lower-class members—is less revealing of the "strength" of class structure than functional analysis of the kind of authority the superordinate group holds over the subordinate group.

For the purpose of qualitative analysis, I submit that a taxonomy of settlement types must take into account not only the characteristics particular to the general cultural and evolutionary type of which it is a part but also that it must distinguish the features that function only on a local level from those that are derived from the settlement's integration in a larger or supracommunity sociocultural system. While inferences about prehistoric communities must obviously be somewhat speculative, archaeology has been unduly hesitant to offer interpretations of settlement types, even when the interpretations can be reasonably well supported. I suggest that this is less because archaeologists lack audacity than because their interests are oriented in other directions. I therefore hazard some interpretative comments on the succession of settlement types in the irrigation areas in the hope of stimulating much-needed research on these matters.

Settlements of the Incipient Farming type can be characterized with considerable certainty. That some of their characteristics are negative ones does not make them less important to studies of culture process. The absence in these settlements of any evidence of intercommunity economic cooperation can be taken as reasonable proof of independence. The scattering of a small number of domiciles around a religious structure in many of the earliest farm communities is fairly indicative of community ceremonial integration. The number and grouping of domiciles is, by analogy with historic societies, often highly suggestive of the kinship composition of the society. (See, for example, my study of the prehistoric Pueblo settlement pattern in relation to kinship, Steward 1937.) The presence of only domestic craft products is ample proof that the societies were not internally divided into groups of occupational specialists.

During the Formative-Florescent Era, supracommunity institutions developed, and the ultimate authority over matters not of purely local concern was evidently held by an upper class of priests. Irrigation was carried out by some form of compulsory labor, precious goods were produced by special artisans, mounds, temples, and other public constructions were erected, and ceremonialism was carried out under the control of this class. Whether the larger settlements in which these centers were located should be classed as "urban" is impossible to say in the absence of adequate conceptualization of this phenomenon. To call them "ceremonial irrigation centers," as distinguished from other kinds of ceremonial centers —for example, "ceremonial trade centers"—is perhaps inept but far better for the present than "cities."

Farm villages or communities continued to exist after ceremonial irrigation or trade centers developed. They differed from the earlier incipient farm communities, however, to the extent that they were linked through irrigation, production, and religion to the institutions of the newer ceremonial irrigation society and that irrigation officials, special craftsmen, temples, and priests might be located in them. Despite the probable retention of such incipient farm culture as certain kinship relations, household handicrafts, local shrines, and the like, these communities could not be classed as incipient farming communities.

During the Militaristic Era, large, complex, compact and often planned settlements appeared as a response to strong central controls over a considerable portion of interpersonal relations. These centers are generally designated as "cities," and culture change during this era is commonly described as "the urban revolution." The propriety of using these terms, however, is contingent upon several other considerations. No meaning of "city" is equally applicable to these militaristic era settlements and modern population centers, except Webster's first definition, "any important town." I am under the impression, however, that many writers have in mind the emergence of a strictly secular, state authority—a kind of power structure that contrasts with that of the earlier theocratic society and has its locus in the city. This concept seems to be linked with that of the city-state, at least in its initial stage, for city and state are assumed to be inextricably related if not identical, regardless of the extent of surrounding territory under state control. A further attribute of the city and state is a system of law, which is ultimately codified, to control economic, military, religious, and social behavior. The authority residing in this kind of state is described as political as against theocratic. A large compact settlement is called a city when it is an administrative center in a state that has political authority.

It seems to me that such reasoning does violence to several concepts and may result in the classification of the population centers of the Militaristic Era in a wrong and misleading taxonomic niche. Within its limited sphere, the authority of the theocratic irrigation society was no doubt as great as that of militaristic society. It differed only in being limited to fewer matters and sanctioned by religion rather than armed might. I think it would be incorrect to view the militaristic society as differing fundamentally in having a purely secular authority that administered a body of civil laws. It continued to control irrigation, corvee labor, construction of monumental works and edifices, and production of precious commodities. Owing to the acquisitive motivations of the society and to the limitations of internal production, the controls were finally extended territorially, they regimented all people more completely, and they were generally strengthened. Owing to the factors causing militarism—competition for resources and goods—the religious sanctions were supplemented and somewhat overshadowed but not replaced by armed force.

Since none of these phenomena really correspond to those designated "city," "state," and "political" in modern cultures, we seem to be at a loss for terms to subsume the data of the irrigation civilizations. While an adequate terminology will surely develop in the future, when new concepts are devised and repeatedly revised after new research, I suggest that the dilemma may be resolved for the present by using these terms in a loose sense to designate levels of integration rather than particular characteristics of sociocultural systems. For example, if "state" signifies a multicommunity system, the partly semantic question of whether Florescent Era ceremonial irrigation societies were states is resolved. These were states in terms of level of organization. Their diagnostic characteristics furnish the qualifying adjectives that mark them as distinctive kinds of states, for example, "ceremonial irrigation" as against "ceremonial trade," "militaristic irrigation," and the like.

Similarly, a city might be regarded as a level of community organization which, since it contains various groups of specialists, necessarily develops coordinating institutions on a higher level than these groups. In part, these institutions may be identical with those of the state. The particular nature of the groups within the city and of the coordinating institutions give them typological distinctiveness.

The concept "political" might also be related to levels. While most monographs on primitive peoples deal with "political organization" and there are several books on "primitive law," it seems to me that heuristically useful distinctions can be made according to the concept of levels. The informally sanctioned controls of customary behavior between members of the same small village or group are of a different order than the religiously- or militaristically-sanctioned rules or codes imposed by the state upon certain areas of individual behavior. When a primitive hunter shares his food with others, he is following a customary rule which is not enforcible by a higher authority. When a militaristic irrigation state farmer yields a portion of his produce to the state, he is obeying an enforcible law. It might be very useful to think of political controls and laws as aspects of any state-level society. The concepts of political authority and law would then be applicable to the early theocratic states. These theocratic states would differ from militaristic ones in the areas and kinds of authority.

Technologies

The sociological effects of technological knowledge in the irrigation civilizations were far simpler than in modern society. Our present-day technology is such that many consumers' goods are the products of a long series of manufacturing steps that begin with the extraction of raw materials from every part of the world and extend through innumerable processes. Consider for example the many specialized kinds of production and sources of material needed to make an automobile. Production in the irrigation societies required comparatively few steps and even fewer kinds of specialists. Instead of an elaborate system of technological interdependencies, the principal sociological requirement of the products of the Florescent Eras was mass labor and a supervisory hierarchy. It entailed organization rather than technological change.

Construction of the large irrigation systems, while entailing a certain knowledge of engineering, was possible mainly because a huge, controlled labor force was available. The development of an irrigation society from incipient farm villages was contingent far more upon enlarged dimensions of the water works than upon crucial inventions or technological innovations in irrigation. In the same way, mounds, temples, palaces, and other structures of incredible size were made when sufficient workers could be mobilized for the job. Constructional principles advanced very little over those of the very beginnings of the evolution. Mounds were still made of heaped-up earth. Doorways and vaults were bridged witth lintels or, occasionally, with the simple corbelled arch.

With the exception of metallurgy, processes used in the manufacturing of household goods and luxury items experienced few important modifications. Pottery, which continued to provide the principal containers, was improved only in ways of manipulating the clay and in knowledge of temper, paints, firing, and the like. Advancement in weaving consisted of little more than use of more kinds of fibers and dyes and elaborations of the basic weave produced on a hand loom. Manufacturing in stone, bone, shell, wood and other materials remained at a primitive level. All craft production and architecture, however, truly flowered in terms of esthetic refinement and of skill in using the fundamentally simple technologies. This flowering resulted from the devotion of full-time specialists to the work, which in turn became possible as irrigation—or, possibly in the case of Mesoamerica, rainfall farming—reached its maximum development.

While the irrigation civilizations flourished without fundamental change in the technologies they had possessed at the beginning of the Formative-Florescent Era, they largely failed to apply several basic intellectual and scientific achievements. In certain areas, the wheel and true arch were discovered but had little practical importance. Mathematics were employed more to keep records of temple affairs, including economic expansion, than to improve techniques of production. The calendar, which probably grew out of the agricultural needs to reckon seasons, contributed little to farm methods. Its refinements became a part of esoteric knowledge that went far beyond practical needs.

Application of theoretical knowledge was not made to an important extent until the subsequent Iron Age, when the inherent limitation upon the development of civilization in the irrigation areas, namely, availability of water, was removed and a new type of culture began to develop in the rainfall areas north of the Mediterranean Sea. While the term "Iron Age" is as inept as the terms "Neolithic Age," "Bronze Age," and others taken from a single technology, it has a certain appropriateness in that the discovery of how to smelt iron was one of the key factors in initiating an entirely new line of cultural evolution. In the irrigation civilizations, knowledge of alloying, smelting, and casting metals had finally led to production of bronze, a tin-copper alloy that is much harder than any of the metals then known. Bronze was first smelted in the Militaristic Era everywhere except China, where it appeared in the Florescent Era. As Collier points out, however, bronze had no bearing upon the florescense of the irrigation cultures. It was used as ornaments and containers but not as tools, because, despite its hardness, it was too rare to be employed widely in manufacturing. Its principal utilitarian function during the Militaristic Era was to make weapons.

The discovery of iron provided a fairly inexpensive and hard metal for everyday utilitarian purposes. While iron could not increase the water supply and thus remove the limitations on the irrigation civilizations, it afforded a means of coping with the forests of the rainfall areas, where it facilitated the development of new cultures. In subsequent eras, the principal changes in the irrigation areas were brought about through their incorporation in larger socio-cultural systems that centered outside these areas.

SUMMARY

I have attempted in these pages first to examine the basic methodology of the multilinear evolutionary approach and to suggest certain refinements of heuristic concepts; second to revise hypotheses explaining the development of the irrigation civilizations; and third to indicate some of the fields in which research, especially archeological research, would be extremely fruitful.

The more important refinements and modifications of conceptual tools pertain to the following: a more adequate terminology, especially for designating the patterns of those large settlements now roughly known as "urban" and those supracommunity sociocultural systems now called "states"; more careful classification of settlement types and sociocultural systems with reference to levels of integration as well as to the substantive phenomena of the different areas; greater attention to the concepts of key area, marginal area, and any other local environmental-cultural variations within the principal areas; and reconsideration of single and mulitple factors as the basis for understanding change and establishing a taxonomy.

The tentative revisions of the original hypotheses concerning the development of these civilizations have entailed principally the following: classification of Incipient Agriculture as a widely-distributed type that is not specific to the irrigation civilizations; classification of Mesoamerica as a Ceremonial Trade or Monopoly State in contrast to the Ceremonial Irrigation States of Mesopotamia, China, and the Central Andes; recognition that the Era of Fusion or Warfare and Cyclical Conquests developed because non-irrigation factors (e.g., warfare stimulated by predatory or acquisitive motivations) became basic causes of change and produced a society very different from the irrigation state; limitation of the hypotheses to the key regions within each area; a tentative explanation of how trade and control of the non-farming labor force may have been a major factor in change.

The outstanding research needs include both comparative study of available materials and new research, especially in the field:

archaeological research concentrated within delimited areas to show
the sociological implications of settlement patterns, the nature of
trade, and the development of irrigation in relation to the local environment on the one hand and to settlements and evidence of
managerial authority on the other; comparative study of historical
and archaeological materials to clarify problems of warfare, property,
slavery and others; and formulation of hypotheses concerning the
development of the one or more types of marginal areas.

BIBLIOGRAPHY

ACOSTA, JORGE R.
1965 "Preclassic and Classic Architecture of Oaxaca," in *Archeology of Southern Mesoamerica* (Gordon R. Willey, ed.), *Handbook of Middle American Indians*, Vol. 3; pp. 814–36. University of Texas Press, Austin.

ACOSTA SAIGNES, MIGUEL
1945 *Los Pochteca Acta Antropologico I.* No. 1. Mexico, D.F.

ADAMS, ROBERT M.
1956a "Some Hypotheses on the Development of Early Civilizations," *American Antiquity*, Vol. 22; pp. 227–32.

ADAMS, ROBERT M.
1956b *Level and Trend in Early Sumerian Civilization.* Unpublished Ph.D. dissertation, University of Chicago.

ADAMS, ROBERT M.
1960 "Early Civilizations: Subsistence and Environment," in *City Invincible: A Symposium on Urbanization and Cultural Development in the Ancient Near East.* (C. H. Kraeling, and R. M. Adams, eds.); pp. 269–95.

ADAMS, ROBERT M.
1962 "Agriculture and Urban Life in Early Southwestern Iran," *Science*, Vol 136; pp. 109–22. Washington, D.C.

ADAMS, ROBERT M.
1965 *Land Behind Baghdad: A History of Settlement on the Diyala Plains.* University of Chicago Press.

ALBANESE, ANTHONY A.
1959 *Protein and Amino Acid Nutrition.* Academic Press, New York.

ALEXANDER, J., and COURSEY, D. G.
1969 "The Origins of Yam Cultivation," in *The Domestication and Exploitation of Plants and Animals.* (Ucko, P. J. and G. W. Dimblebey, eds.) pp. 405–26. Aldine Publishing Co., Chicago.

ALIMEN, H.
1957 *The Prehistory of Africa.* Hutchinson, London.

ALLEE, W. C.; EMERSON, A. E.; PARK, O.; PARK, T.; and SCHMIDT, KARL P.
1949 *Principles of Animal Ecology.* W. B. Saunders, Philadelphia.

ALTSCHUL, AARON M.
1962 "Seed Proteins and World Food Problems," *Economic Botany*, Vol. 16; 2–13.

AMSCHLER, J. WOLFGANG
1939 "Der Ausgrabungen von dem "Grossen Königshügel" Shah Tepé, in Nord-Iran," Reports from the Scientific Expedition to the North-western Provinces of China under the Leadership of Dr. Sven Hedin:

The Sino-Swedish Expedition, *Publication*, No. 9, part 7 Archaeology, No. 4; pp. 35–129.

AMSCHLER, J. WOLFGANG

n.d. "Identification of the Animal Bones from the Amouq," unpublished manuscript in the personal files of Robert J. Braidwood.

ANDERSON, EDGAR

1949 *Introgressive Hybridization*. John Wiley and Sons, New York.

ANDERSON, EDGAR

1952 *Plants, Life and Man*. Little, Brown and Co., Boston.

ANDERSON, EDGAR

1956 "Man as a Maker of New Plants and Plant Communities," in *Man's Role in Changing the Face of the Earth* (William L. Thomas, Jr., ed.); pp. 763–77. University of Chicago Press.

ANDERSON, EDGAR, and CUTLER, HUGH C.

1942 "Races of *Zea mays:* I. Their Recognition and Classification," Missouri Botanical Gardens, *Annals*, Vol. 29; pp. 69–86.

ANDERSON, EDGAR, and ERICKSON, RALPH O.

1941 "Antithetical Dominance in North American Maize," National Academy of Sciences, *Proceedings*, Vol. 27; pp. 436–40. Washington, D.C.

ANDERSON, JAMES E.

1967 "The Human Skeletons," in *Environment and Subsistence* (Douglas S. Byers, gen. ed.) *The Prehistory of the Tehuacán Valley*, Vol. 1; pp. 91–113. University of Texas Press, Austin.

ANTONIUS, O.

1922 *Grundzüge einer Stammesgeschichte der Haustiere*. Fischer, Jena.

ARAMBOURG, C.

1929 "Les Mammifères Quaternaires de l'Algérie," Soc. Hist. Nat. Afrique du Nord, *Bulletin*, Vol. 20; pp. 63–84.

ARKELL, A. J.

1957 "Khartoum's Part in the Development of the Neolithic," *Kush*, Vol. 5; pp. 8–12.

ARMILLAS, PEDRO

1949 "Notas Sobre Sistemas de Cultivo en Mesoamerica," Instituto Nacional de Antropologia e Historia, *Anales*, Vol. 3; pp. 85–115. Mexico.

ARMILLAS, PEDRO

1951 "Tecnologia, Formaciones Socioeconomicas y Religion en Mesoamerica," in *The Civilizations of Ancient America* (Sol Tax, ed.); pp. 19–30. Selected papers of the 29th International Congress of America.

ARNAL, J., and BURNEZ, C.

1958 "Die Struktur des Französischen Neolithikums auf Grund Neuester Stratigraphischer Boebachtungen," *Bericht der Römisch-Germanischen Kommission*, Vol. 37–38; pp. 1–90.

ARRIBAS, A.

1967 "Le Néolithique Ancien de la Péninsula Ibérique," *Palaeohistoria*, Vol. 12; pp. 11–17.

ASCHMAN, HOMER

1960 "Indian Pastoralists of the Guajira Peninsula," Association of American Geographers, *Annals*, Vol. 50; pp. 408–18.

AVELEYRA ARROYO DE ANDA, LUIS

1964 "The Primitive Hunter," in *Natural Environments and Early Cultures* (Robert C. West, ed.), *Handbook of Middle American Indians*, Vol. 1; pp. 384–412. University of Texas Press, Austin.

BAERREIS, DAVID

1951 *The Preceramic Horizons of Northeastern Oklahoma.* University of Michigan, Museum of Anthropology, *Anthropological Papers*, No. 6.

BAILLOUD, G.

1964 *Le Néolithique dans le Basin Parisien.* Centre National de la Recherche Scientifique, Paris.

BANDI, H. G. editor

1963 *Birsmatten-Basisgrotte, Eine Mittelsteinzeitliche Fundstelle im Unteren Birstal.* Stämpfli, Bern.

BANGHAM, A. D.

1957 "Distribution of Electrophoretically Different Hæmoglobins among Cattle Breeds of Great Britain," *Nature*, Vol. 179; pp. 467–68. London.

BARGHOORN, ELSO S.; WOLF, MARGARET K.; and CLISBY, KATHRYN H.

1954 "Fossil Maize from the Valley of Mexico," Harvard University, Botanical Museum, *Leaflets*, Vol. 16; pp. 229–40.

BARLOW, R. H.

1949 "The Extent of the Empire of the Culhua, Mexica," *Ibero-Americana*, Vol. 28.

BARRIÈRE, C.

1947 *Les civilisations Tardenoisiennes en Europe Occidentale.* Briere, Bordeaux-Paris.

BARTA, J.

1959 "Mezolitické a Neolitické Kamenné Nástroje z dún 'Vísky' pri Dolnej Strede," *Slovenska Archeólogia*, Vol. 7; pp. 241–59.

BARTH, FREDRIK

1956 "Ecologic Relationships of Ethnic Groups in Swat, North Pakistan," *American Anthropologist*, Vol. 58; pp. 1079–89. Washington, D.C.

BARTHOLOMEW, GEORGE A., JR., and BIRDSELL, J. B.

1953 "Ecology and the Protohominids," *American Anthropologist*, Vol. 55, pt. 2; pp. 481–98.

BARTON, G. A.

1929 *Royal Inscriptions of Sumer and Akkad.* New Haven.

BATE, DOROTHEA M. A.

1937 *The Stone Age of Mount Carmel.* Clarendon, Oxford.

BATE, DOROTHEA M. A.

1940 "The Fossil Antelopes of Palestine in Natufian (Mesolithic) Times," *Geology Magazine*, Vol. 77; pp. 418–33.

BATE, DOROTHEA M. A.

1942 "The Fossil Mammals of Shukbah," *Proceedings of the Prehistoric Society*, Vol. 8; pp. 15–20.

BATE, DOROTHEA M. A.

1953 "The Vertebrate Fauna," in *Shaheinab* (A. J. Arkell, ed.); pp. 11–19. Oxford University Press, London.

BATOVIĆ, S.

1962 "Neolitsko Nalaziste u Smilčiću," *Diadora,* Vol. 2; pp. 31–116.

BEHRENS, H.

1959 "Die Rössener Kultur and ihre Bedeutung für die Herausbildung der Tiefstichkeramik aus der Trichterbecherkultur," *Die Kunde: Mitteilungen des Niedersächsischen Landesvereins für Urgeschichte,* Neue Folge 10, Heft 1–2; pp. 44–60.

BENAC, A.

1962 "Studien zur Stein- und Kupferzeit im Nordwestlichen Balkan," *Bericht der Römisch-Germanischen Komission,* Vol. 42; pp. 1–170.

BENGSTON, H., and MILOJČIĆ, V.

1958 *Grosser Historischer Weltatlas,* Part I. Bayerischer Schulbuch-Verlag, Munich.

BENNETT, W. C.

1946 "The Andean Highlands: An Introduction," in *Handbook of South American Indians* (Julian H. Steward, ed.) Vol. 2, Bureau of American Ethnology, *Bulletin,* Vol. 143; pp. 1–60.

BENNETT, W. C., and BIRD, J. B.

1949 *Andean Culture History.* The American Museum of Natural History, *Handbook Series,* No. 15.

BENSON, J. L.

1956 "Aegean and Near Eastern Seal Impression from Cyprus," in *The Aegean and the Near East* (S. S. Weinberg, ed.); pp. 59–77. Augustin, Locust Valley, New York.

BERNABO BREA, L.

1957 *Sicily Before the Greeks.* Thames and Hudson, London.

BERNAL, IGNACIO

1965 "Architecture in Oaxaca after the End of Monte Alban," in *Archeology of Southern Mesoamerica* (Gordon R. Willey, ed.) *Handbook of Middle American Indians,* Vol. 3; pp. 837–48. University of Texas Press, Austin.

BETTINI, T. M.

1944 "Die Rinderzucht in Italienisch-Ostafrika," *Beitraege zur Kulturgeschichte Linguistik,* Vol. 6; pp. 109–33.

BEUCHER, F.

1963 "Flores Quarternaires au Sahara Nord-occidental," *C. R. Acad. Sci.,* Vol. 256; pp. 2205–8.

BINFORD, LEWIS R.

1963 "Archaeological Systematics and the Study of Culture Process," *American Antiquity,* Vol. 31; pp. 203–10.

BINFORD, LEWIS R.

1964 *Archaeological and Ethnohistorical Investigations of Cultural Diversity.* Ph.D. dissertation, University of Michigan (microfilm).

BINFORD, LEWIS R.

1968a "Post-Pleistocene Adaptations," in *New Perspectives in Archeology* (Sally R. and Lewis R. Binford, eds.); pp. 313–41. Aldine Publishing Co., Chicago.

BINFORD, LEWIS R.

1968b "An Ethnohistory of the Nottoway, Meherrin and Weanock Indians of Southeastern Virginia," *Ethnohistory,* Vol. 14; No. 3–4.

BINFORD, LEWIS R., and BINFORD, SALLY R.

1966a "A Preliminary Analysis of Functional Variability in the Mousterian of Levallois Facies," *American Anthropologist,* Vol. 68; pp. 238–95.

BINFORD, LEWIS R., and BINFORD, SALLY R.

1966b "The Predatory Revolution: A Consideration of the Evidence for a New Subsistence Level," *American Anthropologist,* Vol. 68; pp. 508–12.

BINFORD, SALLY R.

1968 "Variability and Change in the Near Eastern Mousterian of Levallois Facies," in *New Perspectives in Archeology,* (Sally R. and Lewis R. Binford, eds.); pp. 49–60. Aldine Publishing Co., Chicago.

BIRD, J. B.

1948 "Preceramic Culture in Chicama and Viru," in *Reappraisal of Peruvian Archaeology* (W. C. Bennett, ed.) Society for American Archaeology, *Memoir* 4.

BIRDSELL, JOSEPH B.

1953 "Some Environmental and Cultural Factors Influencing the Structuring of Australian Aboriginal Populations," *American Naturalist,* Vol. 87; pp. 171–207.

BIRDSELL, JOSEPH B.

1957 "Some Population Problems Involving Pleistocene Man," *Cold Spring Harbor Symposia on Quantitative Biology,* Vol. 22; pp. 47–69.

BIRDSELL, JOSEPH B.

1958 "On Population Structure in Generalized Hunting and Collecting Populations," *Evolution,* Vol. 12; pp. 189–205.

BIRDSELL, JOSEPH B.

1966 "Some Predictions for the Pleistocene Based upon Equilibrium Systems among Recent Hunters," statement for conference, "Man the Hunter," University of Chicago, April 6–9, 1966.

BIRDSELL, JOSEPH B.

1968 "Some Predictions for the Pleistocene Based upon Equilibrium Systems among Recent Hunters," in *Man the Hunter* (Richard B. Lee and Irven DeVore, eds.); pp. 229–40. Aldine Publishing Co., Chicago.

BISHOP, CARL W.

1938 "Origin and Early Diffusion of the Traction Plow," Smithsonian Institution, *Annual Report for 1937;* pp. 531–47.

BISSCHOP, J. H. R.

1937 "Parent Stock and Derived Types of African Cattle," *South African Journal of Science,* Vol. 33; pp. 852–70. Johannesburg.

BLACK, GLENN A.

1944 *Angel Site, Vandenburgh County, Indiana.* Indiana Historical Society, *Prehistory Research Series,* Vol. 11, No. 5.

BLACK, MEREDITH

1963 "The Distribution and Archaeological Significance of the Marsh Elder, *Iva Annua* L.," Michigan Academy of Science, Arts and Letters, *Papers,* Vol. 48; pp. 541–47.

BLOCK, RICHARD J., and WEISS, KATHRYN W.
1956 *Amino Acid Handbook.* Charles C. Thomas, Springfield, Illinois.

BODENHEIMER, FRIEDERICH S.
1949 *Hachai bearzot Hamikra.* Bialik Foundation, Jerusalem.

BOESSNECK, J.
1953 "Die Haustiere in Altägypten," Zoologischen Staatssammlung München, *Veröffentlungen,* Vol. 3.

BOETTGER, CAESAR R.
1958 *Die Haustiere Afrikas.* G. Fischer, Jena.

BOHLKEN, HERWART
1958 "Vergleichende Untersuchungen an Wildrindern (*Tribus bovini* Simpson 1945)," *Zoologische Jahrbuch Abteilung für Allgemeine Zoologie und Physiologie der Tiere,* Band 68; pp. 113–202.

BÖHM, J., and DE LAET, S. J., editors.
1961 *L'Europe à la Fin de l'Âge de la Pierre.* Editions de l'Académie Tchécoslovaque des Sciences, Prague.

BOHMERS, A.
1960 "Statistiques et Graphiques dans l'Étude des Industries Lithiques Préhistoriques," *Palaeohistoria,* Vol. 8; pp. 15–39. Groningen.

BOHMERS, A., and WOUTERS, A.
1956 "Statistics and Graphs in the Study of Flint Assemblages. III A Preliminary Report on the Statistical Analysis of the Mesolithic in Northwestern Europe," *Palaeohistoria,* Vol. 5; pp. 27–39.

BÖKÖNYI, S.
1964 "A Maroslele-Panai Neolitikus Telep Gerinces Faunája," *Archaeologiai Értesítö,* Vol. 91; pp. 87–94.

BORCHARDT, LUDWIG
1905 "Ein Königserlass aus Dahschur," *Zeitschrift für Ägyptische Sprache und Altertumskunde,* Vol. 42; pp. 1–11.

BOSE, SARADINDU
1964 "Economy of the Onge of Little Andaman," *Man in India,* Vol. 44; pp. 298–310.

BOSERUP, ESTHER
1965 *The Conditions of Agricultural Growth: The Economics of Agrarian Change Under Population Pressure.* Aldine Publishing Co., Chicago.

BOSTANCI, ENVER Y.
1959 "Researches on the Mediterranean Coast of Anatolia: A New Palaeolithic Site at Beldibi near Antalya," *Anatolia,* Vol. 4; pp. 129–73.

BOSTON, E. J.
1954 "Jersey Cattle," in *Jersey Cattle* (E. J. Boston, ed.); pp. 19–42. Faber, London.

BOURDIER, FRANCK, and DE LUMLEY, HENRY
1954 "Existence d'une Industrie Proto-Azilienne Contemporaire du Renne en Dauphiné," *Société Préhistorique Française, Bulletin,* Vol. 51; pp. 307–9. Paris.

BRAIDWOOD, ROBERT J.
1951a *Prehistoric Men,* 2nd ed. Chicago Natural History Museum, *Popular Series, Anthropology,* No. 37, Chicago.

BRAIDWOOD, ROBERT J.

1951b "From Cave to Village in Prehistoric Iraq," American Schools of Oriental Research, *Bulletin*, Vol. 124; pp. 12–18.

BRAIDWOOD, ROBERT J.

1952a *The Near East and the Foundations for Civilization*. University of Oregon Press, Eugene.

BRAIDWOOD, ROBERT J.

1952b "From Cave to Village," *Scientific American*, Vol. 187, No. 4; pp. 62–66.

BRAIDWOOD, ROBERT J.

1957a "Jericho and Its Setting in Near Eastern History," *Antiquity*, Vol. 31; pp. 73–81.

BRAIDWOOD, ROBERT J.

1957b "Means Toward an Understanding of Human Behavior Before the Present," National Academy of Science–National Research Council, *Publication*, No. 565; pp. 14–16.

BRAIDWOOD, ROBERT J.

1958 "Near Eastern Prehistory," *Science*, Vol. 127; pp. 1419–30.

BRAIDWOOD, ROBERT J.

1959 "Über die Anwendung der Radiokarbon-Chronologie für das Verständnis der Ersten Dorfkulturgemeinschaften in Sudwestasien," Österreichische Akademie der Wissenschaften, Philosophisch-Historische Klasse, *Anzeiger*, No. 95; pp. 249–59.

BRAIDWOOD, ROBERT J.

1960a "The Agricultural Revolution," *Scientific American*, Vol. 203; pp. 130–48.

BRAIDWOOD, ROBERT J.

1960b "Levels in Prehistory: A Model for Consideration of the Evidence," in *The Evolution of Man* (Sol Tax, ed.) *Evolution After Darwin*, Vol. 2. University of Chicago Press.

BRAIDWOOD, ROBERT J.

1960c "Prelude to Civilization," in *City Invincible* (Carl H. Kraeling and Robert M. Adams, eds.); pp. 297–314. University of Chicago Press.

BRAIDWOOD, ROBERT J.

1960d "Preliminary Investigations Concerning the Origins of Food-Production in Iranian Kurdistan," *British Association for the Advancement of Science*, Vol. 17; pp. 214–18.

BRAIDWOOD, ROBERT J.

1962 "The Earliest Village Communities of Southwestern Asia Reconsidered," *Atti del VI Congresso Internazionale della Scienza Preistoriche e Protostoriche*, Vol. 1; pp. 115–26. Collegio Romano, Rome.

BRAIDWOOD, ROBERT J.

1963 *Prehistoric Men*, 6th ed. Chicago Natural History Museum. *Popular Series, Anthropology*, No. 37, Chicago.

BRAIDWOOD, ROBERT J.

1965 "Further Remarks on Radioactive Carbon Age Determination and the Chronology of the Late Prehistoric and Protohistoric Near East," in *Vorderasiatische Archäologie: Studien und Aufsätze* (Kurt Bittel, *et al.*, eds.); pp. 57–68. Anton Moortgat Festschrift, Mann, Berlin.

BRAIDWOOD, ROBERT J.

1967 *Prehistoric Men,* 7th ed. Scott, Foresman and Company, Glenview, Illinois.

BRAIDWOOD, ROBERT J.

n.d. *Cultures Based on Animal and Plant Domestication.* Readings in Anthropology Today. Del Mar, California (*in press*).

BRAIDWOOD, ROBERT J., and BRAIDWOOD, LINDA S.

1949 "On the Treatment of Prehistoric Near Eastern Materials in Steward's 'Cultural Causality and Law,'" *American Anthropologist,* Vol. 51; pp. 665–69.

BRAIDWOOD, ROBERT J., and BRAIDWOOD, LINDA S.

1950 "Jarmo: A Village of Early Farmers in Iraq," *Antiquity,* Vol. 24; pp. 189–95.

BRAIDWOOD, ROBERT J., and BRAIDWOOD, LINDA S.

1953 "The Earliest Village Communities of Southwestern Asia," *Journal of World History,* Vol. 1; pp. 278–310.

BRAIDWOOD, ROBERT J., and BRAIDWOOD, LINDA S.

1960 *Excavations in the Plain of Antioch,* Vol. 1. University of Chicago, Oriental Institute, *Publications,* Vol. 61. Chicago.

BRAIDWOOD, ROBERT J., and HOWE, BRUCE

1962 "Southwestern Asia Beyond the Land of the Mediterranean Littoral," in *Courses Toward Urban Life* (Robert J. Braidwood and Gordon R. Willey, eds.). Aldine Publishing Co., Chicago.

BRAIDWOOD, ROBERT J.; HOWE, BRUCE; and NEGAHBAN, EZAT O.

1960 "Near Eastern Prehistory," *Science,* Vol. 131; pp. 1536–41.

BRAIDWOOD, ROBERT J.; HOWE, BRUCE; and REED, CHARLES A.

1961 "The Iranian Prehistoric Project," *Science,* Vol. 133; pp. 2008–10.

BRAIDWOOD, ROBERT J.; HOWE, BRUCE; *et al.*

1960 *Prehistoric Investigations in Iraqi Kurdistan.* University of Chicago, Oriental Institute, *Studies in Ancient Oriental Civilization,* No. 31. University of Chicago Press.

BRAIDWOOD, ROBERT J., and REED, CHARLES A.

1957 "The Achievement and Early Consequences of Food-Production: A Consideration of the Archeological and Natural-Historical Evidence," *Cold Spring Harbor Symposia on Quantitative Biology,* Vol. 22; pp. 19–31.

BRAIDWOOD, ROBERT J., and WILLEY, GORDON R., editors

1962a *Courses Toward Urban Life.* Aldine Publishing Co., Chicago.

BRAIDWOOD, ROBERT J., and WILLEY, GORDON R.

1962b "Conclusions and Afterthoughts," in *Courses Toward Urban Life* (Robert J. Braidwood and Gordon R. Willey, eds.); pp. 330–59. Aldine Publishing Co. Chicago.

BRAIDWOOD, ROBERT J., *et al.*

1944 "New Chalcolithic Material of Samarran Type and its Implications," *Journal of Near Eastern Studies,* Vol. 3; pp. 47–72.

BREASTED, J. H.

1906 *Ancient Records of Egypt I.* Chicago.

BREUIL, H.

1921 "Observations Suivantes: M. Cartilhac La Question de L'Hiatus Entre le Paléolithique et le Néolithique," *l'Anthropologie,* Vol. 31; pp. 349–55.

BREUIL, H.

1946 "The Discovery of the Antiquity of Man," Royal Anthropological Institute of Great Britain and Ireland, *Journal*, Vol. 75; pp. 21–31.

BRODAR, M.

1958–1959 "Crvena Stijena, Eine Neue Paläolithstation aus dem Balkan in Jugoslawien," *Quartär*, Vol. 10–11; pp. 227–37.

BRØNSTED, J.

1957 *Danmarks Oldtid Stenalderen*, 2nd ed., Vol. 1. Gyldendal, Copenhagen.

BROOKS, R. H.; KAPLAN, L.; CUTLER, H. C.; and WHITAKER, T. W.

1962 "Plant Material from a Cave on the Rio Zape, Durango, Mexico," *American Antiquity*, Vol. 27; pp. 356–69.

BROWN, JOHN ALLEN

1889 "On Some Small Highly Specialized Forms of Stone Implements, Found in Asia, North Africa and Europe," Royal Anthropological Institute of Great Britain and Ireland, *Journal*, Vol. 18; pp. 134–319.

BROWN, JOHN ALLEN

1893 "On the Continuity of the Palaeolithic and Neolithic Periods," Royal Anthropological Institute of Great Britain and Ireland, *Journal*, Vol. 22; pp. 66–98.

BUKASOV, S. M.

1930 "The Cultivated Plants of Mexico, Guatemala, and Colombia," *Bulletin of Applied Botany, of Genetics and Plant-Breeding*, Suppl. 47 (English Summary, pp. 470–553).

BURKILL, I. H.

1935 *A Dictionary of the Economic Products of the Malay Peninsula.* London.

BURKILL, I. H.

1951 "The Rise and Decline of the Greater Yam in the Service of Man," *The Advancement of Science*, Vol. 7; pp. 443–48.

BURKITT, M. C.

1925 "The Transition Between Palaeolithic and Neolithic Times, i.e., the Mesolithic Period," Prehistoric Society of East Anglia, *Proceedings*, Vol. 5; pp. 16–33.

BURTON, MAURICE

1956 "Eland Ignored," *Illustrated London News*, Vol. 229; p. 234.

BUTTLER, W.

1938 "Der Donauländische und der Westische Kulturkreis der Jüngeren Steinzeit," in *Handbuch der Urgeschichte Deutschlands*, Vol. 2. de Gruyter, Berlin.

BUTZER, KARL W.

1957 "Late Glacial and Postglacial Climatic Variations in the Near East," *Erdkunde*, Vol. 11; pp. 21–35.

BUTZER, KARL W.

1958a "Quaternary Stratigraphy and Climate in the Near East," *Bonner Geographisches Abhandlung*, Vol. 24.

BUTZER, KARL W.

1958b "Das Ökologische Problem der Neolitischen Felsbilder der Östlichen Sahara," Adad. Wiss. Lit. (Mainz), *Abhandlungen, Math.-Naturw. Klasse*, Vol. 1; pp. 20–49.

BUTZER, KARL W.

1959 "Die Naturlandschaft Ägyptens während der Vorgeschichte und dem Dynastichen Zeitalter," Akad. Wiss. Lit. (Mainz), *Abhandlungen, Math.-Naturw. Klasse,* Vol. 2; pp 1–80.

BUTZER, KARL W.

1964 *Environment and Archeology: An Introduction to Pleistocene Geography.* Aldine Publishing Co., Chicago.

BUTZER, KARL W.

1970 "Environmental Changes in Southwestern Asia and Egypt during Terminal Pleistocene and Early Holocene Times," *Fundamenta,* Series B, Vol. 3. Cologne (*in press*).

BUTZER, KARL W.

n.d. "Climatic Geomorphologic Interpretation of Upper Pleistocene Sediments in the Eurafrican Subtropics," UNESCO-WMO Symposium on Changes of Climate with Special Reference to the Arid Zones, Rome, October 1961.

BUTZER, KARL W., and HANSEN, C. L.

1968 *Desert and River in Nubia: Geomorphology and Prehistoric Environments at the Aswan Reservoir.* University of Wisconsin Press, Madison.

BYERS, DOUGLAS S., general editor

1967a *Environment and Subsistence. The Prehistory of the Tehuacán Valley,* Vol. 1. University of Texas Press, Austin.

BYERS, DOUGLAS S., general editor

1967b *The Non-Ceramic Artifacts. The Prehistory of the Tehuacán Valley,* Vol. 2. University of Texas Press, Austin.

CALDWELL, JOSEPH R.

1957 *Trend and Tradition in the Prehistory of the Eastern United States.* Ph.D. dissertation, Department of Anthropology, University of Chicago.

CALDWELL, JOSEPH R.

1958 *Trend and Tradition in the Prehistory of the Eastern United States.* American Anthropological Association, *Memoir,* No. 88, Illinois State Museum, *Scientific Papers,* Vol. 10.

CALDWELL, JOSEPH R.

1962 "Eastern North America," in *Courses Toward Urban Life* (Robert J. Braidwood and Gordon R. Willey, eds.); pp. 288–308. Aldine Publishing Co., Chicago.

CALDWELL, JOSEPH R.

n.d. "Appraisal of the Archeological Resources of Hartwell Reservoir, South Carolina and Georgia," Smithsonian Institution, *Smithsonian River Basin Surveys* (mimeographed).

CALLEN, ERIC O.

1965 "Food Habits of Some Pre-Columbian Mexican Indians," *Economic Botany,* Vol. 19, No. 4; pp. 335–43.

CALLEN, ERIC O.

1967 "Analysis of the Tehuacán Coprolites," in *Environment and Subsistence* (Douglas S. Byers, gen. ed.) *The Prehistory of the Tehuacán Valley,* Vol. 1; pp. 261–89. University of Texas Press, Austin.

CALLEN, ERIC, and MACNEISH, RICHARD S.

n.d. "Prehistoric Tamaulipas Food Remains as Determined by a Study of Fecal Remains," unpublished manuscript.

CARDICH, AUGUSTO

1958 *Los Yacimientos de Lauricocha; Nuevas Interpretationes de la Prehistoria Peruana.* Centro Argentino de Estudios Prehistoricos, *Studia Praehistorica,* Vol. 1. Buenos Aires.

CARDICH, AUGUSTO

1964 *Lauricocha; Fundamentos para una Prehistoria de los Andes Centrales.* Centro Argentino de Estudios Prehistoricos, *Studia Praehistorica,* Vol. 3. Buenos Aires.

CARLSON, ROY L.

1963 "Basketmaker III Sites Near Durango, Colorado," in *Faunal and Floral Remains, The Earl Morris Papers,* No. 1. University of Colorado Studies, *Series in Anthropology,* No. 8.

CARNEIRO, ROBERT

1957 *Subsistence and Social Structure: An Ecological Study of the Kuikuru Indians.* Ph.D. dissertation, University of Michigan (mimeographed).

CARR-SAUNDERS, A. M.

1922 *The Population Problem: A Study in Human Evolution.* Clarendon Press, Oxford.

CARTER, G. F.

1945 *Plant Geography and Culture History in the American Southwest.* Viking Fund, *Publications in Anthropology,* No. 5.

CASO, ALFONSO

1952 *Urnas de Oaxaca.* Instituto Nacional de Antropologia e Historia. Mexico.

CASO, ALFONSO

1965 "Zapotec Writing and Calendar," in *Archeology of Southern Mesoamerica* (Gordon R. Willey, ed.), *Handbook of Middle American Indians,* Vol. 3; pp. 931–47. University of Texas Press, Austin.

CHANG, KWANG-CHIH

1968 "Archeology of Ancient China," *Science,* Vol. 162; pp. 519–26

CHARLES, ROBERT P.

1957 "Essai sur la Chronologie des Civilisations Predynastiques d'Egypte," *Journal of Near Eastern Studies,* Vol. 16; pp. 240–53.

CHATFIELD, CHARLOTTE, and ADAMS, GEORGIAN

1940 "Proximate Composition of American Food Materials," U. S. Department of Agriculture, *Circular,* No. 549.

CHAVAILLON, J.

1964 *Les Formations Quaternaires du Sahara Nord-Øccidental.* Centre Nationale Recherches Sciences. Paris.

CHEESMAN, E. E.

1948 "On the Nomenclature of Edible Bananas," *Journal of Genetics,* Vol. 48; pp. 293–96.

1925 *The Dawn of European Civilization.* Alfred A. Knopf, New York.

CHILDE, V. GORDON

1928 *The Most Ancient East.* Kegan Paul, Trench, Trubner, London.

CHILDE, V. GORDON

1929 *The Most Ancient East.* Routledge and Kegan Paul, London.

CHILDE, V. GORDON

1931 "The Forest Cultures of Northern Europe: A Study in Evolution and

Diffusion," Royal Anthropological Institute of Great Britain and Ireland, *Journal*, Vol. 61; pp. 325–48.

CHILDE, V. GORDON

1937 "Adaptation to the Postglacial Forest on the North Eurasiatic Plain," in *Early Man* (G. G. McCurdy, ed.). J. B. Lippincott, New York.

CHILDE, V. GORDON

1941 *Man Makes Himself*. Watts & Co., London.

CHILDE, V. GORDON

1942 *What Happened in History*. Harmondsworth, London.

CHILDE, V. GORDON

1944 *Progress and Archeology*. The Thinkers Library, No. 102. Watts & Co., London.

CHILDE, V. GORDON

1950 "The Urban Revolution," *Town Planning Review*, Vol. 21; pp. 3–17.

CHILDE, V. GORDON

1951a *Social Evolution*. Schuman, New York.

CHILDE, V. GORDON

1951b *Man Makes Himself*. New American Library, Mentor Books, New York.

CHILDE, V. GORDON

1951c "The First Waggons and Carts—From the Tigris to the Severn," Prehistoric Society, *Proceedings*, Vol. 17; pp. 177–94. London.

CHILDE, V. GORDON

1952a *New Light on the Most Ancient East*, 4th edition. Routledge and Kegan Paul, London.

1952b *New Light on the Most Ancient East*, Grove Press, New York.

CHILDE, V. GORDON

1953 "Old World Prehistory: Neolithic," in *Anthropology Today* (A. L. Kroeber, assembler); pp. 193–210. University of Chicago Press.

CHILDE, V. GORDON

1954 "The Diffusion of Wheeled Vehicles," *Ethnographisch-Archäologische Forschungen*, Vol. 2.

CHILDE, V. GORDON

1956 "The New Stone Age," in *Man, Culture and Society* (Harry L. Shapiro, ed.); pp. 94–110. Oxford University Press.

CHILDE, V. GORDON

1957 "Civilization, Cities and Towns," *Antiquity*, Vol. 31; pp. 36–38.

CHILDE, V. GORDON

1958a "Retrospect," *Antiquity*, Vol. 32; pp. 69–74. London.

CHILDE, V. GORDON

1958b *The Prehistory of European Society*. Pelican, Harmondsworth.

CHURCHILL, D. M.

1965 "The Kitchen Midden Site at Westward Ho!, Devon, England: Ecology, Age and Relation to Changes in Land and Sea Level," Prehistoric Society, *Proceedings*, Vol. 31; pp. 74–84. London.

CLARK, JAMES COOPER, editor and translator

1938 *Codex Mendoza*, the Mexican Manuscript known as the *Collection of Mendoza* and preserved in the Bodleian Library Oxford, 3 vols. Waterlow and Sons, Ltd., London.

CLARK, J. DESMOND
1951 "Bushmen Hunters of the Barotse Forests," *The Northern Rhodesia Journal,* Vol. 1, pt. 3; pp. 56–65.

CLARK, J. DESMOND
1962 "Africa South of the Sahara," in *Courses Toward Urban Life* (Robert J. Braidwood and Gordon R. Willey, eds.); pp. 1–33. Aldine Publishing Co., Chicago.

CLARK, J. DESMOND, editor
1967a *Atlas of African Prehistory.* University of Chicago Press.

CLARK, J. DESMOND
1967b "The Problem of Neolithic Culture in Subsaharan Africa," in *Background to Evolution in Africa* (W. W. Bishop & J. D. Clark, ed.); pp. 601–27. University of Chicago Press.

CLARK, J. G. D.
1932 *The Mesolithic Age in Britain.* The University Press, Cambridge, England.

CLARKE, J. G. D.
1936 *The Mesolithic Settlement of Northern Europe: A Study of the Food Gathering Peoples of Northern Europe During the Early Post-Glacial Period.* The University Press, Cambridge, England.

CLARK, J. G. D.
1945 "Farmers and Forests in Neolithic Europe," *Antiquity,* Vol. 19; pp. 57–71. London.

CLARK, J. G. D.
1946 "Farmers and Forests in Neolithic Europe," *Antiquity,* Vol. 19; pp. 57–71. London.

CLARK, J. G. D.
1948a "Fowling in Prehistoric Europe," *Antiquity,* Vol. 22, pt. 8; pp. 116–30. London.

CLARK, J. G. D.
1948b "The Development of Fishing in Prehistoric Europe," *The Antiquaries Journal,* Vol. 28; pp. 45–85.

CLARK, J. G. D.
1952 *Prehistoric Europe, The Economic Basis.* Philosophical Library, New York.

CLARK, J. G. D.
1954 *Excavations at Star Carr.* Cambridge University Press, Cambridge.

CLARK, J. G. D.
1955 "A Microlithic Industry from the Cambridgeshire Fenland and other Industries of Sauveterrian Affinities from Britain," Prehistoric Ssociety, *Proceedings,* Vol. 21; pp. 3–20. London.

CLARK, J. G. D.
1963 "A Survey of the Mesolithic Phase in the Prehistory of Europe and Southwest Asia," *Atti del VI Congresso Internazaionale delle Scienze Preistoriche e Protostoriche,* Vol. 1; pp. 97–111. Collegio Romano, Rome.

CLARK, J. G. D.
1965a "Radiocarbon Dating and the Expansion of Farming Culture from the Near East over Europe," Prehistoric Society, *Proceedings,* Vol. 31; pp. 58–73. London.

CLARK, J. G. D.
   1965b "Traffic in Stone Axe and Adze Blades," *The Economic History Review*, Vol. 18; pp. 1–28.

CLARK, J. G. D.
   1966 "The Invasion Hypothesis in British Archaeology," *Antiquity*, Vol. 40; pp. 172–89.

CLASON, A. T.
   1967 *Animal and Man in Holland's Past.* J. B. Wolters, Groningen.

COE, MICHAEL D.
   1961 *La Victoria, An Early Site on the Pacific Coast of Guatemala.* Harvard University, Peabody Museum of Archeology and Ethnology, *Papers*, Vol. 53. Cambridge.

COE, MICHAEL D.
   1962 *Mexico.* Thames and Hudson, London.

COE, MICHAEL D.
   1963a "Cultural Development in Southeastern Mexoamerica," Smithsonian Institution, *Miscellaneous Collections*, Vol. 146, No. 1; pp. 27–44.

COE, MICHAEL D.
   1963b "Olmec and Chavin: Rejoinder to Lanning," *American Antiquity*, Vol. 29; pp. 101–4.

COE, MICHAEL D., and FLANNERY, KENT V.
   1964 "Microenvironments and Mesoamerican Prehistory," *Science*, Vol. 143; pp. 650–54. Washington, D.C.

COE, MICHAEL D., and FLANNERY, KENT V.
   1967 "Early Cultures and Human Ecology in South Coastal Guatemala," Smithsonian Institution, *Contributions to Anthropology*, Vol. 3. Washington, D.C.

COLE, FAY-COOPER, *et al.*
   1951 *Kincaid: A Prehistoric Illinois Metropolis.* University of Chicago Press.

COLLIER, DONALD
   1955 "Development of Civilization on the Coast of Peru," in *Irrigation Civilizations: A Comparative Study* (Julian Steward, ed.); pp. 19–27. Pan American Union, Washington, D.C.

COLLIER, DONALD
   1959 "Agriculture and Civilization on the Coast of Peru," manuscript presented at the Annual Meeting of the American Anthropological Association.

COOK, SHERBURNE F.
   1949a "The Historical Demography and Ecology of the Teotlalpan," *Ibero-Americana*, Vol. 33.

COOK, SHERBURNE F.
   1949b "Soil Erosion and Population in Central Mexico," *Ibero-Americana*, Vol. 34.

COON, CARLETON S.
   1939 *The Races of Europe.* Macmillan, New York.

COON, CARLETON S.
   1951 *Cave Explorations in Iran 1949.* University of Pennsylvania Museum, Philadelphia.

COOPER, WILLIAM S.

1958 "Terminology of Post-Valders Time," Geological Society of America, *Bulletin*, Vol. 69; pp. 941–45.

COUTIL, L.

1912 "Tardenoisien, Capsien, Getulien, Ibéro-Maurusien Intergetulo-Néolithique, Tellien Loubirien, Geneyenien," *Congrès International d'Anthropologie et d'Archeologie Préhistorique, 14th Session*, Vol. 1; pp. 301–36. Geneva.

CRANE, H. R.

1956 "University of Michigan Radiocarbon Dates I," *Science*, Vol. 124; pp. 665–72.

CRESSEY, GEORGE B.

1960 *Crossroads: Land and Life in Southwest Asia*. J. B. Lippincott, Philadelphia.

CRUXENT, J. M., and ROUSE, I.

1958 "An Archaeological Chronology of Venezuela," Pan American Union, *Social Science Monographs*, No. 6; pp. 263–65.

CUMONT, M.

1907 "Quelques Mots au Sujet de Tardenoisien et de la Transition du Paléolithique au Néolithique," Société Royale Belge d'Anthropologie et de Préhistoire, *Bulletin*, Vol. 26; pp. 205–8.

CURSON, H., and EPSTEIN, H.

1934 "A Comparison of Hamitic Longhorn, West African Shorthorn and Afrikander Cattle Particularly with Regard to the Skull," *Onderstepoort Journal of Veterinary Science*, Vol. 3. Pretoria.

CURSON, H., and THORNTON, R.

1936 "The Study of African Native Cattle," *Onderstepoort Journal of Veterinary Research*, Vol. 7; pp. 618–739. Pretoria.

CUTLER, HUGH C., and WHITAKER, THOMAS W.

1961 "History and Distribution of the Cultivated Cucurbits in the Americas," *American Antiquity*, Vol. 26; pp. 469–85.

CUTLER, HUGH C., and WHITAKER, THOMAS W.

1967 "Cucurbits from the Tehuacán Caves," in *Environment and Subsistence* (Douglas S. Byers, gen. ed.) *The Prehistory of the Tehuacán Valley*, Vol. 1; pp. 212–19. University of Texas Press, Austin.

DAHLBERG, A. A.

1960 "The Dentition of the First Agriculturists (Jarmo, Iraq)," *American Journal of Physical Anthropology*, Vol. 18; pp. 243–56.

DAIFUKU, H.

1952 "A New Conceptual Scheme for Prehistoric Cultures in the Southwestern United States," *American Anthropologist*, Vol. 54; pp. 191–200.

DARBY, H. C.

1956 "The Clearing of the Woodland in Europe," in *Man's Role in Changing the Face of the Earth* (W. L. Thomas, ed.); pp. 183–216. University of Chicago Press.

DARWIN, CHARLES R.

1868 *The Variation of Animals and Plants under Domestication*. J. Murray and Sons, London.

DARWIN, CHARLES R.

1875 *The Variation of Animals and Plants under Domestication*, Vol. 1, 2nd ed. Murray and Sons, London.

DAWKINS, WILLIAM BOYD

1894 "On the Relation of the Palaeolithic to the Neolithic Period," Royal Anthropological Institute of Great Britain and Ireland, *Journal*, Vol. 23; pp. 242–54.

DECANDOLLE, ALPHONSE L. P. P.

1959 *Origin of Cultivated Plants* (reprint of the 2nd ed., 1886). Hafner, New York.

DEEVEY, EDWARD S., JR.

1944 "Pollen Analysis and Mexican Archaeology: An Attempt to Apply the Method," *American Antiquity*, Vol. 10; pp. 135–49.

DEEVEY, EDWARD S., JR.

1960 "The Human Population," *Scientific American*, Vol. 203; pp. 194–204.

DEEVEY, EDWARD S., JR.; FLINT, RICHARD FOSTER; and ROUSE, IRVING, editors

1966 *Radiocarbon*, Vol. 8. American Journal of Science, Yale University, New Haven.

DEEVEY, EDWARD S., JR.; FLINT, RICHARD FOSTER; and ROUSE, IRVING, editors

1967 *Radiocarbon*, Vol. 9. American Journal of Science, Yale University, New Haven.

DEIMEL, ANTON

1924 *Wirtschaftstexte aus Fara*. Deutschen Orient-Gesellschaft, *Wissenschaftliche Veröffentlichung*, No. 45. Leipzig.

DEIMEL, ANTON

1931 "Sumerische Tempelwirtschaft zur Zeit Urukaginas und seiner Vorgänger," *Analecta Orientalia*, Vol. 2. Rome.

DÉLIBRIAS, G., and HUGOT, H. G.

1962 "Datation par la Méthode C-14 de Néolithique de l'Adrar Bous," in *Missions Berliet: Ténéré-Tchad* (H. J. Hugot, ed.); pp. 71–72. Arts et Métier Graphiques, Paris.

DÉLIBRIAS, G.; HUGOT, H.; and QUÉZEL, P.

1959 "Trois Datations de Sédiments Sahariens Récents par le Radiocarbone," *Libyca*, Vol. 5; pp. 267–70.

DELLINGER, S. C., and DICKINSON, S. D.

1942 "Pottery from the Ozark Bluff Shelters," *American Antiquity*, Vol. 7, No. 3; pp. 276–89.

DICK, HERBERT

1954 "The Bat Cave Corn Complex: A Note on its Significance," *El Palacio*, Vol. 61, No. 5; pp. 138–44. Santa Fe.

DIGBY, ADRIAN

1949 "Technique and the Time Factor in Relation to Economic Organization," Royal Anthropological Institute of Great Britain and Ireland, *Man*, Vol. 49; pp. 16–18.

DIGBY, ADRIAN

1962 "Time the Catalyst: Or Why We Should Study the Material Culture of Primitive Peoples," *The Advancement of Science*, Vol. 19; pp. 349–57. of Science, Vol. 19; pp. 349-57.

DIKAIOS, PORPHYRIOS
1953 *Khirokitia.* Oxford University Press, London.

DIKAIOS, PORPHYRIOS
1961 "The Stone Age in Cyprus," in *The Swedish Cyprus Expedition* (Einar Gjerstad, ed.), Vol. 4, pt. 1A. Lund.

DIRECCIÓN DE IRRIGACIÓN. MINISTERIO DE FOMENTO Y OBRAS PUBLICAS. REPUBLICA DEL PERU.
1964 *Aguas e Irrigacion (Publicación Trimestral)*, Vol. 9, No. 3. Lima.

DIXON, KEITH A.
1966 "Obsidian Dates from Temesco, Valley of Mexico," *American Antiquity,* Vol. 31; pp. 640–43.

DOLLFUS, OLIVIER
1965 "Les Andes Centrales du Pérou et Leurs Piemonts (entre Lima et le Pérené); Étude Géomorphologique," *Travaux de l'Institut Français d'Études Andines,* tome 10. Lima.

DONNAN, CHRISTOPHER B.
1964 "An Early House from Chilca, Peru," *American Antiquity,* Vol. 30, No. 2, pt. 1; pp. 137–44.

DOWNS, J. F.
1960 "Domestication: An Examination of the Changing Social Relationships between Man and Animal," Kroeber Anthropological Society, *Publication* No. 22; pp. 18–67.

DRESSLER, R. L.
1953 "The Pre-Columbian Cultivated Plants of Mexico," Harvard University, Botanical Museum, *Leaflets,* Vol. 16; pp. 115–72.

DREYER, T. F., and MEIRING, A. J. D.
1937 "A Preliminary Report on an Expedition to Collect Old Hottentot Skulls," *Soölogiese Navorsing van die Nasionale Museum Bloemfontein,* Vol. 1; pp. 81–88.

DREYER, T. F., and MEIRING, A. J. D.
1952 "The Hottentot," *Navorsinge van die Nasionale Museum Bloemfontein,* Vol. 1; pp. 19–22.

DRIEHAUS, J.
1960 *Die Altheimer Gruppe und das Jungnoelithikum in Mitteleuropa.* Habelt, Bonn.

DRUCKER, PHILIP; HEIZER, ROBERT F.; and SQUIER, ROBERT J.
1959 *Excavations at La Venta Tabasco, 1955.* Bureau of American Ethnology, *Bulletin,* No. 170.

DUCOS, P.
1958 "Le Gisement de Chateauneuf-lez-Martiques," *Bulletin du Musée d'Antropologie Préhistorique de Monaco,* No. 5; pp. 121–33.

DUELL, PRENTICE, *et al.*
1938 *The Masataba of Mereruka I–II.* University of Chicago, Oriental Institute, *Publications,* Nos. 31 and 30. Chicago.

DUERST, J. ULRICH
1899 *Die Rinder von Babylonien, Assyrien und Agypten und Ihr Zusammenhang mit den Rindern der Alten Welt.* Reimar, Berlin.

DUERST, J. ULRICH
1904 "Die Teirwelt der Ansiedlungen am Schlossberg zu Burg a.d. Spree," *Arch. f. Anthropol.*, N.F. 2.

DUERST, J. ULRICH
1908 "Animal Remains from the Excavations at Anau and the Horse of Anau in Relation to the Races of Domestic Horses." Carnegie Institute of Washington, *Publications*, Vol. 73; pp. 339–442.

DUERST, J. ULRICH
1926 *Das Horn der Cavicornia.* Fretz, Zürich.

DUMOND, D. E.
1965 "Population Growth and Cultural Change," *Southwestern Journal of Anthropology*, Vol. 21; pp. 302–24.

DUNHAM, DOWS
1938 "The Biographical Inscriptions of Nekhebu in Boston and Cairo," *Journal of Egyptian Archaeology*, Vol. 24; pp. 1–8.

DURKHEIM, ÉMILE
1897–1898 "Morphologie Sociale," *L'Année Sociologique*, Vol. 2; pp. 520–21.

DYSON, ROBERT H., JR.
1953 "Archeology and the Domestication of Animals in the Old World," *American Anthropologist*, Vol. 5; pp. 661–73. Menasha, Wisconsin.

DYSON, ROBERT H., JR.
1960 "A Note on Queen Shub-Ad's 'Onagers'," *Iraq*, Vol. 22; pp. 102–4.

EBERT, MAX, editor
1924 *Reallexikon der Vorgeschichte.* de Gruyter, Berlin.

EGGAN, FRED
1952 "The Ethnological Cultures and Their Archeological Backgrounds," in *Archeology of Eastern United States* (James B. Griffin, ed.); pp. 35–45. University of Chicago Press.

EHRICH, R. W., editor
1954 *Relative Chronologies in Old World Archeology.* University of Chicago Press.

EHRICH, R. W., editor
1965 *Chronologies in Old World Archeology.* Unviersity of Chicago Press.

ELIOT, H. W.
1950 *Excavations in Mesopotamia and Western Iran.* Harvard University, Peabody Museum, *Special Publication.* Cambridge.

ELLIS, G. P.
1959 "The Maillard Reaction," *Advances in Carbohydrate Chemistry*, Vol. 14; pp. 63–134.

EL-WAILLY, FAISAL
1963 "Tell as-Sawwan (Foreword)," *Sumer*, Vol. 19, Nos. 1 and 2; pp. 1–2. Baghdad.

EL-WAILLY, FAISAL
1964 "Tell as-Sawwan (Foreword)," *Sumer*, Vol. 20, Nos. 1 and 2; pp. 1–2. Baghdad.

EMILIANI, C.
1955 "Pleistocene Temperatures," *Journal of Geology*, Vol. 63; pp. 538–78.

EPSTEIN, H.

1933 "Descent and Origin of the Afrikander Cattle," *Journal of Heredity*, Vol. 24; pp. 449–62. Washington.

EPSTEIN, H.

1934 "Studies in Native Animal Husbandry, 9. The West African Shorthorn," South African Veterinary Medical Association, *Journal*, Vol. 5; pp. 1–15. Johannesburg.

EPSTEIN, H.

1955 "The Zebu Cattle of East Africa," *East African Agricultural Journal*, Vol. 21; pp. 83–95. Nairobi.

EPSTEIN, H.

1957 "The Sanga Cattle of East Africa," *East African Agricultural Journal*, Vol. 22; pp. 149–64. Nairobi.

EPSTEIN, H.

1958 "Die Unbrauchbarkeit einiger Anatomischer Merkmale für die Rassengeschichte Europäischer Longhornrinder," *Zeitschrift für Tierzüchtung und Züchtungsbiologie*, Vol. 71, No. 1; pp. 59–68. Berlin.

ESCALON DE FONTON, M., and DE LUMLEY, H.

1955 "Quelques Civilisations de la Méditerranée Septentrionale et leurs Intercurrences (Epipaléolithique, Leptolithique, Epileptolithique)," Société Préhistorique Française, *Bulletin*, Vol. 52; pp. 379–95.

ESCALON DE FONTON, M.

1956 "Préhistoire de la Basse-Provence," *Préhistoire*, Vol. 12.

ESCALON DE FONTON, M.

1966 "Du Paléolithique Supérieur au Mésolithique dans le Midi Méditerranéen," Société Préhistorique Française, *Bulletin*, Vol. 63; pp. 66–180.

EVANS, J. V.

1956 "Blood Groups in Ruminants and Human Migration." *Advancement of Science*, Vol. 13; pp. 198–200.

EVANS, J. D.

1958 "Two Phases of Prehistoric Settlement in the Western Mediterranean," University of London, Institute of Archaeology, *Annual Report and Bulletin*, Vol. 13; pp. 49–70.

EWING, J. FRANKLIN

1949 "The Treasures of Ksar 'Akil," Fordham University, *Thought*, Vol. 24; pp. 255–88.

EWING, J. FRANKLIN

1951 "Comments on the Report of Dr. Herbert E. Wright, Jr., on his Study of Lebanese Marine Terraces," *Journal of Near Eastern Studies*, Vol. 10; pp. 119–22.

FAIRBANKS, CHARLES H.

1956 "Archeology of the Funeral Mound, Ocmulgee National Monument, Georgia," National Park Service, *Archeological Research Series*, No. 3. Washington.

FAIRBRIDGE, R. W.

1961 "Eustatic Changes in Sea Level," *Physics and Chemistry of the Earth*, Vol. 4; pp. 99–185.

FAIRSERVIS, W. A., JR.

1956 "Excavations in the Quetta Valley, West Pakistan," American Museum of Natural History, *Anthropological Papers*, No. 45; pp. 165–402.

FALKENSTEIN, ADAM

1936 *Archaische Texte aus Uruk.* Deutschen Forschungsgemeinschaft in Uruk Warka, *Ausgrabungen*, Vol. 2. Leipzig.

FALKENSTEIN, ADAM

1939 *Zehnter Vorläufiger Bericht über die von der Notgemeinschaft der Deutschen Wissenschaft in Uruk-Warka Unternommen Ausgrabungen.* Berlin.

FALKENSTEIN, ADAM

1954 "La Cité-Temple Sumérienne," *Journal of World History,* Vol. 1; pp. 784–814.

FAULKNER, D. E., and EPSTEIN, H.

1957 *The Indigenous Cattle of the British Dependent Territories in Africa.* Her Majesty's Stationery Office, London.

FAURE, H.

1966 "Évolution des Grands Lacs Sahariens a l'Holocène," *Quaternaria,* Vol. 8; pp. 167–75.

FECHT, WILLIAM G.

1961 "The Snyders Mound Group and Village Site," *Central States Archeological Journal,* Vol. 8, No. 3; pp. 84–93. Springdale, Arkansas.

FIRBAS, FRANZ

1949 *Waldgeschichte Mitteleuropas,* Vol. 1. G. Fischer, Jena.

FIRBAS, FRANZ

1949–52 *Spät-und Nacheiszeitliche Waldgeschichte Mitteleuropas Nördlich der Alpen.* G. Fischer, Jena.

FLANNERY, KENT V.

1964 *The Middle Formative of the Tehuacán Valley: Its Pattern and Place in Mesoamerican Prehistory.* Unpublished Ph.D. dissertation, Department of Anthropology, University of Chicago.

FLANNERY, KENT V.

1965 "The Ecology of Early Food Production in Mesopotamia," *Science,* Vol. 147; pp. 1247–56. Washington.

FLANNERY, KENT V.

1966 "The Postglacial 'Readaptation' as Viewed from Mesoamerica," *American Antiquity,* Vol. 31; pp. 800–5. Salt Lake City.

FLANNERY, KENT V.

1967 "Vertebrate Fauna and Hunting Patterns," in *Environment and Subsistence* (Douglas S. Byer, gen. ed.) *The Prehistory of the Tehuacán Valley,* Vol. 1; pp. 132–77, 201–11. University of Texas Press, Austin.

FLANNERY, KENT V.

1968a "The Olmex and the Valley of Oaxaca: A Model for Inter-Regional Interaction in Formative Times," paper presented at the Conference on the Olmec, Dumbarton Oaks, Washington, D.C. October 27, 1967.

FLANNERY, KENT V.

1968b "Archeological Systems Theory and Early Mesoamerica," in *Anthropological Archeology in the Americas* (Betty J. Meggers, ed.); pp. 67–87. The Anthropological Society of Washington, Washington, D.C.

FLANNERY, KENT V. and COE, MICHAEL D.
1968 "Social and Economic Systems in Formative Mesoamerica," in *New Perspectives in Archeology* (Salley R. and Lewis R. Binford, eds.); pp. 267–84. Aldine Publishing Co., Chicago.

FLANNERY, KENT V.; KIRKBY, ANNE V. T.; KIRKBY, MICHAEL J.; and WILLIAMS, JR., AUBREY W.
1967 "Farming Systems and Political Growth in Ancient Oaxaca," *Science*, Vol. 158; pp. 445–54.

FLANNERY, KENT V., and WRIGHT, HENRY T.
n.d. "Faunal Remains from the 'Hut Sounding' at Eridu, Iraq," unpublished manuscript submitted to Dr. Fuad Safar, Department of Antiquities, Baghdad.

FLINT, RICHARD FOSTER
1957 *Glacial and Pleistocene Geology*. Wiley, New York.

FOLTINY, STEPHEN
1959 "The Oldest Representations of Wheeled Vehicles in Central and Southeastern Europe," *American Journal of Archaeology*, Vol. 63; pp. 53–58. Concord.

FORDE-JOHNSTON, J.
1959 *Neolithic Cultures of North Africa*. The University Press, Liverpool.

FOWLER, MELVIN L.
1957a *Ferry Site, Hardin County, Illinois*. Illinois State Museum, *Scientific Papers*, Vol. 8, No. 1. Springfield.

FOWLER, MELVIN L.
1957b "Archaic Projectile Point Styles 7000–2000 B.C. in the Central Mississippi River Valley," *Missouri Archeologist*, Vol. 19, Nos. 1 and 2; pp. 7–20. Columbia, Missouri.

FOWLER, MELVIN L.
1957c "The Origin of Plant Cultivation in the Central Mississippi Valley: A Hypothesis," paper presented at the Annual Meeting of the American Anthropological Association, Chicago.

FOWLER, MELVIN L.
1959a "Modoc Rock Shelter: An Early Archaic Site in Southern Illinois," *American Antiquity*, Vol. 24; pp. 257–69.

FOWLER, MELVIN L.
1959b *Summary Report of Modoc Rock Shelter, 1952, 1953, 1955, 1956*. Illinois State Museum, *Reports of Investigations*, No. 8.

FOWLER, MELVIN L., et al.
1962 *First Annual Report: American Bottoms Archaeology July 1, 1961– June 30, 1962*. Illinois Archæological Survey, Urbana.

FOWLER, MELVIN L., et al.
1963 *Second Annual Report: American Bottoms Archaeology July 1, 1962– June 30, 1963*. Illinois Archæological Survey, Urbana.

FRANKFORT, HENRI
1939 *Cylinder Seals*. Macmillan, London.

FRANKFORT, HENRI
1948 *Kingship and the Gods*. Chicago.

FRANKFORT, HENRI

1951 *The Birth of Civilization in the Near East.* London.

FRANKFORT, HENRI, *et al.*

1946 *The Intellectual Adventure of Ancient Man.* Chicago.

FREEMAN, G. F.

1912 "Southwestern Beans and Teparies," University of Arizona Agricultural Experimental Station, *Bulletin 68.*

FRENZEL, B.

1959–1960 "Die Vegetations- und Landschaftszonen Nord-Eurasiens während der Letzten Eiszeit und während der Postglazialen Wärmzeit," Akad. Wiss. Lit. (Mainz), *Abhandlungen, Math.-Naturw. Klasse,* 1959, No. 13; 1960, No. 6.

FRENZEL, B.

1966 "Climatic Change in the Atlantic/Sub-Boreal Transition of the Northern Hemisphere: Botanical Evidence," in *World Climate from 8000 to 0* B.C.; pp. 99–123. Royal Meteorological Society, London.

FRIES, M.

1963 "Vad Myren Berättar," in *Sartryck Sveriges Naturs Arsbok;* pp. 91–107.

FUNKHOUSER, W. D., and WEBB, W. S.

1929 "The So-called 'Ash Caves' in Lee County, Kentucky," University of Kentucky, *Reports in Anthropology and Archeology,* Vol. 1, No. 2.

GABEL, W. CREIGHTON

1958a "The Mesolithic Continuum in Western Europe," *American Anthropologist,* Vol. 60; pp. 658–67.

GABEL, W. CREIGHTON

1958b "European Secondary Neolithic Cultures," The Royal Anthropological Institute of Great Britain and Ireland, *Journal,* Vol. 88; pp. 97–107.

GABEL, W. CREIGHTON

1960 "Seminar on Economic Types in Pre-urban Cultures of Temperate Woodland, Arid and Tropical Areas," *Current Anthropology,* Vol. 1; pp. 437–38.

GAILLARD, C.

1934 "Contribution à l'Étude de la Faune Préhistorique de l'Égypte," *Arch. Musée Hist. Nat. Lyon,* Vol. 14, No. 3; pp. 1–125.

GALINAT, W. C.

1963 "Form and Function of Plant Structures in the American Maydeae and Their Significance for Breeding," *Economic Botany,* Vol. 17; pp. 50–59.

GALINAT, W. C.; CHAGANTI, R. S. K.; and HAGER, F. D.

1964 "Tripsacum as a Possible Amphidiploid of Wild Maize and Manisuris," Harvard University, Botanical Museum, *Leaflets,* Vol. 20; pp. 289–316.

GALINAT, W. C., and GUNNERSON, J. H.

1963 "Spread of Eight-rowed Maize from the Prehistoric Southwest," Harvard University, Botanical Museum, *Leaflets,* Vol. 20; pp. 117–60.

GALINAT, W. C., and RUPPE, R. J.

1961 "Further Archaeological Evidence on the Effects of Teosinte Introgression in the Evolution of Modern Maize," Harvard University, Botanical Museum, *Leaflets,* Vol. 19; pp. 163–81.

GANSSEN, R.
1957 *Bodengeographie*. K. F. Köhler, Stuttgart.

GARROD, DOROTHY A. E.
1930 "The Palaeolithic of Southern Kurdistan: Excavations in the Caves of Zarzi and Hazar Merd," American School of Prehistoric Research, *Bulletin*, Vol. 6; pp. 9–43.

GARROD, DOROTHY A. E.
1932 "A New Mesolithic Industry: The Natufian of Palestine," The Royal Anthropological Institute of Great Britain and Ireland, *Journal*, Vol. 62; pp. 257–69.

GARROD, DOROTHY A. E.
1958 "The Natufian Culture: The Life and Economy of a Mesolithic People in the Near East," The British Academy, *Proceedings*, Vol. 43; pp. 211–27.

GARROD, DOROTHY A. E., and BATE, D. M. A.
1937 *The Stone Age of Mount Carmel*. Clarendon Press, Oxford.

GAUTIER, J. E., and LAMPRE, G.
1905 "Fouilles de Moussian," *Mémoires de la Mission Archéologique de Perse*, Vol. 8; pp. 59–148. Paris.

GEERTZ, CLIFFORD
1963 *Agricultural Involution; The Process of Ecological Change in Indonesia*. University of California Press, Berkeley.

GILMORE, R. MELVIN
1931 "Vegetal Remains of the Ozark Bluff-Dwellers Culture," The Michigan Academy of Science, Arts and Letters, *Papers*, Vol. 14; pp. 83–103. Ann Arbor, Michigan.

GILMORE, RAYMOND M.
1950 "Fauna and Ethnozoology of South America," in *Handbook of South American Indians*, Vol. 6 (Julian H. Steward, ed.) Bureau of American Ethnology, *Bulletin*, Vol. 143; pp. 345–464.

GIMBUTAS, MARIJA
1956 *The Prehistory of Eastern Europe, I: Mesolithic, Neolithic and Copper Age Cultures in Russia and the Baltic Area*. Harvard University, American School of Prehistoric Research, Peabody Museum, *Bulletin*, No. 20. Cambridge.

GIMBUTAS, MARIJA
1963 "European Prehistory: Neolithic to the Iron Age," in *Biennial Review of Anthropology 1963* (Bernard J. Siegel, ed.). Stanford University Press, Stanford.

GIOT, P. R.
1960 *Brittany*. Thames and Hudson, London.

GODWIN, H.
1944 "Neolithic Forest Clearance," *Nature*, Vol. 153; pp. 511–14.

GOODSPEED, THOMAS HARPER
1954 "The Genus *Nicotiana*," *Chronica Botanica*, Vol. 16.

GORDON, E. I.
1953 "Mesilim and Mesannepada—Are They Identical?," American Schools of Oriental Research, *Bulletin*, Vol. 132; pp. 27–30.

GORMAN, C. F.
1969 "Hoabinhian: A Pebble-Tool Complex with Early Plant Associations in Southeast Asia," *Science,* Vol. 163; pp. 671–73.

GOSLIN, ROBERT
1957 "Food of the Adena People," in *The Adena People No. 2.* (William S. Webb and Raymond S. Baby); pp. 41–46. Ohio State University Press, Columbus.

GRADMANN, R.
1906 "Beziehungen zwischen Pflanzengeographie und Siedlungsgeschichte," *Geog. Zeit.,* Vol. 12; pp. 305–25.

GRADMANN, R.
1933 "Die Steppenheide-Theorie," *Geog. Zeit.,* Vol. 39; pp. 265–78.

GRADMANN, R.
1936 "Vorgeschichtliche Landwirtschaft und Besiedlung," *Geog. Zeit.,* Vol. 42; pp. 378–86.

GRIFFIN, JAMES B.
1950 *A Preview of the Ceramic Relationships of the Snyders Site, Calhoun County, Illinois.* Greater St. Louis Archaeological Society, St. Louis.

GRIFFIN, JAMES B.
1952a "Some Early and Middle Woodland Pottery Types in Illinois," Illinois State Museum, *Scientific Papers,* Vol. 5, No. 3. Springfield.

GRIFFIN, JAMES B.
1952b "Culture Periods in Eastern United States Archeology," in *Archeology of Eastern United States* (James B. Griffin, ed.); pp. 352–64. University of Chicago Press.

GRIFFIN, JAMES B.
1958 "The Chronological Position of the Hopewellian Culture in the Eastern United States," University of Michigan, Museum of Anthropology, *Anthropological Papers,* No. 12.

GRIFFIN, JAMES B.
1960a "Climatic Change: A Contributory Cause of the Growth and Decline of Northern Hopewellian Culture," *Wisconsin Archeologist,* Vol. 41, No. 3; pp. 21–33. Lake Mills.

GRIFFIN, JAMES B.
1960b "A Hypothesis for the Prehistory of the Winnebago," in *Culture in History* (S. Diamong, ed.); pp. 809–68. Columbia University Press.

GRIFFIN, JAMES B.
1961 "Comments in Edmonson: Neolithic Diffusion Rates," *Current Anthropology,* Vol. 2; pp. 92–93.

GROBMAN, A.; SALHUANA, W.; SEVILLE, R. in collaboration with MANGELSDORF, P. C.
1961 *Races of Maize in Peru.* National Academy of Science, National Research Council, *Publications,* No. 915.

GULDER, A.
1953 "Beiträge zur Kenntnis des Neiderösterreichischen Mesolithikums," *Archaeologia Austriaca,* Vol. 12; pp. 5–33.

GUNNERSON, J. H.
1960 "The Fremont Culture: Internal Dimensions and External Relationships," *American Antiquity,* Vol. 28; pp. 41–45.

GUNNERSON, J. H.
1962 "Plateau Shoshonean Prehistory: A Suggested Reconstruction," *American Antiquity*, Vol. 28; pp. 41–45.

GUTMANN, J., and TAUTE, W.
1964 "Gibt es in Nordwestdeutschland eine Frühmesolitische 'Kirchdorfer Stufe'?" *Die Kunde, N. F.*, Vol. 15; pp. 88–109.

HAGEN, A.
1967 *Norway*. Thames and Hudson, London.

HAGGETT, PETER
1965 *Locational Analysis in Human Geography*. Edward Arnold Ltd., London.

HAHN, EDUARD
1896 *Die Haustiere und ihre Beziehungen zur Wirtschaft des Menschen*. Duncker and Humblot, Leipzig.

HAHN, EDUARD
1909 *Die Entstehung der Pflugkultur*. C. Winter, Heidelberg.

HAINLINE, JANE
1965 "Culture and Biological Adaptation," *American Anthropologist*, Vol. 67; pp. 1174–97.

HALBWACHS, MAURICE
1960 *Population and Society, Introduction to Social Morphology*. (Translated by Otis Duncan and Harold W. Pfautz.) The Free Press, Glencoe.

HALTENORTH, THEODOR
1961 "Lebensraum, Lebensweise und Vorkommen des Mesopotamischen Damhirsches, Cervus mesopotamicus Brooke, 1875," *Säugetierkundliche Mitteilungen*, BLV-Verlagsgesellschaft München 3, 9. Jhg., No. 1; pp. 15–39.

HANCAR, FRANZ
1956 *Das Pferd in Prähistorischer und Früher Historischer Zeit*. Herold, Vienna.

HARDING, T. G.
1967 *Voyagers of the Vitiaz Strait: A Study of a New Guinea Trade System*. Seattle.

HARLAN, JACK R.
1967 "A Wild Wheat Harvest in Turkey," *Archaeology*, Vol. 20; pp. 197–201.

HARLAN, JACK R., and ZOHARY, DANIEL
1966 "Distribution of Wild Wheats and Barley," *Science*, Vol. 153; pp. 1074–80. Washington.

HARPER, F.
1945 *Extinct and Vanishing Animals of the Old World*. New York Zoological Park, New York.

HARRINGTON, M. R.
1924 "The Ozark Bluff-Dwellers," *American Anthropologist*, Vol. 26, No. 1; pp. 1–21. Menasha.

HARRINGTON, M. R.
1933 *Gypsum Cave, Nevada*. Southwest Museum, *Papers*, No. 8. Los Angeles.

HARRINGTON, M. R.
1960 *The Ozark Bluff Dwellers*. Heye Foundation, Museum of the American Indian, *Indian Notes and Monographs*, Vol. 12. New York.

HARRIS, M.
  1959 "The Economy Has No Surplus?," *American Anthropologist,* Vol. 61; pp. 185–99.
HATT, ROBERT T.
  1959 *The Mammals of Iraq.* University of Michigan, Museum of Zoology, *Miscellaneous Publications,* No. 106. Ann Arbor.
HAUDRICOURT, A. G.
  1948 "Contribution à la Géographie et à l'Ethnologie de la Voiture," *Revue de Géographie Humaine et d'Ethnologie,* Vol. 1.
HAUDRICOURT, A. G., and HÉDIN, LOUIS
  1943 *L'homme et les Plantes Cultivées.* Paris.
HAYES, H. K.
  1963 *A Professor's Story of Hybrid Corn.* Burgess Publishing Co, Minneapolis.
HECK, HEINZ
  1951 "The Breeding-Back of the Aurochs," *Oryx,* Vol. 1, No. 3; pp. 117–22.
HEICHELHEIM, F. M.
  1956 "Effects of Classical Antiquity on the Land," in *Man's Role in Changing the Face of the Earth* (W. L. Thomas, ed.); pp. 165–82. University of Chicago Press.
HEINRICH, ERNST
  1936 *Kleinfunde aus den Archaischen Tempelschichten in Uruk.* Deutschen Forschungsgemeinschaft in Uruk Warka, *Ausgrabungen,* Vol. 1. Leipzig.
HEISER, CHARLES B., JR.
  1949 "Study in the Evolution of the Sunflower Species *Helianthus Annuus* and *H. Bolanderi,*" University of California, *Publications in Botany,* Vol. 23; pp. 157–208.
HEISER, CHARLES B., JR.
  1951 "Hybridization in the Annual Sunflowers: *Helianthus annus X H. debilis var. circumerifolius,*" *Evolution,* Vol. 5; pp. 42–51. Lancaster, Pennsylvania.
HEISER, CHARLES B., JR.
  1955 "The Origin and Development of the Cultivated Sunflower," *American Biology Teacher,* Vol. 17; pp. 161–67.
HEIZER, R. F.
  1960 "Application of Quantitative Methods in Archaeology," *Viking Fund Publications in Anthropology,* No. 28; pp. 93–157.
HELBAEK, HANS
  1959 "Domestication of Food Plants in the Old World," *Science,* Vol. 130; pp. 365–72.
HELBAEK, HANS
  1960a "The Paleoethnobotany of the Near East and Europe," in *Prehistoric Investigations in Iraqi Kurdistan,* (Braidwood and Howe) University of Chicago, Oriental Institute, *Studies in Ancient Oriental Civilization,* No. 31; pp. 99–118.
HELBAEK, HANS
  1960b "Ecological Effects of Irrigation in Ancient Mesopotamia," *Iraq,* Vol. 22; pp. 186–96.

HELBAEK, HANS
1960c "Cereal and Weed Grasses in Phase A," in *Excavations in the Plain of Antioch*, Vol. 1 (R. J. and L. Braidwood, *et al.*) Oriental Institute, *Publications*, Vol. 61; pp. 540–43. University of Chicago Press.

HELBAEK, HANS
1964 "Early Hassunan Vegetable Food at Es-Sawwan Near Sammara," *Sumer*, Vol. 20, Nos. 1 and 2; pp. 45–48. Baghdad.

HELBAEK, HANS
1966a "Commentary on the Phylogenesis of *Triticum* and *Hordeum*," *Economic Botany*, Vol. 20; pp. 350–60.

HELBAEK, HANS
1966b "Pre-Pottery Neolithic Farming at Beidha," in "Five Seasons at the Pre-Pottery Neolithic Village of Beidha in Jordan," (D. Kirkbride) *Palestine Exploration Quarterly*, Vol. 98; pp. 61–66.

HELBAEK, HANS
1969 "Plant Collecting, Dry Farming, and Irrigation Agriculture in Prehistoric Deh Luran," in *Prehistory and Human Ecology of Deh Luran Plain* (Hole, Flannery and Neely) University of Michigan, Museum of Anthropology, *Memoirs*, No. 1; pp. 383–426. Ann Arbor.

HERRE, WOLF
1949 "Neue Ergebnisse Zoologischer Domestikationsforschung," Deutsche Zoologische Gesellschaft, *Verhandlungen;* pp. 40–54. Leipzig.

HERRE, WOLF
1950 "Zur Abstammung und Entwicklung der Haustiere," *Zoologische Garten*, Vol. 17; pp. 103–21. Leipzig.

HERRE, WOLF
1955a "Domestikation und Stammesgeschichte," in *Evolution der Organismen* (Gerhard Heberer, ed.), Vol. 2; pp. 801–56. Stuttgart.

HERRE, WOLF
1955b *Deas Ren als Haustier.* Geest und Portig, Leipzig.

HERRE, WOLF
1956 "Die Züchtungsbiologische Bedeutung neuer Erkenntnisse über Abstammung und Frühentwicklung von Haustieren," *Zuechtungskunde*, Vol. 28; pp. 221–29. Göttigen.

HERRE, WOLF
1958a "Die Geschichtliche Entwicklung der Haustierzüchtung," in *Tierzüchtungslehre* (Zorn, ed.). Ulmer, Stuttgart.

HERRE, WOLF
1958b *Handbuch Tierzüchtung*, Vol. 1. Parey, Berlin.

HERRE, WOLF
1959 "Der Heutige Stand der Domestikationsforschung," *Naturwissenschaftliche Rundschau*, Vol. 12; pp. 87–99.

HERVE, GEORGES
1899 "Populations Mésolithiques et Néolithiques de l'Espagne et du Portugal," *Revue Mensuelle de l'École d'Anthropologie de Paris*, Vol. 9; pp. 265–80.

HESSE, R.; ALLEE, W. C.; and SCHMIDT, K. P.
1951 *Ecological Animal Geography.* New York.

HESTER, J. A.

1952-54 "Agriculture, Economy, and Population Densities of the Maya," Carnegie Institution of Washington, *Yearbook,* Nos. 51-53.

HEUSSER, CALVIN J.

1955 "Pollen Profiles from Prince William Sound and Southeastern Kenai Peninsula, Alaska," *Ecology,* Vol. 36; pp. 185-202. Durham, North Carolina.

HICKERSON, HAROLD

1965 "The Virginia Deer and Intertribal Buffer Zones in the Upper Mississippi Valley," in *Man, Culture and Animals* (Anthony Leeds and Andrew P. Vayda, eds.), American Association for the Advancement of Science, *Publications,* No. 78; pp. 43-65. Washington, D.C.

HIGGS, E. S., and JARMAN, M. R.

1969 "The Origins of Agriculture: A Reconsideration," *Antiquity,* Vol. 43; pp. 31-44.

HILZHEIMER, MAX

1926a *Natuerliche Rassengeschichte der Haussäugetiere.* W. de Gruyter & Co. Berlin.

HILZHEIMER, MAX

1926b *Die Wildrinder im alten Mesopotamien.* Pfeiffer, Leipzig.

HILZHEIMER, MAX

1932 "Dogs," *Antiquity,* Vol. 6; pp. 411-19.

HILZHEIMER, MAX

1941 *Animal Remains from Tell Asmar.* University of Chicago, Oriental Institute, *Studies in Oriental Civilizations,* Vol. 20.

HO, PING-TI

1969 "The Loess and the Origin of Chinese Agriculture," *American Historical Review,* Vol. 75; pp. 1-36.

HOLE, FRANK

1962 "Archeological Survey and Excavation in Iran, 1961," *Science,* Vol. 137; pp. 524-26. Washington, D.C.

HOLE, FRANK

1966 "Investigating the Origins of Mesopotamian Civilization," *Science,* Vol. 153; pp. 605-11. Washington, D.C.

HOLE, FRANK, and FLANNERY, KENT V.

1967 "The Prehistory of Southwestern Iran: A Preliminary Report," Prehistoric Society, *Proceedings,* Vol. 33; pp. 147-206.

HOLE, FRANK; FLANNERY, KENT V.; and NEELY, JAMES A.

1969 *Prehistory and Human Ecology of the Deh Luran Plain.* University of Michigan, Museum of Anthropology, *Memoirs,* No. 1. Ann Arbor.

HOOIJER, D. A.

1961 "The Fossil Vertebrates of Ksar Akil, a Paleolithic Rock Shelter in the Lebanon," *Zoologische Verhandelingen,* No. 49. Leiden.

HOPKINS, D. M.

1959 "Cenozoic History of the Bering Land Bridge," *Science,* Vol. 129; pp. 1519-28.

HOWELL, F. CLARK

1959 "Upper Pleistocene Stratigraphy and Early Man in the Levant," American Philosophical Society, *Proceedings,* Vol. 103; pp. 1-65.

HÜCKRIEDE, R.

1962 "Jung-Quartär und End-Mesolithikum in der Provinz Kerman (Iran)," *Eiszeitalter und Gegenwart*, Vol. 12; pp. 25–42.

HUGOT, H. J.

1968 "The Origins of Agriculture: Sahara," *Current Anthropology*, Vol. 9; pp. 483–88.

HUNTINGFORD, GEORGE W. B.

1953 *The Southern Nilo-Hamites*, pt. 8. International African Institute, London.

HUNTINGFORD, GEORGE W. B.

1955 "The Economic Life of the Dorobo," *Anthropos*, Vol. 50; pp. 605–84.

HUTCHINSON, J. B.; SILOW, R. A.; and STEPHENS, S. G.

1947 *The Evolution of Gossypium*. Oxford University Press.

HYRENIUS, HANNES

1959 "Population Growth and Replacement," in *The Study of Population: An Inventory and Appraisal* (P. M. Hauser and Otis Duncan, eds.). University of Chicago Press.

IRWIN, HENRY J., and BARGHOORN, ELSO S.

1965 "Identification of the Pollen of Maize, Teosinte and Tripsacum by Phase Contrast Microscopy," Harvard University, Botanical Museum, *Leaflets*, Vol. 21; pp. 37–58.

IRWIN, HENRY J., and IRWIN, C. C.

1959 *Excavations at the Lodaiska Site in the Denver, Colorado Area*. Denver Museum of Natural History, *Proceedings*, No. 8.

IVERSEN, J.

1949 "The Influence of Prehistoric Man on Vegetation," *Danmarks Geol. Undersoegelse*, Series IV, Vol. 3, No. 6.

IVERSEN, J.

1960 "Problems of the Early Post-Glacial Forest Development in Denmark," *Danmarks Geol. Undersoegelse*, Series IV, Vol. 4, No. 3.

JACKSON, RAYMOND C.

1960 "A Revision of the Genus *Iva* L.," University of Kansas, *Science Bulletin*, Vol. 41; pp. 793–876.

JACOBSEN, THORKILD

1939 "The Assumed Conflict Between Sumerians and Semites in Early Mesopotamian History," The American Oriental Society, *Journal*, Vol. 59; pp. 485–95.

JACOBSEN, THORKILD

1943 "Primitive Democracy in Ancient Mesopotamia," *Journal of Near East Studies*, Vol. 2; pp. 159–72.

JACOBSEN, THORKILD, and ADAMS, ROBERT M.

1958 "Salt and Silt in Ancient Mesopotamian Agriculture," *Science*, Vol. 128; pp. 1252–58.

JAŻDŻEWSKI, K.

1965 *Poland*. Thames and Hudson, London.

JEFFREYS, M. D. W.

1951 "Pygmies—Human and Otherwise," *South African Journal of Science*, Vol. 47; pp. 227–33. Johannesburg.

JENNINGS, JESSE D.
  1953 "Danger Cave: A Progress Summary," *El Palacio,* Vol. 60; pp. 179–213. Santa Fe.
JENNINGS, JESSE D.
  1957 *Danger Cave.* Society of American Archeology, *Memoir,* No. 14.
JENNINGS, JESSE D., *et al.*
  1956 "The American Southwest: A Problem in Cultural Isolation," in *Seminars in American Archaeology: 1955* (Robert Wauchope, ed.). Society for American Archaeology, *Memoirs,* No. 11; pp. 59–127
JESTIN, R.
  1937 *Tablettes Sumériennes de Suruppak Conservées au Musée de Stamboul.* L'Institut Français d'Archéologie de Stamboul, *Memoirs,* Vol. 3. Paris.
JEWELL, DONALD P.
  1966 "Notes on Projectile Points in Oaxaca, Mexico," *American Antiquity,* Vol. 31; 874–75.
JOHNSON, FREDERICK, assembler
  1951 *Radiocarbon Dating.* Society for American Archaeology, *Memoirs* 8. Supp. to *American Antiquity,* Vol. 17, no. 1, pt. 2.
JONES, D. BREESE; GORSDORF, CHARLES E. F.; and PHILLIPS, SAMMIE
  1938 "Proteins of the Black Bean of the Mayas, *Phaseolus vulgaris,*" *Journal of Biological Chemistry,* Vol. 122; pp. 745–55.
JONES, VOLNEY
  1936 "The Vegetal Remains of Newt Kash Hollow Shelter," University of Kentucky, *Reports in Anthropology and Archaeology,* Vol. 3, No. 4; pp. 147–67.
KAPLAN, DAVID
  1960 "The Law of Cultural Dominance," in *Evolution and Culture* (Marshall D. Sahlins and Elman R. Service, eds.). University of Michigan Press, Ann Arbor.
KAPLAN, LAWRENCE
  1956 "The Cultivated Beans of the Prehistoric Southwest," Missouri Botanical Gardens *Annals,* Vol. 43; pp. 189–251.
KAPLAN, LAWRENCE
  1965 "Archeology and Domestication in American *Phaseolus* (Beans)," *Economic Botany,* Vol. 19; pp. 358–68.
KAPLAN, LAWRENCE
  1967 "Archeological Phaseolus from Tehuacan," in *Environment and Subsistence* (Douglas S. Byers, gen. ed.). *The Prehistory of the Tehuacan Valley,* Vol. 1; pp. 201–11. University of Texas Press, Austin.
KAPLAN, LAWRENCE, and MACNEISH, R. S.
  1960 "Prehistoric Bean Remains from Caves in the Ocampo Region of Tamaulipas, Mexico," Harvard University, Botanical Museum, *Leaflets,* Vol. 19; pp. 33–56.
KEES, HERMANN
  1933 *Ägypten.* Kulturgeschichte des Alten Orients, *Abschnitt* 1, Abt. 3, Teil 1, Band 3. (Handbuch der Altertumswissenschaft I). Munich.
KELLEY, J. CHARLES
  1955 "Juan Sabeata and Diffusion in Aboriginal Texas," *American Anthropologist,* Vol. 57, pp. 981–95. Menasha.

KELM, HANS
  1938 "Die Postembryonale Schädelentwicklung des Wild- und Berkshire-Schweins," *Zeitschrift für Anatomie und Entwicklungsgeschiechte,* Vol. 108; pp. 499–599. Berlin.

KENYON, KATHLEEN M.
  1952 "Early Jericho," *Antiquity,* Vol. 26; pp. 116–22.

KENYON, KATHLEEN M.
  1959a "Earliest Jericho," *Antiquity,* Vol. 33; pp. 5–9.

KENYON, KATHLEEN M.
  1959b "Some Observations on the Beginnings of Settlement in the Near East," The Royal Anthropological Institute of Great Britain and Ireland, *Journal,* Vol. 89; pp. 35–43.

KIRKBRIDE, D.
  1966 "Five Seasons at the Pre-pottery Neolithic Village of Beidha in Jordan," *Palestine Exploration Quarterly,* Vol. 98; pp. 3–72.

KLATT, BERTHOLD
  1927 "Entstehung der Haustier," *Handbuch der Vererbungswissenschaft,* Band III, Lief 2; pp. 1–107. Gebrüder Borntraeger, Berlin.

KLATT, BERTHOLD
  1948 *Haustier und Mensch.* Hermes, Hamburg.

KMOCH, L. L.
  1966 "Eine Mesolith-Station auf dem Bisamberg bei Wien," *Archaeologia Austriaca,* Vol. 40; pp. 13–24.

KNETSCH, G., *et al.*
  1963 "Untersuchungen an Pluvialen Wassern der Ost-Sahara," *Geol. Rundschau,* Vol. 52; pp. 587–610.

KNÖLL, H.
  1959 *Die Nordwestdeutsche Tiefstichkeramik und ihre Stellung im Nord- und Mitteleuropäischen Neolithikum.* Aschendorf, Münster.

KOBY, F.
  1954 "Y a-t-il eu, à Lascaux, 'un Bos Longifrons'?," *Bulletin Société Préhistorique Française,* Vol. 51; pp. 434–41. Paris.

KÖKTEN, I. K.
  1955 "Antalya' da Karain Mağrasinda Yapilan Prehistorya Arastir-malarina Toplu Bir Bakiş," *Türk Tarih Kurumu: Belleten,* Vol. 19; pp. 271–93.

KÖKTEN, I. K.
  1958 "Tarsus-Antalya Arasi Sahil Seriti Üzerinde ve Antalya Bölgesinde Yapilan Tarihöncesi Araştirmalari Hakkinda," *Türk Arkeologi Dergisi,* Vol. 8; pp. 10–16.

KOSCHAKER, P.
  1942 "Zur Staatlichen Wirtschaftsverwaltung in Altababylonischer Zeit, Insbesondere nach Urkunden aus Larsa," *Zeitschrift fur Assyrologie,* Vol. 47; pp. 135–80.

KOZLOWSKI, LEON
  1926 "L'Époque Mésolithique en Pologne," *L'Anthropologie,* Vol. 36; pp. 47–74

KRÄMER, HERMANN
  1960 "Die Haustierfunde von Vindonissa," *Revue Suisse de Zoologie,* Vol. 7; pp. 143–272. Geneva.

KROEBER, ALFRED L.

1917 "The Superorganic," *American Anthropologist*, Vol. 19; pp. 163–213.

KROEBER, ALFRED L.

1939 *Cultural and Natural Areas of Native North America*. University of California, *Publications in American Archeology and Ethnology*, No. 38. Berkeley.

KROEBER, ALFRED

1948 *Anthropology*. Harcourt, Brace & Co., New York.

KURTZ, EDWIN B., LIVERMAN, JAMES L., and TUCKER, HENRY

1960 "Some Problems Concerning Fossil and Modern Corn Pollen," Torrey Botanical Club, *Bulletin*, Vol. 87; pp. 85–94. New York.

KURTZ, EDWIN B., and TURNER, RAYMOND M.

1957 "An Oil-Flotation Method for the Recovery of Pollen from Inorganic Sediments," *Micropaleontology*, Vol. 3; pp. 67–68.

KYLE, JACK H., and RANDALL, T. E.

1963 "A New Concept of the Hard Seed Character in *Phaseolus vulgaris* L. and its Use in Breeding and Inheritance Studies," *Proceedings of the American Society of Horticultural Science*, Vol. 83; pp. 461–75.

LA BAUME, WOLFGANG

1950 "Zur Abstammung des Hausrindes," *Forschungen und Fortschritte*, Vol. 26; pp. 43–45. Berlin.

LAET, S. J. DE

1967 "Quelques Problèmes de Néolithique Belge," *Palaeohistoria*, Vol. 12; pp. 335–62.

LAGERCRANTZ, S.

1950 "Contributions to the Ethnography of Africa," *Studia Ethnographica Upsaliensia*, Vol. 1.

LANDSBERGER, B.

1944 "Die Anfänge der Zivilisation in Mesopotamien," *Turk Tarih Kurumu Basimevi*, Vol. 2, pt. 3.

LANNING, EDWARD P.

1963 "A Pre-Agricultural Occupation on the Central Coast of Peru," *American Antiquity*, Vol. 28, No. 3; pp. 360–71.

LANNING, EDWARD P.

1967 *Preceramic Archaeology of the Ancón-Chillón Region, Central Coast of Peru*. Mimeographed, New York.

LATHRAP, DONALD

1968 "The 'Hunting' Economies of the Tropical Forest Zone of South America: An Attempt at Historical Perspective," in *Man the Hunter*, (Richard B. Lee and Irven DeVore, eds.); pp. 23–29. Aldine Publishing Co., Chicago

LE BRETON, LOUIS

1957 "The Early Periods at Susa, Mesopotamian Relations," *Iraq*, Vol. 19; pp. 79–124. London.

LEE, RICHARD B.

1965 *Subsistence Ecology of Kung Bushmen*. Ph.D. dissertation, University of California (Berkeley), microfilm.

LEE, RICHARD B.

1969 "!Kung Bushmen Subsistence: An Input-Output Analysis," in *Environ-*

ment and Cultural Behavior: An Anthropological Reader (A. P. Vayda, ed.). The Natural History Press, New York.

LEEMANS, W.
1950 *The Old Babylonian Merchant*. Leiden.

LEES, G. M., and FALCON, N. L.
1952 "The Geographical History of the Mesopotamian Plains," *Geographical Journal*, Vol. 118; pp. 24–39. London.

LEES, S. H.
1967 "Regional Integration of Pig Husbandry in the New Guinea Highlands," paper presented at the Michigan Academy of Sciences, Annual Meeting for 1967

LEHMAN, ULRICH
1949 "Der Ur im Deluvium Deutschlands und Seine Verbreitung," *Neues Jahrbuch für Mineralogie, Geologie und Paläontologie*, Band 90; pp. 163–266.

LEISNER, G., and LEISNER, V.
1943 *Die Megalithgräber der Iberischen Halbinsel, Der Süden*. de Gruyter, Berlin.

LEISNER, G., and LEISNER, V.
1956 *Die Megalithgräber der Iberischen Halbinsel. Der Westen*. de Gruyter, Berlin.

LEOPOLD, A. STARKER
1959 *Wild Life of Mexico: The Game Birds and Mammals*. The University of California Press, Berkeley.

LESER, PAUL
1931 *Entstehung und Verbreitung des Pfluges*. Anthropos, Münster.

LHOTE, H.
1959 *The Search for the Tassili Frescoes*. Dutton, New York.

LHOTE, H.
1965 "L'Évolution de la Faune dans les Gravures et les Peintures Rupestres du Sahara et Ses Relations avec l'Évolution Climatique," in *Miscelánea en Homenaje al Abate Henri Breuil*; pp. 83–118. Dip. Prov. de Barcelona, Barcelona.

LINTON, RALPH
1939 "The Tanala of Madagascar," in *The Individual and His Society* (Abram Kardiner, ed.); pp. 251–90. New York.

LINTON, RALPH, and LINTON, A.
1949 *We Gather Together: The Story of Thanksgiving*. Henry Schumann, Inc., New York.

LLABADOR, F.
1962 "Résultats Malacologiques à la Mission Scientifique du Ténéré," in *Missions Berliet: Ténéré-Tchad* (H. J. Hugot, ed.); pp. 234–70. Arts et Métier Graphiques, Paris.

LLOYD, SETON and SAFAR, FUAD
1947 "Excavations at Eridu," *Sumer*, Vol. 3; pp. 85–111.

LLOYD, SETON and SAFAR, FUAD
1948 "Eridu," *Sumer*, Vol. 4; pp. 115–27.

LOE, BARON A. DE

1908 "Contribution à l'Étude des Temps Intermédiares Entre le Paléolithique et le Néolithique," *XIII Congrès International d'Anthropologie et d'Archéologie Préhistorique*, Vol. 1; pp. 422–23. Monaco.

LOFTUS, WILLIAM KENNETH

1857 *Travels and Researches in Chaldaea and Susiana*. James Nisbet & Co., London.

LOGAN, W.

1952 "Graham Cave, An Archaic Site in Montgomery County, Missouri," Missouri Archaeological Society, *Memoir* No. 2. Columbia, Mo.

LORENZ, KONRAD Z.

1955 *Man Meets Dog*. Houghton-Mifflin, Boston.

LORENZ, KONRAD Z.

1959 *Man Meets Dog*. Pan, London.

LORENZO, JOSÉ L.

1960 "Aspectos Físicos del Valley de Oaxaca," *Revista Mexicana de Estudios Antropologicos*, Vol. 16; pp. 49–64.

LOWE, GARETH W.

1959a *Archaeological Exploration of the Upper Grijalva River, Chiapas, Mexico*. The Archaeological Foundation, *Papers*, No. 2. Provo, Utah.

LOWE, GARETH W.

1959b "The Chiapas Project, 1955–1958," New World Archaeological Foundation, *Publications*. Orinda, California.

LOWE, RICHARD T.

1868 *A Manual Flora of Madeira*. London.

LÜDI, W.

1955 "Die Vegetationsentwicklung seit dem Rückzug der Gletscher in den Mittleren Alpen und ihrem Nördlichen Vorland," *Ber. Geobotan. Forschungsinst. Rübel* (Zürich), 1954; pp. 36–38.

LUMHOLTZ, KARL S.

1902 *Unknown Mexico*. C. Scribner's Sons, New York.

LÜTTSCHWAGER, H.

1967 "Kurzbericht über Tierfunde aus Meso- und Neolithischen Moorsiedlungen in Schleswig-Holstein," *Schr. Naturw. Ver. Schlesw.-Holstein*, Vol. 37; pp. 53–64.

MCBURNEY, C. B. M.

1967 *The Haua Fteah (Cyrenaica) and the Stone Age of the Southeast Mediterranean*. Cambridge University Press, Cambridge.

MCCARTHY, FREDERICK D.

1957 "Habitat, Economy, and Equipment of the Australian Aborigines," *The Australian Journal of Science*, Vol. 19; pp. 88–97.

MCCARTHY, FREDERICK D., and MCARTHUR, MARGARET

1960 "The Food Quest and the Time Factor in Aboriginal Economic Life," *Records of the American Australian Scientific Expedition to Arnhemland*, Vol. 2; pp. 145–94. University of Melbourne Press, Parkville, Australia.

MACCURDY, GEORGE GRANT

1924 *Human Origins: A Manual of Prehistory* (2 vols.). D. Appleton, New York.

MCGREGOR, J. C.

1958 *The Pool and Irving Villages: A Study of Hopewellian Occupation in the Illinois River Valley.* University of Illinois Press, Urbana.

MACKIE, W. W.

1943 "Origin, Dispersal and Variability of the Lima Bean, *Phaseolus lunatus,*" *Hilgardia,* Vol. 15; pp. 1–29.

MACNEISH, RICHARD S.

1947 "The Pre-pottery Faulkner Site of Southern Illinois," *American Antiquity,* Vol. 13, No. 3; pp. 232–43.

MACNEISH, RICHARD S.

1954 "An Early Archaeological Site near Panuco, Vera Cruz," American Philosophical Society, *Transactions,* Vol. 44, pt. 5. Philadelphia.

MACNEISH, RICHARD S.

1955 "Ancient Maize and Mexico," *Archaeology,* Vol. 8, No. 2; pp. 108–15.

MACNEISH, RICHARD S.

1958 *Preliminary Archaeological Investigations in the Sierra de Tamaulipas, Mexico.* American Philosophic Society, *Transactions,* Vol. 48, pt. 6. Philadelphia.

MACNEISH, RICHARD S.

1959a "A Speculative Framework of Northern North American Prehistory as of April, 1959," *Anthropologica,* Vol. 1; pp. 7–21.

MACNEISH, RICHARD S.

1959b "Origin and Spread of some Domesticated Plants as Seen from Tamaulipas, Mexico," Manuscript presented at the Annual Meetings of the American Anthropological Association.

MACNEISH, RICHARD S.

1961 *First Annual Report of the Tehuacan Archaeological-Botanical Project.* R. S. Peabody Foundation, Andover, Massachusetts.

MACNEISH, RICHARD S.

1962 *Second Annual Report of the Tehuacan Archaeological-Botanical Project.* R. S. Peabody Foundation, Andover, Massachusetts.

MACNEISH, RICHARD S.

1964a "Ancient Mesoamerican Civilization." *Science,* Vol. 143; pp. 531–37. Washington, D.C.

MACNEISH, RICHARD S.

1964b "The Food-Gathering and Incipient Agriculture Stage of Prehistoric Middle America," in *Natural Environments and Early Cultures* (R. C. West, ed.). *Handbook of Middle American Indians,* Vol. 1; pp. 413–26. University of Texas Press, Austin.

MACNEISH, RICHARD S.

1967a "An Interdisciplinary Approach to an Archeological Problem," in *Environment and Subsistence* (Douglas S. Byers, gen. ed.). *The Prehistory of the Tehuacan Valley,* Vol. 1; pp. 14–24. University of Texas Press, Austin.

MACNEISH, RICHARD S.

1967b "A Summary of the Subsistence," in *Environment and Subsistence* (Douglas S. Byers, gen. ed.). *The Prehistory of the Tehuacán Valley,* Vol. 1; 290–309. University of Texas Press, Austin.

MACNEISH, RICHARD S.

1967c "Introduction," in *The Non-Ceramic Artifacts* (Douglas S. Byers, gen. ed.). *The Prehistory of the Tehuacán Valley,* Vol. 2; pp. 3–13. University of Texas Press, Austin.

MACNEISH, RICHARD S.; NELKIN-TURNER, ANTOINETTE; and JOHNSON, IRMGARD W.

1967a "Projectile Points," in *The Non-Ceramic Artifacts* (Douglas S. Byers, gen. ed.). *The Prehistory of the Tehuacán Valley,* Vol. 2; pp. 52–81. University of Texas Press, Austin.

MACNEISH, RICHARD S.; NELKIN-TURNER, ANTOINETTE; and JOHNSON, IRMGARD W.

1967b "Conclusion," in *The Non-Ceramic Artifacts* (Douglas S. Byers, gen. ed.). *The Prehistory of the Tehuacán Valley,* Vol. 2; pp. 227–45. University of Texas Press, Austin.

MACNUTT, F. A., translator and editor.

1908 *Letters of Cortes.* New York.

MALLOWAN, M. E. L., and ROSE, J. CRUIKSHANK

1935 "Excavations at Tall Arpachiyah, 1933," *Iraq,* Vol. 2; pp. 1–178.

MANGELSDORF, PAUL C.

1954 "New Evidence on the Origin and Ancestry of Maize," *American Antiquity,* Vol. 19; pp. 409–10.

MANGELSDORF, PAUL C.

1958a "Reconstructing the Ancestor of Corn," American Philosophical Society, *Proceedings,* Vol. 102; pp. 454–63.

MANGELSDORF, PAUL C.

1958b "The Mutagenic Effect of Hybridizing Maize and Teosinte," *Cold Spring Harbor Symposium on Quantitative Biology,* Vol. 23; pp. 409–21.

MANGELSDORF, PAUL C.

1958c "Ancestor of Corn," *Science,* Vol. 128; pp. 1313–20. Lancaster.

MANGELSDORF, PAUL C., and LISTER, ROBERT H.

1956 "Archeological Evidence on the Evolution of Maize in Northwestern Mexico," Harvard University, Botanical Museum, *Leaflets,* Vol. 17; pp. 151–78.

MANGELSDORF, PAUL C.; MACNEISH, RICHARD S.; and GALINAT, WALTON C.

1956 "Archaeological Evidence on the Diffusion of Maize in Northeastern Mexico," Harvard University, Botanical Museum, *Leaflets,* Vol. 17; pp. 125–50.

MANGELSDORF, PAUL C.; MACNEISH, RICHARD S.; and GALINAT, WALTON C.

1964 "Domestication of Corn," *Science,* Vol. 143; pp. 538–45.

MANGELSDORF, PAUL C.; MACNEISH, RICHARD S.; and WILLEY, GORDON R.

1964 "Origins of Agriculture in Middle America," in *Natural Environment and Early Cultures* (Robert C. West, ed.) *Handbook of Middle American Indians,* Vol. 1; pp. 427–45. University of Texas Press, Austin.

MANGELSDORF, PAUL C., and OLIVER, D. L.

1951 "Whence Came Maize to Asia?," Harvard University, Botanical Museum, *Leaflets,* Vol. 14; pp. 263–91.

MANGELSDORF, PAUL C., and REEVES, R. G.

1959a "The Origin of Corn. III: Modern Races, the Product of Teosinte Introgression," Harvard University, Botanical Museum, *Leaflets,* Vol. 18; pp. 389–411.

MANGELSDORF, PAUL C., and REEVES, R. G.
1959b "The Origin of Corn. IV: Place and Time of Origin," Harvard University, Botanical Museum, *Leaflets*, Vol. 18; pp. 413–27.

MANGELSDORF, PAUL C., and REEVES, R. G.
1939 "The Origin of Indian Corn and Its Relatives," Texas Agricultural Experiment Station, *Bulletin*, No. 574; pp. 1–315.

MANGELSDORF, PAUL C., and SMITH, JR., C. EARLE
1949 "New Archaeological Evidence on Evolution in Maize," Harvard University, Botanical Museum, *Leaflets*, Vol. 13; pp. 213–60.

MARTIN, PAUL S.; RINALDO, J. B.; BLUHM, E.; CUTLER, H. C.; and GRANGE, JR., R.
1952 *Mogollon Cultural Continuity and Change: The Stratigraphic Analysis of Tularosa and Cordova Caves.* Chicago Natural History Museum, *Fieldiana: Anthropology*, Vol. 40.

MARUYAMA, MAGOROH
1963 "The Second Cybernetics: Deviation-Amplifying Mutual Causal Processes," *American Scientist*, Vol. 51; pp. 164–79.

MARX, KARL
1853 "The British Rule in India," *New York Daily Tribune*, June 25.

MASON, I. L.
1951 "*A World Dictionary of Breed Types and Varieties of Livestock.*" Commonwealth Bureau of Animal Breeding and Genetics, *Technical Communication*, No. 7.

MASSON, V. M.
1965 "The Neolithic Farmers of Central Asia," VIth International Congress of Pre- and Proto-historic Sciences, *Acts*, Vol. 2; pp. 205–15.

MASSOULARD, EMILE
1949 *Préhistoire et Protohistoire d'Égypte*, Université Paris, Institut d'éthnologie, *Travaux et Mémoires*, Vol. 53.

MATTHEY, ROBERT
1954 "Chromosome et Systématique des Canidés." *Mammalia*, Vol. 18; pp. 225–30.

MAUDSLAY, A. P., translator and editor
1908–1916 *The True History of the Conquest of New Spain.* (Bernal Diaz de Castillo). London.

MAUNY, R.
1956 Préhistoire et Zoologie: La Grande 'Faune Éthiopienne' du Nord-Ouest Africaine du Paléolithique à Nos Jours," *Bull. Inst. Franc. d'Afrique, Noire* (Series A), Vol. 18; pp. 246–79.

MAXWELL, MOREAU
1951 "The Woodland Cultures of Southern Illinois," Logan Museum, Papers in Anthropology, *Bulletin*, No. 7. Beloit.

MAY, J. M.
1961 *The Ecology of Malnutrition in the Far and Near East.* New York.

MEGARD, R. O.
1967 "Late Quaternary *Cladocera* of Lake Zeribar, Western Iran," *Ecology*, Vol. 48; pp. 179–89.

MEGGERS, BETTY J.
1954 "Environmental Limitation on the Development of Culture," *American Anthropologist*, Vol. 56; pp. 801–24. Washington.

MELLAART, JAMES
1961a "2,000 Years of Haçilar—Starting from over 9,000 Years Ago: Excavations in Turkey which Throw Light on the Earliest Anatolia," *Illustrated London News*, Vol. 238; pp. 588–91.

MELLAART, JAMES
1961b "Excavations at Haçilar: 4th Preliminary Report," *Anatolian Studies*, Vol. 11; pp. 39–75.

MELLAART, JAMES
1962 "Excavations at Catal-Hüyük," *Anatolian Studies*, Vol. 12; pp. 41–65. London.

MELLAART, JAMES
1963 "Excavations at Catal-Hüyük 1962: 2nd Preliminary Report," *Anatolian Studies*, Vol. 13; pp. 43–103.

MELLAART, JAMES
1965 *Earliest Civilizations of the Near East*. Thames and Hudson, London.

MENGHIN, OSWALD
1929 "Die Mesolithische Kulturentwicklung in Europa," Deutsches Archäologisches Institut, Römisch-Germanische Kommission, *Berichte*, Vol. 17; pp. 154–97.

MENGHIN, OSWALD
1934 "Merimde—Benisalâme und Ma'âdi," Akademie der Wissenschaften in Wien, Philosophisch-Historische Klasse, *Anzeiger*, Vol. 70; pp. 82–97.

MILL, JOHN STUART
1909 *Principles of Political Economy*. Longmans, Green and Co., London.

MILLON, R.
1954 "Irrigation at Teotihuacan," *American Antiquity*, Vol. 20; pp. 177–80.

MILOJČIĆ, VLADIMIR
1959 "Ausgrabungen in Thessalien," in *Neue Deutsche Ausgrabungen im Mittlemeergebiet und im Vorderen Orient* (Erich Boehringer, ed.); pp. 225–36. Deutsches Archäologisches Institut, Verlag Gebr. Mann, Berlin.

MILOJČIĆ, VLADIMIR
1960 "Ergebnisse der Deutschen Ausgrabungen in Thessalien (1953–1958)," *Jahrbuch des Romisch-Germanischen Zentralmuseums Mainz*, Vol. 6; pp. 1–57.

MILOJČIĆ, V.; BOESSNECK, J.; and HOPF, M.
1962 *Das Prákeramische Neolithikum sowie die Tier-und Pflanzenreste*. I. *Die Deutschen Ausgrabungen auf der Argissa-Magula in Thessalian*, Vol. 1. Habelt, Bonn.

MILUKOW, PAUL
1898 *Skizzen Russischer Kulturgeschichte*, Vol. 1. Leipzig.

MINER, HORACE
1950 *Cave Hollow, an Ozark Bluff-Dweller Site*. University of Michigan, Museum of Anthropology, *Anthropological Papers*, No. 3. Ann Arbor.

MISHKIN, BERNARD
1946 "The Contemporary Quechua," in *Handbook of South American Indians* (Julian H. Steward, ed.). Vol. 2, Bureau of American Ethnology, *Bulletin*, Vol. 143; pp. 411–70.

MORGAN, JACQUES DE
1900 "Étude Géographique sur la Susiane," *Mémoires de la Mission Archéologique de Perse*, Vol. 1. Paris.

MORGAN, JACQUES DE
1924 *Prehistoric Man: A General Outline of Prehistory*. Alfred A. Knopf, New York.

MORI, F.
1965 *Tadrart Acacus: Arte Rupestre e Culture del Sahara Preistorico*. Einaudi. Torino.

MORRISON, J. P. E.
1942 "Preliminary Reports on the Mollusca Found in the Shell Mounds of the Pickwick Landing Basin in the Tennessee River Valley," Smithsonian Institution, Bureau of American Ethnology, *Bulletin* 129; pp. 341–92.

MORRISON, H. B.; GILLULY, JAMES; RICHMOND, G. M.; and HUNT, C. B.
1957 "In Behalf of the Recent," *American Journal of Science*, Vol. 255; pp. 385–93.

MORTILLET, ADRIEN DE
1896 "Les Petits Silex Taillés, à Contours Géométriques Trouvés en Europe, Asie et Afrique," *Revue de l'École d'Anthropologie*, Vol. 6; pp. 376–405.

MORTILLET, GABRIEL DE
1885 *Le Préhistorique, Antiquité de l'Homme*, 2nd edition. C. Reinwald, Paris.

MOSELEY, MICHAEL E.
1968 *Changing Subsistence patterns: Late Preceramic Archaeology of the Central Peruvian Coast*. Ph.D. Dissertation in Anthropology, Harvard University, Cambridge.

MOUSTAFA, Y. S.
1955 *"Canis familiaris aegyptica* from Predynastic Maadi, Egypt," Institut d'Égypte, *Bulletin*, Vol. 36; pp. 105–9.

MÜNTZING, ARNE
1959 "Darwin's Views on Variation Under Domestication in the Light of Present-Day Knowledge," American Philosophical Society, *Proceedings*, Vol. 103; pp. 190–219. Philadelphia.

MURRAY, G. W.
1951 "The Egyptian Climate: An Historical Outline," *Geographic Journal*, Vol. 117; pp. 422–34.

NACHTSHEIM, HANS
1949 *Vom Wildtier zum Haustier*. Paul Parey, Berlin.

NARR, KARL J.
1953 "Hirten, Pflanzer, Bauern: Produktionsstufe," in *Historia Mundi* (F. Valjavec, ed.), Vol. 2; pp. 66–100. Francke, Bern.

NARR, KARL J.
1956 "Early Food-Producing Populations," in *Man's Role in Changing the Face of the Earth* (W. L. Thomas, ed.). pp. 134–51. University of Chicago Press

NEELY, JAMES A.
1967 "Organización Hidráulica y Sistemas di Irrigación Prehistóricos en el

Valle de Oaxaca," Instituto Nacional de Antropología e Historia, *Boletin*, No. 27; pp. 15–17. Mexico City.

NELSON, N. C.
1917 "Contributions to the Archaeology of Mammoth Cave and Vicinity, Kentucky," The American Museum of Natural History, *Anthropological Papers*, Vol. 22, pt. 1. New York.

NEUMANN, GEORGE K., and FOWLER, MELVIN L.
1952 "Hopewellian Sites in the Wabash Valley," in *Hopewellian Communities in Illinois* (Thorne Deuel, ed.). Illinois State Museum, *Scientific Papers*, No. 5; pp. 175–248. Springfield.

NEUVILLE, R.
1951 "Le Paléolithique et le Mésolithique de Désert de Judée," *Arch. Inst. Paléontol. Humaine* (Paris), No. 24.

NICOLAISEN, J.
1963 "Ecology and Culture of the Pastoral Tuareg," *Nationalmuseets Skrifter*, Vol. 9. Copenhagen.

NIETSCH, H.
1939 *Wald und Siedlung im Vorgeschichtlichen Mitteleuropa*. Mannus-Bücherei, Vol. 64. Leipzig.

NIR, D., and BEN-ARIEH, D.
1965 "Relics of an Intermediate Terrace Between the Ghor and the Zor in the Central Jordan Valley," *Israel Journal of Earth Science*, Vol. 14; pp. 1–8.

NOBBS, ERIC A.
1927 "The Native Cattle of Southern Rhodesia," *South African Journal of Science*, Vol. 24; pp. 328–42. Johannesburg.

NOBIS, GÜNTER
1955 "Die Entwicklung der Haustierwelt Nordwest- und Mitteldeutschlands in ihrer Beziehung zu Landschaftlichen Gegebenheiten," *Petermanns Geographische Mitteilungen*, Vol. 99; pp. 2–7.

OBERMAIER, H.
1924a *Fossil Man in Spain*. Yale University Press, New Haven.

OBERMAIER, H.
1924b "Asturias-Stufe," in *Reallexicon der Vorgeschichte* (M. Ebert, ed.), Vol. 1; pp. 246–50. de Gruyter, Berlin.

ODUM, EUGENE P., and ODUM, H. T.
1959 *Fundamentals of Ecology*, 2nd ed. W. B. Saunders, Philadelphia.

OSBORN, HENRY FAIRFIELD
1919 *Men of the Old Stone Age, Their Environment, Life and Art*, 3rd ed. C. Scribner's Sons, New York.

PABOT, HENRI
1960 *The Native Vegetation and its Ecology in the Khuzistan River Basins*. Khuzistan Development Service, Ahwaz, Iran. (mimeographed)

PADDOCK, JOHN
1966 "Oaxaca in Ancient Mesoamerica," in *Ancient Oaxaca* (John Paddock, ed.). Stanford University Press, Stanford.

PALERM, ANGEL
1954 "La Distribucion del Regadio en el Area Central de Mesoamerica," *Ciencias Sociales*, Vol. 5; pp. 2–15, 64–74.

PALERM, ANGEL
1955 "The Agricultural Basis of Urban Civilization in Mesoamerica," in *Irrigation Civilizations: A Comparative Study* (Julian H. Steward. ed.). Pan American Union, *Social Science Monographs*, No. 1; pp. 28–42.

PALERM, ANGEL, and WOLF, ERIC R.
1954–55 "El Desarrollo del Area Clave del Imperio Texcocano," *Revista Mexicana de Estudios Antropologicos*, Vol. 14; pp. 337–50.

PALERM, ANGEL, and WOLF, ERIC R.
1957 "Ecological Potential and Cultural Development in Mesoamerica," Pan American Union of Social Sciences, *Monograph*, No. 3; pp. 1–37.

PATTE, ÉTIENNE
1958 "La Domestication du Renne au Paléolithique." *Comptes Rendus Hebdomadaires des Séances de l'Académie des Sciences*, Vol. 246; pp. 3490–92. Paris.

PATTERSON, THOMAS C.
1967 "Current Research: Highland South America," *American Antiquity*, Vol. 32; pp. 427–29. Salt Lake City.

PATTERSON, THOMAS C., and MOSELEY, M. EDWARD
n.d. "Late Preceramic and Early Ceramic Cultures of the Central Coast of Peru," to be published in *Ñawpa Pacha* 6. Berkeley.

PAYNE, E. J.
1892 *History of the New World Called America*. New York.

PEAKE, H. J., and FLEURE, H.
1927 *Peasants and Potters. The Corridors of Time*, Vol. 3. University Press, Oxford.

PEARSON, HARRY W.
1957 "The Economy Has No Surplus: Critique of a Theory of Development," in *Trade and Market in the Early Empires* (Karl Polanyi, Conrad Arensberg, and Harry Pearson, eds.); pp. 320–41. Free Press, Glencoe.

PENNINGTON, CAMPBELL
1963 *The Tarahumar of Mexico*. University of Utah Press, Salt Lake City.

PERKINS, A. L.
1949 "The Comparative Archeology of Early Mesopotamia," *Studies in Ancient Oriental Civilization*, Vol. 25. Chicago.

PERKINS, DEXTER
1964 "The Prehistoric Fauna from Shanidar, Iraq," *Science*, Vol. 144; pp. 1565–66.

PERKINS, DEXTER
1969 "Fauna of Çatal Hüyük: Evidence for Early Cattle Domestication in Anatolia," *Science*, Vol. 164; pp. 177–79.

PERROT, JEAN
1957 "Le Mésolithique de Palestine et les Récentes Découvertes à Eynan (Ain Mallaha)," *Antiquity and Survival*, Vol. 2; pp. 91–110.

PERROT, JEAN
1960 "Excavations at 'Eynan ('Ein Mallaha). Preliminary Report on the 1959 Season," *The Israel Exploration Journal*, Vol. 10; pp. 14–22.

PERROT, JEAN
1962 "Palestine-Syria-Cilicia," in *Courses Toward Urban Life* (R. J. Braidwood and G. R. Willey, eds.); pp. 147–64. Aldine Publishing Co., Chicago.

PERROT, JEAN

1966 "Le Gisement Natufien de Mallaha ('Eynan), Israël," *L'Anthropologie*, Vol 70; pp. 437–84.

PETERSON, FREDERICK A.

1962 *Ancient Mexico*. Capricorn Books Edition, Great Britain.

PHILIPS, PHILIP; FORD, JAMES A.; and GRIFFIN, JAMES B.

1951 *Archaeological Survey in the Lower Mississippi Alluvial Valley*. Peabody Museum of American Archeology and Ethnology, *Papers*, No. 25.

PICARD, LEO

1943 *Structure and Evolution of Palestine*, Hebrew University, Department of Geology, *Bulletin*, Vol. 4. Jerusalem.

PICARD, LEO

1963 "The Quaternary in the Northern Jordan Valley," *Proceedings of the Israel Academy Sci. Hum.*, Vol. 1, No. 4; pp. 1–34.

PICKERSGILL, BARBARA

1969 "The Archaeological Record of Chili Petters (*Capsicum* spp.) and the Sequence of Plant Domestication in Peru," *American Antiquity*, Vol. 34; pp. 54–61. Salt Lake City.

PIETTE, ED

1895a "Études d'Ethnographie Préhistorique," *L'Anthropologie*, Vol. 6; pp. 276–92.

PIETTE, ED

1895b "Hiatus et Lacune Vestiges de la Période de Transition dans la Grotte du Mas-d'Azil," La Société d'Anthropologie de Paris, *Bulletin*, Vol. 6 (4th series); pp. 235–67.

PIGGOTT, S.

1954 *The Neolithic Cultures of the British Isles*. University Press, Cambridge.

PIGGOTT, S.

1965 *Ancient Europe from the Beginnings of Agriculture to Classical Antiquity, A Survey*. University Press, Edinburgh.

PIÑA CHÁN, ROMAN

1958 "Tlatilco," Instituto Nacional de Antropologia e Historia, *Serie Investignaciones*, No. 1. Mexico City.

PIPER, C. V.

1926 "Studies of American Phaseolinae," Smithsonian Institution, U. S. National Museum, U. S. National Herbarium, *Contributions*, Vol. 22; pp. 663–701.

PITTIONI, RICHARD

1954 *Urgeschichte des Österreichischen Raumes*. F. Deuticke, Vienna.

PITTIONI, RICHARD

1962a "Italien, Urgeschichtlichen Kulturen," in *Realencyclopädie der Classischen Altertumswissenschaft* (Pauly-Wissowa, ed.), Supplementband 9; pp. 106–371. Druckenmüller, Stuttgart.

PITTIONI, RICHARD

1962b "Southern Middle Europe and Southeastern Europe," in *Courses Toward Urban Life* (R. J. Braidwood and G. R. Willey, eds.); pp. 211–26. Aldine Publishing Co., Chicago.

PITT-RIVERS, A. LANE-FOX

1906 *The Evolution of Culture and Other Essays.* (J. L. Myres, ed). Clarendon Press, Oxford.

PLATT, B. S.

1962 *Tables of Representative Values of Foods Commonly Used in Tropical Countries.* Medical Research Council, *Special Report Series,* No. 302. Her Majesty's Stationery Office.

PLISCHKE, H.

1954 "Das Kuhblasen eine Völkerkundliche Miszelle zu Herodot," *Zeitschrift für Ethnologie,* Vol. 79; pp. 1–7.

POEBEL, A.

1926 "Der Konflikt Zwischen Lagas and Umma zur Zeit Eannatums I und Entemenas," in *Paul Haupt Anniversary Volume;* pp. 226–67. Baltimore.

POMEL, A.

1898 "Les Ovidés," Service Carte Géologie Algérie, *Paléontol. Monogr.,* No. 13; pp. 1–32.

POOLE, D. M.

1951 "The Spanish Conquest of Mexico: Some Geographical Aspects," *Geographical Journal,* Vol. 117; pp. 27–42.

PREUSS, J.

1966 *Die Baalberger Gruppe in Mitteldeutschland.* Deutscher Verlag der Wissenschaften, Berlin.

PRITCHARD, J. B.

1950 *Ancient Near Eastern Texts Relating to The Old Testament.* Princeton.

PRUFER, OLAF H.

1961 *The Hopewell Complex of Ohio.* Unpublished Ph.D. dissertation, Harvard University, Cambridge.

PRUFER, OLAF H.

n.d. "The McGraw Site: A Middle Woodland Site near Chilocothe, Ross County Ohio," paper presented at the 29th Annual Meeting of the Society for American Archaeology, Chapel Hill.

PUMPELLY, R.

1908 *Explorations in Turkestan: Expedition of 1904: Prehistoric Civilizations of Anau.* Carnegie Institute, *Publications,* No. 73.

QUÉZEL P., and MARTINEZ, C.

1958 "Étude Palynologique de deux Diatomites du Borkou," *Bull. Soc. Hist. Nat. Afrique Nord,* Vol. 49; pp. 230–44.

QUÉZEL, P., and MARTINEZ, C.

1961 "Le Dernier Interpluvial au Sahara Central. Essai de Chronologie Palynologique et Paléoclimatique," *Libyca,* Vol. 6/7; pp. 211–27.

QUIBELL, J. E.

1900 *Hierakonpolis I.* London

QUIMBY, GEORGE I.

1946 "The Possibility of an Independent Agricultural Complex in the Southeastern United States," Human Origins: An Introductory General Course in Anthropology, *Selected Readings Series,* No. 31; pp. 206–10. University of Chicago (mimeographed).

QUIMBY, GEORGE I.
1960 *Indian Life in the Upper Great Lakes.* University of Chicago Press.

QUIMBY, GEORGE I.
1962 "A Year with a Chippewa Family 1763–1764," *Ethnohistory,* Vol. 9; pp. 217–39.

QUITTA, H.
1960 "Zur Frage der Ältesten Bandkeramik in Mitteleuropa," *Praehistorische Zeitschrift,* Vol. 38; pp. 1–38.

QUITTA, H.
1964 "Zur Herkunft des Frühen Neolithikums in Mitteleuropa," in *Varia Archaeologica* (P. Grimm, editor), Vol. 16; pp. 14–24. Akademie, Berlin.

RADIN, PAUL
1920 "The Sources and Authenticity of the History of the Ancient Mexicans," University of California, *Publications in American Archeology and Ethnology,* Vol. 27; pp. 1–150. Berkeley.

RADMILLI, A. M., editor
1962 *Piccola Guida della Preistoria Italiana.* Sansoni, Florence.

RADMILLI, A. M., and TONGIORGI, E.
1958 "Gli Scavi Nella Grotta La Porta di Positano," *Rivista di Scienze Preistoriche,* Vol. 13.

RALPH, ELIZABETH K.
1955 "University of Pennsylvania Radiocarbon Dates I," *Science,* Vol. 121; pp. 149–51.

RANDS, ROBERT L.
1952 *Some Evidence of Warfare in Classic Maya Art,* unpublished Ph.D. dissertation, Columbia University.

RAPPAPORT, ROY A.
1967 "Ritual Regulation of Environmental Relations Among a New Guinea People," *Ethnology,* Vol. 6; pp. 17–30.

RAWLINSON, HENRY C.
1839 "Notes on a March from Zohab through Luristan to Kirmanshah, in the year 1836," Royal Geographic Society, *Journal,* Vol. 9; pp. 26–116. London.

REDFIELD, ROBERT, and SINGER, MILTON
1954 "The Cultural Role of Cities," *Economic Development and Cultural Change,* Vol. 3; pp. 53–73.

REED, CHARLES A.
1959 "Animal Domestication in the Prehistoric Near East," *Science,* Vol. 130; pp. 1629–39. Washington, D.C.

REED, CHARLES A.
1960 "A Review of the Archeological Evidence on Animal Domestication in the Prehistoric Near East," in *Prehistoric Investigations in Iraqi Kurdistan* (Robert J. Braidwood and Bruce Howe, eds.), The University of Chicago, Oriental Institute, *Studies in Ancient Oriental Civilization,* No. 31; pp. 119–45. University of Chicago Press.

REED, CHARLES A.
1961 "Osteological Evidences for Prehistoric Domestication in Southwestern Asia," *Zeitschr. Tierzüchtung und Züchtungs-biologie,* Vol. 76; pp. 31–38.

REED, CHARLES A.
1969 "The Pattern of Animal Domestication in the Prehistoric Near East," in *The Domestication and Exploitation of Plants and Animals.* (P. J. Ucko and G. W. Dimblebey, eds.); pp. 361–80. Aldine Publishing Co, Chicago.

REED, CHARLES A., and BRAIDWOOD, ROBERT J.
1960 "Toward the Reconstruction of the Environmental Sequence of Northeastern Iraq," in *Prehistoric Investigations in Iraqi Kurdistan* (Robert J. Braidwood and Bruce Howe, eds.), The University of Chicago, Oriental Institute, *Studies in Ancient Oriental Civilization*, No. 31; pp. 163–73. University of Chicago Press.

REEDER, J. R.
1967 "Grasses," *Encyclopedia Britannica*, 1967 ed., Vol. 10; p. 700.

RENFREW, J. M.
1969 "The Archaeological Evidence for the Domestication of Plants," in *The Domestication and Exploitation of Plants and Animals.* (P. J. Ucko and G. W. Dimblebey, eds.); pp. 149–72. Aldine Publishing Co., Chicago.

RHOTERT, H.
1952 *Libysche Felsbilder.* L. C. Wittich, Darmstadt.

RICHTER, CURT P.
1952 "Domestication of the Norway Rat and its Implication for the Study of Genetics in Man," *American Journal of Human Genetics*, Vol. 4; pp. 273–85.

RITCHIE, WILLIAM A.
1944 *The Pre-Iroquoian Occupations of New York State.* Rochester Museum of Arts and Sciences, *Memoirs*, No. 1. Rochester.

RITCHIE, WILLIAM A.
1955 "Recent Discoveries Suggesting an Early Woodland Burial Cult in the Northeast," New York State Museum and Science Service, *Circular* 40.

RITCHIE, WILLIAM A., and DRAGOO, DON W.
1960 *The Eastern Dispersal of Adena.* New York State Museum and Science Service, *Bulletin*, No. 379. Albany.

RITCHIE, WILLIAM A., and MACNEISH, RICHARD
1949 "The Pre-Iroquoian Pottery of New York State," *American Antiquity*, Vol. 15; pp. 97–123.

RIZKANA, IBRAHIM
1952 "Centres of Settlement in Prehistoric Egypt in the Area Between Helwan and Heliopolis," l'Institut du Desert, *Bulletin*, Vol. 2, pt. 2; pp. 117–28.

ROBERTS, L. M.; GRANT, U. J.; RAMIREZ, E. R.; HATHEWAY, W. H.; and SMITH, D. L in collaboration with MANGELSDORF, P. C.
1957 *Races of Maize in Colombia.* National Academy of Science, National Research Council, *Publication* 510.

ROCHE, J.
1965 "Observations sur la Stratigraphie et la Chronologie des amas Coquilliers Mésolithiques de Muge (Portugal)," Société Préhistorique Française *Bulletin*, Vol. 62; pp. 130–38.

RODDEN, ROBERT J.
1964 "Recent Discoveries from Prehistoric Macedonia," *Balkan Studies*, Vol. 5; pp. 109–24.

RODDEN, ROBERT J.

1965 "An Early Neolithic Village in Greece," *Scientific American*, Vol. 212; No. 4; pp. 82–92.

ROGNON, P.

1967 *Le Massif de l'Atakor et Ses Bordures (Sahara Central)*. Centre Nat. Rech. Sci. Paris.

RÖHRS, MANFRED

1957 "Ökologische Beobachtungen an Wildebenden Tylopoden Südamerikas," Deutsche Zoologische Gesellschaft, *Verhandlungen*, Vol. 21; pp. 538–54.

ROLINGSON, M. A., and SCHWARTZ, D. W.

1966 *Late Paleo-Indian and Early Archaic Manifestations in Western Kentucky*. University of Kentucky, *Studies in Anthropology*, No. 3. University of Kentucky Press.

ROSSIGNOL, M.

1962 "Analyse Pollinique de Sédiments Marins Quaternaires en Israel, II— Sédiments Pleistocènes," *Pollen et Spores*, Vol. 4; pp. 121–48.

ROSSIGNOL, M.

1963 Analyse Pollinique de Sédiments Quaternaires dans la Plaine de Haifa, Israël," *Israel Journal of Earth Sciences*, Vol. 12; pp. 207–14.

ROTH, H. LING

1887 "On the Origin of Agriculture," Royal Anthropological Institute of Great Britain and Ireland, *Journal*, Vol. 16; pp. 102–36.

ROWE, JOHN H.

1946 "Inca Culture at the Time of the Spanish Conquest," in *Handbook of South American Indians* (Julian H. Steward, ed.). Vol. 2, Bureau of American Ethnology, *Bulletin*, Vol. 143; pp. 183–330.

ROWE, JOHN H.

1948 "The Kingdom of Chimor," *Acta Americana*, Vol. 6; pp. 26–59.

RUST, A.

1950 *Die Höhlenfunde von Jabrud (Syrien)*. K. Wachholtz, Neumünster.

RUST, A.

1962 *Vor 20,000 Jahren, Rentierjäger der Eiszeit*. Karl Wachholtz, Neumünster.

RÜTIMEYER, L.

1877 "Die Rinder der Teriär-Epoche," Schweizerische Palaeontologische Gesellschaft, *Abhandlungen*, Vol. 4.

RYDER, M. L.

1958 "Follicle Arrangement in Skin from Wild Sheep, Primitive Domestic Sheep and in Parchment," *Nature*, Vol. 182; pp. 781–83.

RYDER, M. L.

1965 "Report of Textiles from Çatal Hüyük," *Anatolian Studies*, Vol. 15; pp. 175–76.

SACKETT, JAMES R.

1968 "Method and Theory of Upper Paleolithic Archeology in Southwestern France," in *New Perspectives in Archeology* (Lewis R. and Sally R. Binford, eds.); pp. 61–84. Aldine Publishing Co., Chicago.

SAHLINS, MARSHALL

1958 *Social Stratification in Polynesia*. University of Washington Press, Seattle.

SAHLINS, MARSHALL

1961 "The Segmentary Lineage: An Organization of Predatory Expansion," *American Anthropologist*, Vol. 63; pp. 322–45.

SAHLINS, MARSHALL

1968 "Notes on the Original Affluent Society," in *Man the Hunter* (Richard B. Lee and Irven DeVore, eds.); pp. 85–89. Aldine Publishing Co., Chicago.

SANDERS, WILLIAM T.

1953 The Anthropogeography of Central Vera Cruz," *Huastecos, Totonacos y sus vecinos* (I. Bernal and E. Davalos, eds.), *Revista Mexicana de Estudios Historicos*, Vol. 13, Nos. 2–3; pp. 27–69. Mexico, D.F.

SANDERS, WILLIAM T.

1956 "The Central Mexican Symbiotic Region, A Study in Prehistoric Settlement Patterns," in *Prehistoric Settlement Patterns in the New World* (Gordon R. Willey, ed.), *Viking Fund Publications in Anthropology*, Vol. 23; pp. 115–27. New York.

SANDERS, WILLIAM T.

1961 "Ceramic Stratigraphy at Santa Cruz, Chiapas, Mexico," The New World Archeological Foundation, *Papers*, No. 13. Provo, Utah.

SANDERS, WILLIAM T.

1965 *The Cultural Ecology of the Teotihuacan Valley*. Pennsylvania State University (multilithed).

SANDERS, WILLIAM T., and PRICE, BARBARA J.

1968 *Mesoamerica: The Evolution of a Civilization*. Random House, New York.

SANKALIA, H. D.

1962 "India," *Viking Fund Publications in Anthropology*, Vol. 32; pp. 60–83.

SAUER, CARL O.

1936 "American Agricultural Origins: A Consideration of Nature and Culture," in *Essays in Anthropology in Honor of A. L. Kroeber*, University of California Press.

SAUER, CARL O.

1947 "Early Relations of Man to Plants," *Geographical Review*, Vol. 37; pp. 1–25.

SAUER, CARL O.

1948 "Environment and Culture During the Last Deglaciation," American Philosophical Society, *Proceedings*, Vol. 92; pp. 65–77.

SAUER, CARL O.

1950 "Cultivated Plants of South and Central America," in *Handbook of South American Indians* (Julian H. Steward, ed.) Vol. 6. Bureau of American Ethnology, *Bulletin*, Vol. 143; pp. 487–543.

SAUER, CARL O.

1952 *Agricultural Origins and Dispersals*. Bowman Memorial Lectures, Series 2. American Geographical Society, New York.

SAUER, CARL O.

1959 "Age and Area of American Cultivated Plants," *Actas 33d Internationales Congreso Americanistes*, Vol. 1; pp. 215–29.

SAUER, JONATHAN DEININGER
1950a "Amaranths as Dye Plants Among the Pueblo Peoples," *Southwestern Journal of Anthropology*, Vol. 6; pp. 412–15.

SAUER, JONATHAN DEININGER
1950b "The Grain Amaranths: A Survey of Their History and Classification," Missouri Botanical Garden, *Annals*, Vol. 37, No. 4; pp. 113–25. St. Louis.

SAUER, JONATHAN DEININGER
1969 "Identity of the Archeologic Grain Amaranths from the Valley of Tehuacán, Puebla, Mexico," *American Antiquity*, Vol. 34; pp. 80–81. Salt Lake City.

SAUTER, M. R.
1948 *Préhistoire de la Méditerranée, Paléolithique, Mésolithique.* Payot, Paris.

SCHAEDEL, R. P.
1951 "Major Ceremonical and Population Centers in Northern Peru," in *The Civilizations of Ancient America* (Sol Tax, ed.); pp. 232–43. 29th International Congress of Americanists, New York, 1949, *Selected Papers* I. Chicago.

SCHAEFFER, C. F. A.
1961 "Les Fondements Pré- et Protohistoriques de Syrie du Néolithique Précéramique au Bronze Ancien," *Syria: Revue d'Art Oriental et d'Archéologie*, Vol. 38; pp. 7–22. Paris.

SCHEFFER, F., and SCHACHTSCHABEL, P.
1960 *Bodenkunde*, 5th ed. F. Enke, Stuttgart.

SCHIETZEL, K.
1965 *Müdderscheim. Eine Ansiedlung der Jüngeren Bandkerdnick im Rheinland.* Böhlau, Köln-Graz.

SCHMID, A.
1942 *Rassenkunde des Rindes.* Benteli, Bern.

SCHMIDT-NIELSEN, KNUT
1964 *Desert Animals: Physiological Problems of Heat and Water.* The Clarendon Press, Oxford.

SCHNEIDER, ANNA
1920 *Die Anfänge der Kulturwirtschaft: Die Sumerische Tempelstadt.* Essen.

SCHOTT, C.
1939 "Die Vorgeschichtliche Kulturlandschaft Mitteleuropas," *Zeitschr. Erdkunde*, Vol. 8; pp. 641–50.

SCHWABEDISSEN, HERMAN
1944 *Die Mittlere Steinzeit im Westlichen Norddeutschland.* Karl Wachholtz, Neumünster.

SCHWABEDISSEN, HERMAN
1954 *Die Federmesser-Gruppen des Nordwesteuropäischen Flachlandes.* Karl Wachholtz, Neumünster.

SCHWABEDISSEN, HERMAN
1962 "Northern Continental Europe," in *Courses Toward Urban Life* (R. J. Braidwood and G. R. Willey, eds.); pp. 254–66. Aldine Publishing Co., Chicago.

SCHWABEDISSEN, HERMAN
1967 "Ein Horizontierter 'Breitkeil' aus Satrup und die Mannigfachen Kul-

turverbindungen des Beginnenden Neolithikums un Norden und Nord-western," *Palaeohistoria,* Vol. 12; pp. 409–68.

SCOTT, J. P.
1953 "The Process of Socialization in Higher Animals," in *Interrelations Between the Social Environment and Psychiatric Disorders;* pp. 82–102. Milbank Memorial Fund, New York.

SCOTT, J. P.
1954 "The Effects of Selection and Domestication Upon the Behavior of the Dog," *Journal of the National Cancer Institute,* Vol. 15; pp. 739–58.

SCOTT, J. P.
1968 "Evolution and Domestication of the Dog," *Evolutionary Biology,* Vol. 2; pp. 243–75.

SCOTT, J. P., FREDERICSON, EMIL; and FULLER, JOHN L.
1951 "Experimental Exploration of the Critical Period Hypothesis," *Personality: Symposia on Tropical Issues,* Vol. 1, No. 2; pp. 163–83.

SEHGAL, S. M.
1963 *Effects of Teosinte and 'Tripsacum' Introgression in Maize.* Harvard University, Bussey Institution.

SENYÜREK, MUZAFFER, and BOSTANCI, ENVER
1956 "The Excavation of a Cave Near the Village of Maǧracik in the Vilâyet of the Hatay," *Anatolia,* Vol. 1; pp. 81–83.

SENYÜREK, MUZAFFER, and BOSTANCI, ENVER
1958a "Hatay Vilâyetinde Prehistorya Arastirmalari," *Türk Tarih Kurumu: Belleten,* Vol. 22; pp. 147–66.

SENYÜREK, MUZAFFER, and BOSTANCI, ENVER
1958b "Hatay Vilâyetinin Paleolitik Kültürlei," *Türk Tarih Kurumu: Belleten,* Vol. 22; pp. 171–210.

SERVICE, E. R.
1962 *Primitive Social Organization.* Random House, New York.

SHALEM, N.
1953 "La Stabilité du Climat en Palestine." *Special Publication of the Research Council of Israel,* Vol. 2; pp. 153–75.

SIEGEL, B. J.
1945 "Some Methodological Considerations for a Comparative Study of Slavery," *American Anthropologist,* Vol. 47; pp. 357–92.

SIMPSON, GEORGE GAYLORD
1949 *The Meaning of Evolution.* Yale University Press, New Haven.

SMITH, C. EARLE, JR.
1950 "Prehistoric Plant Remains from Bat Cave," Harvard University, Botanical Museum, *Leaflets,* Vol. 14; pp. 157–80.

SMITH, C. EARLE, JR.
1965a *Agriculture, Tehuacan Valley.* Chicago Natural History Museum, *Fieldiana: Botany,* Vol. 31, No. 3.

SMITH, C. EARLE, JR.
1965b "Flora, Tehuacan Valley," Chicago Natural History Museum, *Fieldiana: Botany,* Vol. 31; pp. 107–43.

SMITH, C. EARLE, JR.
1967 "Plant Remains," in *Environment and Subsistence* (Douglas S. Byer,

gen. ed.), *The Prehistory of the Tehuacan Valley*, Vol. 1; pp. 220–55. University of Texas Press, Austin.

SMITH, C. EARLE, JR., and MACNEISH, RICHARD S.

1964 "Antiquity of American Polyploid Cotton," *Science*, Vol. 143; pp. 675–76.

SMOLLA, G.

1960 "Neolithische Kulturerscheinungen: Studien zur Frage ihrer Herausbildungen," *Antiquitas*, Series 2, Vol. 3; pp. 1–180.

SOLECKI, RALPH S.

1955 "Shanidar Cave, a Paleolithic Site in Northern Iraq," Smithsonian Institution, *Annual Report*, 1954; pp. 389–425.

SOLECKI, RALPH S.

1957a "The 1956 Season at Shanidar," *Sumer*, Vol. 13; pp. 165–71.

SOLECKI, RALPH S.

1957b "The 1956–1957 Season at Shanidar Iraq: A Preliminary Statement," *Quaternaria*, Vol. 4; pp. 23–30.

SOLECKI, RALPH S.

1959 "Early Man in Cave and Village at Shanidar, Kurdistan, Iraq," *Transactions of the New York Academy of Science*, Vol. 21; pp. 712–17.

SOLECKI, RALPH S.

1964a "Shanidar Cave, A Late Pleistocene Site in Northern Iraq," VIth International Congress on the Quaternary, *Reports*, Vol. 4; pp. 413–23.

SOLECKI, RALPH S.

1964b "Zawi Chemi Shanidar, A Post-Pleistocene Village Site in Northern Iraq," VIth International Congress on the Quaternary, *Reports*, Vol. 4; pp. 405–12.

SOLECKI, RALPH S., and RUBIN, MEYER

1958 "Dating of Zawi Chemi, an Early Village Site at Shanidar, Northern Iraq," *Science*, Vol. 127; p. 1446.

SOLLAS, W. J.

1924 *Ancient Hunters and Their Modern Representatives*. Macmillan, New York.

SONNEVILLE-BORDES, DENISE DE

1960 *Le Paléolithique Supérieur en Périgord*. Delmas, Bordeaux.

SONNEVILLE-BORDES, DENISE DE

1963a "Upper Paleolithic Cultures in Western Europe," *Science*, Vol. 142; pp. 347–55.

SONNEVILLE-BORDES, DENISE DE

1963b "Le Paléolithique Supérieur en Suisse," *L'Anthropologie*, Vol. 67; pp. 205–68.

SPEISER, E. A.

1942 "Some Sources of Intellectual and Social Progress in the Ancient Near East," in *Studies in the History of Culture;* pp. 51–62. American Council of Learned Societies Devoted to Humanistic Studies, Published for the Conference of the Secretaries of the Constituent Societies.

SPINDEN, HERBERT J.

1917 "The Origin and Distribution of Agriculture in America," 19th International Congress of the Americas, *Proceedings;* pp. 269–76.

SPINDEN, HERBERT J.
  1928 *Ancient Civilizations of Mexico and Central America,* American Museum of Natural History, *Handbook Series,* No. 3. New York.
STAMPFUSS, R.
  1942 "Die Ersten Altsteinzietlichen Höhlenfunde in Griechenland," *Mannus,* Vol. 34; pp. 132-47.
STEBBINS, G. L., JR.
  1950 *Variation and Evolution in Plants.* Columbia University Press. New York.
STEENSBURG, A.
  1957 "Some Recent Danish Experiments in Neolithic Agriculture," *Agriculture History Review,* Vol. 5; pp. 66-73.
STEGGERDA, MORRIS
  1941 "Maya Indians of Yucatan," Carnegie Institute of Washington, *Publications,* No. 531. Washington, D.C.
STEINDORFF, GEORG
  1913 *Das Grab des Ti.* Leipzig.
STEKELIS, M., and HAAS, G.
  1952 "The Abu Usba Cave (Mount Carmel)," *Israel Exploration Journal,* Vol. 2; pp. 15-47.
STENBERGER, M.
  1965 *Sweden.* Thames and Hudson, London.
STEVENS, RAYFRED L.
  1965 "The Soils of Middle America and Their Relation to Indian Peoples and Cultures," in *Natural Environment and Early Cultures* (R. C. West, ed.), *Handbook of Middle American Indians,* Vol. 1; pp. 265-315. University of Texas Press, Austin.
STEWARD, JULIAN H.
  1936 "The Economic and Social Bases of Primitive Bands," *Essays in Honor of Alfred L. Kroeber,* University of California Press.
STEWARD, JULIAN H.
  1937 "Ecological Aspects of Southwestern Society," *Anthropos,* Vol. 32; pp. 87-104.
STEWARD, JULIAN H.
  1938 "Basin-Plateau Aboriginal Sociopolitical Groups," Bureau of American Ethnology, Smithsonian Institution, *Bulletin* 120.
STEWARD, JULIAN H.
  1949a "South American Cultures: An Interpretive Summary," in *Handbook of South American Indians* (Julian H. Steward, ed.), Vol. 5; pp. 699-772. BAE, *Bulletin* 143.
STEWARD, JULIAN H.
  1949b "Cultural Causality and Law: A Trial Formulation of the Development of Early Civilizations," *American Anthropologist,* Vol. 51; pp. 1-27.
STEWARD, JULIAN H., editor
  1946-50 *Handbook of South American Indians.* Bureau of American Ethnology, *Bulletin,* Vol. 143. 6 vols., Washington, D.C.
STEWARD, JULIAN H.
  1953 "Evolution and Process," in *Anthropology Today* (A. L. Kroeber, assembler); pp. 313-26. University of Chicago Press.

STEWARD, JULIAN H.

1955 *Theory of Culture Change.* University of Illinois Press, Urbana.

STEWARD, JULIAN H., and FARON, LOUIS C.

1959 *Native Peoples of South America.* McGraw-Hill, New York.

STEWARD, JULIAN H., *et al.*

1955 *Irrigation Civilizations: A Comparative Study.* Pan American Union, *Social Science Monographs,* No. 1. Washington, D.C.

STRONACH, DAVID

1961 "The Excavations at Ras al 'Amiya," *Iraq,* Vol. 23; pp. 95–137. London.

STRONG, W. D.

1951 "Cultural Resemblances in Nuclear America: Parallelism or Diffusion?," in *The Civilizations of Ancient America* (Sol Tax, ed.); pp. 271–79. 29th International Congress of Americanists, New York, 1949, *Selected Papers* I. Chicago.

STRONG, W. D., and EVANS, C.

1952 "Cultural Stratigraphy in the Viru Valley, Northern Peru," *Columbia Studies in Archeology and Ethnology,* No. 4. New York.

STRUEVER, STUART

1961 "Further Excavations at the Snyders Site; An Analysis of Snyders Ceramics," *Central States Archeological Journal,* Vol. 8, No. 3; pp. 94–100. Springdale, Arkansas.

STRUEVER, STUART

1962 "Implications of Vegetal Remains from an Illinois Hopewell Site," *American Antiquity,* Vol. 27; pp. 584–86.

STRUEVER, STUART

n.d. "Middle Woodland Culture History in the Southern Great Lakes-Riverine Area," paper presented at the 29th Annual Meeting of the Society for American Archaeology, Chapel Hill.

TACKENBERG, K.

1954 *Fundkarten zur Vorgeschichte der Rheinprovinz.* Habelt, Bonn.

TAUTE, W.

1963 "Funde der Spätpalgolithischen Federmesser-Gruppe aus dem Raum zwischen mittlerer Elbe und Weichsel," *Berliner Jahrbuck für Vor-und Frühgeschichte,* Vol. 3; pp. 62–112.

TAUTE, W.

1967 "Das Felsdach Lautereck, Eine Mesolitisch-Neolithish-Bronze-zeitliche Stratigraphie au der Oberen Donau," *Palaeohistoria,* Vol. 12; pp. 483–505.

TAYLOR, WALTER W.

1957 *The Identification of Non-artifactual Archaeological Materials,* National Academy of Sciences, National Research Council, *Publication* 565. Washington, D.C.

TAX, SOL, editor

1951 *The Civilizations of Ancient America.* 29th International Congress of Americanists, New York, 1949. *Selected Papers* I. Chicago.

TEAL, JOHN J., JR.

1958 "Musk Ox Can Be Tamed." *Explorers Journal,* Vol. 36; p. 13.

TEAL, JOHN J., JR.

1958 "Golden Fleece of the Arctic." *Atlantic Monthly,* March 1958; pp. 76–81.

THEOCHARIS, D. R.
1958 "Pre-ceramic Thessaly," *Thessalika* (Volo), Vol. 1; pp. 70–86. (In Greek.)

THOMPSON, JOHN ERIC
1954 *The Rise and Fall of Maya Civilization.* Norman, Oklahoma.

TIXIER, J.
1963 *Typologie de l'Épipaléolithique du Maghreb.* Art et Métiers Graphiques, Paris.

TOBLER, ARTHUR J.
1950 *Excavations at Tepe Gawra,* Vol. II. University of Pennsylvania, *Museum Monographs,* University of Pennsylvania Press, Philadelphia.

TOBIAS, PHILLIP V.
1955 "Physical Anthropology and Somatic Origins of the Hottentots," *African Studies,* Vol. 14, No. 1; pp. 1–15. Johannesburg.

TOWLE, MARGARET A.
1952 "The Pre-Colombian Occurrence of Lagenaria Seeds in Coastal Peru," Harvard University, Botanical Museum, *Leaflets,* Vol. 15; pp. 171–84.

TOWLE, MARGARET A.
1961 "The Ethnobotany of Pre-Colombian Peru," *Viking Fund Publications in Anthropology,* No. 30. Wenner Gren Foundation for Anthropological Research, Inc., New York.

TOYNBEE, A. J.
1935 *A Study of History,* 2nd ed. Oxford University Press, London.

TREVOR, J. C.
1947 "The Physical Characters of the Sandawe," Royal Anthropological Institute of Great Britain and Ireland, *Journal,* Vol. 77, pt. 1; pp. 61–78. London.

TROELS-SMITH, JORGEN
1953 "Ertebølle Culture-Farmer Culture, Results of the Past Ten Years' Excavations in Asmosen Bog, West Zealand," *Aarboger for Nordisk Oldkyndighed of Historie;* pp. 1–62. Copenhagen.

TROELS-SMITH, JORGEN
1955 "Senglacialtidens Jaegere," *Saertryk af Fre Nationalmuseets Arbejdsmark, Kopenhagen;* pp. 129–53.

TROELS-SMITH, JORGEN
1957 "Maglemosetidens Jaegere og Fiskere," *Saertryk af Fra Nationalmuseets Arbejdsmark, Aarhus;* pp. 101–33.

TROELS-SMITH, JORGEN
1960a "Ivy, Mistletoe and Elm. Climate Indicators—Fodder Plants," *Danmarks Geol. Undersoegelse,* Series IV, Vol. 4, No. 4.

TROELS-SMITH, JORGEN
1960b "Ertebøllefidens Fangstfolk og Bønder," *Fra Nationalmuseets Arbejdsmark, Kopenhagen;* pp. 95–119.

TROELS-SMITH, JORGEN
1967 "The Ertebølle Culture and its Background," *Palaeohistoria,* Vol. 12; pp. 505–28.

TYLOR, E. B.
1881 *Anthropology.* Henry Holt, London.

TZALKIN, V. I.
1951 "Materials for the Recognition of the Fauna and Flora of the U.S.S.R."
Moscow Society of Naturalists, *Zoological*, Vol. 27.

UCKO, P. J., and DIMBLEBEY, G. W., editors
1969 *The Domestication and Exploitation of Plants and Animals.* Aldine
Publishing Co. Chicago.

VAILLANT, GEORGE C.
1930a "Excavations at Zacatenco," The American Museum of Natural History, *Anthropological Papers*, Vol. 32, pt. 1. New York.

VAILLANT, GEORGE C.
1930b "Excavations at Zacatenco," The American Museum of Natural History, *Anthropological Papers*, Vol. 32, pt. 2.

VAILLANT, GEORGE C.
1931 "Excavations at Ticomán," The American Museum of Natural History,
Anthropological Papers, Vol. 32, pt. 2. New York.

VAILLANT, GEORGE C.
1953a "Early Cultures of the Valley of Mexico," The American Museum of
Natural History, *Anthropological Papers*, Vol. 34, pt. 3. New York.

VAILLANT, GEORGE C.
1935b "Excavations at El Arbolillo," The American Museum of Natural
History, *Anthropological Papers*, Vol. 35, pt. 2. New York.

VAN BUREN, E. D.
1939 "The Fauna of Ancient Mesopotamia as Represented in Art," *Analecta
Orientalia*, Vol. 18.

VAN LOON, MAURITS
1966 "Mureybat: An Early Village in Inland Syria," *Archaeology*, Vol. 19;
pp. 215–16.

VAN LOON, MAURITS
1968 "The Oriental Institute Excavations at Mureybit, Syria: Preliminary
Report on the 1965 Campaign," *Journal of Near Eastern Studies*, Vol. 27;
pp. 265–90.

VAN NOTEN, F. L.
1967 "Le Tjongerien en Belgique," Société Royale Belge d'Anthropologie et
Préhistoire, *Bulletin*, Vol. 78; pp. 197–236.

VAN ZEIST, W.
1967 "Late Quaternary Vegetation History of Western Iran," *Review of
Palaeobotany and Palynology*, Vol. 2; pp. 301–11.

VAN ZEIST, W., and WRIGHT, JR., H. E.
1963 "Preliminary Pollen Studies at Lake Zeribar, Zagros Mountains, Southwestern Iran," *Science*, Vol. 140; pp. 65–69.

VAUFREY, R.
1928 "Le Paléolithique Italien," *Archives de l'Institut de Paléontologie
Humaine*, Mémoire 3.

VAUFREY, R.
1955 "Le Maghreb," in *Préhistoire de l'Afrique*, Vol. 1. Masson, Paris.

VAVILOV, N. I.
1951a "Phytogeographic Basis of Plant Breeding," *Chronica Botanica*, Vol.
13; pp. 14–54.

VAVILOV, N. I.
1951b "The Origin, Variation, Immunity and Breeding of Cultivated Plants," *Chronica Botanica*, Vol. 13, No. 1/6.

VAYDA, ANDREW P.
1964 "Anthropologists and Ecological Problems," in *Man, Culture and Animals* (Anthony Leeds and Andrew P. Vayda, eds.) American Association for the Advancement of Science, No. 78; pp. 1–5. Washington, D.C.

VESEY-FITZGERALD, B.
1957 *The Domestic Dog: An Introduction to Its History.* Routledge and Kegan Paul, London.

VIELLE, EDMOND
1890 "Pointes de Flèches Typiques de Fère-en-Tardenois (Aisne)," *Bulletin de Société Anthropologique de Paris*, Vol. 1 (6th series); pp. 959–64.

VITA-FINZI, C.
1969 *The Mediterranean Valleys: Geological Changes in Historical Times.* Cambridge University Press. Cambridge.

VOGT, E.
1961 "Der Stand der Neolithischen Forschung in der Schweiz," in *L'Europe à la fin de l'âge de la pierre*, (J. Bohm and S. J. de Laet, eds.); pp. 459–88. Éditions de l'Académie tchécoslovaque des Sciences. Prague.

VON FÜRER-HAIMENDORF, CHRISTOPH
1955 "Culture History and Cultural Development," *Yearbook of Anthropology*, Vol. 1; pp. 149–68.

VON GONZENBACH, V.
1949 *Die Cortaillodkultur in der Schwiez.* Birkhüser, Basel.

VON LEITHNER, O.
1927 "Der Ur," *Berichse der Internationales Gesellschaft zur Erhaltung des Wissenshaffen*, Vol. 2.

WALKER, E. P.
1964 *Mammals of the World.* Baltimore.

WALLACE, H. A., and BROWN, W. L.
1956 *Corn and Its Early Fathers.* Michigan State University Press, Lakeside Press, Chicago.

WALTER, H.
1954 *Grundlagen der Pflanzenverbreitung II. Arealkunde.* E. Ulmer, Stuttgart.

WARING, ANTONIO J., and HOLDER, PRESTON
1945 "A Prehistoric Ceremonial Complex in the Southeastern United States," *American Anthropologist*, Vol. 47.

WATELIN, LOUIS C., and LANGDON, STEPHEN
1934 *Excavations at Kish*, Vol. 4. Geuthner, Paris.

WATERBOLK, H. T.
1962 "The Lower Rhine Basin," in *Courses Toward Urban Life* (Robert J. Braidwood and Gordon R. Willey, eds.); pp. 227–53. Aldine Publishing Co., Chicago.

WATERBOLK, H. T.
1968 "Food Production in Prehistoric Europe," *Science*, Vol. 162; pp. 1093–1102.

WATERBOLK, H. T., and MODDERMAN, P. J. R.

1959 "Die Grossbauten der Bandkeramik," *Palaeohistoria,* Vols. 6–7; pp. 163–72.

WATSON, P. J.

1966 "Clues to Iranian Prehistory in Modern Village Life," *Expedition,* Vol. 8; p. 13.

WATSON, W.

1969 "Early Animal Domestication and Cereal Cultivation in China," in *The Domestication and Exploitation of Plants and Animals* (P. J. Ucko and G. W. Dimblebey, eds.); pp. 393–402. Aldine Publishing Co. Chicago.

WATTERS, R. F.

1960 "The Nature of Shifting Cultivation, A Review of Recent Research," *Pacific Viewpoint,* Vol. 1; pp. 59–99.

WATTS, W. A.

1960 "C-14 Dating and the Neolithic in Ireland," *Antiquity,* Vol. 34; pp. 111–16. London.

WEBB, WILLIAM S.

1946 *Indian Knoll.* University of Kentucky, *Reports in Anthropology,* Vol. 4, No. 3. Lexington, Kentucky.

WEBB, WILLIAM S., and BABY, RAYMOND S.

1957 *The Adena People No. 2.* The Ohio State Historical Society. Columbus.

WEBB, WILLIAM S., and HAAG, WILLIAM G.

1947 *Archaic Sites in McClean County, Kentucky.* University of Kentucky, *Reports in Anthropology,* Vol. 7, No. 1. Lexington, Kentucky.

WEBERBAUER, AUGUSTO

1936 "Phytogeography of the Peruvian Andes," in *Flora of Peru* (J. F. Mac-Bride), pt. 1; pp. 13–81. Field Museum of Natural History, Chicago.

WEBERBAUER, AUGUSTO

1945 *El Mundo Vegetal de los Andes Peruanos; Estudio Fitogeográfico.* Estación Experimental Agricola de La Molina. Dirección de Agricultura, Ministerio de Agricultura, Lima.

WEDEL, WALDO R.

1943 *Archaeological Investigations in Platte and Clay Counties, Missouri.* Smithsonian Institution, Bureau of American Ethnology, *Bulletin,* No. 183.

WEDEL, WALDO R.

1959 *An Introduction to Kansas Archeology.* Bureau of American Ethnology, *Bulletin,* No. 174. Washington, D.C.

WEINBERG, S. S.

1965 "The Stone Age in the Aegean," in *The Cambridge Ancient History,* Vol. 1, Ch. 10. University Press, Cambridge.

WEISNER, J.

1959 "Review of *Das Pford in Prähistorischer und Früher Historischer Zeit* by Franz Hancar (1956)," *Gnomon,* Vol. 31; pp. 289–301.

WELLHAUSEN, E. J., FUENTES, O., and HERNANDEZ, E.; in collaboration with MANGELSDORF, P. C.

1957 *Races of Maize in Central America.* National Academy of Science, National Research Council, *Publication* 511, Washington, D.C.

WELLHAUSEN, E. J.; ROBERTS, L. M.; HERNANDEZ, E.; in collaboration with MANGELSDORF, P. C.
1952 *Races of Maize in Mexico.* Harvard University, Bussey Institution, Cambridge.

WERTH, E.
1954 *Grabstock, Hacke, Pflug.* Ulmer, Ludwigsburg.

WEST, R., and ARMILLAS, PEDRO
1950 "Las Chinampas de Mexico," *Cuadernos Americanos,* Vol. 50.

WHEELER, MORTIMER
1956 "The First Towns?," *Antiquity,* Vol. 30; pp. 132–36.

WHITAKER, THOMAS W., and BIRD, JUNIUS B.
1949 "Identification and Significance of the Cucurbit Materials from Huaca Prieta, Peru," The American Museum of Natural History, *Novitates,* No. 1426.

WHITAKER, THOMAS W., and CARTER, GEORGE F.
1954 "Oceanic Drift of Gourds—Experimental Observations," *American Journal of Botany,* Vol. 41; pp. 697–700.

WHITAKER, THOMAS W.; CUTLER, HUGH C.; and MACNEISH, RICHARD S.
1957 "Cucurbit Materials from Three Caves near Ocampo, Tamaulipas," *American Antiquity,* Vol. 22, No. 4; pp. 352–58.

WHITE, LESLIE A.
1949 *The Science of Culture.* Farrar, Strauss and Co., New York.

WHITE, LESLIE A.
1959 *The Evolution of Culture.* McGraw-Hill, New York.

WHITE, MARIAN E.
1963 "Settlement Pattern Change and the Development of Horticulture in the New York-Ontario Area," *Pennsylvania Archaeologist,* Vol. 23.

WHITE, THEODORE
1953 "A Method of Calculating the Dietary Percentage of Various Food Animals Utilised by Aboriginal Peoples," *American Antiquity,* Vol. 18; pp. 396–98.

WHITING, ALFRED F.
1939 *Ethnobotany of the Hopi.* Museum of Northern Arizona, *Bulletin,* No. 15. Flagstaff.

WILHEMY, H.
1950 "Das Alter der Schwarzerde und die Steppen Mittel- und Osteuropas," *Erdkunde,* Vol. 4; pp. 5–34.

WILLEY, GORDON R.
1949 *Archaeology of the Florida Gulf Coast.* Smithsonian Institution, *Miscellaneous Collections,* Vol. 113. Washington, D.C.

WILLEY, GORDON R.
1953 *Prehistoric Settlement Patterns in the Viru Valley, Peru.* Bureau of American Ethnology, *Bulletin,* No. 155.

WILLEY, GORDON R.
1955 "The Prehistoric Civilizations of Nuclear America," *American Anthropologist,* Vol. 57; pp. 571–93.

WILLEY, GORDON R.
1956a "Problems Concerning Prehistoric Settlement Patterns in the Maya

Lowlands," in *Prehistoric Settlement Patterns in the New World* (Gordon R. Willey, ed.), Viking Fund, *Publications in Anthropology*, No. 23. New York.

WILLEY, GORDON R., editor

1956b *Prehistoric Settlement Patterns in the New World*. Viking Fund, *Publications in Anthropology*, No. 23. New York.

WILLEY, GORDON R.

1960a "New World Prehistory," *Science*, Vol. 131; pp. 73–86. Washington, D.C.

WILLEY, GORDON R.

1960b "Historical Patterns and Evolution in Native New World Cultures," in *Evolution After Darwin* (Sol Tax, ed.) University of Chicago Press, Vol. 2; pp. 111–41.

WILLEY, GORDON R.

1966 "New World Archeology in 1965," The American Philosophical Society, *Proceedings*, Vol. 110; pp. 140–45.

WILLEY, GORDON R., and CORBETT, JOHN M.

1954 *Early Ancon and Early Supe Culture*. Columbia University, *Studies in Archeology and Ethnology* No. 3. New York.

WILLEY, GORDON R.; EKHOLM, GORDON F.; and MILLON, RENÉ F.

1964 "The Patterns of Farming Life and Civilization," in *Natural Environments and Early Cultures* (Robert C. West, ed.) *Handbook of Middle American Indians*, Vol. 1; pp. 446–500. University of Texas Press, Austin.

WILLEY, GORDON R., and PHILLIPS, PHILIP

1955 "Method and Theory in American Archeology II: Historical-Developmental Interpretation," *American Anthropologist*, Vol. 57, No. 4.

WILLEY, GORDON R., and PHILLIPS, PHILIP

1958 *Method and Theory in American Archaeology*. University of Chicago Press.

WILLIS, J. C.

1951 *Dictionary of the Flowering Plants and Ferns*, 6th ed. revised. Cambridge University Press, Cambridge.

WILSON, THOMAS

1894 "Minute Stone Implements from India," The U. S. National Museum, *Report for 1892*. U. S. Government Printing Office, Washington, D.C.

WINTERS, HOWARD D.

1963 "An Archaeological Survey of the Wabash Valley in Illinois," Illinois State Museum, *Reports of Investigations*, No. 10.

WINTERS, HOWARD D.

n.d.a "Value Systems of the Archaic," paper presented at the 29th Annual Meeting of the Society for American Archaeology, Chapel Hill.

WINTERS, HOWARD D.

n.d.b "The Hopewellian Interaction Sphere: A Reappraisal," paper presented at the 29th Annual Meeting of the Society for American Archaeology, Chapel Hill.

WISSMANN, H. VON

1957 "Ursprung und Ausbreitungswege von Pflanzen- und Tierzucht und ihre Abhängigkeit von der Klimageschichte," *Erdkunde*, Vol. 11; pp. 81–94, 175–93.

WITTFOGEL, KARL A.
1938 "Die Theorie der Orientalischen Gesellschaft," *Zeitschrift für Sozialforschung 7.*

WITTFOGEL, KARL A.
1953a "Oriental Despotism," *Sociologus*, Vol. 3, No. 2.

WITTFOGEL, KARI A.
1953b "The Ruling Bureaucracy of Oriental Despotism: A Phenomenon That Paralyzed Marx," *Review of Politics*, Vol. 15, No. 3.

WITTFOGEL, KARL A.
1957 *Oriental Despotism: A Comparative Study of Total Power.* Yale University Press, New Haven.

WITTHOFT, JOHN
1959 "The Transition Between Archaic and Woodland Cultures in the Northeast and the Mississippi Basin," Southeastern Archaeological Conference, *Newsletter*, Vol. 6, No. 15; pp. 25–28. Chapel Hill.

WITTRY, WARREN L.
1959a "The Raddatz Rockshelter, Sk5, Wisconsin," *The Wisconsin Archeologist*, Vol. 40; pp. 33–68.

WITTRY, WARREN L.
1959b "Archaeological Studies of Four Wisconsin Rockshelters," *The Wisconsin Archaeologist*, Vol. 40; pp. 137–267.

WITTRY, WARREN L.
1964 "An American Woodhenge," Cranbrook Institute of Science, *Newsletter*, Vol. 33, No. 9; pp. 102–7.

WOLF, ERIC R.
1951 "The Social Organization of Mecca and the Origins of Islam," *Southwestern Journal of Anthropology*, Vol. 7; pp. 329–56.

WOLF, ERIC R.
1959 *Sons of Shaking Earth.* University of Chicago Press.

WOLF, ERIC R.
1966 *Peasants.* Prentice-Hall, Englewood Cliffs, New Jersey.

WOLF, ERIC R., and PALERM, ANGEL
1955 "Irrigation in the Old Acolhua Domain, Mexico," *Southwestern Journal of Anthropology*, Vol. 11; pp. 265–81. Albuquerque.

WOODBURN, JAMES
n.d. "Background Material on the Hadze of Tanzania," ms. presented at the conference *Man the Hunter*, University of Chicago, April 1965.

WOOLEY, C. L.
1934 *Ur Excavations*, Vol. 2. Oxford University Press, London.

WRIGHT, HERBERT E., JR.
1952 "The Geological Setting of Four Prehistoric Sites in Northeastern Iraq," *Bulletin of American School Oriental Research*, Vol. 128; pp. 11–24.

WRIGHT, HERBERT E., JR.
1957 "The Late-Glacial Chronology of Europe—A Discussion," *American Journal of Science*, Vol. 255; pp. 447–60.

WRIGHT, HERBERT E., JR.

1960 "Climate and Prehistoric Man in the Eastern Mediterranean," in *Prehistoric Investigations in Iraqi Kurdistan* (Robert J. Braidwood and Bruce Howe, eds.), University of Chicago, the Oriental Institute, *Studies in Oriental Civilization*, No. 31; pp. 71–97. University of Chicago Press.

WRIGHT, HERBERT E., JR.

1961a "Late Pleistocene Climate of Europe: A Review," Geological Society of America. *Bulletin* 72; pp. 933–83.

WRIGHT, HERBERT E., JR.

1961b "Pleistocene Glaciation in Kurdistan," *Eiszeitalter und Gegenwart*, Vol. 12; pp. 131–64. Hannover.

WRIGHT, HERBERT E., JR.

1967 *The Administration of Rural Production in an Early Mesopotamian Town.* Unpublished Ph.D. dissertation, University of Chicago, Department of Anthropology.

WRIGHT, HERBERT E., JR.

1968 "Natural Environment of Early Food Production North of Mesopotamia," *Science*, Vol. 161; pp. 334–39.

WRIGHT, H. E., JR.; ANDREWS, J. H.; and VAN ZEIST, W.

1967 "Modern Pollen Rain in Western Iran and Its Application to Plant Geography and Quaternary Vegetational History," *Journal of Ecology*, Vol. 55; pp. 415–43.

WRIGLEY, E. A.

1967 "Demographic Models and Geography," in *Socio-economic Models in Geography* (Richard J. Chorley and Peter Haggett, eds.); pp. 189–215. University Paperbacks, Methuen, London.

WYNNE-EDWARDS, V. C.

1962 *Animal Dispersion in Relation to Social Behaviour.* Oliver and Boyd, Edinburgh.

WYNNE-EDWARDS, V. C.

1964 "Population Control in Animals," *Scientific American*, Vol. 211; pp. 68–74.

WYSS, R.

1960 "Zur Erforschung des Schweizerischen Mesolithikums," *Zeitschrift für Schweizerische Archäologie und Kunstgeschichte*, Vol. 20; pp. 55–113.

YENGOYAN, ARAM A.

1960 "Preliminary Notes on a Model of the Initial Populating of the Philippines," *Anthropology Tomorrow*, Vol. 6, No. 3; pp. 42–48.

YARNELL, R. A.

1964 "Aboriginal Relationships Between Cultures and Plant Life in the Upper Great Lakes Region," *Anthropological Papers*, Museum of Anthropology, University of Michigan, No. 23. Ann Arbor.

YOUNG, T. C., and SMITH, P. E. L.

1966 "Research in the Prehistory of Central Western Iran," *Science*, Vol. 153; pp. 386–91.

ZEIST, W. VAN

1967 "Late Quaternary Vegetation History of Western Iran," *Revue Palaeobotanie Palynologie*, Vol. 2; pp. 301–11.

ZEUNER, F. E.
1953 "The Colour of the Wild Cattle of Lascaux," Royal Anthropological Institute of Great Britain and Ireland, *Man*, Vol. 53; pp. 68–69.
ZEUNER, F. E.
1954 "Domestication of Animals," in *A History of Technology* (C. Singer, *et al.*, eds.); pp. 327–57. Oxford University Press, London.
ZEUNER, F. E.
1955 "The Goats of Early Jericho," *Palestine Exploration Quarterly*, Vol. 1955; pp. 70–86.
ZEUNER, F. E.
1958 "Dog and Cat in the Neolithic of Jericho," *Palestine Exploration Quarterly*, Vol. 1958; pp. 52–55. London.
ZEUNER, F. E.
1963 *A History of Domesticated Animals*. Hutchinson, London.
ZIEGLER, FREDERICK E.
1953 *Die Keramik von der Qal'a des Haggi Mohammad. Uruk-Warka*, Vol. 5.

INDEX

Acosta, Jorge R., 173
Acosta Saignes, Miguel, 600
Adams, Georgian, 519
Adams, Inez, 640
Adams, Robert M., 51, 64, 69, 70, 71, 72, 73, 75, 239, 249, 252, 253, 257, 260, 280, 286, 287, 295, 300, 303, 307–11, 572–90, 591–614, 616, 617, 618, 622, 624, 628, 632, 635, 639
Africa, northern, agricultural dispersal into. *See* Agricultural dispersal into Europe and northern Africa
Agricultural dispersal: economic motives for, 313–15; migration of races and cultures as factor in, 313–14; chronic overpopulation as factor in, 314; environmental theory of postglacial desiccation as cause of, 314–15; Sauer's theory of agricultural diffusion from southeast Asia, 315–16; hypothesis of Wissmann on, 316
Agricultural dispersal into Europe and northern Africa, 313–34; economic motives for agricultural dispersal, 313–15; Sauer's theory of diffusion from southeast Asia, 315–16; dispersal into Europe during Atlantic phase, 317; European climate during Atlantic phase, 317–18; plants and forests of Europe during Atlantic phase, 317, 318; environmental factors influencing location of early agricultural settlement in Europe, 318–22 (*figs.*); physical

environment of early Danubian culture, 318–21 (*fig.*); similarity between new agricultural lands of mid-latitude Europe and of Near East, 321; changes in crop ecology in European agriculture, 321–22; early village culture in Europe and adjacent areas, 322 (*fig.*); agricultural colonization of Mediterranean Basin, 322; ecological adaptation required in settlement of arid lands, 322, 328–29; Saharan climate during the mid-Holocene, 322–26; evidence of moist intervals in Saharan climate, 323–26; prehistoric cattle-nomads of the Sahara, 326–29; epi-Paleolithic hunting culture of the Sahara, 326–27; Neolithic food-producing culture of of the Sahara, 326–27; economic traits of Saharan pastoralists, 327–28; hunters and cattle nomads in the Sahara, 329 (*fig.*); impact of food production on man-land relationships, 329–34; physical transformation of natural environment, 330, 331; creation of a cultural landscape, 330, 331–33; population explosion, from improved subsistence economy, 330–31

Agricultural Origins and Dispersals (Sauer), 407n; review of, by Paul C. Mangelsdorf, 415–22; summary of Sauer's postulations, 415–18;

LAW AND WARFARE:
Studies in the Anthropology of Conflict
—Paul Bohannan

TRIBAL AND PEASANT ECONOMIES:
Readings in Economic Anthropology
—George Dalton

PERSONALITIES AND CULTURES:
Readings in Psychological Anthropology
—Robert Hunt

COMPARATIVE POLITICAL SYSTEMS:
Studies in the Politics of Preindustrial Societies
—Ronald Cohan and John Middleton

MYTH AND COSMOS:
Readings in Mythology and Symbolism
—John Middleton

GODS AND RITUALS:
Readings in Religious Beliefs and Practices
—John Middleton

MAGIC, WITCHCRAFT, AND CURING:
—John Middleton

BEYOND THE FRONTIER:
Social Process and Cultural Change
—Paul Bohannan and Fred Plog

MARRIAGE, FAMILY, AND RESIDENCE:
—Paul Bohannan and John Middleton

KINSHIP AND SOCIAL ORGANIZATION:
—Paul Bohannan and John Middleton

ENVIRONMENT AND CULTURAL BEHAVIOR:
Ecological Studies in Cultural Anthropology
—Andrew P. Vayda

FROM CHILD TO ADULT:
Studies in the Anthropology of Education
—John Middleton

ANTHROPOLOGY AND ART:
Readings in Cross-Cultural Aesthetics
—Charlotte M. Otten

ECONOMIC DEVELOPMENT AND SOCIAL CHANGE:
The Modernization of Village Communities
—George Dalton